The Theory of Interest

The Theory of Interest

Third Edition

Stephen G. Kellison
University of Central Florida

THE THEORY OF INTEREST
Third Edition
International Edition 2009

Published by McGraw-Hill Education, 2 Penn Plaza, New York, NY 10121.

20
20 19 18 17
SLP

When ordering this title, use ISBN: 978-007-127627-6 or MHID: 007-127627-0

Printed in Singapore

www.mhhe.com

To my family: Toni, Matt, and Lexi.

Preface

This third edition is a substantially revised and expanded treatment of the theory of interest from that contained in the second edition. With a few minor exceptions, all the material in the second edition has been retained and updated. In addition, a significant amount of new material has been added.

The first seven chapters cover the basic mathematical theory of interest as traditionally developed. These seven chapters match the first seven chapters in the second edition. However, the material on yield rates was moved from Chapter 5 to Chapter 7 and the other two chapters were renumbered accordingly.

The coverage of topics in these seven chapters largely tracks the second edition. The consideration of annuities varying in geometric progression has been expanded into a separate section reflecting the increasing importance of indexed annuities in various types of applications. The material on capital budgeting in Chapter 7 has been significantly expanded with the introduction of several techniques not covered in the second edition. Finally, the discussion of short sales has been expanded and repositioned into Chapter 7

Chapter 8 covers practical applications of material presented in the first seven chapters. It is organized into largely independent sections, so that it can readily be used as a reference for the topics covered. One new topic that has been added in Chapter 8 is leasing as an alternative to traditional loan financing, with particular emphasis on automobile leasing. Also, the section introducing the reader to modern financial instruments has been expanded to include additional financial instruments.

Chapters 9 through 13 introduce the reader to the economic and financial theory of interest, in additional to the mathematical theory of interest. Much of this material was covered in the second edition, but the extent and depth of coverage has been significantly expanded in the third edition. For example, Chapter 9 has separate sections devoted to reflecting the effects of inflation, expenses, taxes, currency exchange rates, and risk and uncertainty in calculations involving interest.

Chapters 10 and 11 are two new chapters representing a significantly expanded treatment of two important topics covered in Chapter 9 of the second edition. Chapter 10 covers the term structure of interest rates with expanded consideration of spot rates, forward rates, relationship with bond yields, and a section with a detailed discussion of arbitrage. Chapter 11 covers important techniques in the management of assets and liabilities, such as duration, convexity, and immunization. The analysis of interest sensitive cash flows is considered more explicitly and in more depth. Also, the material on the full immunization technique has been moved from an appendix and expanded into a separate section.

With a couple of notable exceptions, the first eleven chapters largely utilize a deterministic approach to the subject of interest. The final two chapters explicitly address stochastic approaches to interest theory. Chapter 12 contains a number of different models for doing this and consists of an expanded treatment of material from Chapter 10 in the second edition. The use of binomial lattices for interest rate modeling and the development of several continuous stochastic models are new to the third edition.

Chapter 13 addresses options and other derivatives and has been expanded into an entire chapter. Significant non-mathematical introductory material has been added in the early part of the chapter to provide a more complete introduction into the basics of options. The two primary approaches for option valuation, binomial lattices and the Black-Scholes formula, have been updated and expanded. Finally, the reader is briefly introduced to some extensions of option valuation techniques for more complex types of options.

The computational approaches in the third edition have been modernized to reflect the widespread availability of calculators with exponential and logarithmic capability, including those with built-in financial functions. Techniques for solving certain key types of problems, e.g. the determination of an unknown yield rate given a set of cash flows, are illustrated. However, the presentation is generic and not tied to any one particular financial calculator. The coverage of calculator techniques is targeted and is not widespread throughout the book. The importance of the mastery of basic concepts and techniques is stressed throughout and is not sacrificed in those areas in which calculator techniques are illustrated.

The interest tables have been eliminated from the third edition as obsolete. Also, iteration techniques are greatly deemphasized from the presentation in the second edition. An appendix on iteration methods is retained for those reader interested in pursuing this subject in more detail.

The pedagogical approach in the second edition has been retained in the third edition. The textbook narrative emphasizes both the importance of conceptual understanding and the ability to apply the techniques to practical problems. Verbal interpretations of key results are emphasized throughout. Key formulas are numbered for ease of reference. Illustrative examples are provided at the ends of most sections. The number of exercises at the ends of the chapters has been significantly expanded to 545. Each exercise is intended to illustrate a somewhat different point to keep the number of repetitious exercises to a minimum. Answers to the exercises are provided at the back of the book.

A new feature in the third edition is the addition of chapter appendices. These appendices contain such items as the more complex derivations, extended results of interest but not fundamental, and additional formulas and techniques. The purpose is for the primary textbook narrative to be "tighter" and focused on the fundamental material. In addition to these chapter appendices, the book also contains five general appendices at the end of the book. These latter five appendices are lettered rather than numbered to avoid ambiguity.

A working knowledge of calculus is required, since the continuous nature of interest is recognized throughout the book. Also, the last two chapters of the book dealing with stochastic approaches assume knowledge of basic probability and statistics.

The book is designed to be appropriate for both classroom use with an instructor and for self-study by those learning the subject without the aid of an instructor. The amount of material probably exceeds that which can be covered in a one-semester university course.

The author is indebted to a number of students who have used the textbook and a number of other correspondents who have written over the years in connection with the second edition. As a result of this input and correspondence, a number of improvements have been incorporated into the third edition.

The author wishes to express his appreciation to the Society of Actuaries and to the Casualty Actuarial Society for using the second edition as a syllabus reference on the actuarial examination covering financial mathematics for many years. A number of the exercises appearing in this book have been obtained from published examinations of these two actuarial organizations.

The author also wishes to give special recognition and appreciation to two individuals at the University of Central Florida. Kellie Tabor spent uncountable hours typing the manuscript for the book. Since final copy was produced by word processing, this was a very painstaking process. Dandan Xu, a graduate student, used special software to develop the figures in the book and also contributed extensively to the exercises.

Finally, the author wishes to recognize the patience and understanding of his wife Toni for her unfailing support. Without her dedication and support this book could not have been completed.

October 2007 STEPHEN G. KELLISON

Contents

1

The measurement of interest

1.1 INTRODUCTION

Interest may be defined as the compensation that a borrower of capital pays to a lender of capital for its use. Thus, interest can be viewed as a form of rent that the borrower pays to the lender to compensate for the loss of use of the capital by the lender while it is loaned to the borrower. In theory, capital and interest need not be expressed in terms of the same commodity. For example, Farmer A may lend a tractor to Farmer B for use in harvesting B's wheat crop in return for a percentage of the wheat harvested. In this example, the tractor is capital and the portion of wheat that B gives to A is interest. However, for almost all applications, both capital and interest are expressed in terms of money.

In Chapter 1 the various quantitative measures of interest are analyzed. This chapter includes most of the basic principles involved in the measurement of interest. Chapters 2 through 8 elaborate and extend these basic principles to more complex financial transactions. These chapters explore the various methods by which interest is calculated and by which capital and interest are repaid by the borrower to the lender.

Chapters 1-8 in essence are concerned with the mathematical theory of interest on a deterministic basis. Chapters 9-13 introduce the reader to a number of more advanced topics. Among these topics are the following: the economic and financial theory of interest, the term structure of interest rates, techniques relating assets and liabilities, stochastic approaches to interest, and more advanced financial instruments such as options and other derivatives.

1.2 THE ACCUMULATION AND AMOUNT FUNCTIONS

A common financial transaction is the investment of an amount of money at interest. For example, a person may invest in a savings account at a bank. The initial amount of money (capital) invested is called the *principal* and the total amount received after a period of time is called the *accumulated value*. The difference between the accumulated value and the principal is the *amount of interest*, or just *interest*, earned during the period of investment.

For the moment, assume that given the original principal invested, the accumulated value at any point in time can be determined. We will assume that no principal is added or withdrawn during the period of investment, i.e. that any change in the fund is due strictly to the effect of interest. Later we will relax this assumption and allow for contributions and withdrawals during the period of investment.

Let t measure time from the date of investment. In theory, time may be measured in many different units, e.g., days, months, decades, etc. The unit in which time is measured is called the *measurement period*, or just *period*. The most common measurement period is one year, and this will be assumed unless stated otherwise.

Consider the investment of one unit of principal. We can define an *accumulation function* $a(t)$ which gives the accumulated value at time $t \geq 0$ of an original investment of 1.

What properties does this function possess?

1. It is clear that $a(0) = 1$

2. $a(t)$ is generally an increasing function. A decrease in the functional values for increasing t would imply negative interest. Although negative interest is possible mathematically, it is not relevant to most situations encountered in practice. However, there are situations in which negative interest does appear, e.g. an investment fund that loses money over a certain period of time. Constant functional values would imply zero interest, a situation occurring occasionally.

3. If interest accrues continuously, as is usually the case, the function will be continuous. However, there are situations in which interest does not accrue continuously between interest payment dates, in which case $a(t)$ possesses discontinuities.

In general, the original principal invested will not be one unit but will be some amount $k > 0$. We now define an *amount function* $A(t)$ which gives the accumulated value at time $t \geq 0$ of an original investment of k. Then we have

$$A(t) = k \cdot a(t) \tag{1.1}$$

and

$$A(0) = k.$$

The second and third properties of $a(t)$ listed above clearly also hold for $A(t)$.

We will denote the amount of interest earned during the nth period from the date of investment by I_n. Then we have

$$I_n = A(n) - A(n-1) \quad \text{for} \quad n = 1,2,3,\ldots . \tag{1.2}$$

It should be noted that I_n involves the effect of interest over an interval of time, whereas $A(n)$ is an amount at a specific point in time.

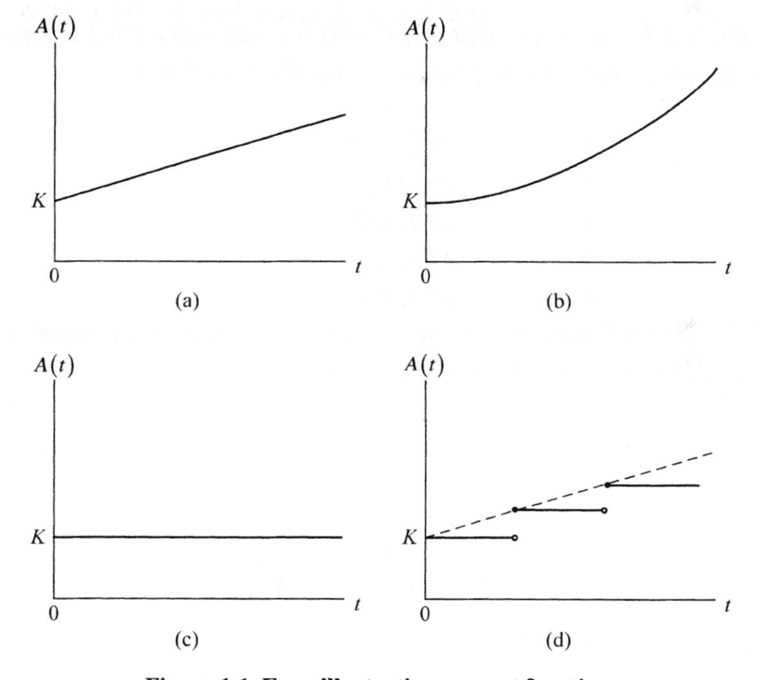

Figure 1.1 Four illustrative amount functions

Actually, the accumulation function is a special case of the amount function for which $k = 1$. However, the accumulation function will be significant enough in the rest of this chapter to warrant a separate definition. In many cases, the accumulation function and the amount function can be used interchangeably.

Figure 1.1 shows four examples of amount functions. Figure (a) is a linear amount function. Figure (b) is nonlinear, in this case an exponential curve. Figure (c) is an amount function which is horizontal, i.e. the slope is zero. This figure represents an amount function in which the principal is accruing no interest. Figure (d) is an amount function in which interest is not accruing continuously but is accruing in discrete segments with no interest accruing between interest payment dates.

In the following sections, various measures of interest will be developed from the accumulation function. In practice, two particular accumulation functions will handle most situations which arise. However, the reader should understand the properties of a general accumulation function as defined in this section and be able to work with it.

Example 1.1 ***An investment of \$10,000 is made into a fund at time t = 0. The fund develops the following balances over the next 4 years:***

t	A(*t*)
0	*10,000.00*
1	*10,600.00*
2	*11,130.00*
3	*11,575.20*
4	*12,153.96*

If \$5000 is invested at time t = 2, under the same interest environment, find the accumulated value of the \$5000 at time t = 4.

Let K be the accumulated value of the \$5000. K can be determined by ratio and proportion

$$\frac{K}{5000} = \frac{A(4)}{A(2)} = \frac{12{,}153.96}{11{,}130.00}$$

and solving for K we have

$$K = \$5460.00$$

1.3 THE EFFECTIVE RATE OF INTEREST

The first measure of interest is called the *effective rate of interest* and is denoted by i. A precise definition is:

> *The effective rate of interest i is the amount of money that one unit invested at the beginning of a period will earn during the period, where interest is paid at the end of the period.*

Note that in terms of the accumulation function, this definition is equivalent to saying that

$$i = a(1) - a(0)$$

or

$$a(1) = 1 + i. \tag{1.3}$$

Several observations about this definition are important:

1. The use of the word "effective" is not intuitively clear. This term is used for rates of interest in which interest is paid once per measurement period. This will be contrasted with "nominal" rates of interest, in which interest is paid more frequently than once per measurement period, to be considered in Section 1.8.

2. The effective rate of interest is often expressed as a percentage, e.g. $i = 8\%$. The concept of the effective rate of interest as a percentage is not inconsistent with the definition above, which states that it is an amount of money, since 8% can be looked upon as .08 per unit of principal.

3. The amount of principal remains constant throughout the period, i.e. no new principal is contributed and no principal is withdrawn during the period.

4. The effective rate of interest is a measure in which interest is paid at the end of the period. The significance of this statement is not immediately clear, but it will become evident in Section 1.7, where a situation is described in which interest is paid at the beginning of the period.

The effective rate of interest can be defined in terms of the amount function as follows:

$$i = \frac{(1+i)-1}{1} = \frac{a(1) - a(0)}{a(0)} = \frac{A(1) - A(0)}{A(0)} = \frac{I_1}{A(0)}. \tag{1.4a}$$

Thus, an alternate definition is:

> *The effective rate of interest i is the ratio of the amount of interest earned during the period to the amount of principal invested at the beginning of the period.*

The same four observations made above also apply to this alternate definition.

Effective rates of interest can be calculated over any measurement period. Let i_n be the effective rate of interest during the nth period from the date of investment. Then we have

$$i_n = \frac{A(n) - A(n-1)}{A(n-1)} = \frac{I_n}{A(n-1)} \quad \text{for} \quad n = 1,2,3,\ldots . \qquad (1.4b)$$

Within this notational framework, the "i" in formula (1.4a) might more properly be labeled i_1.

Although formula (1.4b) allows the various effective rates of interest i_n to vary for different n, it will be demonstrated in Section 1.5 that for one very important accumulation function, the effective rate of interest is constant over successive measurement periods, i.e. for all $n = 1,2,3,\ldots$.

Example 1.2 For the \$10,000 investment given in Example 1.1, find the effective rate of interest for each of the four years.

From the table of values given in Example 1.1 we can apply formula (1.4b) four times to obtain:

$$i_1 = \frac{A(1)-A(0)}{A(0)} = \frac{10,600.00-10,000.00}{10,000.00} = .06, \text{ or } 6\%,$$

$$i_2 = \frac{A(2)-A(1)}{A(1)} = \frac{11,130.00-10,600.00}{10,600.00} = .05, \text{ or } 5\%,$$

$$i_3 = \frac{A(3)-A(2)}{A(2)} = \frac{11,575.20-11,130.00}{11,130.00} = .04, \text{ or } 4\%,$$

and

$$i_4 = \frac{A(4)-A(3)}{A(3)} = \frac{12,153.96-11,575.20}{11,575.20} = .05, \text{ or } 5\%.$$

1.4 SIMPLE INTEREST

It was shown in the preceding sections that $a(0) = 1$ and $a(1) = 1 + i$. There are an infinite number of accumulation functions that pass through these two points. Two of these are most significant in practice. The first, simple interest, will be discussed in this section; and the second, compound interest, will be discussed in Section 1.5.

Consider the investment of one unit such that the amount of interest earned during each period is constant. The accumulated value of 1 at the end of the first period is $1 + i$, at the end of the second period it is $1 + 2i$, etc. Thus, in general, we have a linear accumulation function

$$a(t) = 1 + it \text{ for } t = 1,2,3,\ldots . \tag{1.5}$$

The accruing of interest according to this pattern is called *simple interest.*

It can be shown that a constant rate of simple interest does not imply a constant effective rate of interest. Let i be the constant rate of simple interest and let i_n be the effective rate of interest for the nth period, as defined in Section 1.3. Then we have

$$i_n = \frac{a(n) - a(n-1)}{a(n-1)} = \frac{[1 + in] - [1 + i(n-1)]}{1 + i(n-1)} = \frac{i}{1 + i(n-1)} \tag{1.6}$$

for $n = 1,2,3,\ldots$, which is a decreasing function of n. Thus, a constant rate of simple interest implies a decreasing effective rate of interest.

The accumulation function for simple interest has been defined only for values of t which are positive integers. However, it is natural to extend the definition to nonintegral values of $t > 0$ as well. This is equivalent to the crediting of interest proportionally over any fraction of a period. If this is the case, then the amount function can be represented by Figure 1.1(*a*). If interest is accrued only for completed periods with no credit for fractional periods, then the amount function becomes a step function with discontinuities as illustrated by Figure 1.1(*d*). Unless stated otherwise, it will be assumed that interest is accrued proportionally over fractional periods under simple interest.

A more rigorous derivation of simple interest for fractional periods is given in Appendix 1 at the end of the chapter.

Example 1.3 Find the accumulated value of $2000 invested for four years, if the rate of simple interest is 8% per annum.

Applying formula (1.5) we have

$$2000[1 + (.08)(4)] = \$2640.$$

Note that the amount of interest earned is 2640 - 2000 = $640. This could also have been obtained as 2000(.08)(4), or, in general, as $A(0) \cdot it$. In different notation, this becomes the familiar result from primary and secondary school

$$I = Prt \tag{1.7}$$

which states that the amount of interest is equal to the product of the amount of principal, the rate of interest, and the period of time.

Also, note that the effective rate of interest for the fourth year is

$$i_4 = \frac{.08}{1+.08(4-1)} = .0645, \text{ or } 6.45\%$$

by applying formula (1.6). This effective rate is well below the constant 8% simple interest rate and decreases as n increases.

1.5 COMPOUND INTEREST

Simple interest has the property that the interest is not reinvested to earn additional interest. For example, consider an investment of $100 for two years at 10% simple interest. Under simple interest the investor will receive $10 at the end of each of the two years. However, in reality, for the second year the investor has $110 which could have been invested. Clearly, it would be advantageous to invest the $110 at 10%, since the investor would then receive $11 in interest for the second year instead of $10.

The theory of *compound interest* handles this problem by assuming that the interest earned is automatically reinvested. The word "compound" refers to the process of interest being reinvested to earn additional interest. With compound interest the total investment of principal and interest earned to date is kept invested at all times.

It is now desired to find the accumulation function for compound interest. Consider the investment of 1 which accumulates to $1 + i$ at the end of the first period. This balance of $1 + i$ can be considered as principal at the beginning of the second period and will earn interest of $i(1+i)$ during the second period. The balance at the end of the second period is $(1+i) + i(1+i) = (1+i)^2$. Similarly, the balance of $(1+i)^2$ can be considered as principal at the beginning of the third period and will earn interest of $i(1+i)^2$ during the third period. The balance at the end of the third period is $(1+i)^2 + i(1+i)^2 = (1+i)^3$. Continuing this process indefinitely, we obtain

$$a(t) = (1+i)^t \text{ for } t = 1,2,3,\ldots \tag{1.8}$$

It can be shown that a constant rate of compound interest implies a constant effective rate of interest and, moreover, that the two are equal. Let i be the constant rate of compound interest and let i_n be the effective rate of interest for the nth period, as defined in Section 1.3. Then, we have

$$i_n = \frac{a(n)-a(n-1)}{a(n-1)} = \frac{(1+i)^n-(1+i)^{n-1}}{(1+i)^{n-1}} = \frac{(1+i)-1}{1} = i$$

which is independent of n. Thus, although defined differently, a rate of compound interest and the corresponding effective rate of interest are identical.

The result just derived can be compared with the result obtained in Section 1.4; namely, that a constant rate of simple interest implies a decreasing effective rate of interest. This result should be intuitively clear, since simple interest becomes progressively less favorable to the investor as the period of investment increases.

The accumulation function for compound interest has been defined only for values of t which are positive integers. It is necessary to develop the accumulation function for nonintegral values of $t>0$. The most straightforward method for doing this is simply to assume that formula (1.8) can be used for any value of $t>0$. This is equivalent to assuming compound interest over fractional periods as well as integral periods. A more rigorous derivation justifying this result is given in Appendix 1 at the end of the chapter.

Unless stated otherwise, it will be assumed that interest is accrued over fractional periods according to formula (1.8) under compound interest. Thus the amount function is exponential and can be represented by Figure 1.1(b). The exponential form of the amount function should not be unexpected, since many growth curves encountered in the natural sciences are exponential.

An interesting insight into the mathematical relationship between simple interest and compound interest can be obtained by performing a binomial expansion on $(1+i)^t$ in formula (1.8). If this binomial expansion is carried to two terms, we obtain $1+it$ appearing in formula (1.5) for simple interest.

Some readers may be troubled, on the one hand, by the statement that interest is paid at the end of the period and, on the other hand, by the statement that interest is accruing continuously. At first glance, the two statements appear contradictory. However, there is no inconsistency as long as interest is accrued over fractional periods as well as completed periods. When this is the case, the accumulated values at any point in time are equal from either perspective.

It is clear that simple and compound interest produce the same result over one measurement period. Over a longer period, compound interest produces a larger accumulated value than simple interest while the opposite is true over a shorter period. These results can be immediately obtained from the binomial expansion mentioned above and will be graphically displayed in Section 1.7.

Another insight into the conceptual difference between simple interest and compound interest can be seen from the two growth patterns involved. Under simple interest, it is the *absolute amount* of growth that is constant over equal periods of time; while under compound interest, it is the *relative rate* of growth that is constant. In terms of symbols, under simple interest

$$a(t+s) - a(t)$$

is independent of t, while under compound interest

$$\frac{a(t+s) - a(t)}{a(t)}$$

is independent of t.

Compound interest is used almost exclusively for financial transactions covering a period of one year or more and is often used for shorter term transactions as well. Simple interest is occasionally used for short-term transactions and as an approximation for compound interest over fractional periods.

The use of compound interest for completed periods and simple interest for a final fractional period can be analyzed as follows. Consider the investment of 1 for $n + k$ periods, where n is a non-negative integer and $0 < k < 1$. The use of simple interest for a final fractional period is equivalent to performing a linear interpolation between $(1 + i)^n$ and $(1 + i)^{n+1}$, where n is a non-negative integer. To see this we start with the linear interpolation

$$\begin{aligned}(1 + i)^{n+k} &\approx (1-k)(1+i)^n + k(1+i)^{n+1} \\ &= (1+i)^n\left[(1-k)+k(1+i)\right] \\ &= (1+i)^n(1+ki) \qquad (1.9)\end{aligned}$$

which is the formula if simple interest is used over the final fractional period. This technique will produce a slightly higher accumulated value than using compound interest throughout, as discussed above.

There is an implicit assumption in this section that the interest earned under compound interest is reinvested at the same rate as the original investment. Although this is often the case, many situations do arise in practice in which the interest earned is reinvested at a different rate. Section 7.4 contains an analysis of the results when the reinvestment rate for the interest earned differs from the rate on the original principal.

***Example 1.4** Rework Example 1.3 using compound interest instead of simple interest.*

The answer is

$$2000(1.08)^4 = \$2720.98.$$

This answer is in contrast with the answer of \$2640 using simple interest. The extra \$80.98 is the result of compounding of interest.

***Example 1.5** An investor age 35 deposits \$10,000 in a fund earning 7% compound interest until retirement at age 65. Find the amount of interest earned between ages 35 and 45, between ages 45 and 55, and between ages 55 and 65.*

Between ages 35 and 45 the amount of interest earned will be

$$A(10)-A(0) = 10{,}000\left[(1.07)^{10}-1\right] = \$9{,}671.51.$$

Between ages 45 and 55 the amount of interest earned will be

$$A(20)-A(10) = 10{,}000\left[(1.07)^{20}-(1.07)^{10}\right] = \$19{,}025.33.$$

Between ages 55 and 65 the amount of interest earned will be

$$A(30)-A(20) = 10{,}000\left[(1.07)^{30}-(1.07)^{20}\right] = \$37{,}425.71.$$

The total amount of interest earned over the 30 years is

$$9{,}671.51+19{,}025.33+37{,}425.71 = \$66{,}122.55.$$

This agrees with the total accumulated value

$$A(30)=10{,}000(1.07)^{30} = \$76{,}122.55$$

after deducting the original $10,000 investment.

Note that the amount of interest earned in the last 10-year period is nearly four times the amount earned in the first 10-year period. This vividly demonstrates the power of earning "interest on interest" when investing money over long periods of time at compound interest.

Also note that the ending balance is over 7 ½ times the beginning fund balance. This result clearly demonstrates the importance of starting early when investing for long-term goals such as retirement.

Example 1.6 Find the accumulated value of $5000 at the end of 5 years and 4 months invested at 9% per annum:
(1) Assuming compound interest throughout.
(2) Assuming simple interest during the final fractional period.

1. Assuming compound interest throughout, the answer is

$$5000(1.09)^{5\frac{1}{3}} = \$7197.32$$

by direct calculation.

2. Assuming simple interest during the final fractional period, the answer using formula (1.9) is

$$5000(1.09)^5(1.03) = \$7923.91.$$

The answer to part (2) is larger than part (1), illustrating that simple interest produces larger accumulated values over fractional periods than compound interest does, although the difference is small.

1.6 PRESENT VALUE

We have seen that an investment of 1 will accumulate to $1 + i$ at the end of one period. The term $1 + i$ is often called an *accumulation factor*, since it accumulates the value of an investment at the beginning of a period to its value at the end of the period.

It is often necessary to determine how much a person must invest initially so that the balance will be 1 at the end of one period. The answer is $(1+i)^{-1}$, since this amount will accumulate to 1 at the end of one period. We now define a new symbol v, such that

$$v = \frac{1}{1+i}. \tag{1.10}$$

The term v is often called a *discount factor*, since it "discounts" the value of an investment at the end of a period to its value at the beginning of the period.

We can generalize the above result to periods of time other than one period, i.e. to find the amount which a person must invest in order to accumulate an amount of 1 at the end of t periods. The answer is the reciprocal of the accumulation function $a^{-1}(t)$, since the accumulated value of this amount at the end of t periods is $a^{-1}(t)\cdot a(t)=1$. We will call $a^{-1}(t)$ the *discount function.*

Thus, we obtain the following results for $t \geq 0$:

$$\text{Simple Interest:} \quad a^{-1}(t) = \frac{1}{1+it} \tag{1.11}$$

$$\text{Compound Interest:} \quad a^{-1}(t) = \frac{1}{(1+t)^t} = v^t \tag{1.12}$$

As specified before, we will use compound interest unless stated otherwise.

In a sense, *accumulating* and *discounting* are opposite processes. The term $(1+i)^t$ is said to be the *accumulated value* of 1 at the end of t periods. The term v^t is said to be the *present value* (or *discounted value*) of 1 to be paid at the end of t periods.

The term "accumulated value" as defined above seems to refer strictly to payments made in the past, while the term "present value" seems to refer strictly to payments to be made in the future. This is the sense in which we will use the terms. Some writers have used "present value" to refer to either past or future payments. We will use the term *current value* for this purpose.

It is interesting to relate v^t to the accumulation function for compound interest from an alternate viewpoint. It is immediately clear that the values of v^t extend the definition of the accumulation function to negative values of t. Thus, the accumulation function for compound interest has meaning for all values of t. The graph of this function is shown in Figure 1.2.

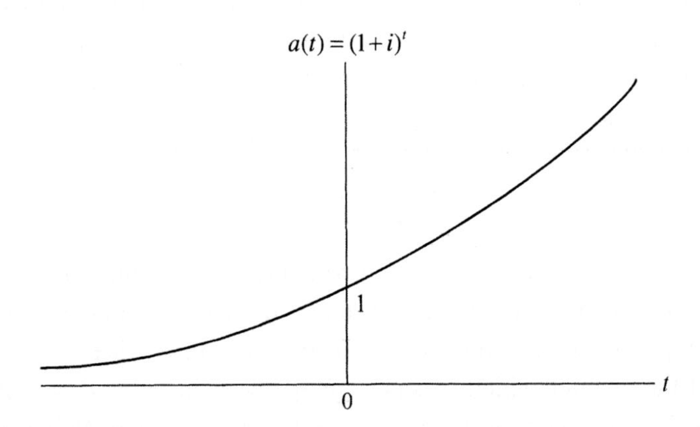

Figure 1.2 Accumulation function for compound interest

Example 1.7 Find the amount which must be invested at 9% per annum in order to accumulate $1000 at the end of three years:
(1) Assuming simple interest.
(2) Assuming compound interest.

1. Applying formula (1.11) the answer is

$$\frac{1000}{1+(.09)(3)} = \frac{1000}{1.27} = \$787.40.$$

2. Applying formula (1.12) the answer is

$$1000v^3 = \frac{1000}{(1.09)^3} = \$772.18.$$

From general reasoning, the reader should justify the relative magnitude of the answers to parts (1) and (2).

1.7 THE EFFECTIVE RATE OF DISCOUNT

In Section 1.3 the effective rate of interest was defined as a measure of interest paid at the end of the period. In this section we define the *effective rate of discount*, denoted by d, as a measure of interest paid at the beginning of the period.

A numerical illustration will help make this distinction clear. If A goes to a bank and borrows \$100 for one year at an effective rate of interest of 6%, then the bank will give A \$100. At the end of the year, A will repay the bank the original loan of \$100, plus interest of \$6, or a total of \$106.

However, if A borrows \$100 for one year at an effective rate of discount of 6%, then the bank will collect its interest of 6% in advance and will give A only \$94. At the end of the year, A will repay \$100.

Thus, it is clear that an effective rate of interest of 6% is not the same as an effective rate of discount of 6%. In the above example, A paid \$6 interest in both cases. However, in the case of interest paid at the end of the year, A had the use of \$100 for the year, while in the case of interest paid at the beginning of the year, A had the use of only \$94 for the year.

Looking at the above illustration in a slightly different manner, in the case of an effective rate of interest, the 6% is taken as a percentage of the balance at the beginning of the year, while in the case of an effective rate of discount, the 6% is taken as a percentage of the balance at the end of the year. Thus, we can formulate a precise definition of the effective rate of discount as follows:

The effective rate of discount d is the ratio of the amount of interest (sometimes called the "amount of discount" or just "discount") earned during the period to the amount invested at the end of the period.

This definition is analogous to the alternate definition of the effective rate of interest given in Section 1.3.

Several observations about the above definition are important:

1. Observations 1, 2, and 3 in Section 1.3 on the definition of the effective rate of interest also apply to the definition of the effective rate of discount.

2. The phrases *amount of discount* and *amount of interest* can be used interchangeably in situations involving rates of discount.

3. The definition does not use the word "principal," since the definition of principal refers to the amount invested at the beginning of the period, not the end of the period.

4. The key distinction between the effective rate of interest and the effective rate of discount can be summarized as follows:

   a) Interest--paid at the end of the period on the balance at the beginning of the period.
   b) Discount--paid at the beginning of the period on the balance at the end of the period.

Some readers may find the use of the word "paid" in connection with rates of discount somewhat confusing, since the borrower does not directly "pay" the interest as with rates of interest. However, the net result of deducting the interest in advance is no different than if the full amount is borrowed and then the borrower immediately pays the interest.

In fact, some readers may find the use of the word "paid" confusing in another sense as well. This confusion involves the possible implication that interest is "paid" in installments as it is earned rather than being accumulated to earn additional interest. We do not attach such a connotation to the word "paid," which can be used in either context above. Terms such as "charged" or "credited" might be preferred by those who find the word "paid" ambiguous in this sense.

Effective rates of discount can be calculated over any particular measurement period. Let d_n be the effective rate of discount during the nth period from the date of investment. A formula analogous to (1.4*b*) is

$$d_n = \frac{A(n) - A(n-1)}{A(n)} = \frac{I_n}{A(n)} \quad \text{for} \quad n = 1, 2, 3, \ldots. \tag{1.13}$$

As mentioned above, I_n may be commonly called either the "amount of discount" or the "amount of interest." In general, d_n may vary from period to period. However, if we have compound interest, in which case the effective rate of interest is constant, then the effective rate of discount is also constant. These situations are referred to as *compound discount*, a term analogous to "compound interest."

The illustration discussed earlier in this section showed that an effective rate of interest of 6% is not the same as an effective rate of discount of 6%. However, there is a definite relationship between effective rates of interest and effective rates of discount. To develop this relationship we need to define a concept of *equivalency* as follows:

Two rates of interest or discount are said to be equivalent if a given amount of principal invested for the same length of time at each of the rates produces the same accumulated value.

As we shall see in Section 1.8, this definition is applicable for nominal rates of interest and discount, as well as effective rates.

Assume that a person borrows 1 at an effective rate of discount d. Then, in effect, the original principal is $1 - d$ and the amount of interest (discount) is d. However, from the basic definition of i as the ratio of the amount of interest (discount) to the principal, we obtain

$$i = \frac{d}{1-d}. \tag{1.14}$$

This formula expresses i as a function of d.

By simple algebra, it is possible to express d as a function of i

$$\begin{aligned} i &= \frac{d}{1-d} \\ i - id &= d \\ d(1+i) &= i \\ d &= \frac{i}{1+i}. \end{aligned} \tag{1.15a}$$

Formula (1.15*a*) can be explained as a restatement of the definition of the effective rate of discount as the ratio of the amount of interest (discount) that 1 will earn during the period to the amount invested at the end of the period.

There are important relationships between d, a rate of discount, and v, a discount factor. One relationship is identical to (1.15*a*)

$$d = iv. \tag{1.15b}$$

This relationship has an interesting verbal interpretation. Interest earned on an investment of 1 paid at the beginning of the period is d. Interest earned on an investment of 1 paid at the end of the period is i. Therefore, if we discount i from the end of the period to the beginning of the period with the discount factor v, we obtain d.

There is another relationship between d and v which is often useful

$$\begin{aligned} d &= \frac{i}{1+i} \\ &= \frac{1+i}{1+i} - \frac{1}{1+i} \\ &= 1 - v. \end{aligned} \tag{1.16}$$

This relationship also can be interpreted verbally. Written in the form $v = 1 - d$, it is seen that both sides of the equation represent the present value of 1 to be paid at the end of the period.

There is one additional relationship between i and d that is significant:

$$\begin{aligned} d &= iv \\ &= i(1-d) \\ &= i - id \end{aligned}$$

or

$$i - d = id. \tag{1.17}$$

This relationship also has an interesting verbal interpretation. A person can either borrow 1 and repay $1 + i$ at the end of the period or borrow $1 - d$ and repay 1 at the end of the period. The expression $i - d$ is the difference in the amount of interest paid. This difference arises because the principal borrowed differs by d. Interest on amount d for one period at rate i is id.

The effective rate of discount, or compound discount, assumes compound interest. However, it is possible to define *simple discount* in a manner analogous to the definition of simple interest. Consider a situation in which the amount of discount earned during each period is constant. Then, the original principal which will produce an accumulated value of 1 at the end of t periods is

$$a^{-1}(t) \;=\; 1-dt \text{ for } 0 \le t < 1/d. \tag{1.18}$$

The second part of the inequality is necessary to keep $a^{-1}(t) > 0$. This contrasts with compound discount, in which case the present value is

$$a^{-1}(t) \;=\; v^t \;=\; (1-d)^t \text{ for } t \ge 0. \tag{1.19}$$

It should be noted that formulas (1.14), (1.15), (1.16), and (1.17) assume effective rates of interest and discount and are not valid for simple rates of interest and discount unless the period of investment happens to be exactly one period.

The reader should note that simple discount is not the same as simple interest. However, simple discount does have properties analogous, but opposite, to simple interest. The following results can be obtained by examining a binomial series expansion for the right-hand term in formula (1.19).

1. A constant rate of simple interest implies a decreasing effective rate of interest, as the period of investment increases, while a constant rate of simple discount implies an increasing effective rate of discount (and interest).

2. Simple and compound discount produce the same result over one measurement period. Over a longer period, simple discount produces a smaller present value than compound discount, while the opposite is true over a shorter period.

It is instructive to illustrate these results graphically. Figure 1.3(a) compares the accumulation function under simple interest and compound interest. Similarly, Figure 1.3(b) compares the discount function under simple discount and compound discount.

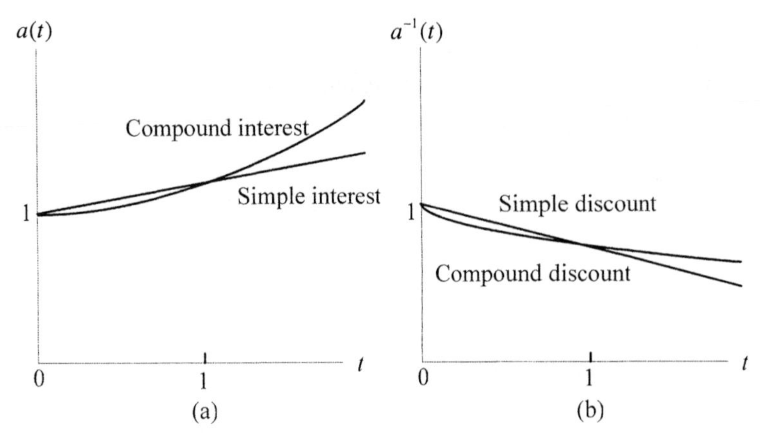

Figure 1.3 Comparisons of: (a) simple and compound interest, and (b) simple and compound discount

Simple discount is used only for short-term transactions and as an approximation for compound discount over fractional periods. It is not as widely used as simple interest. However, it does have one important application which will be discussed in Section 6.2.

The word "discount" unfortunately is used in two different contexts with various shades of meaning in each. It is used in connection with present values (discount factor, discount function, discounting, discounted value) and in connection with interest paid at the beginning of the period (effective rate of discount, amount of discount, compound discount, simple discount).

Unfortunately, terms involving the word "discount" are often misused in practice. For example, in the process of discounting, i.e. taking present values, the phrase "rate of discount" is often used when really "rate of interest" is meant. Yet another usage of the word "discount" will appear in Chapter 6. The term will be used to refer to bonds for which the price is less than the redemption value.

Exacerbating the confusion even further is a fourth use of the word "discount" to refer to price reductions. Although we do not attach this meaning to the word in this book, it commonly has this meaning in business and financial transactions. Needless to say, the reader should be careful in using the term "discount" to keep the meaning completely clear and should not hesitate to seek clarification from others using the term if there is any possibility of ambiguity.

Example 1.8 Rework Example 1.7:
(1) Assuming simple discount instead of simple interest.
(2) Assuming compound discount.

1. Applying formula (1.18) the answer is

$$1000[1-(.09)(3)] = \$730.$$

2. Applying formula (1.19) the answer is

$$1000(.91)^3 = \$753.57.$$

From general reasoning, the reader should justify the relative magnitudes of the answers to parts (1) and (2).

Example 1.9 For the $10,000 investment given in Example 1.1, find the effective rate of discount for the fourth year, i.e. d_4.

One method is to apply formula (1.13) which gives

$$d_4 = \frac{A(4)-A(3)}{A(4)} = \frac{12{,}153.96-11{,}575.20}{12{,}153.96} = .0476, \text{ or } 4.76\%.$$

A second method is to recall that the effective rate of interest for the fourth year, i_4, was found to equal .05 in Example 1.2. Then applying formula (1.15*a*) we have

$$d_4 = \frac{i_4}{1+i_4} = \frac{.05}{1+.05} = .0476, \text{ or } 4.76\%.$$

Example 1.10 Derive a formula analogous to formula (1.9) for computing present values using compound discount for completed periods and simple discount for a final fractional period.

Consider the present value of 1 to be paid at the end of $n+k$ periods, where n is a non-negative integer and $0<k<1$. If we perform a linear interpolation between v^n and v^{n+1}, we obtain

$$\begin{aligned} v^{n+k} = (1-d)^{n+k} &\approx (1-k)(1-d)^n + k(1-d)^{n+1} \\ &= (1-d)^n\left[(1-k)+k(1-d)\right] \\ &= v^n(1-kd). \end{aligned} \qquad (1.20)$$

Formula (1.20) uses compound discount for completed periods and a simple discount approximation for the final fractional period.

1.8 NOMINAL RATES OF INTEREST AND DISCOUNT

In Sections 1.3 and 1.7 effective rates of interest and discount were discussed. The term "effective" is used for rates of interest and discount in which interest is paid once per measurement period, either at the end of the period or at the beginning of the period, as the case may be. In this section, we consider situations in which interest is paid more frequently than once per measurement period. Rates of interest and discount in these cases are called "nominal."

Most persons have encountered such situations in practice. For example, Lender A might charge an annual effective rate of 9% on loans; Lender B might charge 8¾ % compounded quarterly; and Lender C might charge 8½ % payable in advance and convertible monthly. Most persons probably realize that these rates are not directly comparable, but they would probably not be able to make a valid comparison among them.

Lender A is charging an annual effective rate of interest, which has already been discussed. However, Lender B is charging what we call a nominal rate of interest, while Lender C is charging what we call a nominal rate of discount.

Various terms are used in practice to describe situations in which interest is paid more frequently than once per measurement period. Among these are "payable," "compounded," and "convertible," as in "payable quarterly," "compounded semiannually," and "convertible monthly." The frequency with which interest is paid and reinvested to earn additional interest is called the *interest conversion period.*

The three terms "payable," "compounded," and "convertible" are often used interchangeably. However, they do have different connotations to some users. For example, the term "compounded" seems to imply that the interest being earned is reinvested to earn additional interest, while the term "payable" seems to imply instead that the interest is paid out in installments as it is earned. The term "convertible" does not seem to possess either connotation. The reader is cautioned not to rely on such connotations when encountering these terms, but to ascertain exactly how the interest is computed and paid.

This section defines nominal rates of interest and discount and develops a systematic method of finding effective and nominal rates of interest and discount which are equivalent. The definition of "equivalency" was given in Section 1.7.

The symbol for a *nominal rate of interest* payable m times per period is $i^{(m)}$, where m is a positive integer > 1. By a nominal rate of interest $i^{(m)}$, we mean a rate payable $m$thly, i.e. the rate of interest is $i^{(m)}/m$ for each mth of a period and not $i^{(m)}$. For example, a nominal rate of 8% convertible quarterly does not mean an interest rate of 8% per quarter but rather an interest rate of 2% per quarter. In reality, we can say that a nominal rate of interest of $i^{(m)}$ per period is identical to an effective rate of interest of $i^{(m)}/m$ per mth of a period.

Thus, from the definition of equivalency we have

$$1+i = \left(1+\frac{i^{(m)}}{m}\right)^m \tag{1.21a}$$

since each side of the equation gives the accumulated value of 1 invested for one measurement period. Rearranging, we have

$$i = \left(1+\frac{i^{(m)}}{m}\right)^m - 1, \tag{1.21b}$$

and

$$i^{(m)} = m\left[(1+i)^{\frac{1}{m}} - 1\right]. \tag{1.21c}$$

Figure 1.4 illustrates accumulation at a nominal rate of interest for one measurement period. The diagonal arrows to the right can be interpreted as plus signs and downward arrows as equal signs.

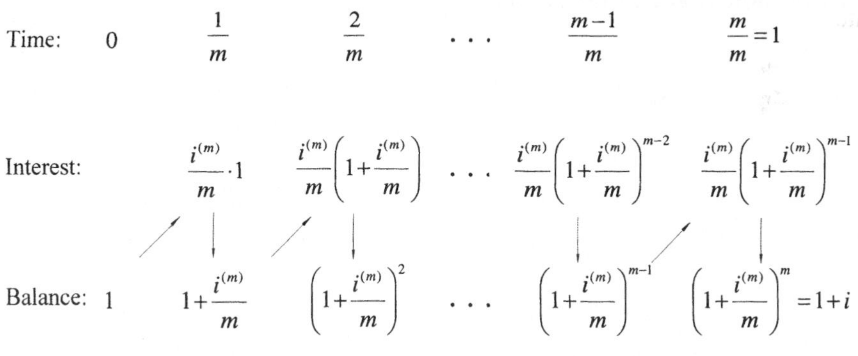

Time:	0	$\frac{1}{m}$	$\frac{2}{m}$	. . .	$\frac{m-1}{m}$	$\frac{m}{m}=1$
Interest:		$\frac{i^{(m)}}{m}\cdot 1$	$\frac{i^{(m)}}{m}\left(1+\frac{i^{(m)}}{m}\right)$	. . .	$\frac{i^{(m)}}{m}\left(1+\frac{i^{(m)}}{m}\right)^{m-2}$	$\frac{i^{(m)}}{m}\left(1+\frac{i^{(m)}}{m}\right)^{m-1}$
Balance:	1	$1+\frac{i^{(m)}}{m}$	$\left(1+\frac{i^{(m)}}{m}\right)^2$	. . .	$\left(1+\frac{i^{(m)}}{m}\right)^{m-1}$	$\left(1+\frac{i^{(m)}}{m}\right)^m = 1+i$

Figure 1.4 Illustration of nominal rates of interest

The symbol for a *nominal rate of discount* payable m times per period is $d^{(m)}$. By a nominal rate of discount $d^{(m)}$, we mean a rate payable $m$thly, i.e. the effective rate of discount is $d^{(m)}/m$ for each mth of a period.

The nominal rate of discount $d^{(m)}$, is a measure of interest paid at the beginning of $m$ths of a period in much the same manner as d is a measure of interest paid at the beginning of the period. By an argument similar to the one used in developing the relationship between $i^{(m)}$ and i, it is possible to develop a formula relating $d^{(m)}$ and d such that they are equivalent.

From the definition of equivalency we have

$$1-d = \left(1-\frac{d^{(m)}}{m}\right)^{m} \tag{1.22a}$$

since each side of the equation gives the present value of 1 to be paid at the end of one measurement period. Rearranging, we have

$$d = 1-\left(1-\frac{d^{(m)}}{m}\right)^{m} \tag{1.22b}$$

and

$$d^{(m)} = m\left[1-(1-d)^{\frac{1}{m}}\right] = m\left[1-v^{\frac{1}{m}}\right]. \tag{1.22c}$$

Figure 1.5 illustrates discounting at a nominal rate of discount for one measurement period. The diagonal arrows to the left can be interpreted as minus signs and downward arrows as equal signs.

Time:	0	$\frac{1}{m}$	$\cdots$	$\frac{m-2}{m}$	$\frac{m-1}{m}$	$\frac{m}{m}=1$
Discount:	$\frac{d^{(m)}}{m}\left(1-\frac{d^{(m)}}{m}\right)^{m-1}$	$\frac{d^{(m)}}{m}\left(1-\frac{d^{(m)}}{m}\right)^{m-2}$	$\cdots$	$\frac{d^{(m)}}{m}\left(1-\frac{d^{(m)}}{m}\right)$	$\frac{d^{(m)}}{m}\cdot 1$	
Balance:	$1-d=\left(1-\frac{d^{(m)}}{m}\right)^{m}$	$\left(1-\frac{d^{(m)}}{m}\right)^{m-1}$	$\cdots$	$\left(1-\frac{d^{(m)}}{m}\right)^{2}$	$1-\frac{d^{(m)}}{m}$	1

Figure 1.5 Illustration of nominal rates of discount

There is a close relationship between nominal rates of interest and nominal rates of discount. The following relationship holds, since both sides of the equation are equal to $1 + i$

$$\left(1+\frac{i^{(m)}}{m}\right)^{m} = \left(1-\frac{d^{(p)}}{p}\right)^{-p}. \tag{1.23a}$$

If $m = p$, then formula (1.22*a*) becomes

$$\left(1+\frac{i^{(m)}}{m}\right) = \left(1-\frac{d^{(m)}}{m}\right)^{-1}. \tag{1.23b}$$

If $m = 1$, then $i^{(m)} = i$, the effective rate of interest; and if $p = 1$, then $d^{(p)} = d$, the effective rate of discount. Thus formula (1.23*a*) can be used in general to find equivalent rates of interest or discount, either effective or nominal, convertible with any desired frequency.

Another relationship between $i^{(m)}$ and $d^{(m)}$ analogous to formula (1.17) is

$$\frac{i^{(m)}}{m} - \frac{d^{(m)}}{m} = \frac{i^{(m)}}{m} \cdot \frac{d^{(m)}}{m}. \tag{1.24}$$

The verbal interpretation of this result is similar to the verbal interpretation of formula (1.17). The derivation can be directly obtained as an algebraic rearrangement of formula (1.23*b*).

In developing the above formulas involving rates of interest and discount which are equivalent, the definition of equivalency given in Section 1.7 was used with a comparison over one measurement period. Although the use of one measurement period is arbitrary, the reader should verify that under compound interest and discount the rates that are equivalent do not depend on the period of time chosen for the comparison. However, for other patterns of interest development, such as simple interest and simple discount, the rates that are equivalent will depend on the period of time chosen for the comparison.

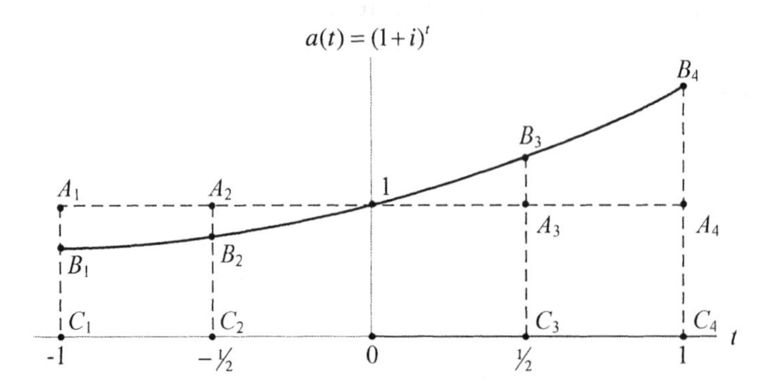

Figure 1.6 Accumulation function illustrating nominal rates of interest and discount

It is instructive to relate nominal rates of interest and discount to the accumulation function $a(t)$. An example is given in Figure 1.6 for $m = 2$. The reader is encouraged to construct other examples. The following relationships hold graphically:

$$A_1B_1 = d \qquad B_1C_1 = v \qquad = \left(1 - \frac{d^{(2)}}{2}\right)^2$$

$$A_2B_2 = \frac{d^{(2)}}{2} \qquad B_2C_2 = v^{1/2} \qquad = 1 - \frac{d^{(2)}}{2}$$

$$A_3B_3 = \frac{i^{(2)}}{2} \qquad B_3C_3 = (1+i)^{1/2} \qquad = 1 + \frac{i^{(2)}}{2}$$

$$A_4B_4 = i \qquad B_4C_4 = 1+i \qquad = \left(1 + \frac{i^{(2)}}{2}\right)^2$$

It is interesting to note that nominal rates of interest and discount are not relevant under simple interest and simple discount. Since the amount of interest or discount is directly proportional to the time involved, a rate of simple interest or simple discount payable *m*thly is no different than one payable once per measurement period.

As with the word "discount," unfortunately the word "nominal" also has multiple meanings. In Section 6.3 "nominal" is used in another sense in connection with yields on bonds, while in Section 9.4 "nominal" takes on a different meaning in connection with the reflection of inflation in rates of interest.

Example 1.11 Find the accumulated value of $500 invested for five years at 8% per annum convertible quarterly.

The answer is

$$500\left(1+\frac{.08}{4}\right)^{4\cdot 5} = 500\,(1.02)^{20} = \$742.97.$$

It should be noted that this situation is equivalent to one in which $500 is invested at a rate of interest of 2% for 20 years.

Example 1.12 Find the present value of $1000 to be paid at the end of six years at 6% per annum payable in advance and convertible semiannually.

The answer is

$$1000\left(1-\frac{.06}{2}\right)^{2.6} = 1000(.97)^{12} = \$693.84.$$

It should be noted that this situation is equivalent to one in which the present value of $1000 to be paid at the end of 12 years is calculated at a rate of discount of 3%.

Example 1.13 Find the nominal rate of interest convertible quarterly which is equivalent to a nominal rate of discount of 6% per annum convertible monthly.

Using formula (1.23*a*)

$$\left(1+\frac{i^{(4)}}{4}\right)^{4} = \left(1-\frac{.06}{12}\right)^{-12}$$

$$1+\frac{i^{(4)}}{4} = (.995)^{-3}$$

$$i^{(4)} = 4\left[(.995)^{-3}-1\right] = .0606, \text{ or } 6.06\%.$$

1.9 FORCES OF INTEREST AND DISCOUNT

The measures of interest defined in the preceding sections are useful for measuring interest over specified intervals of time. Effective rates of interest and discount measure interest over one measurement period, while nominal rates of interest and discount measure interest over $m$ths of a measurement period.

It is also important to be able to measure the intensity with which interest is operating at each moment of time, i.e. over infinitesimally small intervals of time. This measure of interest at individual moments of time is called the *force of interest.*

Consider the investment of a fund such that the amount in the fund at time t is given by the amount function $A(t)$. Recall that the only factor operating on the fund is the growth of the fund through interest, i.e. no principal is added or withdrawn.

The intensity with which interest is operating at time t is measured by the rate of change or the slope of the $A(t)$ curve at time t. From elementary calculus, the slope of the $A(t)$ curve at time t is given by the derivative at that point.

However, as a measure of interest, $A'(t)$ is unsatisfactory, since it depends on the amount invested. For example, if \$200 and \$100 are invested under identical conditions, the rate of change of the \$200 fund will be twice as great as the rate of change of the \$100 fund. However, interest is not operating with twice the intensity on the \$200 fund; in fact, we would say that it is operating with the same intensity on both funds.

We can compensate for this by dividing $A'(t)$ by the amount in the fund at time t, namely $A(t)$. This gives a measure of the intensity with which interest is operating at time t expressed as a rate independent of the amount in the fund, i.e. as a rate per dollar in the fund. Thus, the force of interest at time t, denoted by δ_t, is defined as

$$\delta_t = \frac{A'(t)}{A(t)} = \frac{a'(t)}{a(t)}. \tag{1.25}$$

The following properties of δ_t should be kept in mind:

1. δ_t is a measure of the intensity of interest at exact time t.
2. δ_t expresses this measurement as a rate per measurement period.

It is possible to write an expression for the value of $A(t)$ and $a(t)$ in terms of the function δ_t. It will be seen from formula (1.25) that an alternate expression for δ_t is

$$\delta_t = \frac{d}{dt}\ln A(t) = \frac{d}{dt}\ln a(t). \tag{1.26}$$

Replacing t by r and integrating both sides between the limits 0 and t

$$\int_0^t \delta_r\,dr = \int_0^t \frac{d}{dr}\ln A(r)\,dr$$
$$= \ln A(r)\Big]_0^t = \ln\frac{A(t)}{A(0)}$$

and hence we have

$$e^{\int_0^t \delta_r dr} = \frac{A(t)}{A(0)} = \frac{a(t)}{a(0)} = a(t). \tag{1.27}$$

Another formula can be obtained from formula (1.25) written as $A(t)\delta_t = A'(t)$. Integrating between the limits 0 and n, we obtain

$$\int_0^n A(t)\delta_t\,dt = \int_0^n A'(t)\,dt = A(t)\Big]_0^n = A(n) - A(0). \tag{1.28}$$

Formula (1.28) has an interesting verbal interpretation. The term $A(n)-A(0)$ is the amount of interest earned over n measurement periods. The differential expression $A(t)\delta_t dt$ may be interpreted as the amount of interest earned on amount $A(t)$ at exact time t due to the force of interest δ_t. When this expression is integrated between limits 0 and n, it gives the total amount of interest earned over the n periods.

Further insight into the nature of the force of interest may be gained by analyzing formula (1.25) in terms of the definition of the derivative. The derivative of $A(t)$ may be expressed as

$$A'(t) = \lim_{h\to 0}\frac{A(t+h)-A(t)}{h}$$

and δ_t from formula (1.25) may then be written

$$\delta_t = \frac{A'(t)}{A(t)} = \lim_{h\to 0}\frac{A(t+h)-A(t)}{hA(t)}. \tag{1.29}$$

Now the expression $\dfrac{A(t+h)-A(t)}{hA(t)}$ may be regarded as the rate of interest based upon the interest earned during the interval from time t to time $t + h$. For example, if $h=1$, we have $\dfrac{A(t+1)-A(t)}{A(t)}$, which is one period's increment in the fund divided by the amount in the fund at the beginning of the period. If $h = 1/2$, we have $2 \cdot \dfrac{A(t+1/2)-A(t)}{A(t)}$, which is twice half a period's increment in the fund divided by the amount in the fund at the beginning of the period. As h approaches 0, the limit of this expression, the force of interest, may be described as the nominal rate of interest based upon the intensity of interest at time t.

It is also possible to define a *force of discount* analogous to formula (1.25). For this purpose, we use the discount function $a^{-1}(t)$ instead of the accumulation function $a(t)$. The definition of the force of discount at time t, denoted by δ_t', is given by

$$\delta_t' = -\frac{\frac{d}{dt}a^{-1}(t)}{a^{-1}(t)}. \tag{1.30}$$

The definition of δ_t' is completely analogous to the definition of δ_t except for the minus sign. The minus sign is necessary to make the force of discount a positive quantity. The denominator of formula (1.30) is positive but the numerator is negative, since $a^{-1}(t)$ is a decreasing function.

Later in this section it will be seen that the force of discount bears a relationship to nominal and effective rates of discount similar to the relationship that the force of interest bears to nominal and effective rates of interest. However, it can be shown that $\delta_t' = \delta_t$, so that we may dispense with δ_t' and use δ_t. The proof is as follows:

$$\begin{aligned}
\delta_t' &= -\frac{\frac{d}{dt}a^{-1}(t)}{a^{-1}(t)} \\
&= \frac{a^{-2}(t)\frac{d}{dt}a(t)}{a^{-1}(t)} \\
&= \frac{a^{-2}(t)a(t)\delta_t}{a^{-1}(t)} \quad \text{from formula (1.25)} \\
&= \delta_t.
\end{aligned}$$

In theory, the force of interest may vary instantaneously. However, in practice it is often constant. If the force of interest is constant over an interval of time, then the effective rate of interest will also be constant over that interval. This can be seen by using formula (1.27) over n measurement periods (n a positive integer)

$$\begin{aligned} e^{\int_0^n \delta_t dt} &= e^{n\delta} \text{ if } \delta_t = \delta \text{ for } 0 \le t \le n \\ &= a(n) \\ &= (1+i)^n \end{aligned}$$

so that

$$e^{\delta} = 1+i \tag{1.31}$$

or

$$i = e^{\delta} - 1 \tag{1.32}$$

which expresses i as a function of δ. Taking the logarithm of formula (1.31) expresses δ as a function of i

$$\delta = \ln(1+i). \tag{1.33}$$

Formula (1.33) may also be derived directly from the accumulation function for compound interest

$$\delta_t = \frac{\frac{d}{dt}(1+i)^t}{(1+i)^t} = \frac{(1+i)^t \ln(1+i)}{(1+i)^t} = \ln(1+i)$$

which is constant for all t.

Having related δ and i immediately relates δ and the other measures of interest described in this chapter. The following series of equalities is an expanded version of formula (1.23*a*) which summarizes much of the material contained in this chapter:

$$\left(1 + \frac{i^{(m)}}{m}\right)^m = 1+i = v^{-1} = (1-d)^{-1} = \left(1 - \frac{d^{(p)}}{p}\right)^{-p} = e^{\delta}. \tag{1.34}$$

It is instructive to examine the behavior of the force of interest under simple interest and simple discount. For simple interest we have

$$\begin{aligned}\delta_t &= \frac{\frac{d}{dt}a(t)}{a(t)} \\ &= \frac{\frac{d}{dt}(1+it)}{1+it} \\ &= \frac{i}{1+it} \quad \text{for } 0 \le t. \qquad (1.35)\end{aligned}$$

Similarly, for simple discount we have

$$\begin{aligned}\delta_t = \delta_t' &= -\frac{\frac{d}{dt}a^{-1}(t)}{a^{-1}(t)} \\ &= -\frac{\frac{d}{dt}(1-dt)}{1-dt} \\ &= \frac{d}{1-dt} \quad \text{for } 0 \le t < 1/d. \qquad (1.36)\end{aligned}$$

The upper restriction on values of t in formula (1.36) is necessary to have values of δ_t that are finite and positive. As we would expect, δ_t is a decreasing function of t for simple interest, but an increasing function of t for simple discount.

The reader may be surprised to observe that although a constant force of interest δ leads to a constant effective rate of interest i, the reverse is not necessarily true. To see this possibility, consider n measurement periods (n a positive integer). Again, we have

$$a(n) = (1+i)^n = e^{\int_0^n \delta_r dr}.$$

However, if we subdivide the n-period integral into a sum of one-period integrals, we have

$$\begin{aligned}(1+i)^n &= e^{\left[\int_0^1 \delta_t dt + \int_1^2 \delta_t dt + \cdots + \int_{n-1}^n \delta_t dt\right]} \\ &= e^{\int_0^1 \delta_t dt} e^{\int_1^2 \delta_t dt} \ldots e^{\int_{n-1}^n \delta_t dt}.\end{aligned}$$

If we allow δ_t to vary within each of these measurement periods in such a way that all the one-period integrals are equal, then we would have the result that i is constant for each of the n periods, but δ_t varies within each of these periods.

A good practical example to illustrate this phenomenon is to invest 1 for n periods at compound interest for completed periods, but use simple interest over fractional periods as illustrated in formula (1.9). This produces a growth pattern of $(1+i)^k$ for $k = 1, 2, \ldots, n$, so that the effective rate of interest is constant over the n measurement periods. However, δ_t varies within each of these periods, since δ_t varies under simple interest. Other examples could be constructed to illustrate the same point, but they would generally involve more esoteric patterns for the variation in δ_t.

Another interesting insight into the nature of the force of interest can be obtained by analyzing δ in terms of $i^{(m)}$. From formula (1.34)

$$\left(1+\frac{i^{(m)}}{m}\right)^m = e^{\delta}$$

$$i^{(m)} = m\left[e^{\frac{\delta}{m}}-1\right].$$

Now using a Taylor series expansion for $e^{\delta/m}$, we have

$$\begin{aligned} i^{(m)} &= m\left[\frac{\delta}{m} + \frac{1}{2!}\left(\frac{\delta}{m}\right)^2 + \frac{1}{3!}\left(\frac{\delta}{m}\right)^3 + \cdots\right] \\ &= \delta + \frac{\delta^2}{2!m} + \frac{\delta^3}{3!m^2} + \cdots \end{aligned}$$

and taking the limit as m approaches infinity,

$$\lim_{m\to\infty} i^{(m)} = \delta. \tag{1.37}$$

This formula has intuitive appeal. Since $i^{(m)}$ is a nominal rate of interest convertible $m$thly, we can interpret δ as a nominal rate of interest convertible continuously.

By an analogous argument, it is possible to show that

$$\lim_{m\to\infty} d^{(m)} = \delta. \tag{1.38}$$

The proof is analogous. This formula also has intuitive appeal. Since $d^{(m)}$ is a nominal rate of discount convertible *m*thly, we can interpret δ as a nominal rate of discount convertible continuously. In essence, this is an alternate proof that the force of interest and the force of discount are equal.

The force of interest is a useful conceptual device, making the continuous growth of money at compound interest similar to growth functions encountered in the natural sciences. In theory, the most fundamental measure of interest is the force of interest. In practice, however, effective and nominal rates of interest and discount tend to be used more frequently because they are simpler for most people to comprehend and because most financial transactions involve discrete, not continuous, processes.

This does not mean that the force of interest is devoid of practical significance. Besides being a useful conceptual and analytical tool, it can be used in practice as an approximation to interest converted very frequently, such as daily. Also, some financial institutions actually have started to use continuous compounding in recent years. Finally, the force of interest is important in the development of certain of the more advanced financial models considered in Chapters 9-13.

Example 1.14 Find the accumulated value of $1000 invested for ten years if the force of interest is 5%.

Applying formula (1.31) the answer is

$$1000e^{(.05)(10)} = 1000e^{.5} = \$1648.72.$$

Example 1.15 Find the accumulated value of 1 at the end of n years if

$$\boldsymbol{\delta_t = \frac{1}{1+t}}.$$

Using formula (1.27), the answer is

$$e^{\int_0^n \delta_t dt} = e^{\int_0^n \frac{1}{(1+t)}dt} = e^{\ln(1+t)\big]_0^n} = 1+n.$$

Example 1.16 ***Money accumulates at a varying force of interest***

$$\delta_t = .05 + .01t \quad \text{for} \quad 0 \le t \le 4.$$

Find the present value at time t = 0 of two payments of 100 each to be paid at times t = 2 and t = 4.

Applying the reciprocal of formula (1.27), the present value of the first payment is

$$\begin{aligned} 100e^{-\int_0^2 \delta_t dt} &= 100e^{-\int_0^2 (.05+.01t)dt} \\ &= 100e^{-.12} \\ &= 88.692. \end{aligned}$$

Similarly, the present value of the second payment is

$$\begin{aligned} 100e^{-\int_0^4 \delta_t dt} &= 100e^{-\int_0^4 (.05+.01t)dt} \\ &= 100e^{-.28} \\ &= 75.578. \end{aligned}$$

Thus, the answer is $88.692 + 75.578 = \$164.27$.

1.10 VARYING INTEREST

This section is concerned with situations involving varying interest. Actually we have already seen a few problems involving varying interest in prior sections. First, Examples 1.2 and 1.9 involved varying effective rates of interest and discount, respectively. Second, Examples 1.15 and 1.16 involved varying forces of interest. Third, a few of the Exercises in prior sections involved varying interest.

Any problem involving varying interest can be analyzed from first principles. In the remainder of this section, we will analyze two types of varying interest that are commonly encountered in practice.

The first type of variation considered involves changes in the effective rate of interest over a period of time. This type of variation is probably the one most commonly encountered in practice. As before, let i_k denote the effective rate of interest during the kth period from the date of investment. Then for positive integers $t \ge 1$, we have

$$a(t) = (1+i_1)(1+i_2)\cdots(1+i_t) = \prod_{k=1}^{t}(1+i_k). \tag{1.39}$$

If $i_1 = i_2 = \ldots = i_t = i$, the familiar result $a(t) = (1+i)^t$ is obtained.

Present values with varying effective rates of interest can be handled similarly. Again, for positive integers t ≥ 1 we have

$$a^{-1}(t) = (1+i_1)^{-1}(1+i_2)^{-1}\cdots(1+i_t)^{-1} = \prod_{k=1}^{t}(1+i_k)^{-1} = \prod_{k=1}^{t} v_k. \qquad (1.40)$$

The approach followed in formulas (1.39) and (1.40) can be easily generalized to include nominal rates of interest or discount. All that is necessary is to count the number of interest conversion periods in each bracketed subinterval in which the rates are constant and then multiply the appropriate factors for each subinterval across the entire interval. This procedure is illustrated in Example 1.17.

Frequently, in situations involving varying interest it is desired to find an equivalent level rate to the rates that vary. When this situation is encountered, the definition of equivalency given in Section 1.7 can be applied directly. However, it is important to note that the answers will depend on the period of time chosen for the comparison. Since interest is varying, the rate that would be equivalent over a period of one length would not be the same as that over a period of a different length.

The second type of variation considered involves a force of interest which varies from period to period, but is constant during each period. We have a notational problem, since the symbol δ_k refers to a continuously varying force of interest.

As before, let i_k denote the effective rate of interest during the *k*th period from the date of investment where *k* is a positive integer. We can then define $\delta_{[k]}$ as the (level) force of interest equivalent to i_k during the *k*th period. By adapting formula (1.33) we obtain

$$\delta_{[k]} = \ln(1+i_k). \qquad (1.41)$$

Then for positive integer $t \geq 1$ we can adapt formula (1.27) to give

$$a(t) = e^{\int_0^t \delta_r dr} = e^{\sum_{k=1}^{t} \delta_{[k]}} \qquad (1.42)$$

for accumulated values. The corresponding formula for present values would be

$$a^{-1}(t) = e^{-\sum_{k=1}^{t}\delta_{[k]}} \tag{1.43}$$

for positive integers $t \geq 1$.

This second type of variation may initially strike the reader as a curious, and somewhat artificial, mixture of continuous and discrete processes. However, it is frequently used in more advanced financial analysis beyond the scope of this book. Also, it is quite easy to apply in practice, as will be illustrated in Example 1.19.

***Example 1.17** Find the accumulated value of $1000 at the end of 15 years if the effective rate of interest is 5% for the first 5 years, 4 1/2% for the second 5 years, and 4% for the third 5 years.*

Using formula (1.39), the answer is

$$1000(1.05)^5(1.045)^5(1.04)^5 = \$1935.05.$$

***Example 1.18** An investor in common stock measures investment returns annually using an effective rate of interest. The investor earns 15% during the first year, -5% during the second year, and 8% during the third year. Find the equivalent level effective rate of return over the three-year period.*

This example contains a negative return in one year which has not been considered before. The effective rates of return for the three years are:

$$\begin{aligned} i_1 &= .15 \\ i_2 &= -.05 \\ i_3 &= .08. \end{aligned}$$

The equivalent level effective rate i is determined from

$$\begin{aligned} a(3) = (1+i)^3 &= (1+i_1)(1+i_2)(1+i_3) \\ &= (1.15)(.95)(1.08) \end{aligned}$$

which gives

$$i = \left[(1.15)(.95)(1.08)\right]^{\frac{1}{3}} - 1 = .0567, \text{ or } 5.67\%.$$

Example 1.19 Rework Example 1.18 if the returns given are continuous measures, i.e. forces of interest, rather than effective rates.

We now have the continuous rates of return given as

$$\delta_{[1]} = .15$$
$$\delta_{[2]} = -.05$$
$$\delta_{[3]} = .08.$$

Per dollar originally invested, formula (1.42) gives the value of the investment at time $t = 3$ as

$$a(3) = e^{.15-.05+.08} = e^{.18}.$$

The equivalent level continuous return δ over the three-year period is given by

$$a(3) = e^{3\delta} = e^{.18},$$

so that $\delta = .06$, or 6%. Note that the equivalent level continuous return is simply the arithmetic mean of the individual annual continuous returns.

Amazingly, determining the equivalent level continuous return is a bit more straightforward than determining the equivalent level effective return!

1.11 SUMMARY OF RESULTS

Table 1.1 summarizes much of the material of this chapter

Table 1.1 Summary of Relationships in Chapter 1

Rate of interest or discount	*The accumulated value of* 1 *at time* $t = a(t)$	*The present value of* 1 *at time* $t = a^{-1}(t)$
Compound interest		
i	$(1+i)^t$	$v^t = (1+i)^{-t}$
$i^{(m)}$	$\left(1+\frac{i^{(m)}}{m}\right)^{mt}$	$\left(1+\frac{i^{(m)}}{m}\right)^{-mt}$
d	$(1-d)^{-t}$	$(1-d)^t$
$d^{(m)}$	$\left(1-\frac{d^{(m)}}{m}\right)^{-mt}$	$\left(1-\frac{d^{(m)}}{m}\right)^{mt}$
δ	$e^{\delta t}$	$e^{-\delta t}$
Simple interest		
i	$1 + it$	$(1+it)^{-1}$
Simple discount		
d	$(1-dt)^{-1}$	$1 - dt$

APPENDIX 1

Simple interest for fractional periods

A more rigorous mathematical approach to the definition of $a(t)$ for nonintegral values of t can be developed by starting with the following property we would want simple interest to possess:

$$a(t+s) = a(t) + a(s) - 1 \text{ for } t \geq 0 \text{ and } s \geq 0. \tag{1.44}$$

In essence, formula (1.44) says that under simple interest the amount of interest earned by an initial investment of one unit over $t + s$ periods is equal to the amount of interest earned over t periods plus the amount of interest earned over s periods. The -1 is necessary in formula (1.44), since otherwise there would be an investment of two units on the right-hand side of the equation.

Assuming $a(t)$ is differentiable, from the definition of the derivative we have

$$\begin{aligned} a'(t) &= \lim_{s\to 0}\frac{a(t+s)-a(t)}{s} \\ &= \lim_{s\to 0}\frac{\left[a(t)+a(s)-1\right]-a(t)}{s} \\ &= \lim_{s\to 0}\frac{a(s)-1}{s} \\ &= \lim_{s\to 0}\frac{a(s)-a(0)}{s} \\ &= a'(0), \text{ a constant.} \end{aligned}$$

Replacing t by r and integrating both sides between the limits 0 and t, we have

$$\begin{aligned} \int_0^t a'(r)\,dr &= \int_0^t a'(0)\,dr \\ a(t)-a(0) &= t\cdot a'(0) \\ a(t) &= 1+t\cdot a'(0) \end{aligned}$$

If we let $t = 1$ and remember that $a(1) = 1 + i$, we have

$$a(1) = 1+i = 1+a'(0)$$

so that $a'(0)=i$. Thus, substituting back we have the familiar result

$$a(t) = 1 + it \text{ for } t \geq 0. \tag{1.5}$$

The above derivation does not depend on t being a positive integer, and is valid for all $t \geq 0$.

Compound interest for fractional periods

We start with the following property we would want compound interest to possess:

$$a(t+s) = a(t) \cdot a(s) \text{ for } t \geq 0 \text{ and } s \geq 0. \tag{1.45}$$

In essence, formula (1.45) says that under compound interest the amount of interest earned by an initial investment of one unit over $t + s$ periods is equal to the amount of interest earned if the investment is terminated at the end of t periods and the accumulated value at that point is immediately reinvested for an additional s periods.

Assuming $a(t)$ is differentiable, from the definition of the derivative we have

$$\begin{aligned} a'(t) &= \lim_{s \to 0} \frac{a(t+s)-a(t)}{s} \\ &= \lim_{s \to 0} \frac{a(t) \cdot a(s)-a(t)}{s} \\ &= a(t) \lim_{s \to 0} \frac{a(s)-1}{s} \\ &= a(t) \cdot a'(0). \end{aligned}$$

Thus

$$\frac{a'(t)}{a(t)} = \frac{d}{dt} \ln a(t) = a'(0).$$

Replacing t by r and integrating both sides between the limits 0 and t, we have

$$\begin{aligned} \int_0^t \frac{d}{dr} \ln a(r)\,dr &= \int_0^t a'(0)\,dr \\ \ln a(t) - \ln a(0) &= t \cdot a'(0) \\ \ln a(t) &= t \cdot a'(0) \end{aligned}$$

since $\ln\ a(0) = 0$. If we let $t = 1$ and remember that $a(1) = 1 + i$, we have

$$\ln\ a(1) = \ln\ (1+i) = a'(0).$$

Thus, substituting back we have the result

$$\ln a(t) = t \ln (1+i) = \ln (1+i)^t$$

or

$$a(t) = (1+i)^t \text{ for } t \geq 0. \tag{1.8}$$

The above derivation does not depend on t being a positive integer, and is valid for all $t \geq 0$.

EXERCISES

1.2 The accumulation and amount functions

1. Consider the amount function $A(t) = t^2 + 2t + 3$.
   a) Find the corresponding accumulation function $a(t)$.
   b) Verify that $a(t)$ satisfies the three properties of an accumulation function.
   c) Find I_n.

2. *a*) Prove that $A(n) - A(0) = I_1 + I_2 + \cdots + I_n$.
   b) Verbally interpret the result obtained in (*a*).

3. For the \$5000 investment given in Example 1.1, find the amount of interest earned during the second year of investment, i.e. between times $t = 3$ and $t = 4$.

4. It is known that $a(t)$ is of the form $at^2 + b$. If \$100 invested at time 0 accumulates to \$172 at time 3, find the accumulated value at time 10 of \$100 invested at time 5.

1.3 The effective rate of interest

5. Assume that $A(t) = 100 + 5t$.
   a) Find i_5.
   b) Find i_{10}.

6. Assume that $A(t) = 100(1.1)^t$.
   a) Find i_5.
   b) Find i_{10}.

7. Show that $A(n) = (1 + i_n)A(n-1)$, where n is a positive integer.

8. If $A(4) = 1000$ and $i_n = .01n$, where n is a positive integer, find $A(7)$.

1.4 Simple interest

9. *a*) At what rate of simple interest will \$500 accumulate to \$615 in 2 1/2 years?
   b) In how many years will \$500 accumulate to \$630 at 7.8% simple interest?

10. At a certain rate of simple interest \$1000 will accumulate to \$1110 after a certain period of time. Find the accumulated value of \$500 at a rate of simple interest three fourths as great over twice as long a period of time.

11. Simple interest of $i = 4\%$ is being credited to a fund. In which period is this equivalent to an effective rate of 2 1/2%?

12. A deposit of \$1000 is invested at simple interest at time $t = 0$. The rate of simple interest during year t is equal to $.01t$ for $t = 1, 2, 3, 4,$ and 5. Find the total accumulated value of this investment at time $t = 5$.

1.5 Compound interest

13. It is known that \$600 invested for two years will earn \$264 in interest. Find the accumulated value of \$2000 invested at the same rate of compound interest for three years.

14. Show that the ratio of the accumulated value of 1 invested at rate i for n periods, to the accumulated value of 1 invested at rate j for n periods, $i > j$, is equal to the accumulated value of 1 invested for n periods at rate r. Find an expression for r as a function of i and j.

15. At a certain rate of compound interest, 1 will increase to 2 in a years, 2 will increase to 3 in b years, and 3 will increase to 15 in c years. If 6 will increase to 10 in n years, express n as a function of a, b, and c.

16. An amount of money is invested for one year at a rate of interest of 3% per quarter. Let $D(k)$ be the difference between the amount of interest earned on a compound interest basis and on a simple interest basis for quarter k, where $k = 1, 2, 3, 4$. Find the ratio of $D(4)$ to $D(3)$.

1.6 Present value

17. The two sets of grandparents for a newborn baby wish to invest enough money immediately to pay \$10,000 per year for four years toward college costs starting at age 18. Grandparents A agree to fund the first two payments, while Grandparents B agree to fund the last two payments. If the effective rate of interest is 6% per annum, find the difference between the contributions of Grandparents A and B.

18. The sum of the present value of 1 paid at the end of n periods and 1 paid at the end of $2n$ periods is 1. Find $(1 + i)^{2n}$.

19. It is known that an investment of \$500 will increase to \$4000 at the end of 30 years. Find the sum of the present values of three payments of \$10,000 each which will occur at the end of 20, 40, and 60 years.

1.7 The effective rate of discount

20. *a*) Find d_5 if the rate of simple interest is 10%.
    b) Find d_5 if the rate of simple discount is 10%.

21. Find the effective rate of discount at which a payment of \$200 immediately and \$300 one year from today will accumulate to \$600 two years from today.

22. The amount of interest earned on A for one year is \$336, while the equivalent amount of discount is \$300. Find A.

23. Find the present value of \$5000 to be paid at the end of 25 months at a rate of discount of 8% convertible quarterly:
    a) Assuming compound discount throughout.
    b) Assuming simple discount during the final fractional period.

24. Show that

$$\frac{d^3}{(1-d)^2} = \frac{(i-d)^2}{1-v}.$$

25. If i and d are equivalent rates of simple interest and simple discount over t periods, show that

$$i - d = idt.$$

1.8 Nominal rates of interest and discount

26. *a*) Express $d^{(4)}$ as a function of $i^{(3)}$.
    b) Express $i^{(6)}$ as a function of $d^{(2)}$.

27. *a*) Show that $i^{(m)} = d^{(m)}(1+i)^{1/m}$.
    b) Verbally interpret the result obtained in (*a*).

28. Find the accumulated value of \$100 at the end of two years:
    a) If the nominal annual rate of interest is 6% convertible quarterly.
    b) If the nominal annual rate of discount is 6% convertible once every four years.

29. Given that $i^{(m)} = .1844144$ and $d^{(m)} = .1802608$, find m.

30. It is known that

$$1 + \frac{i^{(n)}}{n} = \frac{1 + \frac{i^{(4)}}{4}}{1 + \frac{i^{(5)}}{5}}.$$

Find n.

31. If $r = \frac{i^{(4)}}{d^{(4)}}$, express v in terms of r.

1.9 Forces of interest and discount

32. Rank i, $i^{(m)}$, d, $d^{(m)}$, and δ in increasing order of magnitude, assuming $m > 1$.

33. *a*) Obtain an expression for δ_t if $A(t) = Ka^t b^{t^2} d^{c^t}$.

    b) Is formula (1.25) or (1.26) more convenient in this case?

34. Fund A accumulates at a simple interest rate of 10%. Fund B accumulates at a simple discount rate of 5%. Find the point in time at which the forces of interest on the two funds are equal.

35. An investment is made for one year in a fund whose accumulation function is a second degree polynomial. The nominal rate of interest earned during the first half of the year is 5% convertible semiannually. The effective rate of interest earned for the entire year is 7%. Find $\delta_{.5}$.

36. Find an expression for the fraction of a period at which the excess of accumulated values computed at simple interest over compound interest is a maximum.

1.10 Varying interest

37. Find the level effective rate of interest over a three-year period which is equivalent to an effective rate of discount of 8% the first year, 7% the second year, and 6% the third year.

38. *a*) Find the accumulated value of 1 at the end of n periods where the effective rate of interest for the kth period, $k = 1, 2, \ldots, n$, is defined by

$$i_k = (1 + r)^k (1 + i) - 1.$$

b) Show that the answer to (*a*) can be written in the form $(1 + j)^n$. Find j.

39. An investor makes a deposit today and earns an average continuous return (force of interest) of 6% over the next five years. What average continuous return must be earned over the subsequent five years in order to double the investment at the end of ten years?

40. In Fund X money accumulates at a force of interest

$$\delta_t = .01t + .1 \text{ for } 0 \le t \le 20.$$

In Fund Y money accumulates at an annual effective interest rate i. An amount of 1 is invested in each fund for 20 years. The value of Fund X at the end of 20 years is equal to the value of Fund Y at the end of 20 years. Calculate the value of Fund Y at the end of 1.5 years.

41. If the effective rate of discount in year k is equal to $.01k + .06$ for $k = 1, 2, 3$, find the equivalent rate of simple interest over the three-year period.

Miscellaneous problems

42. You are given that $A(t)$ is a second degree polynomial for $0 \le t \le 2$ and that $A(0) = 100$, $A(1) = 110$, and $A(2) = 136$.

a) Determine i_2.

b) Determine the equivalent effective rate of discount between $t = .5$ and $t = 1.5$.

c) Determine $\delta_{1.2}$.

d) Find the present value of 1 to be paid at time $t = 1.25$ evaluated at time $t = .75$.

43. You are working on a complex financial model which has an interest component. One of the scenarios the model will test involves an examination of effects if interest rates gradually rise from their current level by 3% over a 6-year period. Since the rest of the model is based on continuous processes, you believe that the force of interest δ should be used for consistency. The current force of interest δ is equal to 5%. You assume that this force of interest will increase linearly to 8% over the 6-year period. If \$1,000,000 will be owed to an outside party at the end of the 6 years, find its present value today.

44. A deposits X into a savings account at time 0 which pays interest at a nominal rate of i compounded semiannually. B deposits $2X$ into a different savings account at time 0 which pays simple interest at annual rate of i. A and B earn the same amount of interest during the last 6 months of the 8th year. Calculate i.

45. A and B each open up new bank accounts at time 0. A deposits 100, while B deposits 50. Each account earns an annual effective discount rate of d. The amount of interest earned in A's account during the 11th year is equal to X. The amount of interest earned in B's account during the 17th year is also equal to X. Calculate X.

46. You are given $\delta_t = \dfrac{2}{t-1}$ for $2 \le t \le 10$. For any one-year interval between times n and $n+1$, with $n = 2, 3, \ldots, 9$, calculate the equivalent $d^{(2)}$.

47. Method A assumes simple interest over final fractional periods, while Method B assumes simple discount over final fractional periods. The annual effective rate of interest is 20%. Find the ratio of the present value of a payment to be made in 1.5 years computed under Method A to that computed under Method B.

48. Write the following as series expansions:

    a) i as a function of δ.

    b) δ as a function of i.

    c) d as a function of i.

    d) δ as a function of d.

49. Find the following derivatives:

    a) $\dfrac{dd}{di}$

    b) $\dfrac{d\delta}{di}$

    c) $\dfrac{d\delta}{dv}$

    d) $\dfrac{dd}{d\delta}$

50. *a*) (1) Derive an expression for $a(t)$ assuming δ_r is linear and positive, i.e. $\delta_r = a + br$, where $a > 0$ and $b > 0$.

(2) Find the accumulation factor during the nth period from the date of investment, i.e. $1 + i_n$.

b) (1) Derive an expression for $a(t)$ assuming δ_r is exponential and positive, i.e. $\delta_r = ab^r$, where $a > 0$ and $b > 0$.

(2) Find the accumulation factor during the nth period from the date of investment, i.e. $1 + i_n$.

2

Solution of problems in interest

2.1 INTRODUCTION

The basic principles in the theory of interest are relatively few. In Chapter 1, various quantitative measures of interest were analyzed. Chapter 2 discusses general principles to be followed in the solution of problems in interest. The purpose of this chapter is to develop a systematic approach by which the basic principles from Chapter 1 can be applied to more complex financial transactions.

With a thorough understanding of the first two chapters it is possible to solve most problems in interest. Successive chapters have two main purposes:

1. To familiarize the reader with more complex types of financial transactions, including definitions of terms, which occur in practice.

2. To provide a systematic analysis of these financial transactions, which will often lead to a more efficient handling of the problem than resorting to basic principles.

As a result of the second purpose above, on occasion, simplifying formulas will be derived. Fortunately, the number of formulas requiring memorization is small. Even so, a common source of difficulty for some is blind reliance on formulas without an understanding of the basic principles upon which the formulas are based. It is important to realize that problems in interest can generally be solved from basic principles and that in many cases resorting to basic principles is not as inefficient as it may first appear to be.

Frequently it is necessary to obtain numerical answers for problems involving interest. This need is considerably facilitated by the widespread availability of inexpensive financial calculators and personal computers. The existence of these modern tools has greatly reduced, or even eliminated, more cumbersome computational and approximation approaches required in the past.

Computational problems in Chapters 1 and 2 can readily be solved using any pocket calculator with exponential and logarithmic functions. From Chapter 3 forward the use of a financial calculator is recommended to take advantage of special financial algorithms available therein.

This book does not directly address the use of personal computers to solve computational problems in interest. However, standard spreadsheet software is ideally suited to solve a wide-range of problems in interest involving discrete processes. The majority of problems encountered in practical applications of interest involve such processes. The reader is encouraged to practice developing spreadsheet solutions for various applications throughout the book.

2.2 THE BASIC PROBLEM

Broken down into its simplest terms, an interest problem involves four basic quantities:

1. The principal originally invested.
2. The length of the investment period.
3. The rate (or force) of interest (or discount).
4. The accumulated value of the principal at the end of the investment period.

If any three of these quantities are known, then the fourth quantity can be determined. In the problems involving accumulated values considered so far, No. 4 is the unknown quantity; whereas, in the problems involving present values, No. 1 is the unknown quantity. Section 2.4 considers the case in which No. 2 is the unknown, while Section 2.5 considers the case in which No. 3 is the unknown.

The following observations may prove helpful in the solution of problems in interest:

a) The length of the investment period is measured in time units. It was mentioned in Chapter 1 that the fundamental measurement period is often assumed to be one year, and many problems are worked with this as the time unit, especially those involving effective rates of interest or discount.

However, if nominal rates of interest or discount are involved, often a time unit other than one year is most advantageous. The most convenient time unit to use is generally the interest conversion period. In problems involving continuous interest, however, some other time unit, such as a year, must typically be used.

b) The phrase "yield rate" is frequently encountered in many different types of applications involving interest. A precise definition of *yield rate* and a thorough examination of it will not be given until Chapter 7.

However, at this early point in the book, it is sufficient to say that the "yield rate" is that rate of interest which will establish an equivalency of value between a financial value at one point in time and a financial value at a different point in time. As a very simple example, \$100 at time $t=0$ is equivalent in value to \$110 at time $t=1$, if and only if the yield rate is equal to 10%.

The concept of "yield rate" also can be readily generalized to multiple values or payments at various points in time. The reader will encounter several examples of this type in Chapters 3 - 6.

c) An interest problem can be viewed from two perspectives, since it involves a financial transaction between two parties, the borrower and the lender. From either perspective, the problem is essentially the same; however, the wording of a problem may be different depending upon the point of view. Examples and exercises phrased from both points of view appear, and the reader should not let the different phraseology be a source of confusion.

As an example, recall the discussion in Section 1.7 involving the use of the words "paid" or "credited." To some readers the word "paid" may seem more normal from the vantage point of the borrower, while "credited" may seem more normal from the vantage point of the lender. Many other such examples could be cited.

Complex financial transactions often involve more than two parties. For example, a business firm analyzing its rate of return on a major investment in a new plant is involved with a multiplicity of parties. However, the basic principles developed to analyze two-party transactions can readily be extended to analyze these more complex transactions.

d) In practical applications involving interest the terminology can become confusing. Many terms have ambiguous meanings (e.g. see the discussion on the use of the word "discount" in Section 1.7). Furthermore, as we shall see in succeeding chapters some terms used unfortunately do not convey an intuitive description of the transactions involved (e.g. see the discussion on the terms "annuity-immediate" and "annuity-due" in Section 3.3). Finally, many parties involved in financial transactions simply do not always use terms with textbook precision.

   The reader is admonished in real-world applications to look beyond the stated terms and be certain to understand the exact nature of the financial transactions in question. There simply is not total consistency in terminology among the large and diverse number of parties involved in financial transactions involving interest.

2.3 EQUATIONS OF VALUE

It is a fundamental principle in the theory of interest that the value of an amount of money at any given point in time depends upon the time elapsed since the money was paid in the past or upon the time which will elapse in the future before it is paid. We have already seen this in many of the examples and exercises considered thus far in the book.

This principle is often characterized as the recognition of the *time value of money*. This process would be in contrast to financial calculations not involving the effect of interest, in which case it would be said that such calculations do not recognize the time value of money. The reader is cautioned that "recognition of the time value of money" reflects the effect of interest, but not the effect of inflation which reduces the purchasing power of money over time. Inflation-adjusted calculations will be discussed in Section 9.4.

As a consequence of the above principle, it is obvious that two or more amounts of money payable at different points in time cannot be compared until all the amounts are accumulated or discounted to a common date. This common date is called the *comparison date*, and the equation which accumulates or discounts each payment to the comparison date is called the *equation of value*.

One device which is often helpful in the solution of equations of value is the *time diagram*. A time diagram is a one-dimensional diagram in which units of time are measured along the one dimension and payments are placed on the diagram at the appropriate points. Note that payments in one direction are placed on the top of the diagram and payments in the other direction are placed on the bottom of the diagram. The comparison date is denoted by an arrow. Figure 2.1 is an example of a time diagram used in the solution of Example 2.1.

The time diagram is not necessary in the solution of equations of value; it is merely an aid in visualizing the problem. With some practice the reader can usually dispense with a time diagram on simpler problems. However, time diagrams are often helpful in the solution of more complex problems.

One of the properties of compound interest is that the choice of the comparison date makes no difference in the answer obtained. Thus, there is a different equation of value for each comparison date, but they all produce the same answer. This important property of compound interest will be illustrated in the solution of Example 2.1.

The reader is cautioned that under other patterns of interest, e.g. simple interest or simple discount, the choice of a comparison date does affect the answer obtained. This illustrates once again the inherent inconsistency in using simple interest or simple discount.

The reader should be aware that the problems involving accumulated values and present values already considered in the first two chapters are examples of equations of value. Example 2.1 illustrates a more general type of problem.

Example 2.1 In return for a promise to receive \$600 at the end of 8 years, a person agrees to pay \$100 at once, \$200 at the end of 5 years, and to make a further payment at the end of 10 years. Find the payment at the end of 10 years if the nominal rate of interest is 8% convertible semiannually.

We shall first work the problem with a comparison date of the present. The time diagram is shown in Figure 2.1.

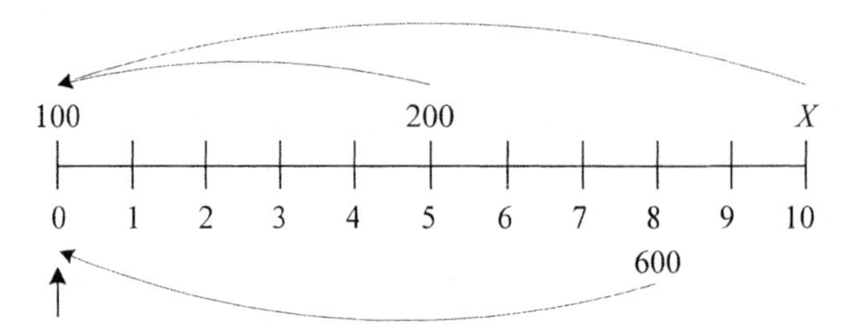

Figure 2.1 Time Diagram for Example 2.1

Since interest is convertible semiannually, we will count time periods in half-years. The equation of value is

$$\begin{aligned} 100 + 200v^{10} + Xv^{20} &= 600v^{16} \text{ at } 4\% \\ X &= \frac{600v^{16} - 100 - 200v^{10}}{v^{20}} \\ &= \frac{600(.53391) - 100 - 200(.67556)}{.45639} \\ &= \$186.76. \end{aligned}$$

We could also have chosen a different comparison date and obtained a different equation of value. For example, if the comparison date were chosen to be the end of the 10th year, then the arrow in the time diagram would be under 10 and the equation of value would be

$$\begin{aligned} 100(1.04)^{20} + 200(1.04)^{10} + X &= 600(1.04)^4 \\ X &= 600(1.04)^4 - 100(1.04)^{20} - 200(1.04)^{10} \\ &= 600(1.16986) - 100(2.19112) - 200(1.48024) \\ &= \$186.76. \end{aligned}$$

Thus, the same answer is obtained. The two equations of value are equivalent. If both sides of the first one are multiplied by $(1.04)^{20}$, the second one is obtained. The reader can verify that if other comparison dates are chosen, the same answer is obtained.

2.4 UNKNOWN TIME

As discussed in Section 2.2, if any three of the four basic quantities entering into an interest problem are given, then the fourth can be determined. In this section we consider the situation in which the length of the investment period is the unknown.

The best method of solving for unknown time involving a single payment is to use logarithms. This technique will be illustrated in Example 2.2. A more general situation involving unknown time with multiple payments will be considered in Section 3.6. Two interesting and useful results can be developed to supplement the basic technique involving logarithms just described.

The first is to develop an index for the average length of a financial transaction. This topic is important in more advanced financial analysis and is considered in depth in Chapter 11. However, it is desirable to lay the groundwork for that development at an early stage in the book.

Consider a situation in which several payments made at various points in time are to be replaced by one payment numerically equal to the sum of the other payments. The problem is to find the point in time at which the one payment should be made such that it is equivalent in value to the payments made separately.

Let amounts $s_1, s_2, \ldots, s_n$ be paid at times $t_1, t_2, \ldots, t_n$ respectively. The problem is to find time t, such that $s_1 + s_2 + \cdots + s_n$ paid at time t is equivalent to the payments of $s_1, s_2, \ldots, s_n$ made separately.

The fundamental equation of value is

$$(s_1 + s_2 + \ldots + s_n)v^t = s_1 v^{t_1} + s_2 v^{t_2} + \cdots + s_n v^{t_n} \tag{2.1}$$

which is one equation in one unknown t. This equation can readily be solved using logarithms.

As a first approximation, t is often calculated as a weighted average of the various times of payment, where the weights are the various amounts paid, i.e.

$$\bar{t} = \frac{s_1 t_1 + s_2 t_2 + \cdots + s_n t_n}{s_1 + s_2 + \cdots + s_n} = \frac{\sum_{k=1}^{n} s_k t_k}{\sum_{k=1}^{n} s_k}. \tag{2.2}$$

This approximation is denoted by $\bar{t}$ and the technique is often called the *method of equated time*.

It is possible to prove that the value of $\bar{t}$ is always greater than the true value of t, or, alternatively, that the present value using the method of equated time is smaller than the true present value. This proof is given in Appendix 2 at the end of the chapter.

The second is to analyze a frequently asked question which is how long it takes money to double at a given rate of interest. We can analyze this problem as follows:

$$(1+i)^n = 2$$

or

$$n \ln(1+i) = \ln 2$$

giving

$$n = \frac{\ln 2}{\ln(1+i)}. \tag{2.3}$$

It is possible to derive an approximation to the exact result given in formula (2.3) as follows:

$$\begin{aligned} n &= \frac{\ln 2}{\ln(1+i)} \\ &= \frac{.6931}{i} \cdot \frac{i}{\ln(1+i)}. \end{aligned}$$

The second factor evaluated for $i = 8\%$ is 1.0395. Thus we have

$$\begin{aligned} n &\approx \frac{.6931}{i}(1.0395) \\ &= \frac{.72}{i}. \end{aligned} \tag{2.4}$$

Formula (2.4) is frequently called the *rule of 72*, since n can be approximated immediately by dividing 72 by the rate of interest expressed as a percentage (i.e. as $100i$).

The rule of 72 produces surprisingly accurate results over a wide range of interest rates. Illustrative values are provided in Table 2.1.

Table 2.1 Length of Time It Takes Money to Double

Rate of interest	*Rule of 72*	*Exact value*
4%	18	17.67
6	12	11.90
8	9	9.01
10	7.2	7.27
12	6	6.12
18	8	4.19

Example 2.2 Find the length of time necessary for \$1000 to accumulate to \$1500 if invested at 6% per annum compounded semiannually.

Let n be the number of half-years. The equation of value is

$$1000(1.03)^n = 1500$$

$$(1.03)^n = 1.5\ .$$

Using logarithms

$$n \ln 1.03 = \ln 1.5$$

$$n = \frac{\ln 1.5}{\ln 1.03} = \frac{.405465}{.029559} = 13.717.$$

Thus, the length of time is $.5(13.717) = 6.859$ years.

Example 2.3 Payments of \$100, \$200, and \$500 are due at the ends of years 2, 3, and 8, respectively. Assuming an effective rate of interest of 5% per annum, find the point in time at which a payment of \$800 would be equivalent:
(1) By the method of equated time.
(2) By an exact method.

1. By the method of equated time using formula (2.2)

$$\bar{t} = \frac{100 \cdot 2 + 200 \cdot 3 + 500 \cdot 8}{100 + 200 + 500} = 6 \text{ years.}$$

2. The exact equation of value is

$$800v^t = 100v^2 + 200v^3 + 500v^8$$

or

$$v^t = \frac{100\,(.90703) + 200\,(.86384) + 500\,(.67684)}{800} = .75236$$

which can be solved for t

$$t = -\frac{\ln\ .75236}{\ln\ 1.05} = -\frac{-.28454}{.04879} = 5.832 \text{ years}.$$

As expected, the true value of t is less than the value using the method of equated time.

2.5 UNKNOWN RATE OF INTEREST

Section 2.4 considered the case in which the length of the investment period is the unknown. In this section we consider the situation in which the rate of interest is the unknown. Problems involving the determination of an unknown rate of interest are widely encountered in practice, since it is often necessary to compute the rate of return or yield rate involved in a particular transaction. Techniques to solve for an unknown rate of interest will be considered again in several later chapters for various important types of applications.

We first consider two somewhat limited, but instructive, methods to use in determining an unknown rate of interest which can be utilized in certain basic types of problems. The first of these is to solve the equation of value for i directly using a calculator with exponential and logarithmic functions. This method will work well if a single payment is involved and can occasionally be adapted to other situations as well. This method is illustrated in Example 2.4.

The second method is to solve the equation of value for i by algebraic techniques. For example, an equation of value with integral exponents on all the terms can be written as an nth degree polynomial in i. If the roots of this polynomial can be determined algebraically, then i is immediately determined. This method is generally practical only for small values of n. This method is illustrated in Example 2.5.

It is obvious that simple techniques such as these can only be applied in certain basic types of problems. More general methods are needed for more complex types of problems. Financial calculators can solve a much wider array of "unknown rate of interest" problems. Several such examples will be illustrated in later chapters of the book.

Financial calculators use techniques and algorithms from numerical analysis for *successive approximation* or *iteration*. In using iteration to solve for an unknown rate of interest, a function involving i, denoted by $f(i)$, is determined using an equation of value, and iteration is used to find a value of i such that $f(i) = 0$. Iteration methods are discussed in more detail in Appendix E for the benefit of readers who would like more insight into what is going on inside the financial calculator's "black box."

Example 2.4 ***At what interest rate convertible quarterly would $1000 accumulate to $1600 in six years?***

Let $j = i^{(4)}/4$ so that the equation of value becomes

$$1000(1+j)^{24} = 1600$$

or

$$j = (1.6)^{1/24} - 1.$$

This equation can be solved directly, which gives

$$j = .019776.$$

The answer is

$$i^{(4)} = 4j = .0791, \text{ or } 7.91\%.$$

Example 2.5 ***At what effective rate of interest will the present value of $2000 at the end of two years and $3000 at the end of four years be equal to $4000?***

An equation of value is

$$4000 = 2000v^2 + 3000v^4$$

which can be rewritten as

$$3v^4 + 2v^2 - 4 = 0.$$

This equation can be solved as a quadratic in v^2, which gives

$$v^2 = \frac{-2 \pm \sqrt{4+4\cdot 3\cdot 4}}{2\cdot 3}.$$

Since $v^2 > 0$, only the positive root is meaningful, and we have

$$v^2 = \frac{-2+\sqrt{52}}{6} = .868517$$

or

$$(1+i)^2 = 1.151388$$

which gives

$$i = .0730, \text{ or } 7.30\% .$$

2.6 DETERMINING TIME PERIODS

In practical problems involving interest it is necessary to determine the exact time period of an investment. Although there would appear to be no ambiguity in this process, different methods of counting the days in a period of investment have arisen in practice. Three methods are commonly encountered.

The first method is to use the exact number of days for the period of investment and to use 365 days in a year. Simple interest computed on this basis is sometimes called *exact simple interest* and is often denoted by "actual/actual." Appendix A contains a table numbering the days of the year, which facilitates counting the number of days between two given dates.

The second method assumes that each calendar month has 30 days and that the entire calendar year has 360 days. Simple interest computed on this basis is sometimes called *ordinary simple interest* and is often denoted by "30/360." Appendix A cannot be used for calculations on this basis. However, a formula for computing the number of days between two given dates is

$$360(Y_2 - Y_1) + 30(M_2 - M_1) + (D_2 - D_1) \tag{2.5}$$

where Y_1 = year of first date
M_1 = month of first date
D_1 = day of first date
Y_2 = year of second date
M_2 = month of second date
D_2 = day of second date.

The third method is a hybrid and uses the exact number of days for the period of investment, but uses 360 days in a year. Simple interest on this basis is sometimes called the *Banker's Rule* and is often denoted by "actual/360." It will be shown in the exercises that the Banker's Rule is always more favorable to a lender than is exact simple interest. Also, it will be shown that the Banker's Rule is usually more favorable to a lender than is ordinary simple interest, although exceptions do exist.

In theory we could have a fourth method denoted by "30/actual" or "30/365." However, this method is almost never encountered in practice.

A further complication arises in a leap year. In most cases, February 29 is counted as a day and the year has 366 days. However, in some cases, February 29 is counted as a day, but the year is still counted as having 365 days. In other cases, February 29 is not counted as day, i.e. no interest is earned. The author has even encountered the assumption that all years have 365 1/4 days! A uniform approach to leap year does not seem to have emerged and different calculation bases are encountered in practice. It should be noted that under ordinary simple interest (30/360), leap year is irrelevant.

The above terms and discussion have been couched in terms of simple interest. However, the three commonly encountered calculation bases, i.e. actual/actual, 30/360, and actual/360, also are used for calculating time periods on a compound interest basis.

The reader should also be aware that most financial calculators have day-counting algorithms as part of their functionality. The exact steps and keystroke entries required vary from calculator to calculator and the owner's manual must be consulted for the particular calculator being used.

It is assumed, unless stated otherwise, that in counting days interest is not credited for both the date of deposit and the date of withdrawal, but for only one of these two dates. If the difference in the two dates is calculated by normal procedures, then this will be the result. However, situations are occasionally encountered in practice in which interest is paid for both the date of deposit and the date of withdrawal, resulting in one extra day's interest.

Not all practical problems involving interest require the counting of days. Many financial transactions are handled on a monthly, quarterly, semiannual, or annual basis. In these cases the counting methods described in this section are not required.

Example 2.6 Find the amount of interest that $2000 deposited on June 17 will earn, if the money is withdrawn on September 10 in the same year and if the rate of simple interest is 8%, on the following bases:
(1) Exact simple interest (actual/actual).
(2) Ordinary simple interest (30/360).
(3) The Banker's Rule (actual/360).

1. From Appendix A, September 10 is day 253 and June 17 is day 168. The actual number of days in the period of investment is 253 – 168 = 85. Thus, the answer is

$$2000(.08)\left(\frac{85}{365}\right) = \$37.26$$

assuming that the year in question is not a leap year. Note that even if a table such as Appendix A is unavailable, it is an easy matter to count the number of days and arrive at 85.

2. Using formula (2.5), the number of days is

$$360(0) + 30(9-6) + (10-17) = 83.$$

Thus, the answer is

$$2000(.08)\left(\frac{83}{360}\right) = \$36.89.$$

3. The counting has already been done above and the answer is

$$2000(.08)\left(\frac{85}{360}\right) = \$37.78.$$

Not surprisingly, the answer using the Banker's Rule is greater than using either exact simple interest or ordinary simple interest.

2.7 PRACTICAL EXAMPLES

Virtually everyone is exposed to interest calculations regularly in their financial affairs. However, in practice interest calculations do not always follow the exact procedures outlined in this book. The purpose of this section is to familiarize the reader with some of the variations encountered in practice. The examples in this section are by no means exhaustive, but they are illustrative of some "real-world" applications of interest. Some terms for types of investments with which the reader may be unfamiliar are used in this section, e.g. "certificate of deposit" and "money market fund." Definitions of these terms are given in Section 8.8.

Financial institutions will sometimes advertise two different rates on deposits. For example, a bank may quote a certificate of deposit as having a "5.20% rate/ 5.30% yield." What is the meaning attached to these two numbers? In this example, the former number is a nominal rate, while the latter is an annual effective rate. The reader should verify that $i^{(4)} = .0520$, is equivalent to $i = .0530$, Interestingly, the frequency of compounding for the nominal rate is not always explicitly stated in such advertisements.

In recent years, financial institutions have started referring to the second rate above as APY, which stands for *annual percentage yield.* This term is similar to another term used for consumer loans called APR, which stands for *annual percentage rate.* These two rates are used for disclosure purposes and will be discussed further in Section 8.2 in connection with "truth-in-lending" requirements.

Section 2.6 deals with some of the variations in counting days. One advertisement the author has seen indicates that a savings bank credits 6% compounded daily which produces a yield of 6.27%. Using either a 360 or 365-day year produces an answer of 6.18%. How can an answer of 6.27% be obtained? After some trial and error, it was discovered that the savings bank was using a mix of 360-day and 365-day years as follows:

$$\left(1+\frac{.06}{360}\right)^{365} - 1 = .0627.$$

When interest is not compounded daily, some interesting variations appear. Consider an investment account which credits interest monthly and on which deposits and withdrawals are occurring. One common variation credits interest on the average daily balance. Another common variation credits interest on the minimum daily balance. Yet a third variation credits interest on the beginning balance, reduced by any withdrawals, but not incremented by any deposits. In this latter case deposits do not start earning interest until the beginning of the following month.

Even the frequency of compounding can be tricky. Usually compounding occurs at some regular, predetermined interval. However, the author has encountered money market funds which compound interest whenever the interest rate being credited is changed. Thus, in a month with unchanged rates interest would be compounded only once, while in another more volatile month interest might be compounded as many as six or more times.

It is also important to distinguish between rates of interest and rates of discount. For example, the United States Government issues Treasury bills for periods of 13, 26, and 52 weeks. The rates on "T-bills," as they are often called, are computed as rates of discount. On the other hand, rates on longer-term Treasury securities are computed as rates of interest. Thus, rates on Treasury bills cannot be directly compared with rates on longer-term Treasury securities unless converted to equivalent rates. Treasury bills are discussed further in Section 6.2.

Rates of discount are also encountered in short-term commercial transactions. For example, if $10,000 is borrowed on a discount basis at 12% for one month, then the borrower receives $9900 immediately and repays $10,000 at the end of the month. Such short-term transactions are often computed on a simple discount basis, as just illustrated. The net effect is equivalent to using a rate of discount convertible at the same frequency as the term of the loan. Thus, if a stated rate, such as the 12% used above, is used for loans of varying lengths, then the equivalent effective rates will differ depending upon the length of the loans.

Credit cards have an interesting way of charging interest. The interest generally is computed on the ending balance of the prior month. Thus, no interest is assessed on new charges during a month for that month, i.e. interest does not begin to be charged until the following month. In essence, this is an interest-free loan from the date of charge until the end of the month. Persons who always pay their credit card charges in full each month are, in essence, borrowing money for short periods of time without paying any interest at all. On the other hand, the interest rate charged on those accounts which do carry outstanding balances from month-to-month tends to be very high.

Another feature that investors need to be careful to consider is a penalty for early withdrawal. For example, such penalties apply to many certificates of deposit. If a two-year certificate of deposit credits an annual rate of 6%, the purchaser is likely to have a rude awakening upon surrendering after one year and learning that less than 6% will be paid. The penalties for early withdrawal often involve either a reduction in the credited interest rate, or not crediting interest for a certain period of time, or some combination of the two. Other types of early withdrawal penalties are also encountered.

Finally, geography may be an important consideration. The techniques and examples provided in this book largely reflect financial calculations involving interest as they are typically done in the United States. Practices in other countries may well differ in certain respects. This factor is becoming increasingly important with the significant globalization of financial markets in recent years.

These illustrations should give the reader a flavor of some of the types of applications encountered. The fact that so many variations exist and that consistent terminology is not used from situation to situation can make seemingly simple financial analysis difficult. In real-world applications the reader is cautioned to look below the surface and ascertain exactly how calculations involving interest actually will be done. Otherwise, comparisons among various options for borrowing and lending may well be flawed.

***Example 2.7** You invest $5000 in a two-year certificate of deposit (CD) crediting 6% convertible quarterly. If the CD is redeemed early, the credited rate will be reduced to 4% convertible quarterly for the final three months of the period of investment. Find the amount you would receive if the CD is redeemed after 18 months.*

The quarterly interest rate on the CD is $y_1 = .06/4 = .015$, if no penalty applies, and $y_2 = .04/4 = .01$, if a penalty applies. The CD earns the full rate for five quarters and the reduced rate for one quarter giving a redemption value of

$$5000(1.015)^5(1.01) \;=\; \$5440.28.$$

APPENDIX 2

Derivation involving method of equated time

Consider s_1 quantities each equal to v^{t_1}, s_2 quantities each equal to v^{t_2}, and so forth until there are s_n quantities each equal to v^{t_n}. The arithmetic mean of these quantities is

$$\frac{s_1 v^{t_1} + s_2 v^{t_2} + \cdots + s_n v^{t_n}}{s_1 + s_2 + \cdots + s_n}.$$

The geometric mean of these quantities is

$$v^{\frac{s_1 v^{t_1} + s_2 v^{t_2} + \cdots + s_n v^{t_n}}{s_1 + s_2 + \cdots + s_n}} = v^{\bar{t}}.$$

However, we know that the arithmetic mean of n positive numbers, not all of which are equal, is greater than the geometric mean, and thus we have

$$\frac{s_1 v^{t_1} + s_2 v^{t_2} + \cdots + s_n v^{t_n}}{s_1 + s_2 + \cdots + s_n} > v^{\bar{t}}$$

or

$$s_1 v^{t_1} + s_2 v^{t_2} + \cdots + s_n v^{t_n} > \left(s_1 + s_2 + \cdots + s_n\right) v^{\bar{t}}.$$

The left-hand side is the true present value which exceeds the present value given by the method of equated time on the right-hand side. Thus, the value of $\bar{t}$ from formula (2.2) is always greater than the true value of t from formula (2.1).

EXERCISES

2.3 Equations of value

1. In return for payments of \$2000 at the end of four years and \$5000 at the end of ten years, an investor agrees to pay \$3000 immediately and to make an additional payment at the end of three years. Find the amount of the additional payment if $i^{(4)} = .06$.

2. You have an inactive credit cart with a \$1000 outstanding unpaid balance. This particular credit card charges interest at the rate of 18% compounded monthly. You are able to make a payment of \$200 one month from today and \$300 two months from today. Find the amount that you will have to pay three months from today to completely pay off this credit card debt. (Note: Work this problem with an equation of value. You will learn an alternative approach for this type of problem in Chapter 5.)

3. At a certain interest rate the present value of the following two payment patterns are equal:

   (*i*) \$200 at the end of 5 years plus \$500 at the end of 10 years.

   (*ii*) \$400.94 at the end of 5 years.

   At the same interest rate \$100 invested now plus \$120 invested at the end of 5 years will accumulate to P at the end of 10 years. Calculate P.

4. An investor makes three deposits into a fund, at the end of 1, 3, and 5 years. The amount of the deposit at time t is $100(1.025)^t$. Find the size of the fund at the end of 7 years, if the nominal rate of discount convertible quarterly is 4/41.

5. Whereas the choice of a comparison date has no effect on the answer obtained with compound interest, the same cannot be said of simple interest. Find the amount to be paid at the end of 10 years which is equivalent to two payments of \$100 each, the first to be paid immediately and the second to be paid at the end of 5 years. Assume 5% simple interest is earned from the date each payment is made and use a comparison date of:

   a) The end of 10 years.

   b) The end of 15 years.

2.4 Unknown time

6. Find how long \$1000 should be left to accumulate at 6% effective in order that it will amount to twice the accumulated value of another \$1000 deposited at the same time at 4% effective.

7. You invest \$3000 today and plan to invest another \$2000 two years from today. You plan to withdraw \$5000 in n years and another \$5000 in $n+5$ years, exactly liquidating your investment account at that time. If the effective rate of discount is equal to 6%, find n.

8. The present value of two payments of \$100 each to be made at the end of n years and $2n$ years is \$100. If $i = .08$, find n.

9. A payment of n is made at the end of n years, $2n$ at the end of $2n$ years, ..., n^2 at the end of n^2 years. Find the value of t by the method of equated time.

10. You are asked to develop a *rule of n* to approximate how long it takes money to triple. Find n, where n is a positive integer.

11. A deposits 10 today and another 30 in five years into a fund paying simple interest of 11% per year. B will make the same two deposits, but the 10 will be deposited n years from today and the 30 will be deposited $2n$ years from today. B's deposits earn an annual effective rate of 9.15%. At the end of 10 years, the accumulated value of B's deposits equals the accumulated value of A's deposits. Calculate n.

12. Fund A accumulates at a rate of 12% convertible monthly. Fund B accumulates with a force of interest $\delta_t = t/6$. At time $t = 0$ equal deposits are made in each fund. Find the next time that the two funds are equal.

2.5 Unknown rate of interest

13. Find the nominal rate of interest convertible semiannually at which the accumulated value of \$1000 at the end of 15 years is \$3000.

14. Find an expression for the exact effective rate of interest at which payments of \$300 at the present, \$200 at the end of one year, and \$100 at the end of two years will accumulate to \$700 at the end of two years.

15. You can receive one of the following two payment streams:

    (*i*) 100 at time 0, 200 at time n, and 300 at time $2n$.

    (*ii*) 600 at time 10.

    At an annual effective interest rate of i, the present values of the two streams are equal. Given $v^n = 0.75941$, determine i.

16. It is known that an investment of $1000 will accumulate to $1825 at the end of 10 years. If it is assumed that the investment earns simple interest at rate i during the 1st year, $2i$ during the 2nd year, ..., $10i$ during the 10th year, find i.

17. It is known that an amount of money will double itself in 10 years at a varying force of interest $\delta_t = kt$. Find an expression for k.

18. The sum of the accumulated value of 1 at the end of three years at a certain effective rate of interest i, and the present value of 1 to be paid at the end of three years at an effective rate of discount numerically equal to i is 2.0096. Find the rate i.

2.6 Determining time periods

19. If an investment was made on the day the United States entered World War II, i.e. December 7, 1941, and was terminated at the end of the war on August 8, 1945, for how many days was the money invested:
    a) On the actual/actual basis?
    b) On the 30/360 basis?

20. A sum of $10,000 is invested for the months of July and August at 6% simple interest. Find the amount of interest earned:
    a) Assuming exact simple interest.
    b) Assuming ordinary simple interest.
    c) Assuming the Banker's Rule.

21. *a*) Show that the Banker's Rule is always more favorable to the lender than is exact simple interest.
    b) Show that the Banker's Rule is usually more favorable to the lender than is ordinary simple interest.
    c) Find a counterexample in (*b*) for which the opposite relationship holds.

2.7 Practical examples

22. A bill for $100 is purchased for $96 three months before it is due. Find:

    a) The nominal rate of discount convertible quarterly earned by the purchaser.

    b) The annual effective rate of interest earned by the purchaser.

23. A two-year certificate of deposit pays an annual effective rate of 9%. The purchaser is offered two options for prepayment penalties in the event of early withdrawal:

    A – a reduction in the rate of interest to 7%.

    B – loss of three months interest.

    In order to assist the purchaser in deciding which option to select, compute the ratio of the proceeds under Option A to those under Option B if the certificate of deposit is surrendered:

    a) At the end of 6 months.

    b) At the end of 18 months.

24. The ABC Bank has an early withdrawal policy for certificates of deposit (CDs) which states that interest still be credited for the entire length the money actually stays with the bank, but that the CD nominal interest rate will be reduced by 1.8% for the same number of months as the CD is redeemed early. An incoming college freshman invests $5000 in a two-year CD with a nominal rate of interest equal to 5.4% compounded monthly on September 1 at the beginning of the freshman year. The student intended to leave the money on deposit for the full two-year term to help finance the junior and senior years, but finds the need to withdraw it on May 1 of the sophomore year. Find the amount that the student will receive for the CD on that date.

25. Many banks quote two rates of interest on certificates of deposit (CDs). If a bank quotes 5.1% compounded daily, find the ratio of the APY (annual percentage yield) to the quoted rate for this CD.

26. A savings and loan association pays 7% effective on deposits at the end of each year. At the end of every three years a 2% bonus is paid on the balance at that time. Find the effective rate of interest earned by an investor if the money is left on deposit:

    a) Two years.

    b) Three years.

    c) Four years.

27. A bank offers the following certificates of deposit (CDs):

Term in years	Nominal annual interest rate (convertible semiannually)
1	5%
2	6%
3	7%
4	8%

The bank does not permit early withdrawal, and all CDs mature at the end of the term. During the next six years the bank will continue to offer these CDs. An investor deposits $1000 in the bank. Calculate the maximum amount that can be withdrawn at the end of six years.

Miscellaneous problems

28. A store is running a promotion during which customers have two options for payment. Option One is to pay 90% of the purchase price two months after the date of sale. Option Two is to deduct X % off the purchase price and pay cash on the date of sale. Determine X such that a customer would be indifferent between the two options when valuing them using an effective annual interest rate of 8%.

29. A manufacturer sells a product to a retailer who has the option of paying 30% below the retail price immediately, or 25% below the retail price in six months. Find the annual effective rate of interest at which the retailer would be indifferent between the two options.

30. You deposit $1000 into a bank account. The bank credits interest at a nominal annual rate of i convertible semiannually for the first 7 years and a nominal annual of $2i$ convertible quarterly for all years thereafter. The accumulated amount in the account at the end of 5 years is X. The accumulated amount in the account at the end of 10.5 years is 1980. Calculate X to the nearest dollar.

31. Fund A accumulates at 6% effective and Fund B accumulates at 8% effective. At the end of 20 years the total of the two funds is $2000. At the end of 10 years the amount in Fund A is half that in Fund B. What is the total of the two funds at the end of 5 years? Answer to the nearest dollar.

32. An investor deposits \$10,000 in a bank. During the first year, the bank credits an annual effective rate of interest i. During the second year, the bank credits an annual effective rate of interest $i - .05$. At the end of two years the account balance is \$12,093.75. What would the account balance have been at the end of three years, if the annual effective rate of interest were $i + .09$ for each of the three years? Answer to the nearest dollar.

33. A signs a one-year note for \$1000 and receives \$920 from the bank. At the end of six months A makes a payment of \$288. Assuming simple discount, to what amount does this reduce the face amount of the note?

3

Basic annuities

3.1 INTRODUCTION

An *annuity* may be defined as a series of payments made at equal intervals of time. Annuities are common in our economic life. House rents, mortgage payments, installment payments on automobiles, and interest payments on money invested are all examples of annuities. Originally the meaning of the word "annuity" was restricted to annual payments, but it has been extended to include payments made at other regular intervals as well.

Consider an annuity such that payments are certain to be made for a fixed period of time. An annuity with these properties is called an *annuity-certain*. The fixed period of time for which payments are made is called the *term* of the annuity. For example, mortgage payments on a home or business constitute an annuity-certain.

Not all annuities are annuities-certain. An annuity under which the payments are not certain to be made is called a *contingent annuity*. A common type of contingent annuity is one in which payments are made only if a person is alive. Such an annuity is called a *life annuity*. For example, monthly retirement benefits from a pension plan, which continue for the life of a retiree, constitute a life annuity.

In this book, we will restrict our attention to annuities-certain. (However, the risk of default or non-payment will be addressed in Section 9.8). It will often be convenient to drop the word "certain" and just use the term "annuity" to refer to an annuity-certain.

The interval between annuity payments is called the *payment period.* In this chapter, we consider annuities for which the payment period and the interest conversion period are equal and coincide, and for which the payments are of level amount. Since the payment period and the interest conversion period are equal and coincide, we will just use the term "period" for both. In Chapter 4, annuities for which payments are made more or less frequently than interest is converted and annuities with varying payments are examined.

3.2 ANNUITY-IMMEDIATE

Consider an annuity under which payments of 1 are made at the end of each period for n periods, where n is a positive integer. Such an annuity is called an *annuity-immediate* (or possibly an *ordinary annuity*). Figure 3.1 is a time diagram for such an annuity. Arrow 1 appears one period before the first payment is made. We assume that the rate of interest is i per period, where $i > 0$. The present value of the annuity at this point in time is denoted by $a_{\overline{n}|}$. Arrow 2 appears n periods after arrow 1, just after the last payment is made. The accumulated value of the annuity at this point in time is denoted by $s_{\overline{n}|}$.

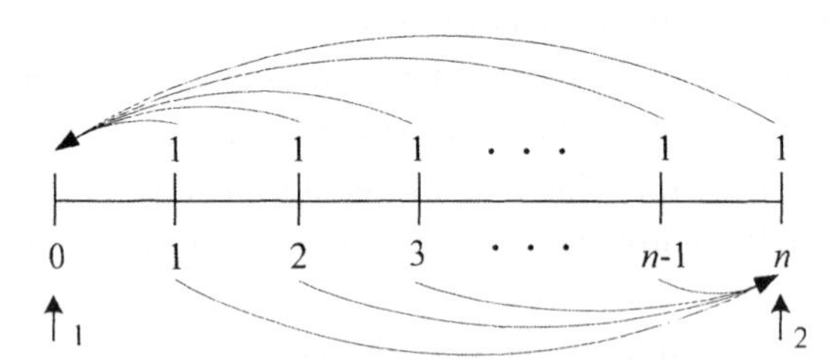

Figure 3.1 Time diagram for an annuity-immediate

We can derive an expression for $a_{\overline{n}|}$ as an equation of value at the beginning of the first period. The present value of a payment of 1 made at the end of the first period is v. The present value of a payment of 1 made at the end of the second period is v^2. This process is continued until the present value of a payment of 1 made at the end of the nth period is v^n. The total present value $a_{\overline{n}|}$ must equal the sum of the present values of each payment, i.e.

$$a_{\overline{n}|} = v + v^2 + \cdots + v^{n-1} + v^n. \tag{3.1}$$

This formula could be used to evaluate $a_{\overline{n}|}$, but it would become inefficient for large n. It is possible to derive a more compact expression by recognizing that formula (3.1) is a geometric progression

$$\begin{aligned} a_{\overline{n}|} &= v+v^2+\cdots+v^{n-1}+v^n \\ &= v\,\frac{1-v^n}{1-v} \\ &= v\,\frac{1-v^n}{iv} \\ &= \frac{1-v^n}{i}\,. \end{aligned} \tag{3.2}$$

An expression for $s_{\overline{n}|}$ can be derived in an analogous manner as an equation of value at the end of the nth period. The accumulated value of a payment of 1 made at the end of the first period is $(1+i)^{n-1}$. The accumulated value of a payment of 1 made at the end of the second period is $(1+i)^{n-2}$. This process is continued until the accumulated value of a payment of 1 made at the end of the nth period is just 1. The total accumulated value $s_{\overline{n}|}$ must equal the sum of the accumulated values of each payment, i.e.

$$s_{\overline{n}|} = 1+(1+i)+\cdots+(1+i)^{n-2}+(1+i)^{n-1}. \tag{3.3}$$

Again, a more compact expression can be derived by summing the geometric progression

$$\begin{aligned} s_{\overline{n}|} &= 1+(1+i)+\cdots+(1+i)^{n-2}+(1+i)^{n-1} \\ &= \frac{(1+i)^n-1}{(1+i)-1} \\ &= \frac{(1+i)^n-1}{i}\,. \end{aligned} \tag{3.4}$$

On occasion, the interest rate is written to the lower right of the symbol, e.g. $a_{\overline{10}|.07}$ or $s_{\overline{25}|.08}$. Since this tends to clutter the symbols, we will do this only if there could be any ambiguity concerning the interest rate to be used in evaluating the annuity function.

It is possible to give a verbal interpretation to formula (3.2) written as

$$1 = ia_{\overline{n}|} + v^n.$$

Consider the investment of 1 for n periods. Each period the investment of 1 will yield interest of i paid at the end of the period. The present value of these interest payments is $ia_{\overline{n}|}$. At the end of n periods the original investment of 1, whose present value is v^n, is returned. Thus, both sides of the equation represent the present value of an investment of 1 at the date of investment. A similar verbal interpretation can be given for formula (3.4).

There is a simple relationship between $a_{\overline{n}|}$ and $s_{\overline{n}|}$

$$s_{\overline{n}|} = a_{\overline{n}|}(1 + i)^n. \tag{3.5}$$

This relationship is obvious from a comparison of either formulas (3.1) and (3.3) or from formulas (3.2) and (3.4). It is also obvious from the time diagram, since $s_{\overline{n}|}$ is the value of the same payments as $a_{\overline{n}|}$, only the value is taken n periods later.

Another relationship between $a_{\overline{n}|}$ and $s_{\overline{n}|}$ is

$$\frac{1}{a_{\overline{n}|}} = \frac{1}{s_{\overline{n}|}} + i. \tag{3.6}$$

This relationship can be derived as follows:

$$\begin{aligned}
\frac{1}{s_{\overline{n}|}} + i &= \frac{i}{(1 + i)^n - 1} + i \\
&= \frac{i + i(1 + i)^n - i}{(1 + i)^n - 1} \\
&= \frac{i}{1 - v^n} \\
&= \frac{1}{a_{\overline{n}|}}.
\end{aligned}$$

Formula (3.6) will be quite significant in another context in Chapter 5. A verbal interpretation of the formula will be given at that time.

Numerical values for annuities are frequently required in practice. One approach is to compute present values using the formula (3.2) and accumulated values using formula (3.4). This method is efficient and can be done on any pocket calculator with exponential and logarithmic functions.

Alternatively, annuity values can directly be obtained using a financial calculator. Readers are encouraged to become familiar with the capabilities of a financial calculator. Although such a calculator is not required to evaluate the elementary annuities considered in this section, it will be required for other financial calculations later in the chapter.

Different financial calculators have different labels and keystroke entries. However, the typical financial calculator will have five keys used to evaluate annuities:

N – the number of payments (i.e. n)
I – the interest rate as a percentage (i.e. $100i$)
PV – present value (i.e. $a_{\overline{n}|}$)
PMT – annuity payment
FV – future value (i.e. $s_{\overline{n}|}$)

One quirk in using a financial calculator is the convention that all cash flows in one direction must be positive, while all cash flows in the opposite direction must be negative. For example, if a financial calculator is being used to evaluate $a_{\overline{n}|}$ and a positive value for PV is needed, the input value for PMT must be negative.

***Example 3.1** Find the present value of an annuity which pays $500 at the end of each half-year for 20 years if the rate of interest is 9% convertible semiannually.*

The answer is

$$500\, a_{\overline{40}|.045}.$$

This can be evaluated using formula (3.2) as

$$500\frac{1-(1.045)^{-40}}{.045} = 500(18.40158) = \$9{,}200.79.$$

Alternatively, using a financial calculator, we set

$$\begin{aligned} N &= 40 \\ I &= 100(.045) = 4.5 \\ PMT &= -500 \end{aligned}$$

and compute PV obtaining

$$PV = \$9{,}200.79.$$

Example 3.2 If a college freshman invests a \$10,000 gift at 8% per annum convertible quarterly, how much can be withdrawn at the end of every quarter to use up the fund exactly at the end of four years of college?

Let R be the amount of each withdrawal. The equation of value at the date of investment is

$$R\, a_{\overline{16}|.02} = 10{,}000.$$

Thus, we have

$$R = \frac{10{,}000}{a_{\overline{16}|.02}} = \frac{10{,}000}{13.57771} = \$736.50.$$

The reader should verify that this answer can also be obtained using a financial calculator by setting

$$\begin{aligned} N &= 16 \\ I &= 100(.02) = 2 \\ PV &= -10{,}000 \end{aligned}$$

and compute PMT obtaining

$$PMT = \$736.50.$$

Example 3.3 Compare the total amount of interest that would be paid on a \$1000 loan over a 10-year period, if the effective rate of interest is 9% per annum, under the following three repayment methods:

(1) The entire loan plus accumulated interest is paid in one lump-sum at the end of 10 years.

(2) Interest is paid each year as accrued and the principal is repaid at the end of 10 years.

(3) The loan is repaid by level payments over the 10-year period.

1. The accumulated value of the loan at the end of 10 years is

$$1000(1.09)^{10} = 2367.36$$

Thus, the total amount of interest paid is equal to

$$2367.36 - 1000.00 = 1367.36.$$

2. Each year the loan accrues interest of 1000(.09) = \$90, so that the total amount of interest paid is equal to

$$10 \cdot 90 = \$900.00.$$

3. Let the level payment be R. An equation of value for R at the inception of the loan is

$$R\, a_{\overline{10}|} = 1000$$

which gives

$$R = \frac{1000}{a_{\overline{10}|}} = \frac{1000}{6.417658} = 155.82.$$

Thus, the total amount of interest paid is equal to

$$10(155.82) - 1000 = \$558.20.$$

The reader should justify by general reasoning the relative answers under the three repayment methods. The later the payments are made on a loan, the higher the total amount of interest will be. Conversely, the sooner the payments are made, the smaller the amount of interest. Although the total amount of payments under the three methods are different, the present value of payments is equal to \$1000, the amount of the loan, for all three.

3.3 ANNUITY-DUE

In Section 3.2 the annuity-immediate was defined as an annuity in which payments are made at the end of the period. In this section, we will consider the *annuity-due* in which payments are made at the beginning of the period instead. The use of the terms "annuity-immediate" and "annuity-due" is unfortunate, since these terms are not descriptive of the properties of these annuities.

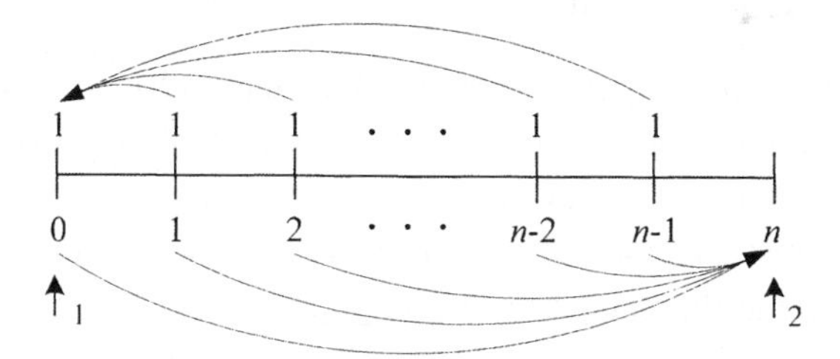

Figure 3.2 Time diagram for an annuity-due

Figure 3.2 is a time diagram for an n-period annuity-due. Arrow 1 appears at the time the first payment is made. The present value of the annuity at this point in time is denoted by $\ddot{a}_{\overline{n}|}$. Arrow 2 appears n periods after arrow 1, one period after the last payment is made. The accumulated value of the annuity at this point in time is denoted by $\ddot{s}_{\overline{n}|}$.

We can write an expression for $\ddot{a}_{\overline{n}|}$ analogous to formula (3.1) as

$$\ddot{a}_{\overline{n}|} = 1+v+v^2+\cdots+v^{n-1}. \tag{3.7}$$

Again summing the geometric progression

$$\begin{aligned}\ddot{a}_{\overline{n}|} &= \frac{1-v^n}{1-v} \\ &= \frac{1-v^n}{iv} \\ &= \frac{1-v^n}{d}\end{aligned} \tag{3.8}$$

which is analogous to formula (3.2).

Similarly for $\ddot{s}_{\overline{n}|}$, we have the following formulas analogous to formulas (3.3) and (3.4)

$$\ddot{s}_{\overline{n}|} = (1+i)+(1+i)^2+\cdots+(1+i)^{n-1}+(1+i)^n \tag{3.9}$$

$$\begin{aligned} &= (1+i)\frac{(1+i)^n-1}{(1+i)-1} \\ &= \frac{(1+i)^n-1}{iv} \\ &= \frac{(1+i)^n-1}{d}.\end{aligned} \tag{3.10}$$

It is instructive to compare formulas (3.2) and (3.8). The numerators are identical; however, the denominator of (3.2) is i and the denominator of (3.8) is d. Under the annuity-immediate, payments are made at the end of the period and i is a measure of interest payable at the end of the period. Under the annuity-due, payments are made at the beginning of the period and d is a measure of interest payable at the beginning of the period. A comparison of formulas (3.4) and (3.10) gives similar results.

The above property, relating the time annuity payments are made to the measure of interest in the denominator, is helpful in remembering annuity formulas. Moreover, this property can be generalized to the more complex annuities which are discussed in Chapter 4.

It is immediately obvious that

$$\ddot{s}_{\overline{n}|} = \ddot{a}_{\overline{n}|}(1+i)^n \tag{3.11}$$

a formula analogous to formula (3.5). It can also be shown that

$$\frac{1}{\ddot{a}_{\overline{n}|}} = \frac{1}{\ddot{s}_{\overline{n}|}} + d \tag{3.12}$$

a formula analogous to formula (3.6). The derivations of formulas (3.11) and (3.12) are similar to those of formulas (3.5) and (3.6).

It is possible to relate the annuity-immediate and the annuity-due. One type of relationship is

$$\ddot{a}_{\overline{n}|} = a_{\overline{n}|}(1+i) \tag{3.13}$$

and

$$\ddot{s}_{\overline{n}|} = s_{\overline{n}|}(1+i). \tag{3.14}$$

Formula (3.13) can immediately be derived by comparing formulas (3.1) and (3.7), or formulas (3.2) and (3.8). Since each payment under $\ddot{a}_{\overline{n}|}$ is made one period earlier than each payment under $a_{\overline{n}|}$, the total present value must be larger by one period's interest. Formula (3.14) can be derived similarly.

There is another type of relationship between the annuity-immediate and the annuity-due

$$\ddot{a}_{\overline{n}|} = 1 + a_{\overline{n-1}|}. \tag{3.15}$$

This formula can be derived from Figure 3.2. The n payments made under $\ddot{a}_{\overline{n}|}$ can be split into the first payment and the remaining $n-1$ payments. The present value of the first payment is 1, and the present value of the remaining $n-1$ payments is $a_{\overline{n-1}|}$ The sum must give the total present value $\ddot{a}_{\overline{n}|}$.

Similarly, we can obtain

$$\ddot{s}_{\overline{n}|} = s_{\overline{n+1}|} - 1. \tag{3.16}$$

This formula can also be derived from Figure 3.2. Temporarily, assume that an imaginary payment of 1 is made at the end of the nth period. Then, the total accumulated value of the $n+1$ payment is $s_{\overline{n+1}|}$. However, we must remove the accumulated value of the imaginary payment, which is just 1. The difference gives the accumulated value $\ddot{s}_{\overline{n}|}$.

Considerable confusion has often been created by treating the annuity-immediate and the annuity-due as if they were greatly different. Actually they refer to exactly the same series of payments evaluated at different points in time. Figure 3.3 clarifies this point.

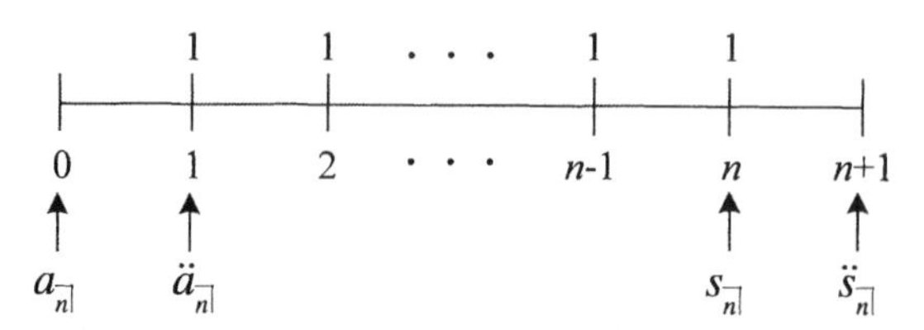

Figure 3.3 Time diagram comparing an annuity-immediate with an annuity-due

Numerical values for an annuity-due can be directly calculated using either formula (3.8) or (3.10). Numerical values for an annuity-due can also be readily obtained using a financial calculator. Typically, financial calculators have a sixth key used to distinguish the annuity-due from the annuity-immediate. The annuity-immediate usually is the default setting or it may be denoted by END (for end of period). The annuity-due usually requires a selection denoted by BEG or BGN (for beginning of period).

An interesting special case in evaluating annuities is the situation in which $i = 0$. In this case formulas such as (3.2), (3.4), (3.8), and (3.10) cannot be applied, since division by zero is impossible. However, any annuity value with $i = 0$ is just the sum of the payments, since nothing is being accumulated or discounted. Thus we have

$$a_{\overline{n}|} = \ddot{a}_{\overline{n}|} = s_{\overline{n}|} = \ddot{s}_{\overline{n}|} = n, \text{ if } i = 0. \tag{3.17}$$

***Example 3.4** An investor wishes to accumulate $100,000 in a fund for retirement at the end of 12 years. To accomplish this the investor plans to make deposits at the end of each year, the final payment to be made one year prior to the end of the investment period. How large should each deposit be if the fund earns 7% effective?*

This problem should be read carefully. There will be only 11 payments, not 12. Since we are interested in the accumulated value one year after the last payment, the equation of value is

$$R\,\ddot{s}_{\overline{11}|} = 100{,}000$$

where R is the annual deposit. Solving for R we have

$$\begin{aligned} R &= \frac{100{,}000}{\ddot{s}_{\overline{11}|}} \\ &= \frac{100{,}000}{16.88845} = \$5921.21. \end{aligned}$$

This example can also be solved using a financial calculator if we set

BEG or BGN
N = 11
I = 100(.07) = 7
FV = -100,000

and compute PMT obtaining

PMT = $5921.21

3.4 ANNUITY VALUES ON ANY DATE

Thus far we have considered evaluating annuities only at the beginning of the term (either one period before, or on the date of, the first payment), or at the end of the term (either on the date of, or one period after, the last payment). However, it is often necessary to evaluate annuities on other dates. We will discuss the following three cases: (1) present values more than one period before the first payment date, (2) accumulated values more than one period after the last payment date, and (3) current values between the first and last payment dates. We will assume that the evaluation date is an integral number of periods from each payment date.

The value of an annuity on any date could be found by accumulating or discounting each separate payment and summing the results. However, this method would become inefficient if a large number of payments are involved. We will see that it is possible to develop values for all three cases in terms of annuity symbols already defined.

The above three cases can best be illustrated by example. Consider an annuity under which seven payments of 1 are made at the end of the 3rd through the 9th periods inclusive. Figure 3.4 is a time diagram for this annuity. The values at the end of the 2nd, 3rd, 9th, and 10th periods are given directly, either by annuities-immediate or by annuities-due, as labeled on the time diagram.

The present value at the beginning of the 1st period is an example of case 1, the accumulated value at the end of the 12th period is an example of case 2, and the current value at the end of the 6th period is an example of case 3. These three cases are denoted by arrows 1, 2, and 3, respectively, on the time diagram.

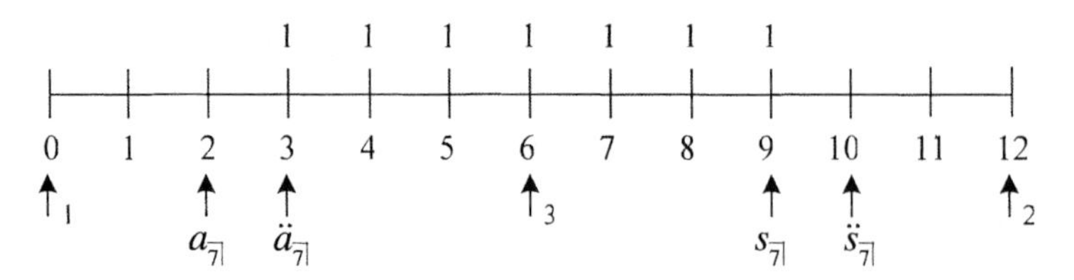

Figure 3.4 Time diagram for illustration in Section 3.4

Present values more than one period before the first payment date

In this case, the present value of the annuity at the beginning of the 1st period is seen to be the present value at the end of the 2nd period discounted for two periods, i.e.

$$v^2 a_{\overline{7}|}.$$

It is possible to develop an alternate expression for this present value strictly in terms of annuity values. Temporarily assume that imaginary payments of 1 are made at the end of the 1st and 2nd periods. Then the present value of all nine payments at time $t = 0$ is $a_{\overline{9}|}$. However, we must remove the present value of the imaginary payments, which is $a_{\overline{2}|}$. Thus, an alternate expression for the present value is

$$a_{\overline{9}|} - a_{\overline{2}|}.$$

This alternative expression offers no computational advantages, but does illustrate a type of reasoning the reader will find useful in other contexts.

This type of annuity is often called a *deferred annuity*, since payments commence only after a deferred period. A symbol given to an annuity-immediate deferred for m periods with a term of n periods after the deferral period is ${}_{m|}a_{\overline{n}|}$. Thus, the annuity being illustrated could be labeled ${}_{2|}a_{\overline{7}|}$.

It is also possible to work with a deferred annuity-due. The reader should verify that the answer to this case, expressed as annuity-due, is

$$v^3\ddot{a}_{\overline{7}|} = \ddot{a}_{\overline{10}|} - \ddot{a}_{\overline{3}|}.$$

A symbol for this annuity would be ${}_{3|}\ddot{a}_{\overline{7}|}$.

Accumulated values more than one period after the last payment date

In this case, the accumulated value of the annuity at the end of the 12th period is seen to be the accumulated value at the end of the 9th period, accumulated for three periods, i.e.

$$s_{\overline{7}|}(1+i)^3.$$

Here it is also possible to develop an alternate expression strictly in terms of annuity values. Temporarily, assume that imaginary payments of 1 are made at the end of the 10th, 11th, and 12th periods. Then the accumulated value of all 10 payments is $s_{\overline{10}|}$. However, we must remove the accumulated value of the imaginary payments, which is $s_{\overline{3}|}$. Thus, an alternate expression for the accumulated value is

$$s_{\overline{10}|} - s_{\overline{3}|}.$$

Again, it is also possible to work with annuities-due instead of annuities-immediate. The reader should verify that the answer in this case, expressed as an annuity-due, is

$$\ddot{s}_{\overline{7}|}(1+i)^2 = \ddot{s}_{\overline{9}|} - \ddot{s}_{\overline{2}|}.$$

Current values between the first and last payment dates

In this case, the current value of the annuity at the end of the 6th period is seen to be the present value at the end of the 2nd period accumulated for four periods or the accumulated value at the end of the 9th period discounted for three periods, i.e.

$$a_{\overline{7}|}(1+i)^4 = v^3 s_{\overline{7}|}.$$

Here it is again possible to develop an alternate expression strictly in terms of annuity values. Separate the seven payments into the first four payments and the last three payments. The accumulated value of the first four payments is $s_{\overline{4}|}$ and the present value of the last three payments is $a_{\overline{3}|}$ Thus, an alternate expression for the current value is

$$s_{\overline{4}|} + a_{\overline{3}|}.$$

Again it is also possible to work with annuities-due instead of annuities-immediate. The reader should verify that the answer in this case, expressed as an annuity-due, is

$$\ddot{a}_{\overline{7}|}(1+i)^3 = v^4\ddot{s}_{\overline{7}|} = \ddot{s}_{\overline{3}|} + \ddot{a}_{\overline{4}|}.$$

Summary

In general, it is possible to express the value of an annuity on any date which is an integral number of periods from each payment date in a variety of ways. The reader should practice translating one form of an answer into alternate forms.

The reader should also be careful to observe that the labels on the time diagram are merely an aid in visualizing the payments involved, but they do not affect the answer. For example, we could label the time diagram in Figure 3.4 from 8 to 20 instead of 0 to 12 and the answers to the various examples would not change. The elements on the time diagram that do affect the answer are the number of payments and the location of the evaluation date or comparison date in relation to the payment dates.

Finally, if it is necessary to find the value of an annuity on a date which is not an integral number of periods from each payment date, the value should be found on a date which is an integral number of periods from each payment date and then the value on this date can be accumulated or discounted for the fractional period to the actual evaluation date. This situation will be illustrated in the exercises.

3.5 PERPETUITIES

A *perpetuity* is an annuity whose payments continue forever, i.e. the term of the annuity is not finite. Although it seems unrealistic to have an annuity with payments continuing forever, examples do exist in practice. The dividends on preferred stock with no redemption provision and the British consols, which are nonredeemable obligations of the British government, are examples of perpetuities. Preferred stock will be defined and discussed further in Chapter 6.

The present value of a perpetuity-immediate is denoted by $a_{\overline{\infty}|}$, which can be evaluated as the sum of an infinite geometric progression, giving

$$\begin{aligned} a_{\overline{\infty}|} &= v + v^2 + v^3 + \cdots \\ &= \frac{v}{1-v} \\ &= \frac{v}{iv} \\ &= \frac{1}{i} \end{aligned} \qquad (3.18)$$

provided $v < 1$, which will be the case if $i > 0$.

Alternatively, we have

$$a_{\overline{\infty}|} = \lim_{n\to\infty} a_{\overline{n}|} = \lim_{n\to\infty} \frac{1-v^n}{i} = \frac{1}{i}$$

since

$$\lim_{n\to\infty} v^n = 0.$$

Formula (3.18) can be interpreted verbally. If principal of $1/i$ is invested at rate i, then interest of $i \cdot 1/i = 1$ can be paid at the end of every period forever, leaving the original principal intact.

By an analogous argument, for a perpetuity-due, we have

$$\ddot{a}_{\overline{\infty}|} = \frac{1}{d}. \qquad (3.19)$$

It should be noted that accumulated values for perpetuities do not exist, since payments continue forever.

It is instructive to use the concept of perpetuities to give a verbal interpretation to formula (3.2)

$$a_{\overline{n}|} = \frac{1-v^n}{i}. \qquad (3.2)$$

Consider two perpetuities. The first pays 1 at the end of each period and has present value $1/i$. The second is deferred n periods and, thus, has present value v^n/i. The difference is the present value of payments of 1 at the end of each period during the deferred period, which is $a_{\overline{n}|}$.

Some readers may feel that perpetuities are of limited practical significance. However, a broader range of transactions than payments literally continuing forever can be looked upon as equivalent to perpetuities. For example, consider the investment of \$1000 at a 10% annual effective rate of interest, payable in installments each year, for an unknown period of time, at the end of which the principal of \$1000 is returned. Such a transaction is equivalent to determining the present value of a perpetuity paying \$100 at the end of each year at an effective rate of interest of 10%.

Example 3.5 below illustrates another type of practical application in which perpetuities are used.

Example 3.5 A leaves an estate of \$100,000. Interest on the estate is paid to beneficiary B for the first 10 years, to beneficiary C for the second 10 years, and to charity D thereafter. Find the relative shares of B, C, and D in the estate, if it is assumed the estate will earn a 7% annual effective rate of interest.

The value of B's share is

$$7000\, a_{\overline{10}|} = 7000(7.02358) = \$49{,}165$$

to the nearest dollar.

The value of C's share is

$$7000\left(v^{10} a_{\overline{10}|}\right) = 7000(1.07)^{-10}(7.02358) = \$24{,}993$$

to the nearest dollar.

The value of D's share is

$$7000\left(v^{20} a_{\overline{\infty}|}\right) = 7000\left(\frac{(1.07)^{-20}}{.07}\right) = \$25{,}842$$

to the nearest dollar.

Note that the sum of the shares of B, C, and D is equal to \$100,000 as expected. Also note that the present value of the estate at the end of 20 years is $100{,}000(1.07)^{-20} = \$25{,}842$, to the nearest dollar, which is equal to D's share. This confirms the fact that charity D continuing to receive the interest into perpetuity or receiving the estate value in a lump-sum at the end of 20 years are equivalent in value.

3.6 UNKNOWN TIME

Thus far, in any problems involving annuities, we have assumed that n and i are both known. In Section 3.6 we will consider the case in which n is unknown, and in Section 3.7 we will consider the case in which i is unknown.

In general, problems involving unknown time will not produce exact integral answers for n. Before tackling the question of determining unknown time, consider first what the symbol $a_{\overline{n+k}|}$ might represent, where n is a positive integer and $0 < k < 1$. Formula (3.1) cannot be applied, since it requires that n be a positive integer. However, it is possible to derive a result which is consistent with formula (3.2) as follows:

$$\begin{aligned} a_{\overline{n+k}|} &= \frac{1-v^{n+k}}{i} \\ &= \frac{1-v^n+v^n-v^{n+k}}{i} \\ &= a_{\overline{n}|} + v^{n+k}\left[\frac{(1+i)^k-1}{i}\right]. \end{aligned} \tag{3.20}$$

Thus, an interpretation for the symbol $a_{\overline{n+k}|}$ consistent with the formula (3.2) is that it is the present value of an n-period annuity-immediate of 1 per period, plus a final payment at time $n+k$ of $\frac{(1+i)^k-1}{i}$.

The amount of this final irregular payment seems rather unusual. A payment that might be more "comfortable" to some readers is k, i.e. the payment would be proportional to the fractional time involved. Fortunately, k is reasonably close to $\frac{(1+i)^k-1}{i}$ which can be seen by using a binomial expansion for $(1+i)^k$.

Unfortunately, the need to interpret annuity symbols for non-integral terms does arise in practice. For example, many courts use an annuity-certain for a person's life expectancy in the measurement of economic damages in personal injury and wrongful death lawsuits. If the injured party in such a lawsuit has a life expectancy of 15.7 years, then what is the correct value of the annuity-certain?

The above approach for solving unknown time problems is seldom used in practice because of the inconvenience and confusion of making a payment at a date which is not an integral number of periods from the dates all other payments are made. For example, making all regular payments on July 1 of each year for a period of years followed by a smaller payment on November 27 is not convenient for either party to the transaction.

What is usually done in practice is either to make a smaller additional payment at the same time as the last regular payment, in effect making a payment larger than the regular payment, called a *balloon payment*, or to make a smaller payment one period after the last regular payment, called a *drop payment.* Naturally, the smaller payments in these two situations are not equal, nor would either be equal to the smaller payment made at an intermediate point as with formula (3.20). However, all these payments would be equivalent in value.

Problems involving unknown time can best be illustrated by example.

***Example 3.6** An investment of $1000 is to be used to make payments of $100 at the end of every year for as long as possible. If the fund earns an annual effective rate of interest of 5%, find how many regular payments can be made and find the amount of the smaller payment:*

(1) To be paid on the date of the last regular payment.

(2) To be paid one year after the last regular payment.

(3) To be paid during the year following the last regular payment, consistent with formula (3.20).

The equation of value is

$$100\, a_{\overline{n}|} = 1000$$

or

$$a_{\overline{n}|} = 10.$$

This example cannot be completely solved just by using the annuity valuation keys on a financial calculator. However, we can use this technique to bracket n between two successive positive integers.

We set

$$\begin{aligned} \text{I} &= 100(.05) = 5 \\ \text{PV} &= 1000 \\ \text{PMT} &= -100 \end{aligned}$$

and compute N. Interestingly, not all financial calculators give the same answer. However, all give an answer sufficient to determine that $14 < n < 15$. Thus, 14 regular payments can be made plus a smaller final payment. Figure 3.5 is a time diagram for this example.

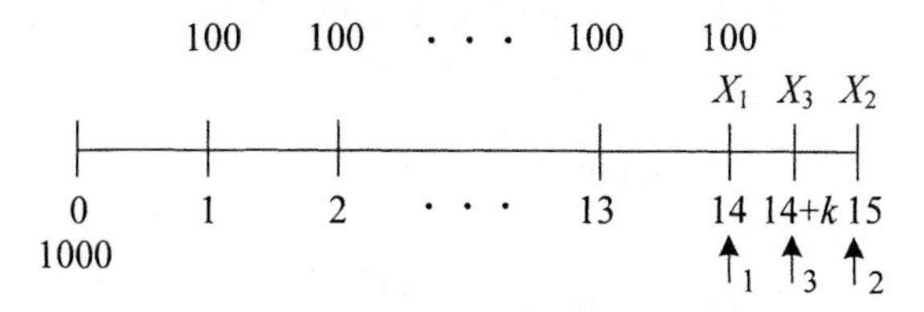

Figure 3.5 Time diagram for Example 3.6

In this figure X_1, X_2, and X_3 are the smaller final payments for the above three cases; arrows 1, 2, and 3 mark comparison dates for the above three cases; and k derives its meaning from formula (3.20).

1. The equation of value at the end of the 14th year is

$$100\, s_{\overline{14|}} + X_1 = 1000(1.05)^{14}.$$

Thus,

$$\begin{aligned} X_1 &= 1000(1.05)^{14} - 100\, s_{\overline{14|}} \\ &= 1979.93 - 1959.86 \\ &= \$20.07. \end{aligned}$$

2. The equation of value at the end of the 15th year is

$$100\, \ddot{s}_{\overline{14|}} + X_2 = 1000(1.05)^{15}.$$

Thus,

$$\begin{aligned} X_2 &= 1000(1.05)^{15} - 100\left(s_{\overline{15|}} - 1\right) \\ &= 2078.93 - 2057.86 \\ &= \$21.07. \end{aligned}$$

It should be noted that 20.07(1.05) = 21.07, or that in general $X_1(1+i) = X_2$. The reader should justify this result by general reasoning.

3. In this case the equation of value becomes

$$100\, a_{\overline{14+k|}} = 1000$$

or

$$a_{\overline{14+k|}} = 10$$

where $0 < k < 1$. This can be written as

$$\frac{1-v^{14+k}}{i} = 10$$

or

$$v^{14+k} = 1 - 10i = .5.$$

Thus,

$$(1.05)^{14+k} = 2$$

giving

$$\begin{aligned} 14+k &= \frac{\ln 2}{\ln 1.05} \\ &= \frac{.693147}{.048790} \\ &= 14.2067 \end{aligned}$$

or

$$k = .2067 .$$

Some financial calculators do give 14.2067 as the computed value of n indicating that these calculators are using an algorithm consistent with formula (3.20). Finally, the exact final irregular payment from formula (3.20) is

$$X_3 = 100 \, \frac{(1.05)^{.2067} - 1}{.05} = \$20.27$$

paid at time 14.2067. A common approximation to the exact amount would be $100k$ or \$20.67. The exact answer obtained lies between the answers to parts 1 and 2, as we would expect. It is obvious that using formula (3.20) is not only inconvenient but that it is also more difficult to use if exact answers are required.

Example 3.7 A fund of \$25,000 is to be accumulated by means of deposits of \$1000 made at the end of every year as long as necessary. If the fund earns an effective rate of interest of 8%, find how many regular deposits will be necessary and the size of a final deposit to be made one year after the last regular deposit.

The equation of value is

$$1000\, s_{\overline{n}|} = 25{,}000$$

or

$$s_{\overline{n}|} = 25.$$

Again, using a financial calculator, we find that $14 < n < 15$.

Thus, it takes 14 regular deposits plus a smaller final deposit, X. The equation of value at the end of the 15th year is

$$1000\ddot{s}_{\overline{14}|} + X = 25{,}000$$

Thus,

$$\begin{aligned} X &= 25{,}000 - 1000\left(s_{\overline{15}|} - 1\right) \\ &= 25{,}000 - 26{,}152 \\ &= -\$1152 \end{aligned}$$

to the nearest dollar.

What has happened here is that the last regular deposit brings the fund close enough to \$25,000 that interest alone over the last year is sufficient to cause the fund to exceed \$25,000. The balance in the fund at the end of the 14th year is

$$1000\, s_{\overline{14}|} = \$24{,}215.$$

The balance in the fund at the end of the 15th year with interest only over the last year is

$$24{,}215(1.08) = \$26{,}152$$

which is in excess of the desired fund by \$1152. The result agrees with the one above. This example should not be thought of as typical, since often a final deposit is necessary. However, it does illustrate that pitfalls do exist and that care must be used in obtaining reasonable answers.

3.7 UNKNOWN RATE OF INTEREST

In this section we consider the situation in which the rate of interest is the unknown. As noted in Section 2.5, problems involving the determination of an unknown rate of interest are widely encountered in practice.

By far, the best way to determine an unknown rate of interest for a basic annuity is to use a financial calculator. The calculator internally is using an algorithm for iteration, as described in Section 2.5 and Appendix E. The availability of such a powerful tool as an inexpensive financial calculator has rendered obsolete a variety of cumbersome techniques and approximations widely used in the past.

Despite the widespread availability of financial calculators, it is nevertheless instructive to note that a simple approximation formula to determine an unknown rate of interest exists. This simple approximation formula can even be computed by hand, yet it often produces reasonable answers if high levels of accuracy are not required.

Consider the situation in which $a_{\overline{n}|i} = g$. An approximation for i is given by

$$i \approx \frac{2(n-g)}{g(n+1)}. \tag{3.21}$$

The derivation of formula (3.21) is given in Appendix 3 at the end of the chapter.

The comparable formula that could be used to find an approximate answer for $s_{\overline{n}|i} = g$ is

$$i \approx \frac{2(g-n)}{g(n-1)} \tag{3.22}$$

One final method, quite limited in its applicability, is to recognize that formula (3.1) for $a_{\overline{n}|}$ and (3.3) for $s_{\overline{n}|}$ are nth degree polynomials. The roots of these nth degree polynomials are then solved by algebraic techniques for i. This method is generally practical only for small values of n.

Example 3.8 At what rate of interest, convertible quarterly, is $16,000 the present value of $1000 paid at the end of every quarter for five years?

Let $j = i^{(4)}/4$, so that the equation of value becomes

$$1000a_{\overline{20}|j} = 16{,}000$$

or

$$a_{\overline{20}|j} = 16.$$

This problem is ideally set up to use a financial calculator. We set

$$\begin{aligned} \text{N} &= 20 \\ \text{PV} &= 16 \\ \text{PMT} &= -1 \end{aligned}$$

and compute I obtaining

$$\text{I} = 2.2262.$$

Thus, we have

$$j = .022262$$

so that

$$i^{(4)} = 4(.022262) = .08905.$$

Example 3.9 ***Use the approximate formula (3.21) to obtain an approximate answer for Example 3.8 without using a financial calculator.***

We have $n = 20$ and $g = 16$, so that formula (3.21) gives

$$j \approx \frac{2(20-16)}{(16)(21)} = .0238$$

This approximate answer for the quarterly interest rate compares with the exact answer of .0223 to four decimal places obtained in Example 3.8.

This is impressive accuracy for an approximation formula that is so easy to apply. Formula (3.21) will give excellent results for small values of n and i, but will give less accurate answers as n and/or i increase.

Example 3.10 ***Find the rate of interest at which*** $\ddot{s}_{\overline{2}|} = 2.5$.

In this example, we can use a simple algebraic approach. Using formula (3.9) we have

$$\ddot{s}_{\overline{2}|} = (1+i)^2 + (1+i) = 2.5.$$

Thus, we have a quadratic which simplifies to $i^2 + 3i - .5 = 0$ and applying the quadratic formula

$$i = \frac{-3 \pm \sqrt{(3)^2 + (4)(.5)}}{2}$$

$$= \frac{-3 \pm \sqrt{11}}{2}.$$

Only the positive root is reasonable, so that

$$i = \frac{-3 + \sqrt{11}}{2} = .1583, \text{ or } 15.83\%.$$

3.8 VARYING INTEREST

Thus far we have assumed a level rate of interest throughout the term of the annuity. In this section we will consider the situation in which the rate of interest can vary each period, but compound interest is still in effect. Other patterns of variation, not involving compound interest, are considered in Section 3.9.

As in Chapter 1, let i_k denote the rate of interest applicable for period k, i.e. for the interval from time k - 1 to time k. We consider first the present value of an n-period annuity-immediate. Two patterns of variation could be involved.

The first pattern would be for i_k to be the applicable rate for period k regardless of when the payment is made. This method could be called the *portfolio rate method* (a term to be defined and analyzed in more detail in Section 7.7), since one rate applies to the entire annuity value ("portfolio") at any point in time. In this case the present value becomes

$$\begin{aligned} a_{\overline{n}|} &= (1+i_1)^{-1} + (1+i_1)^{-1}(1+i_2)^{-1} + \cdots \\ &+ (1+i_1)^{-1}(1+i_2)^{-1}\cdots(1+i_n)^{-1} = \sum_{t=1}^{n}\prod_{s=1}^{t}(1+i_s)^{-1}. \end{aligned} \tag{3.23}$$

The second pattern would be to compute present values using rate i_k for the payment made at time k over all k periods. This method could be called the *yield curve method* (a term to be defined and analyzed in more detail in Section 10.2). In this case the present value becomes

$$\begin{aligned} a_{\overline{n}|} &= (1+i_1)^{-1} + (1+i_2)^{-2} + \cdots + (1+i_n)^{-n} \\ &= \sum_{t=1}^{n}(1+i_t)^{-t}. \end{aligned} \tag{3.24}$$

Present values of the annuity-due can be obtained from present values of the annuity-immediate by using formula (3.15), i.e. $\ddot{a}_{\overline{n}|} = 1 + a_{\overline{n-1}|}$.

We now turn to accumulated values. We will consider values of $\ddot{s}_{\overline{n}|}$ rather than $s_{\overline{n}|}$ so that all values of i_k for k = 1, 2, . . . , n will enter the formula. Again, the same two patterns of variation could be involved. If the applicable rate for period k is i_k regardless of when the payment is made ("portfolio rate method"), we have

$$\begin{aligned} \ddot{s}_{\overline{n}|} &= (1+i_n) + (1+i_n)(1+i_{n-1}) + \cdots + (1+i_n)(1+i_{n-1})\ldots(1+i_1) \\ &= \sum_{t=1}^{n}\prod_{s=1}^{t}(1+i_{n-s+1}). \end{aligned} \tag{3.25}$$

Alternatively, if the payment made at time k earns at rate i_k over the rest of the accumulation period ("yield curve method"), we have

$$\begin{aligned} \ddot{s}_{\overline{n}|} &= (1+i_n)+(1+i_{n-1})^2+\cdots+(1+i_1)^n \\ &= \sum_{t=1}^{n} (1+i_{n-t+1})^t \,. \end{aligned} \tag{3.26}$$

Accumulated values of the annuity-immediate can be obtained from accumulated values of the annuity-due by using formula (3.16), i.e. $s_{\overline{n+1}|} = \ddot{s}_{\overline{n}|} + 1$.

The reader should distinguish carefully between the two different patterns of computing interest described above, since both occur in practice. In essence, formulas (3.23) and (3.25) assume that the interest rate for any given period is the same for all payments whose value is affected by interest during that period. On the other hand, formulas (3.24) and (3.26) assume that each payment has an associated interest rate which remains level over the entire period for which present values or accumulated values are being computed.

In practice, changes in interest rates may not occur each period, but only once every several periods. In such cases, values can be obtained directly from annuity values given earlier in this chapter. This approach is generally easier to use than to directly apply the more general formulas given above and is illustrated in the following two examples.

Example 3.11 Find the accumulated value of a 10-year annuity-immediate of $100 per year if the effective rate of interest is 5% for the first 6 years and 4% for the last 4 years.

We could apply formula (3.25); however, the following approach is simpler. The accumulated value of the first six payments after six years is

$$100\, s_{\overline{6}|.05}\,.$$

This value is accumulated to the end of the 10 years at 4%, giving

$$100\, s_{\overline{6}|.05}\,(1.04)^4.$$

The accumulated value of the last four payments is

$$100\, s_{\overline{4}|.04}\,.$$

Thus, the answer is

$$\begin{aligned} &100\left[s_{\overline{6}|.05}(1.04)^4 + s_{\overline{4}|.04}\right] \\ &= 100\left[(6.8019)(1.16986)+(4.2465)\right] \\ &= \$1220.38. \end{aligned}$$

This is an illustration of the "portfolio rate method."

Example 3.12 Rework Example 3.11 if the first 6 payments are invested at an effective rate of interest of 5% and if the final 4 payments are invested at 4%.

We could apply formula (3.26), but again a simpler approach is available. The set-up is similar to Example 3.11 and the answer is

$$\begin{aligned} &100\left[s_{\overline{6}|.05}(1.05)^4 + s_{\overline{4}|.04}\right] \\ &= 100\left[(6.8019)(1.21551)+ 4.2465\right] \\ &= \$1251.43. \end{aligned}$$

This is an illustration of the "yield curve method". The reader should justify the relative magnitude of the answers to Examples 3.11 and 3.12 by general reasoning.

3.9 ANNUITIES NOT INVOLVING COMPOUND INTEREST

The valuation of annuities not involving compound interest is full of pitfalls and requires careful analysis and interpretation to obtain reasonable results. Multiple values for annuities can result, which in turn requires qualification as to the basis on which the values are calculated. In fact, it is best to avoid dealing with annuities not involving compound interest, if possible.

Unfortunately, it is not always possible to avoid the subject. For example, on occasion some courts have required the use of simple interest in computing the value of an annuity involving lost income in personal injury and wrongful death lawsuits. The "correct" procedure to compute such values is not only ambiguous, but serious distortions will result if a significant period of time is involved in the calculation.

Section 3.9 is not fundamental to an understanding of the theory of interest and can safely be ignored by the reader. However, it is included as a useful reference for those readers who, for whatever reason, find themselves in the unfortunate position of trying to achieve some degree of consistency in an inherently inconsistent framework.

It would seem logical to return to the accumulation function as the basis to compute annuity values. The present value of an n-period annuity-immediate is equal to the sum of the present values of the individual payments. Thus, a generalized version of formula (3.1) is

$$a_{\overline{n}|} = \sum_{t=1}^{n} \frac{1}{a(t)}. \tag{3.27}$$

We turn next to finding a value for $s_{\overline{n}|}$. If we assume that 1 invested at time t, where $t = 1, 2, \ldots n-1$ will accumulate to $\dfrac{a(n)}{a(t)}$ at time n, then we would have

$$s_{\overline{n}|} = \sum_{t=1}^{n} \frac{a(n)}{a(t)} = a(n) \sum_{t=1}^{n} \frac{1}{a(t)}. \tag{3.28}$$

This would seem to be an appropriate procedure in certain cases, e.g. a problem involving a varying force of interest over the n periods.

However, it does not produce correct results in all cases. For example, suppose we wish to find the accumulated value of an n-period annuity-immediate in which each payment is invested at simple interest from the date of payment until the end of the n periods. The accumulated value of such an annuity would be

$$1 + (1+i) + (1+2i) + \cdots + \left[1 + (n-1)i\right].$$

This leads to a generalized version of formula (3.3)

$$s_{\overline{n}|} = \sum_{t=0}^{n-1} a(t) \tag{3.29}$$

which will produce the correct answer for the above simple interest example.

However, it can easily be shown that formulas (3.28) and (3.29) do not produce the same result under simple interest. In fact, it can be shown that formulas (3.28) and (3.29) do not produce the same results in general for any pattern of interest other than compound interest.

For those readers who like symmetry and completeness, we could use formula (3.29) to find another expression for $a_{\overline{n|}}$

$$a_{\overline{n|}} = \sum_{t=0}^{n-1} \frac{a(t)}{a(n)} = \frac{1}{a(n)} \sum_{t=0}^{n-1} a(t) . \tag{3.30}$$

It is not surprising that formulas (3.27) and (3.30) produce different answers unless compound interest is involved.

Further analysis of annuity values at simple interest is instructive. Consider the investment of a sum of money for n periods at simple interest which is just sufficient to permit a withdrawal of 1 the end of each period for n periods. The concept of simple interest means that interest does not earn additional interest. Thus, the original amount of the investment is deposited in a fund which earns interest at rate i, but any interest earned is immediately transferred into a second fund which does not earn interest.

The ambiguity arises whenever a withdrawal is made. How much should be withdrawn from the principal fund, which earns interest, and how much from the interest fund, which does not earn interest? Different answers will be obtained depending on how this allocation is made.

In order to illustrate some of the possible answers which can be obtained, let $n = 6$ and $i = 10\%$. Let the original investment be denoted by K. We will refer to the principal fund as "Fund 1," and the interest fund as "Fund 2."

One extreme case would be to withdraw payments from Fund 2 whenever possible, and to withdraw from Fund 1 only when Fund 2 is exhausted. At the end of the first period interest of $.1K$ is earned on Fund 1 and deposited into Fund 2. A withdrawal of 1 is then made, with $.1K$ coming from Fund 2 and $1 - .1K$ coming from Fund 1. This leaves a new balance in Fund 1 of $K - (1 - .1K) = 1.1K - 1$. At the end of the second period interest of $.1(1.1K - 1)$ is earned on Fund 1 and deposited into Fund 2. A withdrawal of 1 is then made, with $.1[1.1K - 1]$ coming from Fund 2 and $1 - .1(1.1K - 1)$ coming from Fund 1. This leaves a new balance in Fund 1 of

$$\begin{aligned} &(1.1K-1)-\left[1-.1(1.1K-1)\right] \\ &= (1.1)^2 K-(1 + 1.1) . \end{aligned}$$

If this process is continued for four more years, the balance in Fund 1 at the end of six years is

$$(1.1)^6 K - \left[1 + 1.1 + (1.1)^2 + (1.1)^3 + (1.1)^4 + (1.1)^5\right]$$

and the balance in Fund 2 is zero. However, the balance in Fund 1 must also be zero after the final withdrawal. Thus

$$K = \frac{(1.1)^6 - 1}{(1.1)^6 (1.1 - 1)} = \frac{1-(1.1)^{-6}}{.1} = 4.36$$

which is the value of $a_{\overline{6}|.1}$ using compound interest. We will discover in Chapter 5 that this is no coincidence. The results of this approach are summarized in Table 3.1.

Table 3.1 Fund Development - Withdrawals from Fund 2 Prior to Fund 1 for $a_{\overline{6}|}$ at 10%.

	Fund 1 Balance		*Fund 2 Balance*	
Period	*Before withdrawal*	*After withdrawal*	*Before withdrawal*	*After withdrawal*
0	N/A	4.355	N/A	0
1	4.355	3.791	.436	0
2	3.791	3.170	.379	0
3	3.170	2.487	.317	0
4	2.487	1.736	.249	0
5	1.736	.910	.174	0
6	.910	.001*	.091	0

* zero, except for .001 roundoff error

The other extreme case would be to withdraw payments from Fund 1 whenever possible, and to withdraw from Fund 2 only when Fund 1 is exhausted. In view of the answer above, we will assume that Fund 1 becomes exhausted at the end of the fifth period. It will be necessary to confirm that the answer obtained is consistent with this assumption.

At the end of the first period interest of $.1K$ is earned on Fund 1 and deposited into Fund 2. A withdrawal of 1 is then made with all of it coming from Fund 1. This leaves a new balance of $K-1$ in Fund 1 and $.1K$ in Fund 2. At the end of the second period interest of $.1(K-1)$ is earned on Fund 1 and deposited into Fund 2. A withdrawal of 1 is then made with all of it coming from Fund 1. This leaves a new balance of $K-2$ in Fund 1 and $.1K+.1(K-1)=.2K-.1$ in Fund 2.

If this process is continued for two more periods, we have $K-4$ in Fund 1, which we have assumed lies between 0 and 1. Also, we have

$$.1\left[K+(K-1)+(K-2)+(K-3)\right] = .4K-.6$$

in Fund 2. At the end of the fifth period interest of $.1(K-4)$ is earned on Fund 1 and deposited into Fund 2. A withdrawal of 1 is then made with $K-4$ of it coming from Fund 1, which is now exhausted. The rest of the payment, i.e. $1-(K-4)=5-K$, comes from Fund 2. The new balance in Fund 2 is

$$(.4K-.6)+.1(K-4)-(5-K) = 1.5K-6\ .$$

At the end of the sixth period no interest is earned, since Fund 1 is exhausted. The fund balance in Fund 2 is unchanged, since Fund 2 does not earn interest. The final withdrawal of 1 comes entirely from Fund 2 exhausting it, so that we have

$$1.5K-6 = 1$$

$$K = \frac{7}{1.5} = 4.67 = a_{\overline{6|}}.$$

This answer is valid, since the assumption was made that $4 < K < 5$. If an answer had been obtained outside this interval, the problem would have to be reworked until an answer consistent with the assumption about the exhaustion of Fund 1 is obtained. The results of this approach are summarized in Table 3.2.

Table 3.2 Fund Development - Withdrawals from Fund 1 Prior to Fund 2 for $a_{\overline{6}|}$ at 10%

Period	Fund 1 Balance		Fund 2 Balance	
	Before withdrawal	*After withdrawal*	*Before withdrawal*	*After withdrawal*
0	N/A	4.667	N/A	0
1	4.667	3.667	.467	.467
2	3.667	2.667	.834	.834
3	2.667	1.667	1.101	1.101
4	1.667	.667	1.268	1.268
5	.667	0	1.268	1.002**
6	0	0	1.002	.002*

* zero, except for .002 roundoff error
** calculated as 1.268 + .1(.667) - (1 - .667) = 1.002

We next apply formula (3.27) directly and obtain

$$a_{\overline{6}|} = \frac{1}{1.1} + \frac{1}{1.2} + \cdots + \frac{1}{1.6} = 4.52$$

which lies between our two extreme answers already obtained. Apparently, formula (3.27) involves an implicit intermediate allocation of withdrawals from Fund 1 and Fund 2 between the two extremes.

If we apply formula (3.30), we obtain

$$a_{\overline{6}|} = \frac{1 + 1.1 + \cdots + 1.5}{1.6} = 4.69$$

which lies outside the range bounded by the two extremes. Thus, we must question whether formula (3.30) produces a result with any real-world significance at all, at least in this example. The results of this analysis are summarized in Table 3.3.

Table 3.3 Comparison of $a_{\overline{6|}}$ Computed at 10% Simple Interest on Four Different Bases

Basis	*Value*
Low extreme (compound interest)	4.36
Formula (3.27)	4.52
High extreme	4.67
Formula (3.30)	4.69

At this point the reader should be thoroughly convinced that finding annuity values at simple interest is treacherous indeed. Furthermore, simple discount would present just as many difficulties. The reader now should really appreciate the admonition given early in this section to avoid computing annuity values not involving compound interest if at all possible!

Example 3.13 Compare the value of $s_{\overline{6|}}$ at 10% interest:
(1) Assuming compound interest.
(2) Using formula (3.28).
(3) Using formula (3.29).

1. Using compound interest at 10%

$$s_{\overline{6|}} = 7.72.$$

2. From formula (3.28)

$$s_{\overline{6|}} = 1.6\left(\frac{1}{1.1} + \frac{1}{1.2} + \cdots + \frac{1}{1.6}\right) = 7.23\ .$$

3. From formula (3.29)

$$s_{\overline{6|}} = 1 + 1.1 + 1.2 + \cdots + 1.5 = 7.50\ .$$

Answer (3) involves simple interest being earned on each payment from the date of deposit to the end of the six-year period of investment. Answer 1 is larger than either of the other two, verifying the larger accumulation with compound interest.

Example 3.14 Find $s_{\overline{5}|}$***, if*** $\delta_t = .02t$ ***for*** $0 \leq t \leq 5$.

If we accumulate each payment from the date of deposit to the end of the five-year period at the varying force of interest δ_t, we have

$$\begin{aligned} s_{\overline{5}|} &= \sum_{t=1}^{5} e^{\int_t^5 \delta_r\, dr} = \sum_{t=1}^{5} e^{.01 r^2]_t^5} \\ &= e^{.24} + e^{.21} + e^{.16} + e^{.09} + 1 \\ &= 1.27125 + 1.23368 + 1.17351 + 1.09417 + 1 \\ &= 5.7726. \end{aligned}$$

Alternatively, formula (3.28) is applicable in this case. We have

$$\begin{aligned} a(t) &= e^{\int_0^t \delta_r\, dr} \\ &= e^{.01r^2]_0^t} \\ &= e^{.01t^2} \end{aligned}$$

so that

$$\begin{aligned} s_{\overline{5}|} &= a(5) \sum_{t=1}^{5} \frac{1}{a(t)} \\ &= e^{.25}\left(e^{-.01} + e^{-.04} + e^{-.09} + e^{-.16} + e^{-.25}\right) \\ &= e^{.24} + e^{.21} + e^{.16} + e^{.09} + 1 \\ &= 5.7726 \end{aligned}$$

which agrees with the answer obtained from first principles above.

APPENDIX 3

Approximate formula for unknown rate of interest

Consider a situation in which $a_{\overline{n}|i} = g$. The goal is to produce an approximation for i using only the given values of g and n. Taking the reciprocal of formula (3.2) gives

$$\frac{1}{g} = \frac{1}{a_{\overline{n}|i}} = \frac{i}{1-(1+i)^{-n}}$$
$$\approx \frac{1}{n}\left[1+\frac{n+1}{2}i\right]$$

which is a series expansion in i carried to two terms obtained by doing a binomial expansion in the denominator followed by an unpleasant long division. We then have

$$\frac{n+1}{2n}i \approx \frac{1}{g} - \frac{1}{n} = \frac{n-g}{ng}$$

or

$$i \approx \frac{2(n-g)}{g(n+1)}. \tag{3.21}$$

The analogous formula that could be used to find an approximate answer for $s_{\overline{n}|i} = g$ is

$$i \approx \frac{2(g-n)}{g(n-1)} \tag{3.22}$$

The derivation of formula (3.22) is similar.

EXERCISES

3.2 Annuity-immediate

1. A family wishes to accumulate $50,000 in a college education fund at the end of 20 years. If they deposit $1000 in the fund at the end of each of the first 10 years and $1000 + X in the fund at the end of each of the second 10 years, find X if the fund earns 7% effective.

2. The cash price of an automobile is $10,000. The buyer is willing to finance the purchase at 18% convertible monthly and to make payments of $250 at the end of each month for four years. Find the down payment that will be necessary.

3. A sports car enthusiast needs to finance $25,000 of the total purchase price of a new car. A loan is selected having 48 monthly level payments with a lender charging 6% convertible monthly. However, the lender informs the buyer that their policy is not to exceed a $500 monthly payment on any car loan. The buyer decides to accept the loan offer with the $500 payment and then decides to take out a second 12-month loan with a different lender at 7.5% convertible monthly to make up the shortfall not covered by the first loan. Find the amount of the monthly payment on the second loan.

4. A borrows $20,000 for 8 years and repays the loan with level annual payments at the end of each year. B also borrows $20,000 for 8 years, but pays only interest as it is due each year and plans to repay the entire loan at the end of the 8-year period. Both loans carry an effective interest rate of 8.5%. How much more interest will B pay than A pays over the life of the loan?

5. An annuity provides a payment of n at the end of each year for n years. The annual effective interest rate is $1/n$. What is the present value of the annuity?

6. If $a_{\overline{n|}} = x$ and $a_{\overline{2n|}} = y$, express d as a function of x and y.

3.3 Annuity-due

7. Find $\ddot{a}_{\overline{8|}}$ if the effective rate of discount is 10%.

8. Find the present value of payments of \$200 every six months starting immediately and continuing through four years from the present, and \$100 every six months thereafter through ten years from the present, if $i^{(2)} = .06$.

9. A worker aged 40 wishes to accumulate a fund for retirement by depositing \$3000 at the beginning of each year for 25 years. Starting at age 65 the worker plans to make 15 annual withdrawals at the beginning of each year. Assuming that all payments are certain to be made, find the amount of each withdrawal starting at age 65 to the nearest dollar, if the effective rate of interest is 8% during the first 25 years but only 7% thereafter.

10. *a)* Show that $\ddot{a}_{\overline{n}|} = a_{\overline{n}|} + 1 - v^n$.
    b) Show that $\ddot{s}_{\overline{n}|} = s_{\overline{n}|} - 1 + (1+i)^n$.
    c) Verbally interpret the results in (*a*) and (*b*).

11. If $\ddot{a}_{\overline{p}|} = x$ and $s_{\overline{q}|} = y$, show that $a_{\overline{p+q}|} = \dfrac{vx + y}{1 + iy}$.

3.4 Annuity values on any date

12. Payments of \$100 per quarter are made from June 7, Z through December 7, $Z + 11$, inclusive. If the nominal rate of interest convertible quarterly is 6%:
    a) Find the present value on September 7, Z - 1.
    b) Find the current value on March 7, Z + 8.
    c) Find the accumulated value on June 7, Z + 12.

13. Simplify $a_{\overline{15}|}(1 + v^{15} + v^{30})$ to one symbol.

14. It is known that $\dfrac{a_{\overline{7}|}}{a_{\overline{11}|}} = \dfrac{a_{\overline{3}|} + s_{\overline{x}|}}{a_{\overline{y}|} + s_{\overline{z}|}}$. Find x, y, and z.

15. Annuities X and Y provide the following payments:

End of Year	Annuity X	Annuity Y
1-10	1	K
11-20	2	0
21-30	1	K

Annuities X and Y have equal present values at an annual effective interest rate i such that $v^{10} = 1/2$. Determine K.

16. You are given that ${}_{5|}a_{\overline{10|}} = 3 \cdot {}_{10|}a_{\overline{5|}}$. Find $(1+i)^5$.

17. Find the present value to the nearest dollar on January 1 of an annuity which pays \$2000 every six months for five years. The first payment is due on the next April 1 and the rate of interest is 9% convertible semiannually.

3.5 Perpetuities

18. Deposits of \$1000 are placed into a fund at the beginning of each year for the next 20 years. After 30 years annual payments commence and continue forever, with the first payment at the end of the 30th year. Find an expression for the amount of each payment.

19. A deferred perpetuity-due begins payments at time n with annual payments of \$1000 per year. If the present value of this perpetuity-due is equal to \$6561 and the effective rate of interest $i = 1/9$, find n.

20. A woman has an inheritance in a trust fund for family members left by her recently deceased father that will pay \$50,000 at the end of each year indefinitely into the future. She has just turned 60 and does not think that this perpetuity-immediate meets her retirement needs. She wishes to exchange the value of her inheritance in the trust fund for one which will pay her a 5-year deferred annuity-immediate providing her a retirement annuity with annual payments at the end of each year for 20 years following the 5-year deferral period. She would have no remaining interest in the trust fund after 20 payments are made. If the trustee agrees to her proposal, how much annual retirement income would she receive? The trust fund is earning an annual effective rate of interest equal to 5%. Answer to the nearest dollar.

21. A benefactor leaves an inheritance to four charities: A, B, C, and D. The total inheritance is a series of level payments at the end of each year forever. During the first n years A, B, and C share each payment equally. All payments after n years revert to D. If the present values of the shares of A, B, C, and D are all equal, find $(1+i)^n$.

22. A level perpetuity-immediate is to be shared by A, B, C, and D. A receives the first n payments, B the second n payments, C the third n payments, and D all payments thereafter. It is known that the ratio of the present value of C's share to A's share is .49. Find the ratio of the present value of B's share to D's share.

3.6 Unknown time

23. Compute $a_{\overline{5.25}|}$ if $i = 5\%$ using the following definitions:
    a) Formula (3.20).
    b) A payment of .25 at time 5.25.
    c) A payment of .25 at time 6.

24. A loan of $1000 is to be repaid by annual payments of $100 to commence at the end of the fifth year and to continue thereafter for as long as necessary. Find the time and amount of the final payment, if the final payment is to be larger than the regular payments. Assume $i = 4\ 1/2\%$.

25. One annuity pays 4 at the end of each year for 36 years. Another annuity pays 5 at the end of each year for 18 years. The present values of both annuities are equal at effective rate of interest i. If an amount of money invested at the same rate i will double in n years, find n.

26. A fund earning 8% effective is being accumulated with payments of $500 at the beginning of each year for 20 years. Find the maximum number of withdrawals of $1000 that can be made at the ends of years under the condition that once withdrawals start they must continue through the end of the 20-year period.

27. A borrower has the following two options for repaying a loan:
    (*i*) Sixty monthly payments of $100 at the end of each month.
    (*ii*) A single payment of $6000 at the end of K months.
    Interest is at the nominal annual rate of 12% convertible monthly. The two options have the same present value. Find K.
    a) On an exact basis.
    b) Using the method of equated time defined in Section 2.4.

3.7 Unknown rate of interest

28. A 48-month car loan of $12,000 can be completely paid off with monthly payments of $300 made at the end of each month. What is the nominal rate of interest convertible monthly on this loan?
    a) Computed on an exact basis with a financial calculator.
    b) Approximated by formula (3.21).

29. If $a_{\overline{2}|} = 1.75$, find an exact expression for i.

30. A beneficiary receives a $10,000 life insurance benefit. If the beneficiary uses the proceeds to buy a 10-year annuity-immediate, the annual payout will be $1538. If a 20-year annuity-immediate is purchased, the annual payout will be $1072. Both calculations are based on an annual effective interest rate of i. Find i.

31. The present values of the following three annuities are equal:
    (*i*) perpetuity-immediate paying 1 each year, calculated at an annual effective interest rate of 7.25%.
    (*ii*) 50-year annuity-immediate paying 1 each year, calculated at an annual effective interest rate of j %.
    (*iii*) n-year annuity-immediate paying 1 each year, calculated at an annual effective interest rate of $j-1$ %.

    Calculate n.

3.8 Varying interest

32. *a*) Find the present value of an annuity-immediate which pays 1 at the end of each half-year for five years, if the rate of interest is 8% convertible semiannually for the first three years and 7% convertible semiannually for the last two years.
    b) Find the present value of an annuity-immediate which pays 1 at the end of each half-year for five years, if the payments for the first three years are discounted at 8% convertible semiannually and the payments for the last two years are discounted at 7% convertible semiannually.
    c) Justify from general reasoning that the answer to (*b*) is larger than the answer to (*a*).

33. Find the present value of an annuity-immediate for five years, i.e. $a_{\overline{5}|}$, if $i_t = .06 + .002(t-1)$ for $t = 1,2,3,4,5$ where i_t is interpreted according to the:

    a) Yield curve method.
    b) Portfolio method.

34. A loan of P is to be repaid by 10 annual payments beginning 6 months from the date of the loan. The first payment is to be half as large as the others. For the first 4 1/2 years interest is at i effective; for the remainder of the term interest is at j effective. Find an expression for the first payment.

35. You are given:
    (*i*) X is the current value at time 2 of a 20-year annuity-due of 1 per annum.
    (*ii*) The annual effective interest rate for year t is $\dfrac{1}{8+t}$.

    Find X. Express your answer in summation form as a function of t.

3.9 Annuities not involving compound interest

36. Find an expression for $a_{\overline{n}|}$ assuming each payment is valued at simple discount rate d.

37. If $a(t) = \dfrac{1}{\log_2(t+2) - \log_2(t+1)}$, find an expression for $\ddot{a}_{\overline{n}|}$ by directly taking the present value of the payments.

38. Given that $\delta_t = \dfrac{1}{20-t}$, $t \geq 0$, find $s_{\overline{10}|}$.

39. For time $t > 0$, the discount function is defined by

$$a^{-1}(t) = \frac{1}{1 + .01t}.$$

A five-year annuity has payments of 1 at times $t = 1, 2, 3, 4, 5$. A calculates the present value of this annuity at time 0 directly. However, B first accumulates the payments according to the accumulation function

$$a(t) = 1 + .01t.$$

B then multiplies the result by $a^{-1}(5)$. By how much do the answers of A and B differ?

Miscellaneous problems

40. At an annual effective interest rate of i, both of the following annuities have a present value of X:

    (*i*) a 20-year annuity-immediate with annual payments of 55.
    (*ii*) a 30-year annuity-immediate with annual payments that pay 30 per year for the first 10 years, 60 per year for the second 10 years, and 90 per year for the final 10 years.

    Calculate X.

41. To accumulate \$8000 at the end of $3n$ years, deposits of \$98 are made at the end of each of the first n years and \$196 at the end of the next $2n$ years. The annual effective rate of interest is i. You are given that $(1+i)^n = 2$. Determine i.

42. A loan of \$10,000 is to be repaid with annual payments at the end of each year for the next 20 years. For the first 5 years the payments are k per year; the second 5 years, $2k$ per year; the third 5 years, $3k$ per year; and the fourth 5 years, $4k$ per year. Find an expression for k.

43. At an annual effective interest rate i it is known that:
    - (i) The present value of 2 at the end of each year for $2n$ years, plus an additional 1 at the end of each of the first n years, is 36.
    - (ii) The present value of an n-year deferred annuity-immediate paying 2 per year for n years is 6.

    Find i.

44. A depositor puts \$10,000 into a bank account that pays an annual effective interest rate of 4% for 10 years. If a withdrawal is made during the first 5 1/2 years, a penalty of 5% of the withdrawal amount is made. The depositor withdraws K at the end of each of years 4, 5, 6, and 7. The balance in the account at the end of year 10 is \$10,000. Find K to the nearest dollar.

45. Simplify $\sum_{n=15}^{40} s_{\overline{n}|}$.

4

More general annuities

4.1 INTRODUCTION

In Chapter 3 we discussed annuities for which the payment period and the interest conversion period are equal and coincide, and for which the payments are of level amount. In Chapter 4 annuities for which payments are made more or less frequently than interest is convertible and annuities with varying payments will be considered.

4.2 DIFFERING PAYMENT AND INTEREST CONVERSION PERIODS

We first address annuities for which the payment period and the interest conversion period differ and for which the payments are level. There are two distinct approaches that can be followed in handling such annuities.

The first approach is applicable if the only objective is to compute the numerical value of an annuity. In this case a two-step procedure can be followed:

1. Find the rate of interest, convertible at the same frequency as payments are made, that is equivalent to the given rate of interest.

2. Using this new rate of interest, find the value of the annuity using the techniques discussed in Chapter 3.

This approach is general and can be used for annuities payable more or less frequently than interest is convertible. Moreover, unknown time and unknown rate of interest problems can be handled in this fashion. This direct approach will be illustrated in the examples.

The second approach involves an algebraic analysis of such annuities. The intent is to develop algebraic expressions for such annuities in terms of annuity symbols already defined in Chapter 3, with adjustment factors sometimes being required.

The reader might expect that the algebraic development for annuities payable less frequently than interest is convertible would be quite similar to that for annuities payable more frequently than interest is convertible. Surprisingly, however, the two cases have traditionally been developed in the literature with definitions and formulas which look quite different from each other. The algebraic analysis of annuities payable less frequently than interest is convertible is given in Section 4.3, while Section 4.4 analyzes annuities payable more frequently than interest is convertible.

Although these algebraic approaches are not required if the sole purpose is to find numerical values for such annuities, they do provide valuable analytical insight into annuities in general. Also, they provide an important foundation for the analysis of contingent annuities (e.g. a monthly annuity payable for life from a pension plan valued at an effective rate of interest).

Example 4.1 ***Find the accumulated value at the end of four years of an investment fund in which \$100 is deposited at the beginning of each quarter for the first two years and \$200 is deposited at the beginning of each quarter for the second two years, if the fund earns 12% convertible monthly.***

We are given an interest rate of 1% per month. Let j be the equivalent rate of interest per quarter, which is the payment period. We have

$$j = (1.01)^3 - 1 = .030301.$$

The value of the annuity in symbols is

$$100\left(\ddot{s}_{\overline{16}|j} + \ddot{s}_{\overline{8}|j}\right)$$

which can be evaluated as

$$100(20.81704 + 9.17157) = \$2998.86.$$

Example 4.2 A loan of $3000 is to be repaid with quarterly installments at the end of each quarter for five years. If the rate of interest charged on the loan is 10% convertible semiannually, find the amount of each quarterly payment.

We are given an interest rate of 5% per half-year. Let j be the equivalent rate of interest per quarter, which is the payment period. We have

$$j = (1.05)^{1/2} - 1 = .024695.$$

Let the quarterly payment be denoted by R. Then the equation of value is

$$Ra_{\overline{20}|j} = 3000$$

so that

$$R = \frac{3000}{a_{\overline{20}|j}} = \frac{3000}{15.63417} = \$191.89.$$

Example 4.3 At what annual effective rate of interest will payments of $100 at the end of every quarter accumulate to $2500 at the end of five years?

Let $j = i^{(4)}/4$ be the interest rate per quarter which accomplishes the above. Then the equation of value at the end of five years is

$$100\, s_{\overline{20}|j} = 2500$$

or

$$s_{\overline{20}|j} = 25.$$

We can use a financial calculator to solve for an unknown rate of interest. We set

$$\begin{aligned} \text{N} &= 20 \\ \text{FV} &= 35 \\ \text{PMT} &= -1 \end{aligned}$$

and compute I obtaining

$$\text{I} = 2.2854.$$

Thus, we have $j = .022854$. The annual effective rate of interest i is given by

$$i = (1.022854)^4 - 1 = .0946, \text{ or } 9.46\%.$$

4.3 ANNUITIES PAYABLE LESS FREQUENTLY THAN INTEREST IS CONVERTIBLE

In this section annuities payable less frequently than interest is convertible are further analyzed algebraically. This section will be subdivided into the following areas: (1) annuity-immediate, (2) annuity-due, and (3) other considerations.

Annuity-immediate

Let k be the number of interest conversion periods in one payment period, let n be the term of the annuity measured in interest conversion periods, and let i be the rate of interest per interest conversion period. We will assume that each payment period contains an integral number of interest conversion periods; thus k and n are both positive integers. The number of annuity payments made is n/k, which is also a positive integer.

The present value of an annuity which pays 1 at the end of each k interest conversion periods for a total of n interest conversion periods can be found by summing a geometric progression as in Chapter 3

$$\begin{aligned} v^k + v^{2k} + \cdots + v^{\frac{n}{k}\cdot k} &= \frac{v^k - v^{n+k}}{1 - v^k} \\ &= \frac{1 - v^n}{(1+i)^k - 1} \\ &= \frac{a_{\overline{n}|}}{s_{\overline{k}|}} \, . \end{aligned} \tag{4.1}$$

Thus, we have an expression for the present value of this annuity in terms of annuity symbols already defined. The accumulated value of this annuity immediately after the last payment is

$$\frac{a_{\overline{n}|}}{s_{\overline{k}|}}(1+i)^n = \frac{s_{\overline{n}|}}{s_{\overline{k}|}} \, . \tag{4.2}$$

It is possible to derive formulas (4.1) and (4.2) by an alternate argument. There is a value of R such that the series of payments of 1 at the end of each k interest conversion periods for n interest conversion periods can be replaced by a series of payments of R at the end of each interest conversion period so that the present values are equal. The present value of this series is

$$Ra_{\overline{n|}}.$$

Now consider any one payment period which contains k interest conversion periods. At the end of the payment period the accumulated value of payments of R at the end of each interest conversion period must equal the payment of 1 made at that point. Thus,

$$Rs_{\overline{k|}} = 1$$

and substituting $R = 1/s_{\overline{k|}}$ into $Ra_{\overline{n|}}$, formula (4.1) is obtained. Formula (4.2) can be derived by a similar argument.

Figure 4.1. is a time diagram clarifying the above argument.

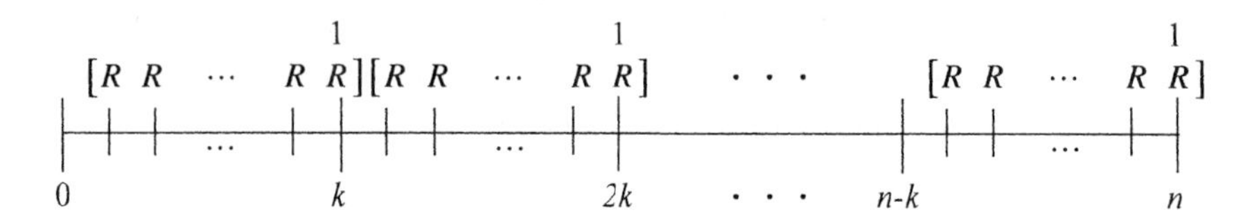

Figure 4.1 Time diagram for an annuity-immediate payable less frequently than interest is convertible

Annuity-due

The present value of an annuity which pays 1 at the beginning of each k interest conversion periods for a total of n interest conversion periods is

$$\begin{aligned} 1 + v^k + v^{2k} + \cdots + v^{n-k} &= \frac{1-v^n}{1-v^k} \\ &= \frac{a_{\overline{n|}}}{a_{\overline{k|}}}. \end{aligned} \tag{4.3}$$

Formula (4.3) can also be obtained by multiplying formula (4.1) by $(1+i)^k$, reflecting each payment occurring k interest conversion periods earlier.

The accumulated value of this annuity k interest conversion periods after the last payment is

$$\frac{a_{\overline{n}|}}{a_{\overline{k}|}}(1+i)^n = \frac{s_{\overline{n}|}}{a_{\overline{k}|}}. \tag{4.4}$$

It is also possible to derive formulas (4.3) and (4.4) by an alternate argument analogous to the argument used above for the annuity-immediate. The reader should fill in the details for this argument. Figure 4.2 is a time diagram for this case. Similarly, formula (4.4) can be obtained by multiplying formula (4.2) by $(1+i)^k$.

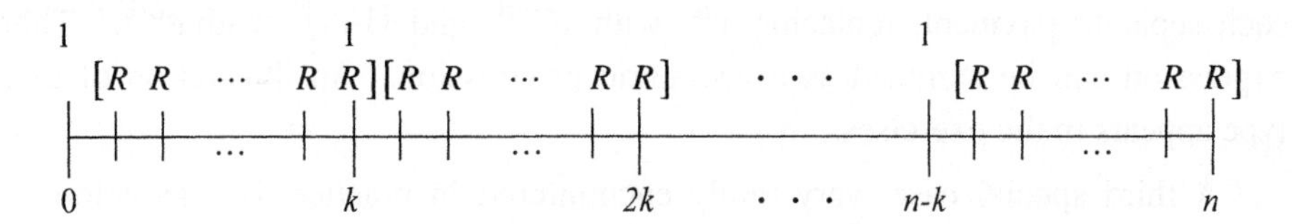

Figure 4.2 Time diagram for an annuity-due payable less frequently than interest is convertible

It is interesting to note in the above formulas that the denominator for the annuities-immediate is $s_{\overline{k}|}$, while the denominator for the annuities-due is $a_{\overline{k}|}$.

Other considerations

On occasion a perpetuity payable less frequently than interest is convertible is encountered. The present value of such a perpetuity-immediate is

$$\begin{aligned} v^k + v^{2k} + \cdots &= \frac{v^k}{1-v^k} \\ &= \frac{1}{(1+i)^k - 1} \\ &= \frac{1}{is_{\overline{k}|}} \end{aligned} \tag{4.5}$$

which is also seen to be the limit of formula (4.1) as n approaches infinity. Similarly, the present value of a perpetuity-due is

$$\frac{1}{ia_{\overline{k|}}}. \tag{4.6}$$

which is also the limit of formula (4.3) as n approaches infinity.

A second special case sometimes encountered is to find the value of a series of payments at a given force of interest δ. Although technically coming under the category of annuities payable less frequently than interest is convertible, this situation is not adequately handled by the methods discussed above, since n and k are both infinite. This situation can best be handled by writing an expression for the value of the annuity as the sum of present values or accumulated values of each separate payment, replacing v^{tk} with $e^{-\delta tk}$ and $(1+i)^{tk}$ with $e^{\delta tk}$. This expression can be summed as a geometric progression. An illustration of this type appears in the exercises.

A third special case, very rarely encountered in practice, is a situation in which each payment period does not contain an integral number of interest conversion periods (i.e. $k > 1$, but k is not an integer). Here again, the best approach would be to resort to basic principles, i.e. to write an expression as the sum of present values or accumulated values of each separate payment, and then to sum this expression as a geometric progression. An illustration of this type also appears in the exercises.

It should be observed that no one-symbol expressions for the annuity values given by formulas (4.1) through (4.6) have been defined. The only expressions are those in terms of ordinary annuity symbols given by formulas (4.1) through (4.6).

Example 4.4 ***Rework Example 4.1 using the approach developed in Section 4.3.***

The rate of interest is 1% per month, the term of the annuity is 48 interest conversion periods, and each payment period contains three interest conversion periods. Since this is an annuity-due, the accumulated value is

$$100\frac{s_{\overline{48|}.01}+s_{\overline{24|}.01}}{a_{\overline{3|}.01}} = 100\frac{61.22261 + 26.97346}{2.94099} = \$2998.86.$$

The answer agrees with that obtained in Example 4.1.

***Example 4.5** An investment of $1000 is used to make payments of $100 at the end of each year for as long as possible with a smaller final payment to be made at the time of the last regular payment. If interest is 7% convertible semiannually, find the number of payments and the amount of the total final payment.*

The equation of value is

$$100\frac{a_{\overline{n}|.035}}{s_{\overline{2}|.035}} = 1000$$

or

$$a_{\overline{n}|.035} = 10s_{\overline{2}|.035} = 20.35.$$

Using a financial calculator and the approach for determining unknown time discussed in Section 3.6, we find that $36 < n < 37$. Thus, 18 regular payments and a smaller final payment can be made. Let the smaller additional payment at the time of the final regular payment be denoted by R. Then an equation of value at the end of 18 years is

$$R+100\frac{s_{\overline{36}|.035}}{s_{\overline{2}|.035}} = 1000\,(1.035)^{36}$$

or

$$R = 1000\,(3.45027)-100\frac{70.00760}{2.035} = \$10.09.$$

The total final payment would thus be $110.09.

4.4 ANNUITIES PAYABLE MORE FREQUENTLY THAN INTEREST IS CONVERTIBLE

In this section annuities payable more frequently than interest is convertible are further analyzed algebraically. In practice annuities payable more frequently than interest is convertible are more common than annuities payable less frequently than interest is convertible. This section will be subdivided into the following areas: (1) annuity-immediate, (2) annuity-due, and (3) other considerations.

Annuity-immediate

Let m be the number of payment periods in one interest conversion period, let n be the term of the annuity measured in interest conversion periods, and let i be the interest rate per interest conversion period. We will assume that each interest conversion period contains an integral number of payment periods; thus m and n

are both positive integers. The number of annuity payments made is mn, which is also a positive integer.

The present value of an annuity which pays $1/m$ at the end of each mth of an interest conversion period for a total of n interest conversion periods is denoted by $a_{\overline{n}|}^{(m)}$. Again by summing a geometric progression we have

$$\begin{aligned} a_{\overline{n}|}^{(m)} &= \frac{1}{m}\left[v^{1/m} + v^{2/m} + \cdots + v^{n-1/m} + v^n\right] \\ &= \frac{1}{m}\left[\frac{v^{1/m} - v^{n+1/m}}{1 - v^{1/m}}\right] \\ &= \frac{1 - v^n}{m\left[(1+i)^{1/m} - 1\right]} \\ &= \frac{1 - v^n}{i^{(m)}}. \end{aligned} \tag{4.7}$$

The accumulated value of this annuity immediately after the last payment is made is denoted by $s_{\overline{n}|}^{(m)}$ and we have

$$\begin{aligned} s_{\overline{n}|}^{(m)} &= a_{\overline{n}|}^{(m)}(1+i)^n \\ &= \frac{(1+i)^n - 1}{i^{(m)}}. \end{aligned} \tag{4.8}$$

Formulas (4.7) and (4.8) should be compared to formulas (3.2) and (3.4), respectively. They are identical except that the denominators of (4.7) and (4.8) are $i^{(m)}$ instead of i. Since $i^{(m)}$ is a measure of interest paid at the end of $m$ths of an interest conversion period, the points at which interest is paid under this measure are consistent with the points at which payments are made. This property, relating the manner in which payments are made and the measure of interest in the denominator, was originally mentioned in Section 3.3.

Annuity-due

The present value of an annuity which pays $1/m$ at the beginning of each mth of an interest conversion period for a total of n interest conversion periods is denoted by $\ddot{a}_{\overline{n}|}^{(m)}$. We have

$$\ddot{a}_{\overline{n}|}^{(m)} = \frac{1 - v^n}{d^{(m)}}. \tag{4.9}$$

The derivation of formula (4.9) is similar to formula (4.7).

The accumulated value of this annuity one *m*th of an interest conversion period after the last payment is made is denoted by $\ddot{s}^{(m)}_{\overline{n}|}$ and we have

$$\begin{aligned} \ddot{s}^{(m)}_{\overline{n}|} &= \ddot{a}^{(m)}_{\overline{n}|}(1+i)^n \\ &= \frac{(1+i)^n - 1}{d^{(m)}}. \end{aligned} \tag{4.10}$$

Here, again, the relationship between the manner in which payments are made and the measure of interest in the denominator should be noted.

A number of other interesting identities involving annuities payable *m*thly can be developed. Several of these are listed in Appendix 4 at the end of the chapter as a reference for interested readers.

Other considerations

On occasion a perpetuity payable more frequently than interest is convertible is encountered. The following formulas are analogous to formulas (3.18) and (3.19):

$$a^{(m)}_{\overline{\infty}|} = \frac{1}{i^{(m)}} \tag{4.11}$$

and

$$\ddot{a}^{(m)}_{\overline{\infty}|} = \frac{1}{d^{(m)}}. \tag{4.12}$$

A second special case, very rarely encountered in practice, is a situation in which each interest conversion period does not contain an integral number of payment periods (i.e. $m > 1$, but m is not integer). In this case, the best approach would be to resort to basic principles, i.e. to write an expression as the sum of present values or accumulated values of each separate payment, and then to sum this expression as a geometric progression. An illustration of this type appears in the exercises.

One important consideration in practical applications involves the proper coefficients for annuities payable *m*thly. Each payment made is of amount $1/m$, while the coefficient of the symbol is 1. In general, the proper coefficient is the amount paid during one interest conversion period, and not the amount of each actual payment. The amount paid during one interest conversion period is often called the *annual rent* of the annuity. This is an appropriate term if the interest conversion period is one year, as is often the case; but it is confusing if the interest conversion period is other than one year. Sometimes the term *periodic rent* is used instead of "annual rent" to avoid this confusion.

Example 4.6 Rework Example 4.2 using the approach developed in Section 4.4.

The rate of interest is 5% per half-year, the term of the loan is ten interest conversion periods, and each interest conversion period contains two payment periods. Thus, the equation of value is

$$2\,Ra^{(2)}_{\overline{10}|.05} = 3000.$$

Note that the coefficient is $2R$, the periodic rent of the annuity. From formula (1.20c)

$$i^{(2)} = 2\left[(1.05)^{.5} - 1\right] = .0493902$$

and we have

$$R = \frac{1500}{a^{(2)}_{\overline{10}|.05}} = \frac{1500 i^{(2)}}{1-(1.05)^{-10}}$$

$$= \frac{(1500)(.0493902)}{1-(1.05)^{-10}} = \$191.89.$$

The answer agrees with that obtained in Example 4.2.

Example 4.7 At what annual effective rate of interest is the present value of a series of payments of $1 every six months forever, with the first payment made immediately, equal to $10?

The equation of value is

$$10 = 1 + v^{.5} + v + v^{1.5} + \cdots = \frac{1}{1-v^{.5}}.$$

Thus,

$$v^{.5} = .9$$

and

$$(1+i)^{.5} = \frac{1}{.9}$$

which gives

$$i = \left(\frac{1}{.9}\right)^2 - 1 = .2346, \text{ or } 23.46\%.$$

Note that a basic principles approach works quite well for this problem, which is often the case for perpetuities.

4.5 CONTINUOUS ANNUITIES

A special case of annuities payable more frequently than interest is convertible is one in which the frequency of payment becomes infinite, i.e. payments are made continuously. Although difficult to visualize in practice, a continuous annuity is of considerable theoretical and analytical significance. Also, it is useful as an approximation to annuities payable with great frequency, such as daily.

We will denote the present value of an annuity payable continuously for n interest conversion periods, such that the total amount paid during each interest conversion period is 1, by the symbol $\bar{a}_{\overline{n}|}$. An expression for $\bar{a}_{\overline{n}|}$ is

$$\bar{a}_{\overline{n}|} = \int_0^n v^t dt \qquad (4.13)$$

since the differential expression $v^t dt$ is the present value of the payment dt made at exact moment t.

A simplified expression can be obtained by performing the integration

$$\begin{aligned} \bar{a}_{\overline{n}|} &= \int_0^n v^t dt \\ &= \left.\frac{v^t}{\ln v}\right]_0^n \\ &= \frac{1-v^n}{\delta}. \end{aligned} \qquad (4.14)$$

Formula (4.14) is analogous to formula (3.2). Again, there is consistency between the manner in which payments are made and the denominator of the expression.

Also formula (4.14) could have been obtained as follows:

$$\bar{a}_{\overline{n}|} = \lim_{m\to\infty} a_{\overline{n}|}^{(m)} = \lim_{m\to\infty} \frac{1-v^n}{i^{(m)}} = \frac{1-v^n}{\delta}$$

or

$$\bar{a}_{\overline{n}|} = \lim_{m\to\infty} \ddot{a}_{\overline{n}|}^{(m)} = \lim_{m\to\infty} \frac{\left(1-v^n\right)}{d^{(m)}} = \frac{1-v^n}{\delta}.$$

Thus, the continuous annuity is seen to be the limiting case of annuities payable $m$thly as $m \to \infty$.

The accumulated value of a continuous annuity at the end of the term of the annuity is denoted by $\bar{s}_{\overline{n}|}$. The following relationships hold:

$$\bar{s}_{\overline{n}|} = \int_0^n (1+i)^t \, dt \tag{4.15}$$

$$= \left. \frac{(1+i)^t}{\ln(1+i)} \right]_0^n$$

$$= \frac{(1+i)^n - 1}{\delta} \tag{4.16}$$

$$= \lim_{m \to \infty} s_{\overline{n}|}^{(m)} = \lim_{m \to \infty} \ddot{s}_{\overline{n}|}^{(m)} .$$

Additional insight into continuous annuities can be obtained by differentiating formula (4.15) with respect to its upper limit n, and then replacing n with t, which gives

$$\frac{d}{dt} \bar{s}_{\overline{t}|} = (1 + i)^t$$

$$= 1 + \delta \bar{s}_{\overline{t}|} \tag{4.17}$$

upon substituting formula (4.16).

Formula (4.17) has an interesting verbal interpretation. Consider an investment fund in which money is continuously being deposited at the rate of 1 per interest conversion period. The fund balance at time t is equal to $\bar{s}_{\overline{t}|}$. The fund balance is changing instantaneously for two reasons. First, new deposits are occurring at the constant rate of 1 per interest conversion period, and second, interest is being earned at force δ on the fund balance $\bar{s}_{\overline{t}|}$.

Similarly, by differentiating formula (4.13) we have

$$\frac{d}{dt} \bar{a}_{\overline{t}|} = v^t$$

$$= 1 - \delta \, \bar{a}_{\overline{t}|} . \tag{4.18}$$

Formula (4.18) also has a verbal interpretation, which is deferred until some additional material is presented in Chapter 5.

Finally, we can express the value of continuous annuities strictly in terms of the force of interest δ. When this is done, formula (4.14) becomes

$$\bar{a}_{\overline{n}|} = \frac{1 - e^{-n\delta}}{\delta} \tag{4.19}$$

and formula (4.16) becomes

$$\bar{s}_{\overline{n|}} = \frac{e^{n\delta}-1}{\delta}. \tag{4.20}$$

In a sense, this is a case of an annuity in which the payment period and interest conversion period are equal, but which was not considered in Chapter 3.

Example 4.8 Find the force of interest at which $\bar{s}_{\overline{20|}} = 3\bar{s}_{\overline{10|}}$.

Using formula (4.20) we have

$$\frac{e^{20\delta}-1}{\delta} = 3\,\frac{e^{10\delta}-1}{\delta}$$

or

$$e^{20\delta} - 3e^{10\delta} + 2 = 0$$

which factors into

$$\left(e^{10\delta}-2\right)\left(e^{10\delta}-1\right) = 0.$$

However, $e^{10\delta}-1 = 0$ implies that $\delta = 0$, which clearly is an extraneous root. Thus, we have

$$e^{10\delta} = 2$$

so that

$$\delta = \frac{\ln 2}{10} = .0693, \text{ or } 6.93\%.$$

4.6 PAYMENTS VARYING IN ARITHMETIC PROGRESSION

Thus far all the annuities considered have had level payments. We now remove this restriction and consider annuities with varying payments. In Sections 4.6 and 4.7 it will be assumed that the payment period and interest conversion period are equal and coincide. As in Chapter 3, we will just use the term "period" for both.

Any type of *varying annuity* can be evaluated by taking the present value or the accumulated value of each payment separately and summing the results. On occasion, this may be the only feasible approach. However, there are two types of commonly-encountered varying annuities for which relatively simple expressions can be developed, and we will consider these. In Section 4.6 we will examine annuities with payments varying in arithmetic progression, while in Section 4.7 we will examine annuities with payments varying in geometric progression.

In practical applications the value of varying annuities in which other payment patterns exist are generally best handled from basic principles. The annuity value can be computed by finding the present value or accumulated value of each payment separately and summing the results.

The reader should also be careful to distinguish the term "varying annuity" from the term "variable annuity." A *variable annuity* is a type of life annuity in which payments vary according to the investment experience of an underlying investment account, usually one invested in common stocks. Variable annuities are beyond the scope of this book and are not considered further. The varying annuities considered in this book have variations which are specified in advance and do not depend on some external event.

Consider first a general annuity-immediate with a term of n periods in which payments begin at P and increase by Q per period thereafter. The interest rate is i per period. Figure 4.3 is a time diagram for this annuity. It should be noted that P must be positive but that Q can be either positive or negative as long as $P+(n-1)Q>0$ to avoid negative payments.

Let A be the present value of the annuity. Then we have

$$A = Pv + (P+Q)v^2 + (P+2Q)v^3 + \cdots + \left[P+(n-2)Q\right]v^{n-1} + \left[P+(n-1)Q\right]v^n .$$

This series is a combination of an arithmetic progression and a geometric progression. Such a series can be solved algebraically by multiplying by the common ratio in the geometric progression to give

$$(1+i)A = P+(P+Q)v + (P+2Q)v^2 + (P+3Q)v^3 + \cdots + \left[P+(n-1)Q\right]v^{n-1}.$$

Now subtracting the first equation from the second we have

$$\begin{aligned} iA &= P+Q\left(v+v^2+v^3+\cdots+v^{n-1}\right)-Pv^n-(n-1)Qv^n \\ &= P\left(1-v^n\right)+Q\left(v+v^2+v^3+\cdots+v^{n-1}+v^n\right)-Qnv^n . \end{aligned}$$

Thus,

$$\begin{aligned} A &= P\frac{1-v^n}{i} + Q\frac{a_{\overline{n}|}-nv^n}{i} \\ &= Pa_{\overline{n}|} + Q\frac{a_{\overline{n}|}-nv^n}{i} . \qquad (4.21) \end{aligned}$$

The accumulated value is given by

$$Ps_{\overline{n}|} + Q\frac{s_{\overline{n}|} - n}{i} \tag{4.22}$$

since it must be the present value accumulated for n periods.

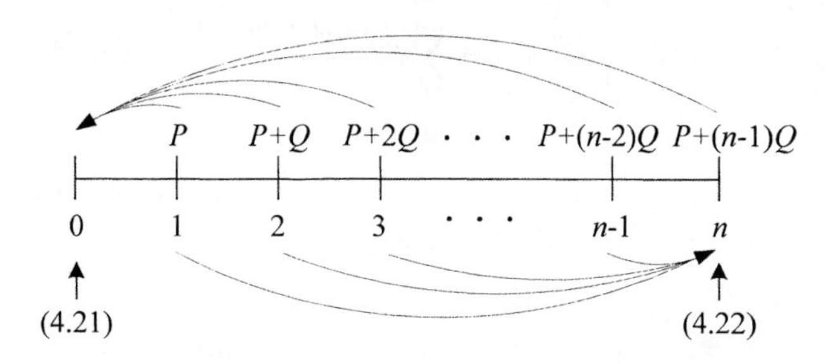

Figure 4.3 Time diagram for formulas (4.21) and (4.22)

Formulas (4.21) and (4.22) can be used in solving any problem in which payments vary in arithmetic progression. However, there are two special cases which often appear and have special notation.

The first of these is the *increasing annuity* in which $P = 1$ and $Q = 1$. Figure 4.4 is a time diagram for this annuity. The present value of this annuity, denoted by $(Ia)_{\overline{n}|}$, can be obtained from formula (4.21)

$$\begin{aligned}(Ia)_{\overline{n}|} &= a_{\overline{n}|} + \frac{a_{\overline{n}|} - nv^n}{i} \\ &= \frac{1 - v^n + a_{\overline{n}|} - nv^n}{i} \\ &= \frac{\ddot{a}_{\overline{n+1}|} - (n+1)v^n}{i} \\ &= \frac{\ddot{a}_{\overline{n}|} - nv^n}{i} .\end{aligned} \tag{4.23}$$

The accumulated value of this annuity, denoted by $(Is)_{\overline{n}|}$, is

$$\begin{aligned}(Is)_{\overline{n}|} &= (Ia)_{\overline{n}|}(1+i)^n \\ &= \frac{\ddot{s}_{\overline{n}|} - n}{i}.\end{aligned} \tag{4.24}$$

Formula (4.23) can be derived by an alternative approach which considers an increasing annuity to be the summation of a series of level deferred annuities. Using this approach, we have

$$\begin{aligned}(Ia)_{\overline{n|}} &= \sum_{t=0}^{n-1} v^t a_{\overline{n-t|}} \\ &= \sum_{t=0}^{n-1} v^t . \frac{1-v^{n-t}}{i} \\ &= \frac{\ddot{a}_{\overline{n|}} - nv^n}{i}. \end{aligned} \tag{4.23}$$

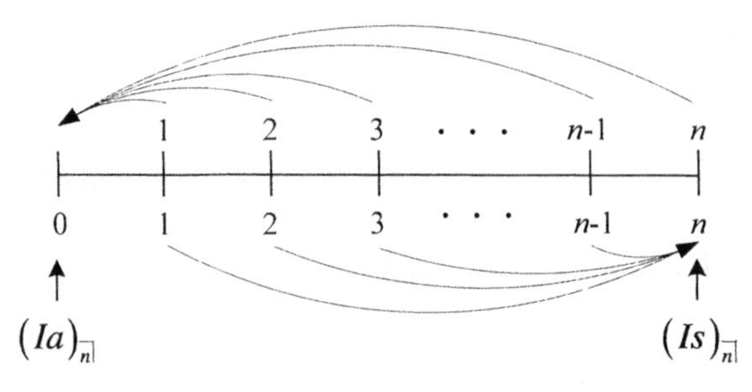

Figure 4.4 Time diagram for an increasing annuity

Not only is this derivation quite efficient, but it also provides valuable insight into the nature of an increasing annuity.

The second special case is the *decreasing annuity* in which $P = n$ and $Q = -1$. Figure 4.5 is a time diagram for this annuity. The present value of this annuity, denoted by $(Da)_{\overline{n|}}$, can be obtained from formula (4.21)

$$\begin{aligned}(Da)_{\overline{n|}} &= na_{\overline{n|}} - \frac{a_{\overline{n|}} - nv^n}{i} \\ &= \frac{n - nv^n - a_{\overline{n|}} + nv^n}{i} \\ &= \frac{n - a_{\overline{n|}}}{i}. \end{aligned} \tag{4.25}$$

The accumulated value of this annuity, denoted by $(Ds)_{\overline{n|}}$, is

$$\begin{aligned}(Ds)_{\overline{n|}} &= (Da)_{\overline{n|}}(1+i)^n \\ &= \frac{n(1+i)^n - s_{\overline{n|}}}{i}. \end{aligned} \tag{4.26}$$

Formula (4.25) can also be derived by the alternative approach which considers a decreasing annuity to be the summation of a series of level annuities. Using this approach, we have

$$\begin{aligned}(Da)_{\overline{n}|} &= \sum_{t=1}^{n} a_{\overline{t}|} \\ &= \sum_{t=1}^{n} \frac{1-v^t}{i} \\ &= \frac{n-a_{\overline{n}|}}{i}. \end{aligned} \tag{4.25}$$

Again, the alternative derivation is quite efficient and provides valuable insight into the nature of a decreasing annuity.

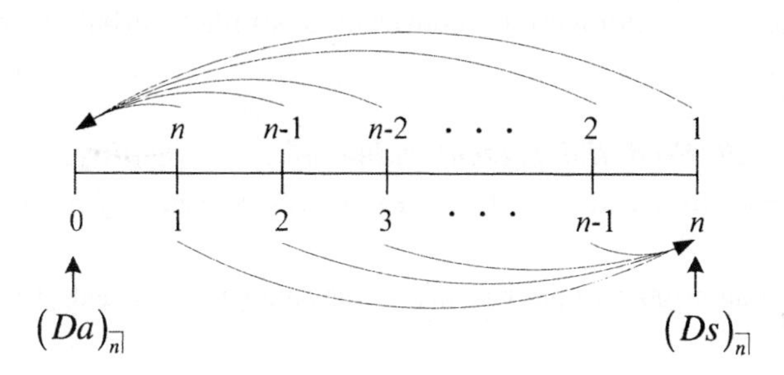

Figure 4.5 Time diagram for a decreasing annuity

All the above formulas are for annuities-immediate. However, we may use the previously mentioned relationship between the manner in which payments are made and the denominator of the expression for the annuity value to find formulas for annuities-due. Changing i in the denominator of any of the above formulas to d will produce values for annuities-due.

Also, it is possible to have varying perpetuities. We can find the general form for a perpetuity-immediate by taking the limit of formula (4.21) as n approaches infinity, obtaining

$$\frac{P}{i} + \frac{Q}{i^2} \tag{4.27}$$

since

$$\lim_{n\to\infty} a_{\overline{n}|} = \frac{1}{i} \quad \text{and} \quad \lim_{n\to\infty} nv^n = 0.$$

Note that P and Q must both be positive to avoid negative payments.

An alternative approach to finding expressions for varying annuities is given in Appendix 4 at the end of the chapter.

Formulas developed in this section have challenging, but enlightening, verbal interpretations. For example, consider formula (4.23). The expression $\ddot{a}_{\overline{n}|}/i$ [expanding the numerator with formula (3.7)] can be interpreted as the sum of the present values at time $t=0$ of n level perpetuities, paying 1 per period, whose payments start at times $t=1,2,\ldots,n$. This provides exactly the correct present value for $(Ia)_{\overline{n}|}$ for the first n periods. However, it also includes the present value at time $t=0$ of a deferred perpetuity paying n per period forever starting at time $n+1$. Subtracting nv^n/i removes the present value of this deferred perpetuity giving us the correct present value at time $t=0$ of the payments for the first n periods.

The reader is encouraged to construct a similar verbal interpretation for formula (4.25).

Example 4.9 Find the present value of a perpetuity-immediate whose successive payments are 1, 2, 3, 4, . . . , at an effective rate of interest of 5%.

An appropriate symbol would be $(Ia)_{\overline{\infty}|}$. Substituting P = 1 and Q = 1 into formula (4.27), we obtain

$$\frac{1}{i}+\frac{1}{i^2} = \frac{1}{.05}+\frac{1}{.0025} = 420.$$

Example 4.10 Find the present value of an annuity-immediate such that payments start at 1, increase by annual amounts of 1 to a payment of n, and then decrease by annual amounts of 1 to a final payment of 1.

The present value is

$$\begin{aligned}
(Ia)_{\overline{n}|}+v^n(Da)_{\overline{n-1}|} &= \frac{\ddot{a}_{\overline{n}|}-nv^n}{i}+v^n\frac{(n-1)-a_{\overline{n-1}|}}{i} \\
&= \frac{1}{i}\left[a_{\overline{n-1}|}+1-nv^n+nv^n-v^n-v^n a_{\overline{n-1}|}\right] \\
&= \frac{1}{i}\left[a_{\overline{n-1}|}(1-v^n)+(1-v^n)\right] \\
&= \frac{1}{i}(1-v^n)(a_{\overline{n-1}|}+1) \\
&= a_{\overline{n}|}\cdot\ddot{a}_{\overline{n}|}.
\end{aligned}$$

Example 4.11 Find the present value of an annuity-immediate such that payments start at 1, each payment thereafter increases by 1 until reaching 10, and then remain at that level until 25 payments in total are made.

A symbol for an n-period increasing annuity-immediate in which increases are limited to the first m periods only, $0 < m < n$, is given by

$$\left(I_{\overline{m|}}a\right)_{\overline{n|}}.$$

Thus, the present value of the annuity in this example can be written as $\left(I_{\overline{10|}}a\right)_{\overline{25|}}$. The reader should verify that the following are all valid expressions for the present value of this annuity:

- $(Ia)_{\overline{10|}} + 10v^{10}a_{\overline{15|}}$
- $(Ia)_{\overline{25|}} - v^{10}(Ia)_{\overline{15|}}$
- $10a_{\overline{25|}} - (Da)_{\overline{9|}}$
- $\sum_{t=0}^{9} v^t a_{\overline{25-t|}}$

4.7 PAYMENTS VARYING IN GEOMETRIC PROGRESSION

The concept underlying annuities with payments varying in geometric progression is that the annuity payments is that the annuity payments themselves follow a compound rate of increase or decrease. This type of varying annuity has several important practical applications. We will examine two of these in more depth in Sections 6.10 and 9.4.

Annuities with payments varying in geometric progression can readily be evaluated by directly expressing the annuity value as a series with each payment multiplied by its associated present or accumulated value. Since the payments and the present or accumulated values are both geometric progressions, the terms in the series for the annuity value constitute a new geometric progression.

First, consider an annuity-immediate with a term of n periods in which the first payment is 1 and successive payments increase in geometric progression with common ratio $1 + k$. The present value of this annuity is

$$v + v^2(1 + k) + \cdots + v^n(1 + k)^{n-1}. \tag{4.28}$$

This is a geometric progression whose sum is

$$v\left[\frac{1-\left(\frac{1+k}{1+i}\right)^n}{1-\left(\frac{1+k}{1+i}\right)}\right] = \frac{1-\left(\frac{1+k}{1+i}\right)^n}{i-k}. \tag{4.29}$$

This expression can be evaluated by direct calculation. If $k = i$, then formula (4.29) is undefined. However, then the present value is just nv, which is obvious from formula (4.28).

The present value of an otherwise identical n-period annuity-due would be given by

$$1+v(1+k)+\cdots+v^{n-1}(1+k)^{n-1} \tag{4.30}$$

which is analogous to formula (4.28). This present value could also be expressed as formula (4.29) multiplied by $1+i$. This involves the same type of adjustment between the value of an annuity-immediate and an annuity-due that was used in Formula (3.13).

However, there is an alternative way of expressing this present value, when $k<i$, that is enlightening. Define a new rate of interest i' such that

$$i+i' = \frac{1+i}{1+k} \tag{4.31a}$$

so that

$$i' = \frac{i-k}{1+k} \tag{4.31b}$$

Formula (4.30) then becomes

$$\begin{aligned} &1+\frac{1+k}{1+i}+\cdots+\frac{(1+k)^{n-1}}{(1+i)^{n-1}} \\ &= 1+\frac{1}{1+i'}+\cdots+\frac{1}{(1+i')^{n-1}} \\ &= \ddot{a}_{\overline{n}|\,i'}. \end{aligned} \tag{4.32}$$

Thus, we obtain the intriguing result that the present value of an n-period annuity having payments increasing in geometric progression with common ratio $1+k$ where $(k<i)$ is equal to the present value of a level n-period annuity evaluated at rate i'.

Accumulated values of annuities with payments varying in geometric progression can be similarly handled. For example, the accumulated value at the end of n periods for the annuity-immediate given in formula (4.28) is

$$(1+i)^{n-1}+(1+i)^{n-2}(1+k)+\cdots+(1+i)(1+k)^{n-2}+(1+k)^{n-1}. \tag{4.33}$$

This is a geometric progression with common ratio $1+k/1+i$ whose sum is

$$\frac{(1+i)^{n-1}-\dfrac{(1+k)^n}{1+i}}{1-\dfrac{1+k}{1+i}}=\frac{(1+i)^n-(1+k)^n}{i-k} \tag{4.34}$$

which can also be obtained by multiplying formula (4.29) by $(1+i)^n$.

The accumulated values of an n-period annuity-due could be similarly computed. The reader should be careful to note that basing this accumulated value on Formula (4.32) does not equal $\ddot{s}_{\overline{n}|\,i'}$, but rather equals

$$\ddot{a}_{\overline{n}|\,i'}(1+i)^n. \tag{4.35}$$

The present-value of a perpetuity will exist if $k<i$, in which case the sum of the infinite geometric progression exists. In that case, the present value of a perpetuity-immediate becomes

$$\frac{1}{i-k} \tag{4.36}$$

which is the limit as $n\to\infty$ of Formula (4.29). Similarly, the present value of a perpetuity-due becomes

$$\frac{1+i}{i-k}. \tag{4.37}$$

If $k>i$, then the infinite geometric progression diverges, and the present value of the perpetuity does not exist.

The reader is cautioned against overly relying on the numbered formulas developed in this section. The present value or accumulated value of any annuity whose payments vary in geometric progression can be directly expressed as a new geometric progression and summed. Such a first principles approach to working problems in this area can always be applied and is usually not excessively time-consuming.

Example 4.12 An annuity provides for 20 annual payments, the first payment a year hence being $1000. The payments increase in such a way that each payment is 4% greater than the preceding payment. Find the present value of this annuity at an annual effective rate of interest of 7%.

The present value of this annuity is

$$1000\left[\frac{1}{1.07}+\frac{1.04}{(1.07)^2}+\cdots+\frac{(1.04)^{19}}{(1.07)^{20}}\right]$$

which can be evaluated using formula (4.29) to give

$$1000\,\frac{1-\left(\frac{1.04}{1.07}\right)^{20}}{.07-.04} = \$14{,}459$$

to the nearest dollar.

Example 4.13 A perpetuity-due makes annual payments which begin at $100 for the first year, then increase at 6% per year through the 10th year, and then remain level thereafter. Calculate the present value of this perpetuity, if the annual effective rate of interest is equal to 8%.

The present value of the first 10 payments is

$$100\left[1+\frac{1.06}{1.08}+\cdots+\left(\frac{1.06}{1.08}\right)^9\right]$$

$$= 100\left[\frac{1-\left(\frac{1.06}{1.08}\right)^{10}}{1-\frac{1.06}{1.08}}\right] = 920.65.$$

Note that the 10th annual payment is made at time $t=9$.

The present value of the rest of the payments is

$$100(1.06)^9\left[\frac{1}{(1.08)^{10}}+\frac{1}{(1.08)^{11}}+\cdots\right]$$

$$= 100\left(\frac{1.06}{1.08}\right)^9\left[\frac{1}{1.08}+\frac{1}{(1.08)^2}+\cdots\right]$$

$$= 100\left(\frac{1.06}{1.08}\right)^9\frac{1}{.08} = 1056.45.$$

Thus, the total present value equals

$$920.65+1056.45 = \$1977.10.$$

***Example 4.14** A participant in a pension plan aged 45 currently earns $50,000 per year. This participant plans to contribute 5% of salary at the end of each year into the pension fund for 20 years. Find the accumulated value at age 65 of these contributions, if the participant receives annual 3% salary increases until retirement and if the pension fund earns 7% effective per year.*

The accumulated value of the contributions made by this participant at the end of 20 years (i.e. at age 65) is

$$50{,}000(.05)\left[(1.07)^{19}+(1.03)(1.07)^{18}+\cdots+(1.03)^{18}(1.07)+(1.03)^{19}\right]$$

which can be evaluated using formula (4.34) to give

$$2500\frac{(1.07)^{20}-(1.03)^{20}}{.07-.03} = \$128{,}973$$

to the nearest dollar.

4.8 MORE GENERAL VARYING ANNUITIES

The varying annuities considered in Sections 4.6 and 4.7 assumed that the payment period and the interest conversion period are equal and coincide. In Section 4.8 this restriction is removed. In practice, varying annuities with payments made more or less frequently than interest is convertible occur infrequently.

It is often possible to apply the technique illustrated in Section 4.2 to this situation. Find the rate of interest convertible at the same frequency as payments are made and then apply the results developed in Sections 4.6 and 4.7.

We will next consider generalizations of the increasing annuity, $(Ia)_{\overline{n}|}$, in which interest is convertible more or less frequently than payments are made. Other annuities in which payments vary in arithmetic progression can be handled analogously.

Consider first the case in which payments are made less frequently than interest is convertible. Let k be the number of interest conversion periods in one payment period, let n be the term of the annuity measured in interest conversion periods, and let i be the rate of interest per interest conversion period. The number of payments is n/k, which is an integer.

Let A be the present value of the generalized increasing annuity. We have

$$A = v^k + 2v^{2k} + \cdots + \left(\frac{n}{k} - 1\right)v^{n-k} + \frac{n}{k}v^n$$

and

$$(1+i)^k A = 1 + 2v^k + \cdots + \left(\frac{n}{k} - 1\right)v^{n-2k} + \frac{n}{k}v^{n-k}.$$

Now subtracting the first equation from the second

$$A\left[(1+i)^k - 1\right] = 1 + v^k + v^{2k} + \cdots + v^{n-k} - \frac{n}{k}v$$

which can be expressed as

$$A = \frac{\dfrac{a_{\overline{n}|}}{a_{\overline{k}|}} - \dfrac{n}{k}v^n}{is_{\overline{k}|}}. \tag{4.38}$$

Formula (4.38) is a generalized version of formula (4.23) and the reader should note the similarity.

Consider next the case in which payments are made more frequently than interest is convertible. Two different results arise depending on whether the rate of payment is constant or varies during each interest conversion period.

Consider first the situation in which the rate of payment is constant during each interest conversion period with increases occurring only once per interest conversion period. We can utilize the relationship between the manner in which payments are made and the measure of interest in the denominator to obtain the following generalized version of formula (4.23)

$$(Ia)^{(m)}_{\overline{n}|} = \frac{\ddot{a}_{\overline{n}|} - nv^n}{i^{(m)}}. \tag{4.39}$$

Formula (4.39) gives the present value of n-period annuity-immediate, payable $m$thly, in which each payment during the first interest conversion period is $1/m$, each payment during the second interest conversion period is $2/m$, and so forth, until each payment during the nth interest conversion period is n/m.

Consider next the situation in which the rate of payment changes with each payment period. Suppose that an increasing annuity is payable at the rate of $1/m$ per interest conversion period at the end of the first mth of an interest conversion period, $2/m$ per interest conversion period at the end of the second mth of an interest conversion period, and so forth. Then the first payment will be $1/m^2$, the second will be $2/m^2$, and so forth. Denoting the present value of such an annuity by $\left(I^{(m)}a\right)_{\overline{n}|}^{(m)}$, we have

$$\begin{aligned}\left(I^{(m)}a\right)_{\overline{n}|}^{(m)} &= \frac{1}{m^2}\left[v^{\frac{1}{m}} + 2v^{\frac{2}{m}} + \cdots + nmv^{\frac{nm}{m}}\right] \\ &= \frac{\ddot{a}_{\overline{n}|}^{(m)} - nv^n}{i^{(m)}}. \end{aligned} \tag{4.40}$$

The derivation of formula (4.40) is left as an exercise.

Annuities in which the payments vary in geometric progression and in which the payment period and the interest conversion period differ are occasionally encountered. However, such annuities present no new difficulties. They can be readily handled by expressing the annuity value as a summation of the present value or accumulated value of each payment. This summation is a geometric progression which can be directly evaluated. This technique will be illustrated in Example 4.16.

Example 4.15 Find the present value of a perpetuity which pays 1 at the end of the third year, 2 at the end of the sixth year, 3 at the end of the ninth year, . . .

Denote the present value of this perpetuity by A. Then

$$A = v^3 + 2v^6 + 3v^9 + \cdots$$

and

$$v^3A = v^6 + 2v^9 + \cdots$$

Now subtracting the second equation from the first

$$A\left(1-v^3\right) = v^3 + v^6 + v^9 + \cdots = \frac{v^3}{1-v^3}$$

so that

$$A = \frac{v^3}{\left(1-v^3\right)^2}.$$

Example 4.16 Find the accumulated value at the end of ten years of an annuity in which payments are made at the beginning of each half-year for five years. The first payment is $2000, and each payment is 98% of the prior payment. Interest is credited at 10% convertible quarterly.

We count periods in quarters of a year. The accumulated value is

$$2000\left[(1.025)^{40} + (.98)(1.025)^{38} + (.98)^2(1.025)^{36} + \cdots + (.98)^9(1.025)^{22}\right]$$

$$= 2000\,\frac{(1.025)^{40} - (.98)^{10}(1.025)^{20}}{1-(.98)(1.025)^{-2}}$$

$$= \$40{,}052$$

to the nearest dollar.

4.9 CONTINUOUS VARYING ANNUITIES

The last type of varying annuity we will consider is one in which payments are being made continuously at a varying rate. Such annuities are primarily of theoretical interest.

Consider an increasing annuity for n interest conversion periods in which payments are being made continuously at the rate of t per period at exact moment t. The present value of this annuity is denoted by $(\bar{I}\,\bar{a})_{\overline{n|}}$ and an expression for it would be

$$(\bar{I}\,\bar{a})_{\overline{n|}} = \int_0^n tv^t\,dt \tag{4.41}$$

since the differential expression $tv^t dt$ is the present value of the payment tdt made at exact moment t.

A simplified expression can be obtained by performing an integration by parts. We have

$$
\begin{aligned}
(\bar{I}\,\bar{a})_{\overline{n}|} &= \int_0^n tv^t dt \\
&= \frac{tv^t}{\ln v}\Bigg]_0^n - \int_0^n \frac{v^t}{\ln v}\,dt \\
&= \frac{tv^t}{\ln v}\Bigg]_0^n - \frac{v^t}{(\ln v)^2}\Bigg]_0^n \\
&= -\frac{nv^n}{\delta} - \frac{v^n}{\delta^2} + \frac{1}{\delta^2} \\
&= \frac{1-v^n}{\delta^2} - \frac{nv^n}{\delta} \\
&= \frac{\bar{a}_{\overline{n}|} - nv^n}{\delta}\,. \qquad (4.42)
\end{aligned}
$$

It should be noted that formula (4.42) can also be derived from formula (4.40)

$$
(\bar{I}\,\bar{a})_{\overline{n}|} = \lim_{m\to\infty} \left(I^{(m)}a\right)_{\overline{n}|}^{(m)} = \lim_{m\to\infty} \frac{\ddot{a}_{\overline{n}|}^{(m)} - nv^n}{i^{(m)}} = \frac{\bar{a}_{\overline{n}|} - nv^n}{\delta}\,.
$$

In general, if the amount of the payment being made at exact moment t is $f(t)dt$, then an expression for the present value of an n-period continuous varying annuity would be

$$
\int_0^n f(t)v^t dt. \qquad (4.43)
$$

An even more general continuous varying annuity would not only be one in which the payments are being made continuously and the variations are occurring continuously, but also one in which the force of interest is varying continuously. In this case, a generalized version of formula (4.43) would be

$$
\int_0^n f(t)e^{-\int_0^t \delta_r dr}dt. \qquad (4.44)
$$

Example 4.18 Find an expression for the present value of a continuously increasing annuity with a term of n years if the force of interest is δ and if the rate of payment at time t is t^2 ***per annum.***

The answer is obtained by performing an integration by parts

$$\int_0^n t^2 e^{-\delta t}\,dt = -\frac{t^2}{\delta}e^{-\delta t}\Big]_0^n + \frac{2}{\delta}\int_0^n te^{-\delta t}\,dt$$

$$= -\frac{n^2}{\delta}e^{-\delta n} - \frac{2t}{\delta^2}e^{-\delta t}\Big]_0^n + \frac{2}{\delta^2}\int_0^n e^{-\delta t}\,dt$$

$$= -\frac{n^2}{\delta}e^{-\delta n} - \frac{2n}{\delta^2}e^{-\delta n} - \frac{2}{\delta^3}e^{-\delta t}\Big]_0^n$$

$$= -\frac{n^2}{\delta}e^{-\delta n} - \frac{2n}{\delta^2}e^{-\delta n} - \frac{2}{\delta^3}e^{-\delta n} + \frac{2}{\delta^3}$$

$$= \frac{2}{\delta^3} - e^{-\delta n}\left(\frac{n^2}{\delta} + \frac{2n}{\delta^2} + \frac{2}{\delta^3}\right).$$

4.10 SUMMARY OF RESULTS

Table 4.1 summarizes the expressions for present values of level annuities for various payment periods and interest conversion periods. The annuity illustrated pays 60 per annum for 10 years at 12% per annum.

Table 4.1 Summary of Relationships for Level Annuities in Chapter 4

Interest conversion period	*Payment period*			
	Annual	*Quarterly*	*Monthly*	*Continuous*
Annual	$60a_{\overline{10}\rvert .12}$	$60a^{(4)}_{\overline{10}\rvert .12}$	$60a^{(12)}_{\overline{10}\rvert .12}$	$60\,\bar{a}_{\overline{10}\rvert .12}$
Quarterly	$60\dfrac{a_{\overline{40}\rvert .03}}{s_{\overline{4}\rvert .03}}$	$15\,a_{\overline{40}\rvert .03}$	$15\,a^{(3)}_{\overline{40}\rvert .03}$	$15\,\bar{a}_{\overline{40}\rvert .03}$
Monthly	$60\,\dfrac{a_{\overline{120}\rvert .01}}{s_{\overline{12}\rvert .01}}$	$15\,\dfrac{a_{\overline{120}\rvert .01}}{s_{\overline{3}\rvert .01}}$	$5\,a_{\overline{120}\rvert .01}$	$5\,\bar{a}_{\overline{120}\rvert .01}$
Continuous	$60\,\dfrac{1-e^{-1.2}}{e^{.12}-1}$	$15\,\dfrac{1-e^{-1.2}}{e^{.03}-1}$	$5\,\dfrac{1-e^{-1.2}}{e^{.01}-1}$	$60\,\dfrac{1-e^{-1.2}}{.12}$

APPENDIX 4

Other formulas for annuities payable more frequently than interest is convertible

The following two formulas involve computing annuities-immediate with an adjustment factor on Chapter 3 annuity values.

$$a_{\overline{n}|}^{(m)} = \frac{i}{i^{(m)}} a_{\overline{n}|} \tag{4.45}$$

$$s_{\overline{n}|}^{(m)} = \frac{i}{i^{(m)}} s_{\overline{n}|} \tag{4.46}$$

The following two formulas are comparable for annuities-due.

$$\ddot{a}_{\overline{n}|}^{(m)} = \frac{i}{d^{(m)}} a_{\overline{n}|} \tag{4.47}$$

$$\ddot{s}_{\overline{n}|}^{(m)} = \frac{i}{d^{(m)}} s_{\overline{n}|} \tag{4.48}$$

The following two formulas are variations of the prior two that were useful before the advent of financial calculators.

$$\ddot{a}_{\overline{n}|}^{(m)} = \left(\frac{i}{i^{(m)}} + \frac{i}{m}\right) a_{\overline{n}|} \tag{4.49}$$

$$\ddot{s}_{\overline{n}|}^{(m)} = \left(\frac{i}{i^{(m)}} + \frac{i}{m}\right) s_{\overline{n}|} \tag{4.50}$$

The following two formulas are comparable for continuous annuities

$$\bar{a}_{\overline{n}|} = \frac{i}{\delta} a_{\overline{n}|} \tag{4.51}$$

$$\bar{s}_{\overline{n}|} = \frac{i}{\delta} \bar{a}_{\overline{n}|} \tag{4.52}$$

The following two formulas are analogous to formulas (3.6) and (3.12).

$$\frac{1}{a_{\overline{n}|}^{(m)}} = \frac{1}{s_{\overline{n}|}^{(m)}} + i^{(m)} \tag{4.53}$$

$$\frac{1}{\ddot{a}_{\overline{n}|}^{(m)}} = \frac{1}{\ddot{s}_{\overline{n}|}^{(m)}} + d^{(m)} \tag{4.54}$$

The following two formulas are analogous to formulas (3.13) and (3.14).

$$\ddot{a}_{\overline{n}|}^{(m)} = a_{\overline{n}|}^{(m)} (1+i)^{1/m} \tag{4.55}$$

$$\ddot{s}_{\overline{n}|}^{(m)} = s_{\overline{n}|}^{(m)} (1+i)^{1/m} \tag{4.56}$$

The following two formulas are analogous to formulas (3.15) and (3.16).

$$\ddot{a}_{\overline{n}|}^{(m)} = 1/m + a_{\overline{n-1/m}|}^{(m)} \tag{4.57}$$

$$\ddot{s}_{\overline{n}|}^{(m)} = s_{\overline{n+1/m}|}^{(m)} - 1/m \tag{4.58}$$

Alternative approach for payments varying in arithmetic progression

An alternative approach to finding expressions for varying annuities is to make use of the following three quantities:

$$F_n = v^n \tag{4.59}$$

= The present value of a payment of 1 at the end of n periods.

$$G_n = \frac{v^n}{d} \tag{4.60}$$

= The present value of a level perpetuity of 1 per period, first payment at the end of n periods.

$$H_n = \frac{v^n}{d^2} \tag{4.61}$$

= The present value of an increasing perpetuity of 1, 2, 3,..., first payment at the end of n periods.

These symbols are very useful in setting up expressions for varying annuities. By appropriately describing the pattern of payments, expressions for the annuity can be immediately written down.

The following examples illustrate the technique:

- Example 4.9

$$(Ia)_{\overline{\infty}|} = H_1 = \frac{v}{d^2} = \frac{1+i}{i^2} = \frac{1.05}{.0025} = 420.$$

- Example 4.10

$$\begin{aligned}(H_1 - H_{n+1}) - (H_{n+1} - H_{2n+1}) &= H_1 - 2H_{n+1} + H_{2n+1} \\ &= \frac{v - 2v^{n+1} + v^{2n+1}}{d^2} \\ &= \frac{1 - 2v^n + v^{2n}}{id} \\ &= \frac{(1-v^n)^2}{id} \\ &= a_{\overline{n}|} \cdot \ddot{a}_{\overline{n}|}.\end{aligned}$$

- Example 4.11

$$H_1 - H_{11} - 10G_{26}$$

EXERCISES

4.2 Differing payment and interest conversion periods

1. Find the accumulated value 18 years after the first payment is made of an annuity on which there are 8 payments of \$2000 each made at two-year intervals. The nominal rate of interest convertible semiannually is 7%. Answer to the nearest dollar.

2. Find the present value of a ten-year annuity which pays \$400 at the beginning of each quarter for the first 5 years, increasing to \$600 per quarter thereafter. The annual effective rate of interest is 12%. Answer to the nearest dollar.

3. A sum of \$100 is placed into a fund at the beginning of every other year for eight years. If the fund balance at the end of eight years is \$520, find the rate of simple interest earned by the fund.

4. An annuity-immediate that pays 400 quarterly for the next 10 years costs \$10,000. Calculate the nominal interest rate convertible monthly earned by this investment.

4.3 Annuities payable less frequency than interest is convertible

5. Rework Exercise 1 using the approach developed in Section 4.3.

6. Give an expression in terms of functions assuming a rate of interest per month for the present value, 3 years before the first payment is made, of an annuity on which there are payments of \$200 every 4 months for 12 years:
   a) Expressed as an annuity-immediate.
   b) Expressed as an annuity-due.

7. Find an expression for the present value of an annuity-due of \$600 per annum payable semiannually for 10 years if $d^{(12)} = .09$.

8. The present value of a perpetuity paying 1 at the end of every three years is 125/91. Find i.

9. Find an expression for the present value of an annuity on which payments are \$100 per quarter for five years, just before the first payment is made, if $\delta = .08$.

10. Find an expression for the present value of an annuity on which payments are 1 at the beginning of each 4-month period for 12 years, assuming a rate of interest per 3-month period.

4.4 Annuities payable more frequently than interest is convertible

11. Rework Exercise 2 using the approach developed in Section 4.4.

12. *a*) Show that $a_{\overline{n}|}^{(m)} = \frac{1}{m}\sum_{t=1}^{m} v^{t/m}\, \ddot{a}_{\overline{n}|}$.

    b) Verbally interpret the result obtained in (*a*).

13. A sum of $10,000 is used to buy a deferred perpetuity-due paying $500 every six months forever. Find an expression for the deferred period expressed as a function of *d*.

14. If $3\,a_{\overline{n}|}^{(2)} = 2\,a_{\overline{2n}|}^{(2)} = 45\,s_{\overline{1}|}^{(2)}$, find *i*.

15. Find an expression for the present value of an annuity that pays 1 at the beginning of each 3-month period for 12 years, assuming a rate of interest per 4-month period.

4.5 Continuous annuities

16. Show algebraically and verbally that $a_{\overline{n}|} < a_{\overline{n}|}^{(m)} < \bar{a}_{\overline{n}|} < \ddot{a}_{\overline{n}|}^{(m)} < \ddot{a}_{\overline{n}|}$ where $m > 1$.

17. There is $40,000 in a fund which is accumulating at 4% per annum convertible continuously. If money is withdrawn continuously at the rate of $2400 per annum, how long will the fund last?

18. If $\bar{a}_{\overline{n}|} = 4$ and $\bar{s}_{\overline{n}|} = 12$, find δ.

19. Find an expression for $\bar{a}_{\overline{n}|}$ if $\delta_t = \frac{1}{1+t}$ for $0 \le t \le n$.

20. Find the value of *t*, $0 < t < 1$, such that 1 paid at time *t* is equivalent to 1 paid continuously between time 0 and 1.

4.6 Payments varying in arithmetic progression

21. Show algebraically, and by means of a time diagram, the following relationship between $(Ia)_{\overline{n}|}$ and $(Da)_{\overline{n}|}$:

$$(Da)_{\overline{n}|} = (n+1)\,a_{\overline{n}|} - (Ia)_{\overline{n}|}.$$

22. Simplify $\sum_{t=1}^{20}(t+5)v^t$.

23. The following payments are made under an annuity: 10 at the end of the fifth year, 9 at the end of the sixth year, decreasing by 1 each year until nothing is paid. Show that the present value is

$$\frac{10 - a_{\overline{14}|} + a_{\overline{4}|}(1-10i)}{i}.$$

24. Find the present value of a perpetuity under which a payment of 1 is made at the end of the first year, 2 at the end of the second year, increasing until a payment of n is made at the end of the nth year, and thereafter payments are level at n per year forever.

25. A perpetuity-immediate has annual payments of 1, 3, 5, 7. . . If the present value of the sixth and seventh payments are equal, find the present value of the perpetuity.

26. If X is the present value of a perpetuity of 1 per year with the first payment at the end of the second year and $20X$ is the present value of a series of annual payments 1, 2, 3, . . . with the first payment at the end of the third year, find d.

27. An annuity-immediate has semiannual payments of 800, 750, 700, ..., 350, at $i^{(2)} = .16$. If $a_{\overline{10}|.08} = A$, find the present value of the annuity in terms of A.

4.7 Payments varying in geometric progression

28. Find the present value of a 20-year annuity with annual payments which pays $600 immediately and each subsequent payment is 5% greater than the preceding payment. The annual effective rate of interest is 10.25%. Answer to the nearest dollar.

29. In Exercise 28, find the interest rate i' such that the present value would be equal to the present value of the level annuity-due $600\ddot{a}_{\overline{20}|i'}$.

30. Annual deposits are made into a fund at the beginning of each year for 10 years. The first 5 deposits are $1000 each and deposits increase by 5% per year thereafter. If the fund earns 8% effective, find the accumulated value at the end of 10 years. Answer to the nearest dollar.

31. A perpetuity makes payments starting five years from today. The first payment is $1000 and each payment thereafter increases by $k\%$ per year. The present value of this perpetuity is equal to $4096 when computed at $i = 25\%$. Find k.

32. An employee currently is aged 40, earns $40,000 per year, and expects to receive 3% annual raises at the end of each year for the next 25 years. The employee decides to contribute 4% of annual salary at the beginning of each year for the next 25 years into a retirement plan. How much will be available for retirement at age 65 if the fund can earn a 5% effective rate of interest? Answer to the nearest dollar.

33. A series of payments is made at the beginning of each year for 20 years with the first payment being $100. Each subsequent payment through the tenth year increases by 5% from the previous payment. After the tenth payment, each payment decreases by 5% from the previous payment. Calculate the present value of these payments at the time the first payment is made using an annual effective rate of 7%. Answer to the nearest dollar.

4.8 More general varying annuities

34. Derive formula (4.40).

35. *a)* Find the sum of the payments in $(Ia)_{\overline{2|}}^{(12)}$.

    b) Find the sum of the payments in $(I^{(12)}a)_{\overline{2|}}^{(12)}$.

36. Show that the present value of a perpetuity on which payments are 1 at the end of the 5th and 6th years, 2 at the end of the 7th and 8th years, 3 at the end of the 9th and 10th years, . . . , is

$$\frac{v^4}{i - vd}.$$

37. A perpetuity has payments at the end of each four-year period. The first payment at the end of four years is 1. Each subsequent payment is 5 more than the previous payment. It is known that $v^4 = .75$. Calculate the present value of this perpetuity.

38. A perpetuity provides payments every six months starting today. The first payment is 1 and each payment is 3% greater than the immediately preceding payment. Find the present value of the perpetuity if the effective rate of interest is 8% per annum.

4.9 Continuous varying annuities

39. Find the ratio of the total payments made under $(\bar{I}\,\bar{a})_{\overline{10}|}$ during the second half of the term of the annuity to those made during the first half.

40. Evaluate $(\bar{I}\,\bar{a})_{\overline{\infty}|}$ if $\delta = .08$.

41. Payments under a continuous perpetuity are made at the periodic rate of $(1+k)^t$ at time t. The annual effective rate of interest is i, where $0 < k < i$. Find the present value of the perpetuity.

42. *a*) Find an integral expression for $(\bar{D}\,\bar{a})_{\overline{n}|}$.
    b) Find an expression not involving integrals for $(\bar{D}\,\bar{a})_{\overline{n}|}$.

43. A one-year deferred continuous varying annuity is payable for 13 years. The rate of payment at time t is $t^2 - 1$ per annum, and the force of interest at time t is $(1+t)^{-1}$. Find the present value of the annuity.

Miscellaneous problems

44. A perpetuity paying 1 at the beginning of each 6-month period has a present value of 20. A second perpetuity pays X at the beginning of every 2 years. Assuming the same annual effective interest rate, the two present values are equal. Determine X.

45. For a given n, it is known that $\bar{a}_{\overline{n}|} = n - 4$ and $\delta = 10\%$. Find $\int_0^n \bar{a}_{\overline{t}|}\,dt$.

46. A family wishes to provide an annuity of \$100 at the end of each month to their daughter now entering college. The annuity will be paid for only nine months each year for four years. Show that the present value one month before the first payment is

$$1200\,\ddot{a}_{\overline{4}|}\,a^{(12)}_{\overline{9/12}|}.$$

47. There are two perpetuities. The first has level payments of p at the end of each year. The second is increasing such that the payments are $q, 2q, 3q, \ldots$ Find the rate of interest which will make the difference in present value between these perpetuities:
    a) Zero.
    b) A maximum.

48. Fence posts set in soil last 9 years and cost 2. Posts set in concrete last 15 years and cost $2 + X$. The posts will be needed for 35 years. Show that the break-even value of X, i.e. the value at which a buyer would be indifferent between the two types of posts is

$$2\left(\frac{a_{\overline{36}|}\, a_{\overline{15}|}}{a_{\overline{9}|}\, a_{\overline{45}|}} - 1\right).$$

49. If $\bar{a}_{\overline{n}|} = a$ and $\bar{a}_{\overline{2n}|} = b$, express $(\bar{I}\,\bar{a})_{\overline{n}|}$ in terms of a and b.

50. *a*) (1) Show that $\frac{d}{di}\, a_{\overline{n}|} = -v\,(I\,a)_{\overline{n}|}$.

(2) Find $\frac{d}{di}\, a_{\overline{n}|}$ evaluated at $i = 0$.

b) (1) Show that $\frac{d}{di}\, \bar{a}_{\overline{n}|} = -v\,(\bar{I}\,\bar{a})_{\overline{n}|}$.

(2) Find $\frac{d}{di}\, \bar{a}_{\overline{n}|}$ evaluated at $i = 0$.

5

Amortization schedules and sinking funds

5.1 INTRODUCTION

In Chapter 5 various methods of repaying a loan are analyzed in more depth than in previous chapters. In particular, two methods of repaying a loan are discussed:

1. *The amortization method.* In this method the borrower repays the lender by means of installment payments at periodic intervals. This process is called "amortization" of the loan.

2. *The sinking fund method.* In this method the borrower repays the lender by means of one lump-sum payment at the end of the term of the loan. The borrower pays interest on the loan in installments over this period. It is also assumed that the borrower makes periodic payments into a fund, called a "sinking fund," which will accumulate to the amount of the loan to be repaid at the end of the term of the loan.

Chapter 5 also considers the following two important questions which are related to the repayment methods mentioned above:

1. How can the outstanding loan balance at any given point in time be determined?

2. How can any payments made by the borrower be divided into repayment of principal and payment of interest?

Sections 5.2 and 5.3 consider the amortization method, while Section 5.4 considers the sinking fund method. Succeeding sections develop extensions and generalization of both methods.

5.2 FINDING THE OUTSTANDING LOAN BALANCE

If a loan is being repaid by the amortization method, the installment payments form an annuity whose present value is equal to the original amount of the loan. Section 5.2 is concerned with determining the amount of the outstanding loan balance at any point in time after the inception date of the loan. The reader may encounter a variety of terms synonymous with "outstanding loan balance" in common usage. Among these are "outstanding principal," "unpaid balance," and "remaining loan indebtedness."

Determining the amount of the outstanding loan balance is of great significance in practice. For example, if a family is buying a home with a 30-year mortgage, after making mortgage payments for 12 years, how much would they have to pay in one lump sum in order to completely pay off the mortgage?

There are two approaches used in finding the amount of the outstanding loan balance; namely, the "prospective method" and the "retrospective method." The names chosen are appropriate, since the prospective method calculates the outstanding loan balance looking into the future, while the retrospective method calculates the outstanding loan balance looking into the past.

According to the *prospective method*, the outstanding loan balance at any point in time is equal to the present value at that date of the remaining installment payments. According to the *retrospective method*, the outstanding loan balance at any point in time is equal to the original amount of the loan accumulated to that date less the accumulated value at that date of all installment payments previously made.

It is possible to show that, in general, the prospective and retrospective methods are equivalent. At the inception date of the loan we have the following equality:

$$\text{Present Value of Payments} = \text{Amount of Loan.}$$

We now accumulate each side of this equation to the date at which the outstanding loan balance is desired, obtaining:

Current Value of Payments = Accumulated Value of Loan.

However, the payments can be divided into past and future payments giving:

Accumulated Value of Past Payments + Present Value of Future Payments = Accumulated Value of Loan.

Now, rearranging, we obtain:

Present Value of Future Payments = Accumulated Value of Loan − Accumulated Value of Past Payments,

or,

Prospective Method = Retrospective Method.

We will denote the outstanding loan balance at time t by the symbol B_t. As an aid in using this symbol, we can denote the prospective form by B_t^p and the retrospective form by B_t^r. However, the usage of the superscripts p and r should be considered optional. The original loan balance B_0 is often denoted by L.

In specific cases it is possible to prove that the prospective method is equal to the retrospective method algebraically. For example, consider a loan of $a_{\overline{n}|}$ at interest rate i per period being repaid with payments of 1 at the end of each period for n periods. The outstanding loan balance t periods after the inception date of the loan is desired where $0 < t < n$. The outstanding loan balance at time t is computed after making the tth payment.

The prospective method gives

$$B_t^p = a_{\overline{n-t}|}. \tag{5.1}$$

The retrospective method gives

$$B_t^r = a_{\overline{n}|}(1+i)^t - s_{\overline{t}|}. \tag{5.2}$$

We can show algebraically that the retrospective form is equal to the prospective form

$$
\begin{aligned}
a_{\overline{n}|}(1+i)^t - s_{\overline{t}|} &= \frac{1-v^n}{i}(1+i)^t - \frac{(1+i)^t - 1}{i} \\
&= \frac{(1+i)^t - v^{n-t} - (1+i)^t + 1}{i} \\
&= \frac{1-v^{n-t}}{i} \\
&= a_{\overline{n-t}|}.
\end{aligned}
$$

In any given problem the prospective method or the retrospective method may be more efficient depending upon the nature of the problem. If the size and number of payments are known, then the prospective method is usually more efficient. If the number of payments or the size of a final irregular payment is not known, then the retrospective method is usually more efficient.

***Example 5.1** A loan is being repaid with 10 payments of $2000 followed by 10 payments of $1000 at the end of each half-year. If the nominal rate of interest convertible semiannually is 10%, find the outstanding loan balance immediately after five payments have been made by:*
(1) The prospective method.
(2) The retrospective method.

1. The rate of interest is 5% per half-year. Prospectively, the outstanding loan balance is

$$B_5^p = 1000\left(a_{\overline{15}|} + a_{\overline{5}|}\right) = 1000(10.37966 + 4.32948) = \$14,709$$

to the nearest dollar.

2. The original loan was

$$L = 1000\left(a_{\overline{20}|} + a_{\overline{10}|}\right) = 1000(12.46221 + 7.72173) = 20,183.95.$$

Retrospectively, the outstanding loan balance is

$$
\begin{aligned}
B_5^r &= 20,183.95(1.05)^5 - 2000\, s_{\overline{5}|} = 20,183.95(1.27628) - 2000(5.52563) \\
&= \$14,709
\end{aligned}
$$

to the nearest dollar. Thus, the prospective and retrospective methods produce the same answer.

Example 5.2 A loan is being repaid with 20 annual payments of $1000 each. At the time of the fifth payment, the borrower wishes to pay an extra $2000 and then repay the balance over 12 years with a revised annual payment. If the effective rate of interest is 9%, find the amount of the revised annual payment.

The balance after five years, prospectively, is

$$B_5^p = 1000a_{\overline{15}|} = 1000(8.06069) = 8060.69.$$

If the borrower pays an additional 2000, the balance becomes 6060.69. An equation of value for the revised payment, denoted by X, is

$$Xa_{\overline{12}|} = 6060.69$$

so that

$$X = \frac{6060.69}{7.16073} = \$846.38.$$

5.3 AMORTIZATION SCHEDULES

If a loan is being repaid by the amortization method, each payment is partially repayment of principal and partially payment of interest. Section 5.3 is concerned with determining how each payment can be divided between principal and interest.

Determining the amount of principal and interest contained in each payment is important for both the borrower and lender. For example, principal and interest are often treated quite differently for income tax purposes.

An *amortization schedule* is a table which shows the division of each payment into principal and interest, together with the outstanding loan balance after each payment is made. Consider a loan of $a_{\overline{n}|}$ at interest rate i per period being repaid with payments of 1 at the end of each period for n periods. Table 5.1 is an amortization schedule for this case.

Table 5.1 Amortization Schedule for a Loan of $a_{\overline{n}|}$ Repaid Over n Periods at Rate i.

Period	*Payment amount*	*Interest paid*	*Principal repaid*	*Outstanding loan balance*
0				$a_{\overline{n}\|}$
1	1	$ia_{\overline{n}\|} = 1-v^n$	v^n	$a_{\overline{n}\|} - v^n = a_{\overline{n-1}\|}$
2	1	$ia_{\overline{n-1}\|} = 1-v^{n-1}$	v^{n-1}	$a_{\overline{n-1}\|} - v^{n-1} = a_{\overline{n-2}\|}$
.	.	.	.	.
.	.	.	.	.
.	.	.	.	.
t	1	$ia_{\overline{n-t+1}\|} = 1-v^{n-t+1}$	v^{n-t+1}	$a_{\overline{n-t+1}\|} - v^{n-t+1} = a_{\overline{n-t}\|}$
.	.	.	.	.
.	.	.	.	.
.	.	.	.	.
$n-1$	1	$ia_{\overline{2}\|} = 1-v^2$	v^2	$a_{\overline{2}\|} - v^2 = a_{\overline{1}\|}$
n	1	$ia_{\overline{1}\|} = 1-v$	v	$a_{\overline{1}\|} - v = 0$
Total	n	$n - a_{\overline{n}\|}$	$a_{\overline{n}\|}$	

Consider the first period of the loan. At the end of the first period the interest due on the balance at the beginning of the period is $ia_{\overline{n}|} = 1-v^n$. The rest of the total payment of 1, i.e. v^n, must be principal repaid. The outstanding loan balance at the end of the period equals the outstanding loan balance at the beginning of the period less the principal repaid, i.e. $a_{\overline{n}|} - v^n = a_{\overline{n-1}|}$. The same reasoning applies for each successive line of the schedule.

Several additional observations are possible. First, it should be noted that the outstanding loan balance agrees with that obtained by the prospective method in formula (5.1). Second, the sum of the principal repayments equals the original amount of the loan. Third, the sum of the interest payments is equal to the difference between the sum of the total payments and the principal repayments. Fourth, the principal repayments form a geometric progression with common ratio 1 + i. Thus, it is a simple matter to find any one principal repayment knowing any other principal repayment and the rate of interest.

Further insight into the nature of the amortization schedule can be gained by the following argument. The original loan balance $a_{\overline{n}|}$ will accumulate to $a_{\overline{n}|}(1+i) = \ddot{a}_{\overline{n}|}$ at the end of the first period. However, $\ddot{a}_{\overline{n}|} = 1+a_{\overline{n-1}|}$, i.e. $\ddot{a}_{\overline{n}|}$ is sufficient to make the annuity payment of 1 and leave an outstanding balance of $a_{\overline{n-1}|}$ at the end of the first period. The same reasoning applies for each successive line of the schedule.

This line of reasoning can be generalized to develop a recursion formula that connects successive outstanding loan balances. If the installment payment at the end of each period is R, then we have the relationship

$$B_{t+1} = B_t(1+i) - R. \tag{5.3}$$

In essence, formula (5.3) represents the *recursion method*, a third method for calculating loan balances in addition to the prospective and retrospective methods developed in Section 5.2. It is particularly useful if multiple loan balances in succession are required.

For convenience, we will denote the amount of interest paid in the tth installment by I_t and the amount of principal repaid in the same installment by P_t. Thus, for the amortization schedule given in Table 5.1 we have

$$I_t = 1 - v^{n-t+1} \tag{5.4}$$

and

$$P_t = v^{n-t+1} \tag{5.5}$$

The reader should note that the notation I_t was also used in Chapter 1 in a different context. However, in both cases the symbol refers to an amount of interest earned between times $t-1$ and t, so there should be little risk of ambiguity.

It should be noted that Table 5.1 is based on an original loan of $a_{\overline{n}|}$. If the original loan were some other amount, then all the values in the schedule would be proportional. For example, if the original loan were \$1000, then each number in the last four columns of the schedule would be multiplied by $1000/a_{\overline{n}|}$.

For a specific problem, the amortization schedule can be constructed from basic principles. For example, consider the construction of an amortization schedule for a \$1000 loan repaid in four annual payments if the annual effective rate of interest is 8%. Then we have

$$R = \frac{1000}{a_{\overline{4}|}} = \frac{1000}{3.31213} = 301.92.$$

Table 5.2 is the amortization schedule for this example.

Table 5.2 Amortization Schedule for a Loan of $1000 Repaid Over Four Years at 8%

Year	*Payment amount*	*Interest paid*	*Principal repaid*	*Outstanding loan balance*
0				1000.00
1	301.92	80.00	221.92	778.08
2	301.92	62.25	239.67	538.41
3	301.92	43.07	258.85	279.56
4	301.92	22.36	279.56	0

In the first line of Table 5.2 we have the following calculations. The interest contained in the first payment is

$$I_1 = i \cdot B_0 = .08(1000) = 80.00.$$

The principal contained in the first payment is

$$P_1 = R - I_1 = 301.92 - 80.00 = 221.92.$$

The outstanding loan balance at the end of the first year is

$$B_1 = B_0 - P_1 = 1000.00 - 221.92 = 778.08.$$

Each successive line of the schedule is calculated in similar fashion.

In this particular example the last line exactly balances. However, more typically some roundoff error is likely to accumulate. Standard practice is to adjust the last payment so that it is exactly equal to the amount of interest for the final period plus the outstanding loan balance at the beginning of the final period (i.e. at the end of the next-to-final period). This adjustment will bring the outstanding loan balance exactly to zero at the end of the term of the loan.

It is also possible to construct the amortization schedule by alternate methods utilizing the various relationships in the table. As one example, the values of the outstanding loan balance can be calculated as in Section 5.2, or with the recursion formula (5.3), and then the rest of the schedule can be deduced from these values. As a second example, the principal repaid column can be calculated using the fact that the successive values are in geometric progression, and then the rest of the schedule can be deduced from these values.

It should be noted that if it is desired to find the amount of principal and interest in one particular payment, it is not necessary to construct the entire amortization schedule. The outstanding loan balance at the beginning of the period in question can be determined as described above, and then that one line of the amortization schedule can be calculated.

It is also possible to construct some, or all, of an amortization schedule using a financial calculator. Typically, the provisions of the original loan are entered and computed using the approach for basic annuities discussed in Chapter 3. For example, in Table 5.2 we could set

$$\begin{aligned} \text{N} &= 4 \\ \text{I} &= 100(.08) = 8 \\ \text{PV} &= -1000 \end{aligned}$$

and compute PMT obtaining

$$\text{PMT} = 301.92.$$

Financial calculators typically have another key labeled AMORT, which is then used to construct the amortization schedule. Values for interest paid, principal repaid, and outstanding loan balance appear in various registers and can readily be accessed by scrolling. By specifying various periods the user can generate the entire amortization schedule or some subset of it. The specific details for generating an amortization schedule vary from calculator to calculator.

The reader might wonder about the amortization schedule for a perpetuity. With a perpetuity the entire payment represents interest and the outstanding loan balance remains unchanged. Thus, amortization of perpetuity is really a contradiction in terms.

Several assumptions have been implicit in the preceding discussion of amortization schedules. First, we have assumed a constant rate of interest. An amortization schedule at a fixed, but varying rate of interest will be considered in the exercises. Second, we have assumed that the annuity payment period and the interest conversion period are equal. The cases in which they are not equal will be considered in Section 5.5. Third, we have assumed that annuity payments are level. The situation in which they are level except for a final irregular payment will be considered in Example 5.3. The general case of a varying series of payments will be considered in Section 5.6.

Certain special types of loan transactions are discussed in more detail in Chapter 8. In particular, consumer loans are considered in Section 8.2, automobile financing is considered in Section 8.3, and real estate mortgages are considered in Section 8.4.

Example 5.3 A $1000 loan is being repaid by payments of $100 at the end of each quarter for as long as necessary, plus a smaller final payment. If the nominal rate of interest convertible quarterly is 16%, find the amount of principal and interest in the fourth payment.

The rate of interest is 4% per quarter. Since the irregular final payment is unknown, the retrospective method should be used. The outstanding loan balance at the beginning of the fourth quarter, i.e. the end of the third quarter, is

$$B_3^r = 1000(1.04)^3 - 100s_{\overline{3}|} = 1124.86 - 312.16 = \$812.70.$$

The interest contained in the fourth payment is

$$I_4 = .04(812.70) = \$32.51.$$

The principal contained in the fourth payment is

$$P_4 = 100.00 - 32.51 = \$67.49.$$

Note that it was not necessary to find the duration and amount of the smaller final payment in order to solve this example.

Example 5.4 A borrows $10,000 from B and agrees to repay it with equal quarterly installments of principal and interest at 8% convertible quarterly over six years. At the end of two years B sells the right to receive future payments to C at a price that will yield C 10% convertible quarterly. Find the total amount of interest received:
(1) By C.
(2) By B.

1. The quarterly installment paid by A is

$$\frac{10,000}{a_{\overline{24}|.02}} = \frac{10,000}{18.91393} = 528.71\,.$$

The price C pays is the present value of the remaining payments at a rate of interest equal to 2.5% per quarter, i.e.

$$528.71a_{\overline{16}|.025} = (528.71)(13.0550) = 6902.31.$$

The total payments made by A over the last four years are

$$(16)(528.71) = 8459.36.$$

Thus, the total interest received by C is

$$8459.36 - 6902.31 = 1557.05.$$

2. The outstanding loan balance on B's original amortization schedule at the end of two years is

$$528.71 a_{\overline{16}|.02} = (528.71)(13.57771) = 7178.67.$$

The total payments made by A over the first two years are

$$(8)(528.71) = 4229.68.$$

The total principal repaid by A over this period is

$$10{,}000 - 7178.67 = 2821.33.$$

Thus, the total interest received by B apparently is

$$4229.68 - 2821.33 = 1408.35.$$

However, the total interest paid by A over the entire loan is equal to

$$(24)(528.71) - 10{,}000 = 2689.04$$

which does not equal the sum of the interest received by C and B, i.e.

$$1557.05 + 1408.35 = 2965.40.$$

What has happened is that B incurred a loss at the end of two years equal to the difference between the outstanding loan balance and the price to C, i.e.

$$7178.67 - 6902.31 = 276.36.$$

If this loss is offset against the interest received by B, then B's net investment income from this transaction is

$$1408.35 - 276.36 = 1131.99.$$

The system now balances, since adding this amount to the amount of interest received by C is equal to the total interest paid by A, i.e.

$$1557.05 + 1131.99 = 2689.04\ .$$

***Example 5.5** An amount is invested at an annual effective rate of interest i which is just sufficient to pay 1 at the end of each year for n years. In the first year the fund actually earns rate i and 1 is paid at the end of the year. However, in the second year the fund earns rate j where j > i. Find the revised payment which could be made at the ends of years 2 through n:*
(1) Assuming the rate earned reverts back to i again after this one year.
(2) Assuming the rate earned remains at j for the rest of the n-year period.

1. The initial investment is $B_0 = a_{\overline{n}|\,i}$ and the account balance at the end of the first year is $B_1 = a_{\overline{n-1}|\,i}$. Let X be the revised payment. We now construct the next line of the amortization schedule on the revised basis, obtaining

$$I_2 = ja_{\overline{n-1}|\,i}$$
$$P_2 = X - ja_{\overline{n-1}|\,i}$$

and

$$B_2 = a_{\overline{n-1}|\,i} - \left(X - ja_{\overline{n-1}|\,i}\right)$$
$$= (1+j)a_{\overline{n-1}|\,i} - X.$$

However, prospectively B_2 must equal the present value of the future payments. Thus, we have

$$(1+j)a_{\overline{n-1}|\,i} - X = Xa_{\overline{n-2}|\,i}$$
$$X\left(1 + a_{\overline{n-2}|\,i}\right) = (1+j)a_{\overline{n-1}|\,i}$$
$$X\ddot{a}_{\overline{n-1}|\,i} = (1+j)a_{\overline{n-1}|\,i}$$
$$X(1+i)a_{\overline{n-1}|\,i} = (1+j)a_{\overline{n-1}|\,i}$$

which gives

$$X = \frac{1+j}{1+i}.$$

2. The development is identical to case 1 above, except that the prospective value for the future payments, which equals B_2, is computed at rate j instead of i. Thus, we have

$$(1+j)a_{\overline{n-1}|\,i} - X = X\,a_{\overline{n-2}|\,j}$$
$$X\left(1 + a_{\overline{n-2}|\,j}\right) = (1+j)a_{\overline{n-1}|\,i}$$
$$X\ddot{a}_{\overline{n-1}|\,j} = (1+j)a_{\overline{n-1}|\,i}$$
$$X(1+j)a_{\overline{n-1}|\,j} = (1+j)a_{\overline{n-1}|\,i}$$

which gives

$$X = \frac{a_{\overline{n-1|}\,i}}{a_{\overline{n-1|}\,j}} .$$

5.4 SINKING FUNDS

Rather than repay a loan in installments by the amortization method, in some cases a borrower may choose to repay it by means of one lump-sum payment at the end of a specified period of time. In many of these cases the borrower will accumulate a fund that will be sufficient to exactly repay the loan at the end of the specified period of time. In fact, in some cases the lender will insist that the borrower accumulate such a fund, which is often called a *sinking fund.*

In some cases payments into a sinking fund may vary irregularly at the discretion of the borrower. However, we shall be primarily interested in those cases in which the payments follow a regular pattern, i.e. where they are some form of an annuity.

It is usually required that the borrower pay interest on the entire amount of the loan periodically over the term of the loan. Such interest is sometimes called *service* on the loan. Thus, the amount of the loan remains constant.

Since the balance in the sinking fund at any point could presumably be applied against the loan, the net amount of the loan is equal to the original amount of the loan minus the accumulated value of the sinking fund. This concept plays the same role for the sinking fund method that the outstanding loan balance, discussed in Section 5.2, does for the amortization method.

It is possible to show that if the rate of interest paid on the loan equals the rate of interest earned on the sinking fund, then the sinking fund method is equivalent to the amortization method.
Recall formula (3.6) from Chapter 3

$$\frac{1}{a_{\overline{n|}}} = \frac{1}{s_{\overline{n|}}} + i . \qquad (3.6)$$

Consider a loan of amount 1 repaid over n periods. The expression $1/a_{\overline{n|}}$ is the amount of each payment necessary to repay the loan by the amortization method. However, the expression $1/s_{\overline{n|}}$ is the periodic sinking fund deposit necessary to accumulate the amount of the loan at the end of n periods, while i is the amount of interest paid on the loan each period. Thus, the two methods are equivalent.

It is instructive to consider this equivalence from an alternate viewpoint. Consider a loan of amount $a_{\overline{n}|}$ being repaid with installments of 1 at the end of each period for n periods. The amount of interest each period is $ia_{\overline{n}|}$. Thus, $1-ia_{\overline{n}|}$ is left to go into the sinking fund each period. However, the sinking fund will accumulate to

$$\left(1-ia_{\overline{n}|}\right)s_{\overline{n}|} = v^n s_{\overline{n}|} = a_{\overline{n}|}$$

which is the original amount of the loan.

At first glance it might seem that the two methods cannot be equivalent, since from Table 5.1, the interest paid in the amortization method decreases $1-v^n,\ 1-v^{n-1},\ \ldots,\ 1-v$; while the interest paid in the sinking fund method is a constant $ia_{\overline{n}|} = 1-v^n$ each period. However, each period the sinking fund earns interest which exactly offsets the seeming discrepancy, so that the net amount of interest is the same for the sinking fund method as for the amortization method.

For example, during the tth period, where $t = 1, 2, \ldots, n$, the amount of interest in the amortization schedule is

$$ia_{\overline{n-t+1}|} = 1-v^{n-t+1}.$$

The net amount of interest in the sinking fund method is the amount of interest paid $ia_{\overline{n}|}$ less the amount of interest earned on the sinking fund. The amount in the sinking fund is the accumulated value of the sinking fund deposits of $1-ia_{\overline{n}|}$ at the end of $t-1$ periods, i.e.

$$\left(1-ia_{\overline{n}|}\right)s_{\overline{t-1}|}.$$

Thus, the net amount of interest in the sinking fund method in the tth period is

$$\begin{aligned} ia_{\overline{n}|} - i\left(1-ia_{\overline{n}|}\right)s_{\overline{t-1}|} &= \left(1-v^n\right) - v^n\left[(1+i)^{t-1}-1\right] \\ &= 1-v^n - v^{n-t+1} + v^n \\ &= 1-v^{n-t+1}. \end{aligned}$$

Therefore, the net amount of interest in the sinking fund method is equal to the amount of interest in the amortization method if the rate of interest on the loan equals the rate of interest earned on the sinking fund.

The equivalence in the two methods can be seen from a consideration of a *sinking fund schedule.* Table 5.3 is a sinking fund schedule for the same example considered in Table 5.2. Let the sinking fund deposit be denoted by D. Then we have

$$D = \frac{1000}{s_{\overline{4}|}} = \frac{1000}{4.50611} = 221.92.$$

The reader should verify the entries in Table 5.3.

Table 5.3 Sinking Fund Schedule for a Loan of $1000 Repaid Over Four Years at 8%

Year	*Interest paid*	*Sinking fund deposit*	*Interest earned on sinking fund*	*Amount in sinking fund*	*Net amount of loan*
0					1000.00
1	80.00	221.92	0	221.92	778.08
2	80.00	221.92	17.75	461.59	538.41
3	80.00	221.92	36.93	720.44	279.56
4	80.00	221.92	57.64	1000.00	0

The following relationships between Table 5.2 and Table 5.3 should be noted:

1. The total payment in the sinking fund method, i.e. interest paid on the loan plus the sinking fund deposit, equals the payment amount in the amortization method.
2. The net interest paid in the sinking fund method, i.e. interest paid on the loan minus interest earned on the sinking fund, equals the interest paid in the amortization method.
3. The annual increment in the sinking fund, i.e. the sinking fund deposit plus the interest earned on the sinking fund, equals the principal repaid in the amortization method.
4. The net amount of the loan in the sinking fund method, i.e. the original amount of the loan minus the amount in the sinking fund, equals the outstanding loan balance in the amortization method.

It now remains to consider the operation of the sinking fund method when the rate of interest earned on the sinking fund differs from the rate of interest paid on the loan. We will denote the rate of interest paid on the loan by i and the rate of interest earned on the sinking fund by j.

In practice j is usually less than or equal to i. It would be unusual for a borrower to be able to accumulate money in a sinking fund at a higher rate of interest than is being paid on the loan. However, this is not necessarily the case mathematically, and the following analysis is valid even if j is greater than i.

The same basic approach will be used for the case in which $i \neq j$ as was previously used in the case in which the two rates were equal. The total payment will be split into two parts. First, interest at rate i will be paid on the amount of the loan. Second, the remainder of the total payment not needed for interest will be placed into a sinking fund accumulating at rate j.

Let $a_{\overline{n}|\, i\&j}$ represent the present value of an annuity of 1 at the end of each period for n periods under the conditions just described. Then if a loan of 1 is made, the periodic installment under the amortization method will be $1/a_{\overline{n}|\, i\&j}$. However, from the sinking fund method this payment must pay interest at rate i on the loan and provide for a sinking fund deposit which will accumulate at rate j to the amount of the loan at the end of n periods. Thus

$$\frac{1}{a_{\overline{n}|\, i\&j}} = \frac{1}{s_{\overline{n}|\, j}} + i\,. \tag{5.6}$$

We can now find an expression for $a_{\overline{n}|\, i\&j}$ as follows:

$$\begin{aligned} \frac{1}{a_{\overline{n}|\, i\&j}} &= \frac{1}{s_{\overline{n}|j}} + i \\ &= \frac{1}{a_{\overline{n}|j}} + (i-j). \end{aligned} \tag{5.7}$$

Thus,

$$a_{\overline{n}|\, i\&j} = \frac{a_{\overline{n}|j}}{1+(i-j)a_{\overline{n}|j}}\,. \tag{5.8}$$

It should be noted that if $i = j$, then $a_{\overline{n}|\, i\&j} = a_{\overline{n}|\, i}$ as would be expected.

The construction of a sinking fund schedule at two rates of interest is very similar to the construction of a sinking fund schedule at a single rate of interest. As an example, consider a \$1000 loan for four years on which an annual effective rate of interest of 10% is charged if the borrower accumulates the amount necessary to repay the loan by means of four annual sinking fund deposits in a fund earning an annual effective rate of 8%. The total semiannual payment made by the borrower is

$$\frac{1000}{a_{\overline{4}|.10\&.08}} = \frac{1000}{s_{\overline{4}|.08}} + 1000(.10) = 221.92 + 100.00 = 321.92.$$

This example is a generalization of the example considered in Table 5.3. Note that the sinking fund schedule is identical to Table 5.3, except that each entry in the interest paid column is $100 instead of $80.

In general, the sinking fund schedule at two rates of interest is identical to the sinking fund schedule at one rate of interest equal to the rate of interest earned on the sinking fund, except that a constant addition of $(i-j)$ times the amount of the loan is added to the interest paid column.

***Example 5.6** A wishes to borrow $1000. Lender B offers a loan in which the principal is to be repaid at the end of four years. In the meantime 10% effective is to be paid on the loan and A is to accumulate the amount necessary to repay the loan by means of annual deposits in a sinking fund earning 8% effective. Lender C offers a loan for four years in which A repays the loan by the amortization method. What is the largest effective rate of interest that C can charge so that A is indifferent between the two offers?*

Under either method A will make four equal payments at the end of each year to repay the loan. Thus, A will be indifferent between the two offers if the annual payment is equal on both of them.

On the sinking fund offer from B the annual payment is

$$\frac{1000}{a_{\overline{4}|.10\&.08}} = 321.92$$

as shown earlier in this section. Thus, on the amortization offer, C could charge i' where

$$321.92\, a_{\overline{4}|\,i'} = 1000$$

or

$$a_{\overline{4}|} = 3.1064.$$

We can use the technique of Section 3.7 to solve for the unknown rate of interest on this annuity. Using a financial calculator, we set

$$\text{N} = 4$$
$$\text{PV} = 3.1064$$
$$\text{PMT} = -1$$

and compute I obtaining

$$\text{I} = 10.94\%$$

In essence we have shown that

$$a_{\overline{4}|.10\&.08} = a_{\overline{4}|.1094}.$$

This example illustrates that to a borrower the total periodic payment is of primary concern and that the difference between the amortization method and the sinking fund method is somewhat artificial.

The reader may find the answer of .1094 surprising, since the answer might be expected to lie between .08 and .10. In general, if the equivalent rate of interest in the amortization method is denoted by i', we have the following approximate equality:

$$i' \approx i + \frac{1}{2}(i - j). \tag{5.9}$$

This formula would produce an answer for this example equal to $.10 + \frac{1}{2}(.10 - .08) = .11$, which is close to the true answer of .1094.

The equivalent rate i' is greater than i because the borrower not only is paying i per unit borrowed but also is investing in a sinking fund on which interest is being sacrificed at rate $i - j$. Since the average balance in the sinking fund per unit borrowed is 1/2, the extra interest cost is approximately $\frac{1}{2}(i - j)$. Thus, the total interest cost per unit borrowed is approximately

$$i + \frac{1}{2}(i - j).$$

It is also instructive to consider B's yield rate on this transaction. If A invests the sinking fund with B, then B's yield rate over the four-year term of the loan is the same as the cost to A, i.e. 10.94%. However, if A invests the sinking fund elsewhere, then B's yield rate is just 10%. Thus, B's overall yield rate is affected by whether or not B has the advantage of holding the sinking fund on which only 8% is credited.

Example 5.7 An investor buys an n-year annuity with a present value of $1000 computed at 8%. The investor pays a price which will permit the replacement of the original investment in a sinking fund earning 7% and will also produce an overall yield rate of 9% on the entire transaction. Find the price which the investor should pay for the annuity.

This is a complex problem involving three different interest rates. The annual payment of the annuity is

$$\frac{1000}{a_{\overline{n}|.08}}.$$

Let P be the purchase price and let D be the sinking fund deposit. Now the total annual payment is split into interest on the purchase price $.09P$ and the sinking fund deposit D. Thus, we have

$$D + .09P = \frac{1000}{a_{\overline{n}|.08}}.$$

However, we also know that the accumulated value of the sinking fund after n years must be P. Thus, we also have

$$P = Ds_{\overline{n}|.07}.$$

Now we see that we have two equations in two unknowns, and we can solve for P

$$P = \left(\frac{1000}{a_{\overline{n}|.08}} - .09P\right) s_{\overline{n}|.07}$$

or

$$P = \frac{1000\, s_{\overline{n}|.07}}{a_{\overline{n}|.08}\left(1 + .09 s_{\overline{n}|.07}\right)}.$$

5.5 DIFFERING PAYMENT PERIODS AND INTEREST CONVERSION PERIODS

In Sections 5.3 and 5.4 it has been assumed that the payment period and he interest conversion period are equal and coincide. Section 5.5 discusses the implications of removing this assumption. Problems involving differing frequencies are best handled from basic principles rather than attempting to develop new formulas.

Consider first an amortization schedule in which payments are made at a different frequency than interest is convertible. The amortization schedule will contain a line for each payment, since the primary purpose of the schedule is to divide each payment between interest paid and principal repaid. In this case, a two-step procedure analogous to Section 4.2, can be followed:

1. Find the rate of interest, convertible at the same frequency as payments are made, that is equivalent to the given rate of interest.

2. Using this new rate of interest, construct the amortization schedule using the techniques developed in Section 5.3.

This approach is general and can be used whether interest is convertible more or less frequently than payments are made. Example 5.8 illustrates this technique.

In the case of sinking funds, the approach is similar, but the details may be a bit more complex, since the frequency of the following may differ: (1) interest payments on the loan, (2) sinking fund deposits, and (3) interest conversion period on the sinking fund. Example 5.9 is illustrative of such a case.

***Example 5.8** A debt is being amortized by means of monthly payments at an annual effective rate of interest of 11%. If the amount of principal in the third payment is $1000, find the amount of principal in the 33rd payment.*

Since payments are made monthly and interest is convertible annually, the principal repaid column in the amortization schedule will be a geometric progression with common ratio $(1+i)^{1/12}$. The interval from the 3rd payment to the 33rd payment is $(33-3)/12 = 2.5$ years. Thus, the principal in the 33rd payment is

$$1000(1.11)^{2.5} = \$1298.10.$$

***Example 5.9** A borrower takes out a loan of $2000 for two years. Construct a sinking fund schedule if the lender receives 10% effective on the loan and if the borrower replaces the amount of the loan with semiannual deposits in a sinking fund earning 8% convertible quarterly.*

In this case all three frequencies differ: (1) interest payments on the loan are made annually, (2) sinking fund deposits are made semiannually, and (3) interest on the sinking fund is convertible quarterly.

The interest payments on the loan are 200 at the end of each year. Let the sinking fund deposit be D. Then

$$D\frac{s_{\overline{8}|.02}}{s_{\overline{2}|.02}} = 2000$$

or

$$D = 2000\frac{s_{\overline{2}|.02}}{s_{\overline{8}|.02}} = 2000\frac{2.02}{8.5830} = 470.70.$$

The complete sinking fund schedule is given in Table 5.4.

Table 5.4 Sinking Fund Schedule for Example 5.9

Year	*Interest paid*	*Sinking fund deposit*	*Interest earned on sinking fund*	*Amount in sinking fund*	*Net amount of loan*
0					
1/4	0	0	0	0	2000.00
1/2	0	470.70	0	470.70	1529.30
3/4	0	0	9.41	480.11	1519.89
1	200.00	470.70	9.60	960.41	1039.59
1 1/4	0	0	19.21	979.62	1020.38
1 1/2	0	470.70	19.59	1469.91	530.09
1 3/4	0	0	29.40	1499.31	500.69
2	200.00	470.70	29.99	2000.00	0

5.6 VARYING SERIES OF PAYMENTS

If a loan is being repaid by the amortization method, it is possible that the borrower repays the loan with installments which are not level. The case in which all the payments are level except for an irregular final payment was considered in Section 5.3. In this section we consider more general patterns of variation. We will assume that the interest conversion period and the payment period are equal and coincide.

Consider a loan L to be repaid with n periodic installments $R_1, R_2, \ldots, R_n$. Then we have

$$L = \sum_{i=1}^{n} v^t R_t \,. \tag{5.10}$$

Often the series of payments R_t follows some regular pattern so that the results of Sections 4.6 and 4.7 can be used.

If it is desired to construct an amortization schedule, it can be constructed from basic principles as in Section 5.3. Alternatively, the outstanding loan balance column can be found prospectively, retrospectively, or recursively, and then the interest paid and principal repaid columns can be determined.

One pattern of variation that is fairly common involves the borrower making level payments of principal. Since successive outstanding loan balances decrease, successive interest payments will also decrease. Thus, successive total payments consisting of principal and interest will decrease. Example 5.12 is an illustration of this type.

It is possible that when a loan is amortized with varying payments, the interest due in a payment is larger than the total payment. In this case, the principal repaid would be negative and the outstanding loan balance would increase instead of decrease. The increase in the outstanding loan balance arises from interest deficiencies being *capitalized* and added to the amount of the loan. This situation is often called *negative amortization*. Example 5.13 is an illustration of this type.

It is also possible to have a varying series of payments with the sinking fund method. We will assume that the interest paid to the lender is constant each period so that only the sinking fund deposits vary.

Assume that the varying payments by the borrower are $R_1, R_2, \ldots, R_n$ and that $i \neq j$. Let the amount of the loan be denoted by L. Then the sinking fund deposit for the tth period is $R_t - iL$. Since the accumulated value of the sinking fund at the end of n periods must be L, we have

$$\begin{aligned} L &= (R_1 - iL)(1+j)^{n-1} + (R_2 - iL)(1+j)^{n-2} + \cdots + (R_n - iL) \\ &= \sum_{t=1}^{n} R_t (1+j)^{n-1} - iL s_{\overline{n}|j} \end{aligned}$$

or

$$L = \frac{\sum_{t=1}^{n} R_t (1+j)^{n-t}}{1 + i s_{\overline{n}|j}} = \frac{\sum_{t=1}^{n} v_j^t R_t}{1 + (i-j) a_{\overline{n}|j}}. \qquad (5.11)$$

If $R_t = 1$, for $t = 1, 2, \ldots, n$, then formula (5.8) is seen to be a special case of formula (5.11). If $i = j$, then formula (5.11) becomes

$$L = \sum_{t=1}^{n} v^t R_t$$

which is just formula (5.10). Thus, the amortization method and the sinking fund method are equivalent if $i = j$.

It should be noted that we have implicitly assumed that the sinking fund deposit $R_t - iL$ is positive. If it were negative, then it would mean that the payment in that year is not even sufficient to pay the interest on the loan. We would then have a negative sinking fund deposit, i.e. a withdrawal, from the sinking fund for that year. Example 5.14 is an illustration of this type.

***Example 5.10** A borrower is repaying a loan at 5% effective with payments at the end of each year for 10 years, such that the payment the first year is $200, the second year $190, and so forth, until the 10th year it is $110.*
(1) Find the amount of the loan.
(2) Find the principal and interest in the fifth payment.

1. The amount of the loan is

$$L = 100a_{\overline{10|}} + 10(Da)_{\overline{10|}} = 100(7.72173) + 10\frac{10-7.72173}{.05} = \$1227.83.$$

2. We have:

$$\begin{aligned} R_5 &= 160.00 \\ B_4^p &= 100\,a_{\overline{6|}} + 10(Da)_{\overline{6|}} \\ I_5 &= iB_4^p = 100(1-v^6) + 10(6-a_{\overline{6|}}) \\ &= 100(1-.74622) + 10(6-5.0757) = \$34.62 \\ P_5 &= R_5 - I_5 = 160.00 - 34.62 = \$125.38. \end{aligned}$$

***Example 5.11** Assuming the same payment pattern as in Example 5.10, find the amount of the loan if the borrower pays 6% effective on the loan and accumulates a sinking fund to replace the amount of the loan at 5% effective.*

Using formula (5.11) the amount of the loan is

$$\frac{100\,a_{\overline{10}|.05} + 10(Da)_{\overline{10}|.05}}{1 + (.06-.05)a_{\overline{10}|.05}} = \frac{1227.83}{1 + (.01)(7.72173)} = \$1139.82.$$

This answer is less than the answer to Example 5.10(1), since these terms are less favorable to the borrower.

Example 5.12 A borrows \$20,000 from B and agrees to repay it with 20 equal annual installments of principal plus interest on the unpaid balance at 3% effective. After 10 years B sells the right to future payments to C, at a price that yields C 5% effective over the remaining 10 years. Find the price which C should pay to the nearest dollar.

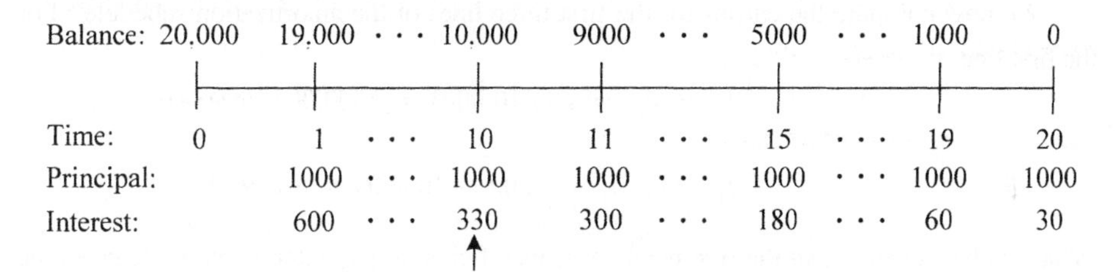

Figure 5.1 Time diagram for Example 5.12

Each year A pays \$1000 principal plus interest on the unpaid balance at 3%. The payments are shown in the lower portion of Figure 5.1. The price to C at the end of the 10th year is the present value of the remaining payments, i.e.

$$\begin{aligned} & 1000a_{\overline{10}|.05} + 30(Da)_{\overline{10}|.05} \\ &= 1000a_{\overline{10}|.05} + 30\frac{10-a_{\overline{10}|.05}}{.05} \\ &= 1000(7.72173) + 30\frac{10-7.72173}{.05} \\ &= \$9089 \end{aligned}$$

to the nearest dollar. The answer must be less than the outstanding loan balance of \$10,000, since C has a yield rate in excess of 3%.

Example 5.13 A borrows \$10,000 from B and agrees to repay it with a series of ten installments at the end of each year such that each installment is 20% greater than the preceding installment. The rate of interest on the loan is 10% effective. Find the amount of principal repaid in the first three installments.

Using formula (4.29) we have

$$10{,}000 = R_1 \left[\frac{1 - \left(\frac{1.2}{1.1} \right)^{10}}{.1 - .2} \right] = 13.87182 R_1$$

so that

$$R_1 = \frac{10{,}000}{13.87182} = 720.89 .$$

We now compute the entries for the first three lines of the amortization schedule. For the first line

$$I_1 = iB_0 = (.1)(10{,}000) = 1000.00$$

and

$$P_1 = R_1 - I_1 = 720.89 - 1000.00 = -279.11 .$$

What has happened is that the first payment is insufficient to pay interest on the loan, so the principal payment is negative. This results in an increase in the outstanding loan balance, i.e.

$$B_1 = B_0 - P_1 = 10{,}000 + 279.11 = 10{,}279.11 .$$

The calculations for the second line of the amortization schedule are:

$$\begin{aligned} R_2 &= 1.2 R_1 = (1.2)(720.89) = 865.07 \\ I_2 &= iB_1 = (.1)(10{,}279.11) = 1027.91 \\ P_2 &= R_2 - I_2 = 865.07 - 1027.91 = -162.84 \\ B_2 &= B_1 - P_2 = 10{,}279.11 + 162.84 = 10{,}441.95. \end{aligned}$$

Continuing for the third line we have:

$$\begin{aligned} R_3 &= 1.2\, R_2 = (1.2)(865.07) = 1038.08 \\ I_3 &= iB_2 = (.1)(10{,}441.95) = 1044.20 \\ P_3 &= R_3 - I_3 = 1038.08 - 1044.20 = -6.12 \\ B_3 &= B_2 - P_3 = 10{,}441.95 + 6.12 = 10{,}448.07 . \end{aligned}$$

Thus, the amount of principal repaid in the first three installments is

$$P_1 + P_2 + P_3 = -279.11 - 162.84 - 6.12 = -\$448.07$$

which could also be computed as $B_0 - B_3$. The principal repaid in the fourth and succeeding installments is positive and the loan is ultimately amortized to zero at the end of ten years. This example illustrates negative amortization for the first three years of the loan.

Example 5.14 What is the maximum amount that A can borrow from B if A is willing to make four successive annual payments of 100, 100, 1000 and 1000, if B is to receive 12% effective on the loan, and if A is to replace the amount of the loan in a sinking fund held by B earning 8% effective?

Let L be the amount of the loan. Annual interest on the loan is then $.12L$. The four successive sinking fund deposits are then $100-.12L$, $100-.12L$, $1000-.12L$, and $1000-.12L$. Since the accumulated value of the sinking fund must equal the original amount of the loan, we have

$$(100-.12L)\, s_{\overline{4}|.08} + 900\, s_{\overline{2}|.08} = L$$

or

$$L = \frac{100\, s_{\overline{4}|.08} + 900\, s_{\overline{2}|.08}}{1+.12\, s_{\overline{4}|.08}}$$

$$= \frac{(100)(4.5061)+(900)(2.08)}{1+(.12)(4.5061)} = \$1507.47.$$

However, this answer is subject to criticism. It is evident that the payments by A for the first two years are not sufficient to pay B 12% on the amount of the loan. Thus, the sinking fund will be negative. It is not reasonable to assume that this negative sinking fund earns 8% because that would imply that A could borrow money at 8%. Since B holds the sinking fund, it is much more reasonable to assume that A would have to borrow at 12%. Thus, the interest deficiencies during the first two years should be capitalized and added to the amount of the loan. Let L' be the amount of the loan under these conditions. We then have

$$B_2^r = L'(1.12)^2 - 100\, s_{\overline{2}|.12}$$

or

$$B_2^r = 1.2544\, L' - 212.$$

However, B_2^r is the increased amount of the loan which must be accumulated in the sinking fund. Thus, we have

$$B_2^r = \left(1000 - .12\,B_2^r\right) s_{\overline{2}|.08}$$

or

$$B_2^r = \frac{1000\, s_{\overline{2}|.08}}{1 + .12\, s_{\overline{2}|.08}} = \frac{1000(2.08)}{1 + (.12)(2.08)} = 1664.53\ .$$

The original loan is then calculated as

$$L' = \frac{B_2^r + 212}{1.2544} = \$1495.96.$$

Thus, L' is slightly less than L, as would be expected.

5.7 AMORTIZATION WITH CONTINUOUS PAYMENTS

It is possible to develop formulas for amortization of loans with continuous payments. Such formulas have conceptual and theoretical value, but are not widely used in practical applications.

We first examine the case in which the rate of payment is constant. Consider a loan of $\bar{a}_{\overline{n}|}$ being repaid with continuous payments at the rate of 1 per period over n periods. We can readily generalize formulas (5.1) and (5.2) to find the outstanding loan balance at time t, $0 \le t \le n$, as

$$B_t^p = \bar{a}_{\overline{n-t}|} \tag{5.12}$$

and

$$B_t^r = \bar{a}_{\overline{n}|}(1+i)^t - \bar{s}_{\overline{t}|}\,. \tag{5.13}$$

Also, we know that the continuous payments are partially interest and partially repayment of principal. Let $\bar{I}_t$ be the instantaneous rate at which interest is being paid and $\bar{P}_t$ be the instantaneous rate at which principal is being repaid at time t. By general reasoning, the generalizations of formulas (5.4) and (5.5) become

$$\bar{I}_t = \delta \cdot B_t \tag{5.14}$$

and

$$\bar{P}_t = 1 - \delta \cdot B_t\,. \tag{5.15}$$

We will verify formulas (5.14) and (5.15) if we are able to show that

$$\frac{d}{dt}B_t = -\bar{P}_t$$

since the instantaneous rate of decrease in the outstanding loan balance must equal the rate of principal repayment. If we differentiate formula (5.12), we have

$$\begin{aligned}
\frac{d}{dt}B_t &= \frac{d}{dt}\bar{a}_{\overline{n-t|}} = \frac{d}{dt}\frac{1-v^{n-t}}{\delta} \\
&= -\frac{d}{dt}\frac{(1+i)^{t-n}}{\delta} = -\frac{(1+i)^{t-n}\ \ln(1+i)}{\delta} \\
&= -(1+i)^{t-n} = -v^{n-t} \\
&= \delta\bar{a}_{\overline{n-t|}} - 1 = \delta B_t - 1 = -\bar{P}_t
\end{aligned}$$

from formula (5.15).

In Section 4.5 we developed the identity

$$\frac{d}{dt}\bar{a}_{\overline{t|}} = 1 - \delta\,\bar{a}_{\overline{t|}} \tag{4.18}$$

and indicated that it was possible to give the formula a verbal interpretation. The discussion immediately above provides that verbal interpretation.

We next consider a generalization in which the rate of payment varies. Assume that payments on the loan are being made continuously at the rate of R_t per period. The original amount of the loan is the present value of the payments,

$$L = B_0 = \int_0^n v^s R_s ds. \tag{5.16}$$

The two formulas for the outstanding loan balance then become

$$B_t^p = \int_t^n v^{s-t} R_s ds \tag{5.17}$$

and

$$B_t^r = B_0(1+i)^t - \int_0^t R_s (1+i)^{t-s}\, ds. \tag{5.18}$$

The above formulas have assumed a constant force of interest. It is relatively straightforward to generalize the above results even further by assuming a varying force of interest using the formulas developed in Section 1.9.

Example 5.15 Show that

$$\int_0^n v'^t \bar{a}'_{\overline{n-t}|}\, dt = \int_0^n v'^t \bar{a}_{\overline{n-t}|}\, dt$$

where unprimed symbols are based on force of interest δ and primed symbols are based on force of interest δ'.

We have

$$\int_0^n v^t \bar{a}'_{\overline{n-t}|} dt = \int_0^n \int_0^{n-t} v^t v'^r drdt.$$

We now reverse the order of integration as illustrated in Figure 5.2.

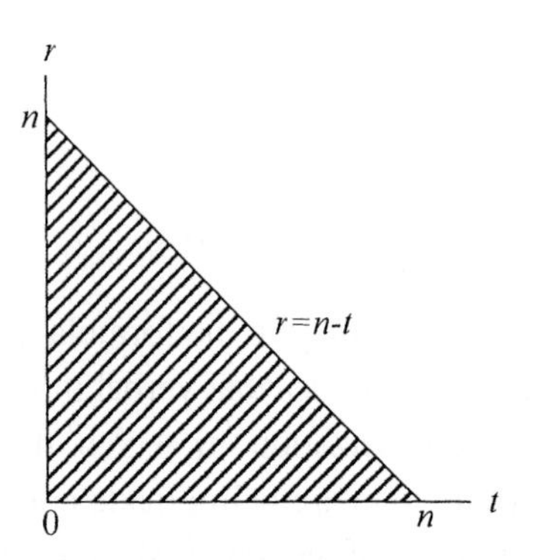

Figure 5.2 Area of integration for Example 5.15

The double integral now becomes

$$\int_0^n \int_0^{n-t} v^t v'^r drdt = \int_0^n \int_0^{n-r} v^t v'^r dtdr$$
$$= \int_0^n v'^r \bar{a}_{\overline{n-r}|} dr$$

which is the result we wanted to show upon substituting t for r. The reader will probably find it surprising that this identity is true.

5.8 STEP-RATE AMOUNTS OF PRINCIPAL

A problem occasionally encountered in practical applications involves the amortization of a loan in which the loan balance is subdivided and different rates of interest are charged on the subdivided portions. For example, a credit institution may charge 1 1/2% per month on the first $1000 of outstanding loan balance and 1% per month on any excess. We call these subdivided portions of loan balance *step-rate amounts of principal.*

The determination of a level periodic payment which will repay a loan involving step-rate amounts of principal is surprisingly a non-routine problem and involves trial-and-error to find a solution. In this section we give a solution to this type of problem for loans involving two step-rates. The approach can be generalized to more than two step-rates.

Consider a loan L which is being repaid with level payments of R over n periods. Interest is computed at rate i per period on the first L' of outstanding loan balance, $0 < L' < L$, and at rate j per period on the excess over L'. In practice $i > j$ in most situations, although this is not required for the derivation. It is desired to find the level payment R.

Before R can be determined it is necessary to find the "crossover" period when the outstanding loan balance first becomes less than or equal to L'. Denote this duration by a, so that a is the smallest integer such that

$$B_a \leq L'. \tag{5.19}$$

The progression of loan balances is illustrated in Figure 5.3.

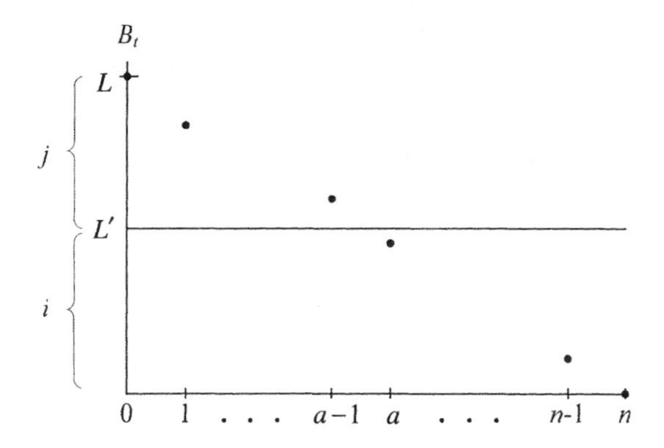

Figure 5.3 Outstanding loan balances for a loan involving step-rate amounts of principal

A formula for R can be developed by the following procedure:

1. Find B_a^p.

2. Find B_a^r.

3. Equate the two and solve for R.

The prospective approach gives

$$B_a^p = R\, a_{\overline{n-a}|\, i}\,. \tag{5.20}$$

The retrospective approach gives

$$B_a^r = (L-L')(1+j)^a + L' + iL'\, s_{\overline{a}|\, j} - R s_{\overline{a}|\, j}. \tag{5.21}$$

Equating formulas (5.20) and (5.21) and solving for R produces

$$R = \frac{(L-L')(1+j)^a + L' + iL' s_{\overline{a}|\, j}}{a_{\overline{n-a}|\, i} + s_{\overline{a}|\, j}}\,. \tag{5.22}$$

Formula (5.22) is the desired formula for the level periodic payment.

Although formula (5.22) is the desired formula for R, the crossover period a is unknown. A simple criterion can be developed to minimize the trial-and-error involved in finding a.

If formulas (5.20) and (5.22) are substituted into formula (5.19), then a is the smallest integer such that

$$\frac{(L-L')(1+j)^a + L' + iL' s_{\overline{a}|\, j}}{a_{\overline{n-a}|\, i} + s_{\overline{a}|\, j}}\, a_{\overline{n-a}|\, i} \le L'\,.$$

The above inequality is a criterion which could be used to determine a.
However, it is possible to substantially simplify the criterion as follows:

$$(L-L')(1+j)^a\, a_{\overline{n-a}|\, i} + iL'\, s_{\overline{a}|\, j}\, a_{\overline{n-a}|\, i} \le L'\, s_{\overline{a}|\, j}$$

$$(L-L')(1+j)^a\, a_{\overline{n-a}|\, i} \le L' v_i^{n-a}\, s_{\overline{a}|\, j}$$

$$\frac{L-L'}{L'} \le \frac{a_{\overline{a}|\, j}}{s_{\overline{n-a}|\, i}}\,. \tag{5.23}$$

Formula (5.23) is a simple criterion which can be used to determine a.

An alternative computer-oriented approach to deal with this type of trial-and-error problem is to solve for R by iteration. The procedure would be as follows:

1. Determine an approximate starting value R_0. For example, R_0 could be based on a rate of interest between i and j.

2. $B_0 = L$.

3. Use the recursion formulas:

$$B_t = B_{t-1} - R + iL' + j(B_{t-1} - L'), \text{ if } B_{t-1} > L' \tag{5.24a}$$

$$B_t = B_{t-1} - R + iB_{t-1}, \text{ if } B_{t-1} \le L'. \tag{5.24b}$$

4. $B_n = 0$.

Successive values of $R_1, R_2, \ldots$ can be generated with these formulas by standard numerical methods on a computer.

Example 5.16 Consider a loan of \$3000 which is being repaid with level monthly payments over 12 months. Interest is computed at 1 1/2% per month on the first \$1000 of outstanding loan balance and at 1% per month on any excess over \$1000. Find the level payment which will exactly amortize this loan.

We have $L = 3000$, $L' = 1000$, $n = 12$, $i = .015$, and $j = .01$, so that formula (5.23) gives

$$2 \le \frac{a_{\overline{a}|.01}}{s_{\overline{12-a}|.015}}.$$

The smallest integer a satisfying this inequality is $a = 9$. The level monthly payment given by formula (5.22) is

$$R = \frac{2000(1.01)^9 + 1000 + 15s_{\overline{9}|.01}}{a_{\overline{3}|.015} + s_{\overline{9}|.01}} = 270.98545.$$

The complete amortization schedule carrying five decimal places is given in Table 5.5. The criterion is verified, since $B_8 > 1000$ and $B_9 < 1000$. The interest paid column is computed as 1 1/2% on the first $1000 of outstanding loan balance and 1% on any excess.

Table 5.5 Amortization Schedule for a Loan of $3000 Repaid Over 12 Months at 1 1/2% Per Month on the First $1000 and 1% on Any Excess

Month	*Payment amount*	*Interest paid*	*Principal repaid*	*Outstanding loan balance*
0				3000.00000
1	270.98545	35.00000	235.98545	2764.01455
2	270.98545	32.64015	238.34530	2525.66925
3	270.98545	30.25669	240.72876	2284.94049
4	270.98545	27.84940	243.13605	2041.80445
5	270.98545	25.41804	245.56741	1796.23704
6	270.98545	22.96237	248.02308	1548.21396
7	270.98545	20.48214	250.50331	1297.71065
8	270.98545	17.97711	253.00834	1044.70231
9	270.98545	15.44702	255.53843	789.16388
10	270.98545	11.83746	259.14799	530.01589
11	270.98545	7.95024	263.03521	266.98068
12	270.98545	4.00471	266.98074	- 0.00006*

* zero, except for .00006 roundoff error

EXERCISES

5.2 Finding the outstanding loan balance

1. A loan of \$1000 is being repaid with quarterly payments at the end of each quarter for five years at 6% convertible quarterly. Find the outstanding loan balance at the end of the second year.

2. A loan of \$10,000 is being repaid by installments of \$2000 at the end of each year, and a smaller final payment made one year after the last regular payment. Interest is at the effective rate of 12%. Find the amount of outstanding loan balance remaining when the borrower has made payments equal to the amount of the loan. Answer to the nearest dollar.

3. A loan is being repaid by quarterly installments of \$1500 at the end of each quarter at 10% convertible quarterly. If the loan balance at the end of the first year is \$12,000, find the original loan balance. Answer to the nearest dollar.

4. A \$20,000 loan is to be repaid with annual payments at the end of each year for 12 years. If $(1+i)^4 = 2$, find the outstanding balance immediately after the fourth payment. Answer to the nearest dollar.

5. A \$20,000 mortgage is being repaid with 20 annual installments at the end of each year. The borrower makes five payments and then is temporarily unable to make payments for the next two years. Find an expression for the revised payment to start at the end of the 8th year if the loan is still to be repaid at the end of the original 20 years.

6. A loan of 1 was originally scheduled to be repaid by 25 equal annual payments at the end of each year. An extra payment K with each of the 6th through the 10th scheduled payments will be sufficient to repay the loan 5 years earlier than under the original schedule. Show that

$$K = \frac{a_{\overline{20}|} - a_{\overline{15}|}}{a_{\overline{25}|}\ a_{\overline{5}|}}.$$

7. A husband and wife buy a new home and take out a \$150,000 mortgage loan with level annual payments at the end of each year for 15 years on which the effective rate of interest is equal to 6.5%. At the end of 5 years they decide to make a major addition to the house and want to borrow an additional \$80,000 to finance the new construction. They also wish to lengthen the overall length of the loan by 7 years (i.e. until 22 years after the date of the original loan). In the negotiations the lender agrees to these

modifications, but only if the effective interest rate for the remainder of the loan after the first 5 years is raised to 7.5%. Find the revised annual payment which would result for the remainder of the loan. Answer to the nearest dollar.

5.3 Amortization schedules

8. A loan is being repaid with quarterly installments of $1000 at the end of each quarter for five years at 12% convertible quarterly. Find the amount of principal in the sixth installment.

9. A loan of $10,000 is being repaid with 20 installments at the end of each year at 10% effective. Show that the amount of interest in the 11th installment is

$$\frac{1000}{1 + v^{10}}.$$

10. A loan is being repaid with a series of payments at the end of each quarter for five years. If the amount of principal in the third payment is $100, find the amount of principal in the last five payments. Interest is at the rate of 10% convertible quarterly.

11. A loan is being repaid with installments of 1 at the end of each year for 20 years. Interest is at effective rate i for the first 10 years and effective rate j for the second 10 years. Find expressions for:
    a) The amount of interest paid in the 5th installment.
    b) The amount of principal repaid in the 15th installment.

12. A borrower has a mortgage that calls for level annual payments of 1 at the end of each year for 20 years. At the time of the seventh regular payment an additional payment is made equal to the amount of principal that according to the original amortization schedule would have been repaid by the eighth regular payment. If payments of 1 continue to be made at the end of the eighth and succeeding years until the mortgage is fully repaid, show that the amount saved in interest payments over the full term of the mortgage is

$$1 - v^{13}.$$

13. A loan of L is being amortized with payments at the end of each year for 10 years. If $v^5 = 2/3$, find the following:
    a) The amount of principal repaid in the first 5 payments.
    b) The amount due at the end of 10 years, if the final 5 payments are not made as scheduled.

14. A 35-year loan is to be repaid with equal installments at the end of each year. The amount of interest paid in the 8th installment is \$135. The amount of interest paid in the 22nd installment is \$108. Calculate the amount of interest paid in the 29th installment.

15. A 10-year loan of L is repaid by the amortization method with payments of \$1000 at the end of each year. The annual effective interest rate is i. The total amount of interest repaid during the life of the loan is also equal to L. Calculate the amount of interest paid during the first year of the loan.

16. A bank customer borrows X at an annual effective rate of 12.5% and makes level payments at the end of each year for n years.
    (*i*) The interest portion of the final payment is \$153.86.
    (*ii*) The total principal repaid as of time $n-1$ is \$6009.12.
    (*iii*) The principal repaid in the first payment is Y.
    Calculate Y.

5.4 Sinking funds

17. A has borrowed \$10,000 on which interest is charged at 10% effective. A is accumulating a sinking fund at 8% effective to repay the loan. At the end of 10 years the balance in the sinking fund is \$5000. At the end of the 11th year A makes a total payment of \$1500.
    a) How much of the \$1500 pays interest currently on the loan?
    b) How much of the \$1500 goes into the sinking fund?
    c) How much of the \$1500 should be considered as interest?
    d) How much of the \$1500 should be considered as principal?
    e) What is the sinking fund balance at the end of the 11th year?

18. A loan of \$1000 is being repaid with level annual payments of \$120 plus a smaller final payment made one year after the last regular payment. The effective rate of interest is 8%. Show algebraically and verbally that the outstanding loan balance after the fifth payment has been made is:
    a) $1000(1.08)^5 - 120s_{\overline{5}|}$.
    b) $1000 - 40s_{\overline{5}|}$.

19. On a loan of \$10,000 interest at 9% effective must be paid at the end of each year. The borrower also deposits \$$X$ at the beginning of each year into a sinking fund earning 7% effective. At the end of 10 years the sinking fund is exactly sufficient to pay off the loan. Calculate X.

20. A borrower is repaying a loan with 10 annual payments of \$1000. Half of the loan is repaid by the amortization method at 5% effective. The other half of the loan is repaid by the sinking fund method in which the lender receives 5% effective on the investment and the sinking fund accumulates at 4% effective. Find the amount of the loan. Answer to the nearest dollar.

21. A borrows \$12,000 for 10 years and agrees to make semiannual payments of \$1000. The lender receives 12% convertible semiannually on the investment each year for the first 5 years and 10% convertible semiannually for the second 5 years. The balance of each payment is invested in a sinking fund earning 8% convertible semiannually. Find the amount by which the sinking fund is short of repaying the loan at the end of the 10 years. Answer to the nearest dollar.

22. *a*) A borrower takes out a loan of \$3000 for 10 years at 8% convertible semiannually. The borrower replaces one third of the principal in a sinking fund earning 5% convertible semiannually and the other two thirds in a sinking fund earning 7% convertible semiannually. Find the total semiannual payment.

    b) Rework (*a*) if the borrower each year puts one third of the total sinking fund deposit into the 5% sinking fund and the other two thirds into the 7% sinking fund.

    c) Justify from general reasoning the relative magnitude of the answers to (*a*) and (*b*).

23. A payment of \$36,000 is made at the end of each year for 31 years to repay a loan of \$400,000. If the borrower replaces the capital by means of a sinking fund earning 3% effective, find the effective rate paid to the lender on the loan.

24. A borrows \$1000 for 10 years at an annual effective interest rate of 10%. A can repay this loan using the amortization method with payments of P at the end of each year. Instead, A repays the loan using a sinking fund that pays an annual effective rate of 14%. The deposits to the sinking fund are equal to P minus the interest on the loan and are made at the end of each year for 10 years. Determine the balance in the sinking fund immediately after repayment of the loan.

5.5 Differing payment periods and interest conversion periods

25. An investor buys an annuity with payments of principal and interest of \$500 per quarter for 10 years. Interest is at the effective rate of 8% per annum. How much interest does the investor receive in total over the 10-year period? Answer to the nearest dollar.

26. A borrows \$10,000 for five years at 12% convertible semiannually. A replaces the principal by means of deposits at the end of every year for five years into a sinking fund which earns 8% effective. Find the total dollar amount which A must pay over the five-year period to completely repay the loan. Answer to the nearest dollar.

27. A borrower is repaying a loan with payments of \$3000 at the end of every year over an unknown period of time. If the amount of interest in the third installment is \$2000, find the amount of principal in the sixth installment. Assume that interest is 10% convertible quarterly.

28. A borrows \$5000 for 10 years at 10% convertible quarterly. A does not pay interest currently and will pay all accrued interest at the end of 10 years together with the principal. Find the annual sinking fund deposit necessary to liquidate the loan at the end of 10 years if the sinking fund earns 7% convertible semiannually.

5.6 Varying series of payments

29. A loan is repaid with payments which start at \$200 the first year and increase by \$50 per year until a payment of \$1000 is made, at which time payments cease. If interest is 4% effective, find the amount of principal in the fourth payment.

30. A borrower is repaying a \$1000 loan with 10 equal payments of principal. Interest at 6% convertible semiannually is paid on the outstanding balance each year. Find the price to yield an investor 10% convertible semiannually.

31. A borrows \$2000 at an effective rate of interest of 10% per annum and agrees to repay the loan with payments at the end of each year. The first payment is to be \$400 and each payment thereafter is to be 4% greater than the preceding payment, with a smaller final payment made one year after the last regular payment.
    a) Find the outstanding loan balance at the end of three years.
    b) Find the principal repaid in the third payment.

32. A has money invested at effective rate i. At the end of the first year A withdraws 162 1/2% of the interest earned, at the end of the second year A withdraws 325% of the interest earned, and so forth with the withdrawal factor increasing in arithmetic progression. At the end of 16 years the fund is exactly exhausted. Find i.

33. A 10-year loan of \$2000 is to be repaid with payments at the end of each year. It can be repaid under the following two options:

    (*i*) Equal annual payments at an annual effective rate of 8.07%.

    (*ii*) Installments of \$200 each year plus interest on the unpaid balance at an annual effective rate of i.

    The sum of the payments under Option (*i*) equals the sum of the payments under Option (*ii*). Determine i.

34. A loan is amortized over five years with monthly payments at a nominal interest rate of 9% compounded monthly. The first payment is \$1000 and is to be paid one month from the date of the loan. Each succeeding monthly payment will be 2% lower than the prior payment. Calculate the outstanding loan balance immediately after the 40th payment is made. Answer to the nearest dollar.

35. A 30-year loan of \$1000 is repaid with payments at the end of each year. Each of the first ten payments equals the amount of interest due. Each of the next ten payments equals 150% of the amount of interest due. Each of the last ten payments is X. The lender charges interest at an annual effective rate of 10%. Calculate X.

5.7 Amortization with continuous payments

36. A loan of $\bar{a}_{\overline{25|}}$ is being repaid with continuous payments at the annual rate of 1 per annum for 25 years. If $i = .05$, find the total amount of interest paid during the sixth through the tenth years inclusive.

37. *a*) Show that

$$(1+i)^t - \frac{\bar{s}_{\overline{t|}}}{\bar{a}_{\overline{n|}}} = \frac{\bar{a}_{\overline{n-t|}}}{\bar{a}_{\overline{n|}}}.$$

    b) Verbally interpret the result obtained in (*a*).

38. A loan is being repaid over n periods with continuous payments at the rate of t per period at time t. Find expressions for the outstanding loan balance at time k, $0 \le k \le n$:

    a) Prospectively.

    b) Retrospectively.

39. A loan of 1 is being amortized over a 10-year period with continuous payments which vary in such a fashion that the outstanding loan balance is linear. The force of interest is 10%. Find:
    a) The principal repaid over the first 5 years.
    b) The interest paid over the first 5 years.

40. It is known that the remaining undiscounted payout on an insurance claim t periods after the claim was incurred is given by $\alpha e^{-\beta t}$.
    a) If the instantaneous rate of claim payment is $P(t)$, find an expression for $P(t)$.
    b) Find the undiscounted total payout on the claim at time 0.
    c) Find the present value of the total payout on the claim at time 0, if the force of interest is δ.
    d) Find the present value of the remaining payout on the claim at time t, if the force of interest is δ.

5.8 Step-rate amounts of principal

41. In order to pay off a $2000 loan, payments of P are made at the end of each quarter. Interest on the first $500 of the unpaid balance is at rate $i^{(4)} = 16\%$, while interest on the excess is at $i^{(4)} = 14\%$. If the outstanding loan balance is $1000 at the end of the first year, find P. Answer to the nearest dollar.

42. A loan of $1000 is to be amortized with quarterly installments of $100 for as long as necessary plus a smaller final payment one quarter after the last regular payment. Interest is computed at 12% convertible quarterly on the first $500 of outstanding loan balance and at 8% convertible quarterly on any excess.
    a) Find the principal repaid in the fourth installment.
    b) Show that prior to the "crossover" point, the successive principal repayments form a geometric progression. What is the common ratio?

43. Consider a loan of $3000 which is being repaid with level monthly payments over 12 months. Interest is computed at 1 1/2% per month on the first $1000 of outstanding loan balance, at 1 1/4% per month on the next $1000, and at 1% per month on any excess over $2000. Find the level payment which will exactly amortize this loan. (Hint: Assume that the two "crossover" points are $t = 5$ and $t = 9$. These can be confirmed as correct from the resulting amortization schedule.)

Miscellaneous problems

44. *a)* Show that

$$a_{\overline{n}|} + i \sum_{t=0}^{n-1} a_{\overline{n-t}|} = n .$$

b) Verbally interpret the result obtained in (*a*).

45. *a)* Show that if a loan is amortized with n level payments of R

$$B_t = R\left(a_{\overline{n}|} - v^n s_{\overline{t}|}\right).$$

b) Verbally interpret the result obtained in (*a*).

46. The original amount of an inheritance was just sufficient at 3 1/2% effective to pay \$10,000 at the end of each year for 10 years. The payments were made as scheduled for the first five years even though the fund actually earned 5% effective. How much excess interest was in the fund at the end of the fifth year? Answer to the nearest dollar.

47. An investor is making level payments at the beginning of each year for 10 years to accumulate \$10,000 at the end of the 10 years in a bank which is paying 5% effective. At the end of five years the bank drops its interest rate to 4% effective.

a) Find the annual deposit for the first five years.

b) Find the annual deposit for the second five years.

48. Two loans for equal amounts are amortized at 4% effective. Loan L is to be repaid by 30 equal annual payments. Loan M is to be repaid by 30 annual payments, each containing equal principal amounts with the interest portion of each payment based upon the unpaid balance. The payment for loan L first exceeds the payment for loan M at the end of year k. Find k.

49. Nine years ago a family incurred a 20-year \$80,000 mortgage at 8% effective on which they were making annual payments. They desire now to make a lump-sum payment of \$5000 and to pay off the mortgage in nine more years. Find an expression for the revised annual payment:

a) If the lender is satisfied with an 8% yield for the past nine years but insists on a 9% yield for the next nine years.

b) If the lender insists on a 9% yield during the entire life of the mortgage.

50. A loan of $1000 is to be repaid with equal annual payments at 5% effective over a 10-year period. The borrower may accelerate the amortization of the loan. However, there is a prepayment penalty of 2% of the excess of any payment over the originally scheduled payment. If the borrower makes a $300 payment at the end of the first year and a $250 payment at the end of the second year, find the outstanding loan balance just prior to the payment at the end of the third year. Answer to nearest dollar.

6

Bonds and other securities

6.1 INTRODUCTION

One of the major applications of the theory of interest is the determination of prices and values for bonds and other securities, such as preferred stock and common stock. There are three main questions which Chapter 6 considers:

1. Given the desired yield rate of an investor, what price should be paid for a given security?

2. Given the purchase price of a security, what is the resulting yield rate to an investor?

3. What is the value of a security on a given date after it has been purchased?

It should be noted that no new basic principles are introduced in this chapter. However, several new terms and formulas are introduced to efficiently handle financial calculations involving these types of securities.

6.2 TYPES OF SECURITIES

Section 6.2 considers three common traditional types of securities which are widespread in financial markets. This section should not be considered as a complete discussion of these securities, since only a very brief description is presented. For a more complete discussion the reader is encouraged to refer to any of several standard textbooks on finance or securities.

The description of securities in this chapter reflects the characteristics of securities as they are issued in the United States. Variations from the characteristics contained herein may exist for securities issued in other countries.

In recent years there has been a proliferation of newer, more exotic financial instruments. These are not discussed at this stage, since it is important to deal with the basics first. However, these newer financial instruments are discussed in Section 8.8.

The three main categories of securities which will be discussed in this chapter are: (1) bonds, (2) preferred stock, and (3) common stock.

Bonds

A *bond* is an interest-bearing security which promises to pay a stated amount (or amounts) of money at some future date (or dates). It is a formal certificate of indebtedness issued by a borrower, usually for some round figure such as $1000 or $5000. Bonds are commonly issued by corporations and governmental units as a means of raising capital.

Bonds are generally redeemed at the end of a fixed period of time. This fixed period of time is called the *term* of the bond. The end of the term of a bond is called the *maturity date*. On occasion, bonds with an infinite term are issued, e.g. the British consols. Such bonds are called *perpetuals*. Also bonds may be issued with a term which varies at the discretion of the borrower or lender. A *callable bond* may be redeemed early at the discretion of the borrower, while a *putable bond* may be redeemed early at the discretion of the lender. Any date prior to, or including, the maturity date on which a bond may be redeemed is termed a *redemption date*.

Bonds may be classified in several different ways. One such classification is the distinction between *accumulation bonds* and *coupon bonds*. The coupons are periodic payments made by the issuer of the bond prior to its redemption. An accumulation bond is one in which the redemption price includes the original loan plus all accumulated interest. The Series E Savings Bonds issued by the United States Treasury are a traditional example of this type of bond. More recently, so-called *zero coupon bonds* have become popular with investors.

However, most bonds have coupons payable periodically, and this will be assumed unless stated otherwise. This chapter will largely be confined to coupon bonds, since accumulation or zero coupon bonds can easily be handled with basic techniques already discussed in earlier chapters.

A second classification is the distinction between *registered bonds* and *unregistered bonds*. A registered bond is one in which the lender is listed in the records of the borrower. If the lender decides to sell the bond, the change of ownership must be reported to the borrower. The periodic coupon payments are paid by the borrower to the owners of record on each coupon payment date. An unregistered bond is one in which the lender is not listed in the records of the borrower. Since the bond belongs to whomever has legal possession of it, an unregistered bond is often called a *bearer bond*.

A third classification is made according to the type of security behind the bond. A *mortgage bond* is secured by a mortgage on real property called *collateral*. A *debenture bond* is one secured only by the general credit of the borrower. Variations within these two major classifications exist. In general, mortgage bonds possess a higher degree of security than debenture bonds, since the lenders can foreclose on the collateral in the event of the default of a mortgage bond.

A type of bond with a high degree of risk to the lender is the *income bond* or *adjustment bond*. Under this type of bond, the periodic coupons are paid only if the borrower has earned sufficient income to pay them. Income bonds were once fairly common, but they have largely disappeared in recent years.

The more modern version of a *high-risk bond* is often called a *"junk" bond*. Such bonds are issued by corporations, often in connection with corporate mergers, acquisitions, or other takeovers. They have a significantly higher risk of default in payments than corporate bonds in general. Accordingly, they must pay commensurately higher rates of interest to the lenders for assuming this higher risk. As a result, such bonds are also called *high-yield bonds*. Such bonds are sometimes characterized as *below investment grade*. The phrase "investment grade" refers to a schedule of quality rankings for various bonds provided by certain rating organizations. Financial calculations involving the risk of default will not be covered in this chapter, but will be addressed in Section 9.8.

A type of bond which is somewhat of a hybrid is the *convertible bond*. This type of bond can be converted into the common stock of the issuing corporation at some future date under certain conditions, at the option of the owner of the bond. Convertible bonds are generally debenture bonds. Such bonds offer an investor a choice between continuing the security as a bond or switching it into common stock, depending upon the performance of the corporation in the future.

A borrower in need of a large amount of funds may not be able to issue bonds with a common maturity date. A large volume of indebtedness falling due at one time can present problems in redeeming or refinancing the debt. For this reason, some borrowers will divide a large issue of bonds so that individual bonds will have a series of staggered redemption dates. These types of bonds are called *serial bonds.* An alternative approach is for the lenders to require the establishment of a sinking fund to accumulate the amount necessary to repay the indebtedness for a large issue of bonds.

The United States Treasury issues indebtedness with a wide range of maturities. Long-term debt of seven or more years duration is issued in the form of *Treasury bonds.* Short-term debt is issued in the form of *Treasury bills*, often called "T-bills." These are issued on a discount basis for maturities of 13, 26, or 52 weeks, and were mentioned briefly in Section 2.7. Debt of an intermediate duration, i.e. one to seven years, is typically issued in the form of *Treasury notes.* Although called "notes," these securities are mathematically equivalent to bonds; the term is just shorter. Calculations involving Treasury bills have some significant differences from those on longer-term Treasury securities. These differences are explored in Example 6.2.

Treasury securities are sometimes packaged as *STRIPS* ("Separate Trading of Registered Interest and Principal of Securities"). When structured in this fashion, the coupons are "stripped" from the bond and are repackaged into separate securities. These securities, along with the maturity value, are functionally equivalent to a series of zero coupon bonds with various maturity dates.

In recent years Treasury securities have also become available as *TIPS* ("Treasury Inflation Protection Securities"). This is a new class of security in which the face amount and coupons are indexed to future changes in the Consumer Price Index (CPI), a major index measuring inflation in the economy. Financial calculations involving TIPS, and inflation more generally, will not be covered in this chapter, but will be addressed in Section 9.4.

Preferred stock

Preferred stock is a type of security which provides a fixed rate of return similar to bonds. However, it differs from a bond in that it technically is an ownership security rather than a debt security, i.e. the owner of preferred stock is part owner of the issuing corporation, while the bond owner is a creditor of the corporation. Despite technically being an ownership security, preferred stockholder typically have limited voting rights, or perhaps none at all.

In general, preferred stock has no maturity date, although on occasion preferred stock with a redemption provision is issued. However, preferred stock is often callable and can be redeemed by the borrower under certain conditions. The periodic payment on preferred stock is usually called a *dividend*, since it is being paid to an owner.

In terms of the degree of security, preferred stock ranks behind bonds and other debt instruments, since all payments on indebtedness must be made before the preferred stock receives a dividend. However, preferred stock ranks ahead of common stock in the degree of security involved, since preferred stock dividends must be paid before common stock dividends can be paid.

To increase the degree of security behind preferred stock, some corporations have issued *cumulative preferred stock*. This type of preferred stock has the feature that any dividends which the corporation is not able to pay are carried forward to future years when they presumably will be paid. For example, if a corporation has preferred stock on which it is paying a $5 dividend per share and can make only a $3 payment in one year, the $2 balance is carried forward (perhaps without interest) to future years. All arrears on preferred stock must be paid before any dividends on common stock can be paid.

Some preferred stocks receive a share of earnings over and above the regular dividend if earnings are at a sufficient level. This type of preferred stock is called *participating preferred stock*, since it participates in the earnings with the common stock. Participating preferred stock has become relatively uncommon.

Some preferred stock has a convertible privilege similar to convertible bonds and is called *convertible preferred stock*. Owners of this type of preferred stock have the option to convert their preferred stock to common stock under certain conditions.

Common stock

Common stock is a type of ownership security, as is preferred stock. However, it does not earn a fixed dividend rate as preferred stock does. Common stock dividends are paid only after interest payments on all bonds and other debt and dividends on preferred stock are paid. The dividend rate is completely flexible and can be set by the corporation's board of directors at its discretion.

Since the dividend rates on common stocks are variable, the prices of common stocks tend to be much more volatile than either bonds or preferred stocks. However, all residual profits after dividends to the preferred stockholders belong to the common stockholders. Furthermore, common stockholders have voting rights for the corporation's board of directors and certain other important matters. The common stockholders are, in reality, the true owners of the corporation.

Example 6.1 A zero coupon bond will pay $1000 at the end of 10 years and is currently selling for $400. Find the yield rate convertible semiannually that would be earned by a purchaser.

Let j be the yield rate per half-year. The equation of value is

$$400(1+j)^{20} = 1000$$

or

$$(1+j)^{20} = 2.5$$

which gives $j = .0469$. Thus, the yield rate convertible semiannually is equal to $2(.0469) = .0938$, or 9.38%.

Example 6.2 A 13-week Treasury bill matures for $10,000 and is bought at discount to yield 7.5%. Find the price which must be paid.

As noted in Section 2.7, T-bill yields are computed as rates of discount rather than rates of interest. These yields are computed on a simple discount basis, which, in effect, results in a rate of discount convertible at the same frequency as the term of the T-bill. Also, it is necessary to know the basis for measuring time periods as described in Section 2.6. The basis typically used for T-bills is actual/360. A 13-week T-bill has a term of 13x7 = 91 days. On this basis the price would be

$$10{,}000\left[1-\frac{91}{360}(.075)\right] = \$9810.42.$$

It should be stressed that the basis for determining time periods for longer-term Treasury securities is actual/actual rather than actual/360 and that rates of interest are used rather than rates of discount.

6.3 PRICE OF A BOND

As mentioned in Section 6.1, one of the three primary questions under consideration in this chapter is the determination of a purchase price which will produce a given yield rate to an investor. This section considers this question for bonds.

The following assumptions are made:

1. All obligations will be paid by the bond issuer on the specified dates of payment. Market prices of bonds will vary depending upon the probability of default in payments, but we will ignore any possibility of default in this chapter. Financial calculations reflecting the probability of default will be discussed in Section 9.8.

2. The bond has a fixed maturity date. Bonds with no maturity date are mathematically equivalent to preferred stock and are considered in Section 6.10. Callable or putable bonds with optional redemption dates are considered in Section 6.7.

3. The price of the bond is desired immediately after an coupon payment date. The price of a bond between two coupon payment dates is considered in Section 6.5.

The following symbols will be used in connection with bonds in this and succeeding sections:

P = the *price* of a bond.

F = the *par value* or *face amount* of a bond. This value is printed on the front of the bond and is often the amount payable at the maturity date. Its sole purpose is to define the series of payments to be made by the borrower. It is not a measure of the price or the value of a bond prior to maturity. It is customary to quote bond prices in terms of a par value of \$100, even though bonds are rarely issued in such small denominations, and this will be assumed unless stated otherwise.

C = the *redemption value* of a bond, i.e. the amount of money paid at a redemption date to the holder of the bond. Often C is equal to F; for example, the common case of a bond redeemed at its maturity date for its par value. It is possible for C to differ from F in the following cases: (1) a bond which matures for an amount not equal to its par value, or (2) a bond which has a redemption date prior to the maturity date on which the bond is redeemed for an amount not equal to its par value. It will be assumed that a bond is redeemable at par unless stated otherwise.

r = the *coupon rate* of a bond, i.e. the rate per coupon payment period used in determining the amount of the coupon. The most common frequency for bond coupons in the United States is semiannual. For example, an 8% bond with semiannual coupons has $r = .04$. In international financial markets other coupon frequencies may be encountered. It is assumed that coupons are constant. The case of varying coupons is considered in Section 6.9.

Fr = the amount of the coupon.

g = the *modified coupon rate* of a bond. The rate g is defined by $Fr = Cg$ or $g = Fr/C$, i.e. g is the coupon rate per unit of redemption value rather than per unit of par value. It should be noted that g will always be convertible at the same frequency as r. In practice, g will often equal r, which is the case whenever C is equal to F.

i = the *yield rate* of a bond, often called the *yield to maturity*, i.e. the interest rate actually earned by the investor, assuming the bond is held until it is redeemed or matures. It is customary that yield rates are convertible at the same frequency as the coupon rate, and this will be assumed unless stated otherwise. The case in which the coupon payment period and the yield rate conversion period are not equal is considered in Section 6.9. It is also assumed that the yield rate is constant. The case in which this is not true is also discussed in Section 6.9.

n = the number of coupon payment periods from the date of calculation to the maturity date, or to a redemption date.

K = the present value, computed at the yield rate, of the redemption value at the maturity date, or a redemption date, i.e. $K = Cv^n$ at the yield rate i.

G = the *base amount* of a bond. The amount G is defined by $Gi = Fr$ or $G = Fr/i$. Thus, G is the amount which, if invested at the yield rate i, would produce periodic interest payments equal to the coupons on the bond.

Figure 6.1 displays the cash flows of a bond using the symbols just defined.

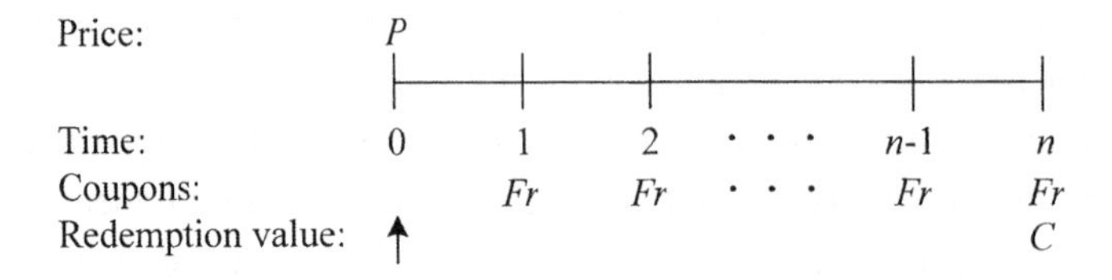

Figure 6.1 Cash flows in a standard coupon bond

The reader should be aware that in everyday business and financial usage there are three different "yields" associated with a bond:

1. *Nominal yield* is simply the annualized coupon rate on the bond. For example, if a $100 par value bond has coupons totaling $9 per year, then the nominal yield on the bond is 9% per annum. The reader should note that the use of the word "nominal" in this context is different than the meaning in Section 1.8 and has yet another meaning to be introduced in Section 9.4, which is an unfortunate source of ambiguity.

2. *Current yield* is the ratio of the annualized coupon to the original price of the bond. For example, if the bond described above is selling for $90 in the market, then the current yield on the bond is 10% per annum. Note that the current yield does not reflect any gain or loss when the bond is sold, redeemed, or matures.

3. *Yield to maturity* is the actual annualized yield rate, i.e. the level rate of interest earned over the life on the bond reflecting the original price and all payments made by the borrower. The determination of an unknown yield to maturity will be discussed in Section 6.6.

We will use the phrase "yield rate" to refer only to the third of these meanings. However, again the reader is reminded that in practical applications not everyone uses terms with textbook precision, and it is important to ascertain exactly what is meant by the user when encountering terms such as the "yield" on a bond.

The reader should be aware that F, C, r, g, and n are given by the terms of a bond and remain fixed throughout its life. In essence, these parameters define exactly what payments will be made by the borrower. On the other hand, P and i will vary throughout the life of the bond. The price and the yield rate have a precise inverse relationship to each other, i.e. as the price rises the yield rate falls, and vice versa. Yield rates on bonds will fluctuate with prevailing rates of interest in financial markets for securities of a similar type. Fluctuating market rates of interest will thus lead to fluctuating bond prices.

However, these fluctuating bond prices, do not usually reflect any increase or decrease in the degree of safety or security attributed to the bond, but rather they reflect changing rates of interest in the securities markets. This inverse relationship between bond prices and yield rates has not always been understood by unsophisticated bondholders, who, in periods of rising rates of interest, have attributed the declining prices of their bonds to a deterioration in the credit rating of the borrower, when this was not a factor at all.

There are four types of formulas which can be used to find the price of a bond. The first of these, called the *basic formula*, is the most straightforward. According to this method the price must be equal to the present value of future coupons plus the present value of the redemption value

$$P = Fra_{\overline{n|}} + Cv^n = Fra_{\overline{n|}} + K \tag{6.1}$$

where the interest functions are calculated at the yield rate i.

The second formula, called the *premium/discount formula*, can be obtained from formula (6.1)

$$\begin{aligned} P &= Fra_{\overline{n|}} + Cv^n \\ &= Fra_{\overline{n|}} + C\left(1 - ia_{\overline{n|}}\right) \\ &= C + (Fr - Ci)a_{\overline{n|}}. \end{aligned} \tag{6.2}$$

The rationale for the name of this method will become evident in Section 6.4.

The third formula, called the *base amount formula*, can also be obtained from formula (6.1)

$$\begin{aligned} P &= Fra_{\overline{n}|} + Cv^n \\ &= Gia_{\overline{n}|} + Cv^n \\ &= G(1-v^n) + Cv^n \\ &= G + (C-G)v^n \end{aligned} \qquad (6.3)$$

Formula (6.3) is simple to compute, since the only interest function in the formula is v^n.

The fourth formula, called the *Makeham formula* (after a British actuary of the 19th Century), can also be obtained from formula (6.1)

$$\begin{aligned} P &= Cv^n + Fra_{\overline{n}|} \\ &= Cv^n + Cg\left(\frac{1-v^n}{i}\right) \\ &= Cv^n + \frac{g}{i}\left(C - Cv^n\right) \\ &= K + \frac{g}{i}(C-K). \end{aligned} \qquad (6.4)$$

Makeham's formula has an interesting verbal interpretation. From the basic formula, the price of a bond must be equal to the present value of the redemption value plus the present value of future coupons. K is present value of the redemption value. If the modified coupon rate g is equal to the yield rate i, then the bond will sell for its redemption value C, so that $C - K$ is the present value of future coupons. However, if the modified coupon rate g is different than the yield rate i, then the present value of future coupons will be proportionally higher or lower, i.e. it will be equal to $\frac{g}{i}(C-K)$.

Financial calculators can also be used to determine bond prices or values if the yield rate is given. However, the data entry required is significant and they are less efficient than the formulas given above for computing prices or values on coupon payment dates. Financial calculators do offer a computational advantage for computing bond prices or values between coupon payment dates and for determining the yield to maturity when the bond price or value is given. These two applications will be demonstrated in Sections 6.5 and 6.6, respectively.

Example 6.3 Find the price of a $1000 par value 10-year bond with coupons at 8.4% payable semiannually, which will be redeemed at $1050. The bond is bought to yield 10% convertible semiannually. Use all four formulas.

In this example we have:

$$F = 1000$$
$$C = 1050$$
$$r = \frac{.084}{2} = .042$$
$$g = \frac{1000}{1050}(.042) = .04$$
$$i = \frac{.10}{2} = .05$$
$$n = 20$$
$$K = 1050(1.05)^{-20} = 395.7340$$
$$G = \frac{.042}{.05}(1000) = 840.$$

1. *Basic formula*:

$$\begin{aligned} P &= Fra_{\overline{n}|} + K \\ &= 42a_{\overline{20}|.05} + 395.7340 \\ &= (42)(12.4622) + 395.7340 = \$919.15. \end{aligned}$$

2. *Premium/discount formula*:

$$\begin{aligned} P &= C + (Fr - Ci)a_{\overline{n}|} \\ &= 1050 + (42 - 52.50)\,a_{\overline{20}|.05} \\ &= 1050 + (42 - 52.50)(12.4622) = \$919.15. \end{aligned}$$

3. *Base amount formula*:

$$\begin{aligned} P &= G + (C - G)\,v^n \\ &= 840 + (1050 - 840)(1.05)^{-20} \\ &= 840 + (1050 - 840)(.37689) = \$919.15. \end{aligned}$$

4. *Makeham formula*:

$$\begin{aligned} P &= K + \frac{g}{i}(C - K) \\ &= 395.7340 + \frac{.04}{.05}(1050 - 395.7340) = \$919.15. \end{aligned}$$

6.4 PREMIUM AND DISCOUNT

If the purchase price of a bond exceeds its redemption value, i.e. if $P > C$, then the bond is said to sell at a *premium* and the difference between P and C is called the "premium." Similarly, if the purchase price is less than the redemption value, i.e. if $P < C$, then the bond is said to sell at a *discount*, and the difference between C and P is called the "discount." The reader should note that this is yet another meaning for the overused word "discount" in addition to the various meanings given in Chapter 1.

We can derive expressions for the premium and the discount from formula (6.2):

$$\text{Premium} = P-C = (Fr-Ci)a_{\overline{n}|i} = C(g-i)a_{\overline{n}|i} \text{ if } g>i \qquad (6.5)$$

$$\text{Discount} = C-P = (Ci-Fr)a_{\overline{n}|i} = C(i-g)a_{\overline{n}|i} \text{ if } i>g \qquad (6.6)$$

It is clear that premium and discount, although bearing different names, are essentially the same concept, since discount is merely a negative premium. It should also be noted that in many cases $F = C$ and therefore $g = r$. However, formulas (6.5) and (6.6) will handle the cases in which this is not true.

The price of a bond depends upon two quantities, the present value of future coupons and the present value of the redemption value. Since the purchase price of a bond is usually less than or greater than the redemption value, there will be a profit (equal to the discount) or a loss (equal to the premium) at the redemption date. This profit or loss is reflected in the yield rate for the bond, when calculated as the yield to maturity.

However, as a result of this profit or loss at the redemption date, the amount of each coupon should not be considered as interest income to an investor. It will be necessary to divide each coupon into interest earned and principal adjustment portions similar to the separation of payments on a loan between interest and principal in Chapter 5.

When this approach is used, the value of the bond will be continually adjusted from the price on the purchase date to the redemption value on the redemption date. These adjusted values of the bond are called the *book values* of the bond. The book values provide a smooth series of values for bonds and historically have been used by certain investors, such as insurance companies and pension funds, in reporting the asset values of bonds for financial statements.

The determination of asset values for bonds and other securities will be discussed further in Section 6.11.

The reader should be careful to note, however, that the book value after purchase will differ from the *market value*, i.e. price of the bond if the bond were bought anew. The market value of the bond will vary as prevailing interest rates change. However, the book values will follow a smooth progression, since they are all based on the original yield rate at purchase.

We will use similar notation for bonds to that developed in Chapter 5 for loans. Thus, the book value t periods after purchase is denoted by B_t, the amount of interest earned in the tth coupon by I_t, and the amount of principal adjustment in the tth coupon by P_t. The level coupon will continue to be denoted by Fr. Note that the price P is equal to B_0, while the redemption value C is equal to B_n.

A *bond amortization schedule* is a table which shows the division of each coupon into its interest earned and principal adjustment portions, together with the book value after each coupon is paid. Consider a bond for which C is equal to 1, the coupon is equal to g, and the price is equal to $1 + p$ (where p can be either positive or negative). Table 6.1 is a bond amortization schedule for this bond.

Consider the first coupon period of the bond. At the end of the first coupon period the interest earned on the balance at the beginning of the period is

$$I_1 = i\left[1 + (g-i)\,a_{\overline{n}|\,i}\right].$$

The rest of the total coupon of g, i.e.

$$P_1 = g - i\left[1 + (g-i)a_{\overline{n}|\,i}\right] = (g-i)\left(1 - ia_{\overline{n}|\,i}\right) = (g-i)v^n$$

must be used to adjust the book value. The book value at the end of the period equals the book value at the beginning of the period less the principal adjustment amount, i.e.

$$B_1 = \left[1 + (g-i)a_{\overline{n}|\,i}\right] - (g-i)v^n = 1 + (g-i)\,a_{\overline{n-1}|\,i}.$$

The same reasoning applies for each successive line of the schedule.

Table 6.1 Bond Amortization Schedule for a $1 *n*-period Bond with Coupons at Rate *g* Bought to Yield Rate *i*.

Period	*Coupon*	*Interest earned*	*Principal adjustment*	*Book value*
0				$1+p=1+(g-i)a_{\overline{n}\mid i}$
1	g	$i\left[1+(g-i)a_{\overline{n}\mid i}\right]$	$g-i\left[1+(g-i)a_{\overline{n}\mid i}\right]=(g-i)v^n$	$\left[1+(g-i)a_{\overline{n}\mid i}\right]-(g-i)v^n=1+(g-i)a_{\overline{n-1}\mid i}$
2	g	$i\left[1+(g-i)a_{\overline{n-1}\mid i}\right]$	$g-i\left[1+(g-i)a_{\overline{n-1}\mid i}\right]=(g-i)v^{n-1}$	$\left[1+(g-i)a_{\overline{n-1}\mid i}\right]-(g-i)v^{n-1}=1+(g-i)a_{\overline{n-2}\mid i}$
.	.	.	.	.
.	.	.	.	.
.	.	.	.	.
t	g	$i\left[1+(g-i)a_{\overline{n-t+1}\mid i}\right]$	$g-i\left[1+(g-i)a_{\overline{n-t+1}\mid i}\right]=(g-i)v^{n-t+1}$	$\left[1+(g-i)a_{\overline{n-t+1}\mid i}\right]-(g-i)v^{n-t+1}=1+(g-i)a_{\overline{n-t}\mid i}$
.	.	.	.	.
.	.	.	.	.
.	.	.	.	.
n 1	g	$i\left[1+(g-i)a_{\overline{2}\mid i}\right]$	$g-i\left[1+(g-i)a_{\overline{2}\mid i}\right]=(g-i)v^2$	$\left[1+(g-i)a_{\overline{2}\mid i}\right]-(g-i)v^2=1+(g-i)a_{\overline{1}\mid i}$
n	g	$i\left[1+(g-i)a_{\overline{1}\mid i}\right]$	$g-i\left[1+(g-i)a_{\overline{1}\mid i}\right]=(g-i)v$	$\left[1+(g-i)a_{\overline{1}\mid i}\right]-(g-i)v=1$
Total	ng	$ng-p$	$(g-i)a_{\overline{n}\mid}=p$	

Several additional observations are possible. First, it should be noted that the book values on each line agree with the prices given by formula (6.2) computed at the original yield rate. Second, the sum of the principal adjustment column is equal to p, the amount of premium or discount. Third, the sum of the interest earned column is equal to the difference between the sum of the coupons and the sum of the principal adjustment column. Fourth, the principal adjustment column is a geometric progression with common ratio $1 + i$. Thus, it is a simple matter to find any one principal adjustment amount knowing any other principal adjustment amount and the yield rate.

When a bond is bought at a premium, the book value will gradually be adjusted downward. This process is called *amortization of premium* or *writing down*. In these cases the principal adjustment amount is often called the "amount for amortization of premium."

When a bond is bought at a discount, the book value will gradually be adjusted upward. This process is called *accumulation of discount* or *writing up*. In these cases the principal adjustment amount is often called the "amount for accumulation of discount."

It should be noted that Table 6.1 is based on a value of $C = 1$. The values in the table are proportional for other values of C. In any particular case, the bond amortization schedule can be constructed from basic principles.

As an example of a bond bought at a premium, consider a $1000 par value two-year 8% bond with semiannual coupons bought to yield 6% convertible semiannually. The price of the bond is computed to be $1037.17. The semiannual coupon is $40. Table 6.2 is a bond amortization schedule for this example.

Table 6.2 Bond Amortization Schedule for a $1000 Two-Year Bond with 8% Coupons Paid Semiannually Bought to Yield 6% Convertible Semiannually

Half-year	*Coupon*	*Interest earned*	*Amount for amortization of premium*	*Book value*
0				1037.17
1	40.00	31.12	8.88	1028.29
2	40.00	30.85	9.15	1019.14
3	40.00	30.57	9.43	1009.71
4	40.00	30.29	9.71	1000.00
Total	160.00	122.83	37.17	

In the first line of Table 6.2 we have the following calculations. The interest earned portion of the first coupon is

$$I_1 = iB_0 = .03(1037.17) = 31.12.$$

The principal adjustment portion of the first coupon is

$$P_1 = Fr - I_1 = 40.00 - 31.12 = 8.88.$$

The book value at the end of the first period is

$$B_1 = B_0 - P_1 = 1037.17 - 8.88 = 1028.29.$$

Each successive line of the schedule is calculated in similar fashion.

As an example of a bond bought at a discount, consider the same $1000 par value two-year 8% bond with semiannual coupons bought to yield 10% convertible semiannually. The price of the bond is computed to be $964.54. The semiannual coupon is $40. Table 6.3 is a bond amortization schedule for this example. The reader should verify the entries in Table 6.3.

It should be noted that the amounts for accumulation of discount are really the negatives of the numbers shown in Table 6.3, i.e. they are increments to the book value rather than decrements. However, they are usually written as positive numbers to avoid minus signs. Thus, the reader should be careful to ascertain in any bond amortization schedule whether the bond is selling at a premium or at a discount, so that the entries in the principal adjustment column can be appropriately interpreted.

Table 6.3 Bond Amortization Schedule for a $1000 Two-Year Bond with 8% Coupons Paid Semiannually Bought to Yield 10% Convertible Semiannually

Half-year	*Coupon*	*Interest earned*	*Amount for accumulation of discount*	*Book value*
0				964.54
1	40.00	48.23	8.23	972.77
2	40.00	48.64	8.64	981.41
3	40.00	49.07	9.07	990.48
4	40.00	49.52	9.52	1000.00
Total	160.00	195.46	35.46	

It should also be noted that if it is desired to find the interest earned or principal adjustment portion of any one coupon, it is not necessary to construct the entire bond amortization schedule. The book value at the beginning of the period in question is equal to the price at that point computed at the original yield rate (which will almost certainly differ from the current market price) and can be determined by the methods of Section 6.3. Then that one line of the schedule can be calculated.

The bond amortization schedule discussed in this section is closely related to the loan amortization schedule described in Chapter 5. In fact, the only conceptual difference is that in the bond amortization schedule the intermediate values are amortized to an ending value equal to the redemption value of the bond, while in the loan amortization schedule intermediate values are amortized to an ending value of zero.

Additional insight into the bond amortization schedule can also be obtained from the sinking fund method. For example, in Table 6.2 the investor can be considered to be investing 1037.17 on which there is a semiannual return of 31.12. This leaves 8.88 each period to place into a sinking fund to replace the premium paid for the bond, since there will be a loss of the premium upon redemption. If the sinking fund can be invested at the yield rate, then the balance in the sinking fund at the end of two years is

$$8.88\, s_{\overline{4}|.03} = (8.88)(4.1836) = 37.15$$

which is the amount of premium (with .02 roundoff error). Example 6.4 illustrates a situation in which the sinking fund earns a rate of interest different than the yield rate.

Similarly, in Table 6.3 we have

$$8.23\, s_{\overline{4}|.05} = (8.23)(4.3101) = 35.47$$

which is the amount of discount (with .01 roundoff error). It should be noted that the sinking fund in this case is a negative sinking fund.

Another method of writing up or writing down the book values of bonds is the *straight line method.* This method does not produce results which are consistent with compound interest theory. However, the method is very simple to apply and the reader is likely to encounter it in practice.

In the straight line method the book values are linear, grading from $P = B_0$ to $C = B_n$. Thus, the principal adjustment column is constant

$$P_t = \frac{P-C}{n} \text{ for } t = 1, 2, \ldots, n. \tag{6.7}$$

Note that $P_t > 0$ for premium bonds and $P_t < 0$ for discount bonds. The interest earned column also is constant

$$I_t = Fr - P_t \text{ for } t = 1, 2, \ldots, n. \tag{6.8}$$

Some additional properties of the straight line method are explored in the exercises. Typically, the larger the amount of premium or discount and the longer the term of the bond, the greater the error in using this method.

Example 6.4 Find the price of a $1000 par value two-year 8% bond with semiannual coupons bought to yield 6% convertible semiannually if the investor can replace the premium by means of a sinking fund earning 5% convertible semiannually.

The bond will sell at a premium, i.e. $P > 1000$. The semiannual coupon is $40, and the interest earned is $.03P$. The difference is placed into the sinking fund which must accumulate to the amount of premium. Thus, in general, the fundamental equation of value is

$$(Cg - iP) s_{\overline{n}|j} = P - C$$

which becomes

$$(40 - .03P) s_{\overline{4}|.025} = P - 1000$$

or

$$P = \frac{1000 + 40 s_{\overline{4}|.025}}{1 + .03 s_{\overline{4}|.025}} = \frac{1000 + (40)(4.1525)}{1 + (.03)(4.1525)} = \$1036.93.$$

This price is smaller than the bond in Table 6.2. The reader should justify the relative magnitude of the two prices from general reasoning. In general, the price of a bond under these conditions is given by

$$P = \frac{C\left(1 + g s_{\overline{n}|j}\right)}{1 + i s_{\overline{n}|j}} \tag{6.9}$$

where i is the yield rate of interest and j the sinking fund rate of interest. Note that formula (6.9) simplifies to formula (6.1) if $i = j$.

6.5 VALUATION BETWEEN COUPON PAYMENT DATES

The preceding sections have assumed that the price or book value of a bond is being calculated just after a coupon has been paid. It remains to consider the determination of prices and book values between coupon payment dates.

Let B_t and B_{t+1} be the prices or book values of a bond on two consecutive coupon payment dates. Let Fr be the amount of the coupon. A recursion formula connecting these two values is given by

$$B_{t+1} = B_t(1+i) - Fr \tag{6.10}$$

assuming a constant yield rate i over this interval. This formula is analogous to formula (5.3) connecting successive loan balances and can be interpreted by general reasoning. It can readily be derived algebraically from the relationships displayed in Table 6.1.

We now need to analyze the behavior of B_{t+k} for $0<k<1$. When a bond is bought between coupon payment dates, it is necessary to allocate the coupon for the current period between the prior owner and the new owner. Since the new owner will receive the entire coupon at the end of the period, the purchase price should include a payment to the prior owner for the portion of the coupon attributable to the period from the prior coupon payment date to the date of purchase. This value is called the *accrued coupon* and is denoted by Fr_k. Clearly, at the end points of the interval we would have $Fr_0 = 0$ and $Fr_1 = Fr$, where Fr_1 is computed just before the coupon is paid.

We define the *flat price* of a bond as the money which actually changes hands at the date of sale and denote it by B^f_{t+k}. We define the *market price* of a bond as the price excluding accrued coupon and denote it by B^m_{t+k}. We then have

$$B^f_{t+k} = B^m_{t+k} + Fr_k \quad \text{for} \quad 0<k<1. \tag{6.11}$$

In practice, bond prices are quoted as market price plus accrued coupon. As we shall see, this leads to a smooth progression of market prices (assuming a constant yield rate i).

The relationship between the flat price and the market price is illustrated in Figure 6.2. This figure uses the book values for the bond in Table 6.3 as prices. The flat price is denoted by the solid line, while the market price is denoted by the dashed line. The accrued coupon at any date is equal to the vertical distance between the solid line and the dashed line.

The book value of a bond can be considered as an asset value assigned to a bond after its purchase. Historically, it has been common practice for book values to be equal to market values computed at the original yield rate at date of purchase. Of course, these values are quite likely to differ from the current market price if the bond were to be purchased anew. Since both book values and market values do not include accrued coupons, any accrued coupon must be handled as a separate item in the financial statements of the owner of the bond.

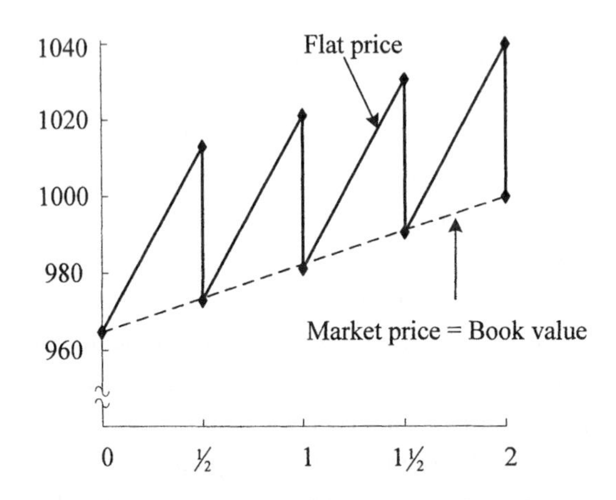

Figure 6.2 Comparison of flat price and market price

There are three methods used to compute the values in formula (6.11). Note that the values on the coupon payment dates are known, so that differences among the three methods arise only for the interim values between coupon payment dates.

The first method is an exact method based on compound interest and is often called the *theoretical method.* The flat price on the interim date is the value on the preceding coupon date accumulated with compound interest at the yield rate for the fractional period

$$B_{t+k}^f = B_t\,(1+i)^k. \tag{6.12}$$

The accrued coupon is computed as in formula (3.20)

$$Fr_k = Fr\left[\frac{(1+i)^k - 1}{i}\right]. \tag{6.13}$$

The market price or book value then is the difference

$$B^m_{t+k} = B_t\,(1+i)^k - Fr\left[\frac{(1+i)^k - 1}{i}\right]. \tag{6.14}$$

The second method is an approximate method based on simple interest for the interim period and is often called the *practical method.* The flat price is determined from the simple interest approximation to formula (6.12)

$$B^f_{t+k} = B_t\,(1+ki). \tag{6.15}$$

An alternative approach that could be used is to perform a linear interpolation between the value at the beginning of the interval B_t and the value at the end of the interval just before the next coupon is paid, i.e. $B_{t+1} + Fr$. Then we would have

$$B^f_{t+k} = \left[(1-k)B_t + kB_{t+1}\right] + k\,Fr. \tag{6.16}$$

It can be shown algebraically that formulas (6.15) and (6.16) are equivalent.

The accrued coupon is computed as the pro rata portion of the coupon

$$Fr_k = k\,Fr. \tag{6.17}$$

The market price or book value then is the difference

$$B^m_{t+k} = B_t\,(1+ki) - kFr \tag{6.18}$$

or

$$= (1-k)B_t + kB_{t+1}. \tag{6.19}$$

Formula (6.18) is based on formula (6.15), while formula (6.19) is based on formula (6.16).

The third method is a mixture of the first two methods and is often called the *semi-theoretical method.* Under this method, the flat price is the same as the theoretical method

$$B^f_{t+k} = B_t\,(1+i)^k. \tag{6.12}$$

However, the accrued coupon is the same as the practical method

$$Fr_k = k\,Fr. \tag{6.17}$$

The market price or book value then is the difference

$$B^m_{t+k} = B_t\,(1+i)^k - k\,Fr. \tag{6.20}$$

In essence, under this method book values are computed on a compound interest basis, but the accrued coupon is computed on a linear pro rata, i.e. simple interest, basis.

The semi-theoretical method has a significant aberration. Consider a bond for which $i = g$ and $P = C$. Then there is no amortization of premium or accumulation of discount, so that the book values on all the coupon dates are equal. It would seem logical that all interim book values should also be equal to that same value for such a bond. This property holds for either of the first two methods, but not for the semi-theoretical method.

Despite conceptual inconsistencies in the semi-theoretical method, it is the most widely used method in practice. The Securities Industry and Financial Markets Association (formerly the Securities Industry Association) publishes a manual entitled *Standard Securities Calculation Methods*. The purpose of this manual is to standardize calculation algorithms for prices and yields on securities. This manual sanctions the use of the semi-theoretical method for calculations on bonds with more than six months to maturity.

For convenient reference, Table 6.4 summarizes the formulas for the three methods.

Table 6.4 Bond Values Between Coupon Payment Dates on Three Different Bases

	Flat price B^f_{t+k}	*Accrued coupon* Fr_k	*Market price* B^m_{t+k}
Theoretical method	$B_t\,(1+i)^k$	$Fr\left[\frac{(1+i)^k-1}{i}\right]$	$B_t\,(1+i)^k - Fr\left[\frac{(1+i)^k-1}{i}\right]$
Practical method	$B_t\,(1+ki)$	kFr	$B_t\,(1+ki) - kFr$
Semi-theoretical method	$B_t\,(1+i)^k$	kFr	$B_t\,(1+i)^k - kFr$

In computing bond prices in the financial markets, the value of k is based on an actual count of days, as described in Section 2.6. Both the actual/actual and 30/360 methods are used depending on the type of bond involved.

The reader should note that Figure 6.2 is drawn to fit the practical method, i.e. both the flat prices and market prices are linear over each coupon payment period (the latter being piecewise linear over the entire term of the bond). The graphs for the other two methods would differ slightly, although the values on the coupon payment dates would be identical.

Another issue to consider is the amount of premium or discount between coupon payment dates. It is evident that these values should be based on the market price or book value rather than on the flat price. For example, a $1000 par value bond with a market value of $980 and accrued coupon of $30 is still a discount bond despite the fact it is selling for $1010.

Thus we have

$$\text{Premium} = B_{t+k}^{m} - C \text{ if } g > i \tag{6.21}$$

and

$$\text{Discount} = C - B_{t+k}^{m} \text{ if } i > g \tag{6.22}$$

for which B_{t+k}^{m} can be calculated by any of the three methods described above.

Financial calculators typically have a special subroutine or worksheet for bond calculations. This feature can be used for finding prices or values between coupon dates. The following data entry is required:

- Purchase (valuation) date
- Redemption (maturity) date
- Actual/actual or 30/360 method
- Redemption value (per 100)
- Annual coupon rate (per 100)
- Coupon frequency rate (e.g. semiannual)
- Annual yield rate (same frequency as coupon rate)

The market price is then computed from these inputs. The accrued coupon is also displayed so that the flat price can be readily determined.

Readers wishing to use a financial calculator for bond calculations are referred to the owner's manual, or other instructions, for the particular calculator being used. The detailed steps for performing the above operations vary form calculator to calculator.

Example 6.5 Compute the flat price, accrued interest, and market price (book value) five months after purchase for the bond in Table 6.2. Use all three methods.

For convenience in illustrating the three methods, we will set $k = 5/6$. For the theoretical method, we have:

$$B^f_{5/6} = 1037.17(1.03)^{5/6} = 1063.04$$

$$Fr_{5/6} = 40\left[\frac{(1.03)^{5/6}-1}{.03}\right] = 33.25$$

$$B^m_{5/6} = 1063.04 - 33.25 = 1029.79.$$

For the practical method, we have:

$$B^f_{5/6} = 1037.17\left[1 + \frac{5}{6}(.03)\right] = 1063.10$$

$$Fr_{5/6} = \frac{5}{6}(40) = 33.33$$

$$B^m_{5/6} = 1063.10 - 33.33 = 1029.77.$$

For the semi-theoretical method, we have:

$$B^f_{5/6} = 1063.04$$

$$Fr_{5/6} = 33.33$$

$$B^m_{5/6} = 1029.71.$$

In practice, actual calendar dates would be used rather than counting calendar months. For sake of illustration, assume that the bond has January 1 issue and redemption dates and is being purchased on June 1. Assume that the day count basis is actual/actual. A financial calculator gives the following answers to this question:

$$B^f_k = 1063.06$$

$$Fr_k = 33.37$$

$$B^m_k = 1029.69.$$

The number of days in the first five months of the year is 151, while the number of days in the first six months of the year is 181. The reader should verify that using $k = 151/181$ in the formulas for the semi-theoretical method produces the answers given by the financial calculator.

6.6 DETERMINATION OF YIELD RATES

As mentioned in Section 6.1, one of the three primary questions under consideration in this chapter is the determination of the yield rate to an investor, given the purchase price of a security. This section discusses this question for bonds. The determination of the yield to maturity on a bond is similar to the determination of an unknown rate of interest for an annuity, discussed in Section 3.7.

As in Section 3.7, the best way to determine an unknown yield to maturity on a bond is to use a financial calculator. The process is identical to that described in Section 6.5 except on the last step. In Section 6.5 on the last step we entered the yield rate and the calculator then computed the price. Here we reverse the order and enter the price. The calculator then computes the yield rate. This technique will be illustrated in Examples 6.6 and 6.7.

The approach just described works for any date. However, there is a simpler procedure for determining an unknown yield rate on a coupon payment date. This alternative procedure is based on annuity functionality and avoids the more complex bond functionality.

The procedure is to set

N	=	n	term of bond, number of coupon
PV	=	P	price (negative)
PMT	=	Fr	coupon amount
FV	=	C	redemption value

and then compute the yield rate i, i.e.,

CPT I.

This alternative procedure will be illustrated in Example 6.6.

As in Section 3.7, a simple approximation formula that can be calculated by hand is available. This formula produces reasonable answers without requiring a financial calculator or other complex iteration approach if high levels of accuracy are not required.

We define k by

$$k = \frac{P-C}{C}. \tag{6.23}$$

The approximate formula to determine the yield to maturity is then given by

$$i \approx \frac{g - \dfrac{k}{n}}{1 + \dfrac{n+1}{2n}k} \tag{6.24}$$

where all other symbols are defined in Section 6.3. The derivation of formula (6.24) is given in Appendix 6 at the end of the chapter.

Formula (6.24) has an interesting verbal interpretation. The amount by which the value of the bond needs to be amortized is k per unit of redemption value. Since the number of periods is n, the average amount of principal adjustment per unit of redemption value each period is k/n. Thus, the portion of each coupon which is interest is approximately $g - k/n$. Per unit of redemption value, the average amount invested is the average of the initial book value for each period, i.e.

$$\frac{1}{n}\left[\left(1+\frac{n}{n}k\right)+\left(1+\frac{n-1}{n}k\right)+\cdots+\left(1+\frac{2}{n}k\right)+\left(1+\frac{1}{n}k\right)\right] = 1+\frac{n+1}{2n}k .$$

Thus, formula (6.24) can be interpreted as the average interest return divided by the average amount invested.

From another viewpoint, the verbal interpretation of formula (6.24) above considers book values to be linear. This is the same assumption as the straight line method of writing bond values up or down described in Section 6.4.

Formula (6.24) forms the basis of an even simpler method for calculating approximate yield rates called the *bond salesman's method.* As usually applied, the bond salesman's method replaces $(n+1)/2n$ with 1/2 in formula (6.24) obtaining

$$i \approx \frac{g - \dfrac{k}{n}}{1 + \dfrac{1}{2}k}. \tag{6.25}$$

In general, formula (6.25) produces less accurate results than formula (6.24).

***Example 6.6** A $100 par value 10-year bond with 8% semiannual coupons is selling for $90. Find the yield rate convertible semiannually.*

We will illustrate the various methods discussed in this section. We have

$$k = \frac{P-C}{C} = \frac{90-100}{100} = -.1.$$

1. The bond salesman's method, formula (6.25), gives the following approximate semiannual yield rate

$$i = \frac{.04 + \dfrac{.1}{20}}{1 + (.5)(-.1)} = .0474$$

i.e. 4.74%, or 9.48% convertible semiannually.

2. The more refined version of the bond salesman's method, formula (6.24), gives

$$i = \frac{.04 + \dfrac{.1}{20}}{1 + \left(\dfrac{21}{40}\right)(-.1)} = .0475$$

i.e. 4.75%, or 9.50% convertible semiannually, which should be closer to the true yield rate.

3. We use bond functionality on a financial calculator with the following inputs:

- Purchase date and redemption date 10 years apart (use any dates)
- Either actual/actual or 30/360 (does not matter in this case)
- Coupon rate = 8%
- Coupon frequency is semiannual
- Price = 90

We then compute the yield to maturity obtaining 9.5761%. Note that the refined version of the bond salesman's method, formula (6.24), gives a reasonable approximation.

4. We use annuity functionality on a financial calculator with the following inputs:

$$\begin{aligned} N &= 20 \\ PV &= -90 \\ PMT &= 4 \\ FV &= 100 \end{aligned}$$

and

CPT I

to obtain $i = .0478807$. The nominal annual rate convertible semiannually is $2(.0478807) = .095761$, or 9.7561%, the same as the answer obtained in part 3 above.

Example 6.7 Assume that the bond in Example 6.6 was issued on March 1. Slightly over two years later on May 15 the market price of the bond is 88, compute the yield rate if the bond is bought on that date.

A financial calculator produces the answer 10.2694%. We will attempt to confirm this answer. The price of the bond on the immediately preceding March 1 at a yield rate of 10.2694% convertible semiannually is computed to be 87.8194. The number of days from March 1 to May 15 is 75, while the number of days from March 1 to September 1 is 184. Using formula (6.20), the semi-theoretical method produces

$$87.8194(1.051347)^{75/184} - \frac{75}{184}\cdot 4 \; = \; 87.9998$$

which confirms the price of 88 with a roundoff error of .0002.

6.7 CALLABLE AND PUTABLE BONDS

A *callable bond* is a bond for which the issuer (borrower) has an option to redeem prior to the normal maturity date. The earliest such *call date* at which the bond can be redeemed will generally be several years after the issue date.

A *putable bond* (or just *put bond*) is a bond for which the owner (lender) has an option to redeem prior to the normal maturity date. Again the earliest such *put date* at which the bond can be redeemed will generally be several years after the issue date.

The terms "callable" and "putable" may seem picturesque at first. In the case of a callable bond, the issuer (borrower) has the right to "call" back the bond early from its owner (lender). In the case of a "putable" bond, it is the owner (lender) of the bond who has the right to "put" the bond back to the issuer (borrower).

Actually, the words "call" and "put" are well established terms for the two primary types of options which have become widespread in financial markets in recent years. Readers with no background in options are encouraged to read the brief subsection of Section 8.8 which provides a non-technical, definitional introduction to option terminology. Options will be discussed on a more technical level in Chapter 13.

Callable bonds are quite widespread in financial markets. In fact, most bonds issued by corporations and by state and local governmental entities are callable. In contrast, bonds issued by the U.S. Treasury are generally not callable.

Putable bonds are much less common than callable bonds or "regular" bonds with no optional features available to either party. However, they do exist and readers should be aware of them and their properties.

A callable bond will sell at a higher yield rate (i.e. lower price) than an otherwise identical non-callable bond because of the uncertainty attached to the ultimate term of the bond. Why would a borrower issue a security on which they will receive a lower initial price and/or pay a higher coupon rate? One possible reason is to obtain the flexibility to pay off the indebtedness early and avoid paying the coupon after the bond is called. A second possible reason is that if interest rates decline, they may be able to call one issue of bonds early and then refinance the indebtedness at a lower rate.

By contrast, a putable bond will sell at a lower yield rate (i.e. higher price) than an otherwise identical non-putable bond. Why would the bond issuer (borrower) be willing to create uncertainty for itself by granting the owner (lender) this option? The most common reason is that it allows the issuer (borrower) to issue indebtedness and receive a higher initial price and/or pay a lower coupon rate.

Callable and putable bonds present a problem in calculating prices and yield rates, because the term of the bond is uncertain. Consider first the callable bond. Since the borrower has an option whether or not to call the bond, the lender should assume that the borrower will exercise that option to the disadvantage of the lender and should calculate the price or yield rate accordingly.

This principle is relatively simple to apply if the redemption values on all the redemption dates, including the maturity date, are equal. The following general rules will hold if this is the case:

1. If the yield rate is less than the modified coupon rate, i.e. if the bond sells at a premium, then assume that the redemption date will be the earliest possible date.

2. If the yield rate is greater than the modified coupon rate, i.e. if the bond sells at a discount, then assume that the redemption date will be the latest possible date.

The rationale for the above rules should be clear. In case 1 there will be a loss at redemption, since the bond was bought at a premium. The most unfavorable situation to the lender occurs when the loss is as early as possible. In case 2 there will be a gain at redemption, since the bond was bought at a discount. The most unfavorable situation to the lender occurs when the gain is as late as possible.

If the redemption values on all the redemption dates, including the maturity date, are not equal, then the above principle is more difficult to apply. In general, it may be necessary to make some trial calculations at the various possible redemption dates to see which is the most unfavorable to the lender. The most unfavorable date will not necessarily be either the earliest or latest possible redemption date. The most unfavorable call date is the one that produces the smallest purchase price at the yield rate. Example 6.8 will illustrate this situation.

As expected, the rules are reversed for putable bonds. The most unfavorable put date is the one that produces the largest purchase price at the yield rate. In this way, the borrower is assured of paying no higher rate on their indebtedness regardless of what the lender does.

It should be noted that if a callable or putable bond is redeemed at a date other than that assumed initially, the yield rate, after the fact, is higher than originally calculated. However, in this situation the original purchase price and the term are both fixed so that the methods of Section 6.6 can be applied directly to determine the yield rate the investor actually earned.

The approach taken in this section does not introduce any new theory to analyze callable and putable bonds. Rather it adopts a "worst case" approach to determine yield rates and prices. This type of approach is sometimes termed *yield to worst* in the financial literature.

A more sophisticated approach to analyze callable and putable bonds does exist. However, it is based on option pricing theory to be introduced in Chapter 13.

Example 6.8 ***Consider a \$100 par value 4% bond with semiannual coupons callable at \$109 on any coupon date starting 5 years after issue for the next 5 years, at \$104.50 starting 10 years after issue for the next 5 years, and maturing at \$100 at the end of 15 years. Find the highest price which an investor can pay and still be certain of a yield of:***

(1) 5% convertible semiannually.

(2) 3% convertible semiannually.

1. If the yield rate is 5%, then the latest possible redemption date is least favorable to an investor, since the bond will be selling at a discount. Thus, the price is

$$100 + (2-2.50)\,a_{\overline{30}|.025} = 100-(.50)(20.9303) = \$89.53\ .$$

2. If the yield rate is to be 3%, then it is not immediately clear which redemption date is least favorable, since the bond will be selling at a premium. The price would be:

$$\begin{aligned} &109.00 + (2-1.6350)\,a_{\overline{n}|.015} \quad \text{for } n = 10, 11, \ldots, 19 \\ &104.50 + (2-1.5675)\,a_{\overline{n}|.015} \quad \text{for } n = 20, 21, \ldots, 29 \\ &100.00 + (2-1.5000)\,a_{\overline{n}|.015} \quad \text{for } n = 30. \end{aligned}$$

The lowest price in each category will result when the lowest value of n is used, i.e. n = 10, 20, and 30. Thus, the prices to compare are:

$$\begin{aligned} 109.00+(.3650)\,a_{\overline{10}|.015} &= 109.00+(.3650)(9.2222) &&= \$112.37 \\ 104.50+(.4325)\,a_{\overline{20}|.015} &= 104.50+(.4325)(17.1686) &&= \$111.93 \\ 100.00+(.5000)\,a_{\overline{30}|.015} &= 100.00+(.5000)(24.0158) &&= \$112.01. \end{aligned}$$

The lowest price \$111.93 occurs for $n = 20$, i.e. for redemption 10 years after issue.

This example illustrates that the least favorable redemption date can occur between the earliest and latest possible redemption dates when the redemption values are not equal at all the possible redemption dates. It is fairly common in practice for a callable bond to have redemption values which decrease as the term of the bond increases, as in this example. The excess of the redemption value over the par value, i.e. \$9 and \$4.50 in this example, is often termed the *call premium.*

Example 6.9 Consider a $100 par value 10-year bond with coupons at 6% payable semiannually bought to yield 8% convertible semiannually. If the bond is putable anytime starting 5 years after issue, what will the price be?

Since the bond will be selling at a discount, the highest possible price will occur when the redemption date is the earliest possible date, i.e. at the end of 5 years. Thus the price is

$$\begin{aligned} &100 + (3-4)a_{\overline{10}|.04} \\ &= 100-8.1109 = \$91.89. \end{aligned}$$

6.8 SERIAL BONDS

As mentioned in Section 6.2, a borrower in need of a large amount of funds may issue a series of bonds with staggered redemption dates instead of using a common maturity date. These types of bonds are called *serial bonds* and are considered further in this section.

If the redemption date of each individual bond is known, then the valuation of any one bond can be performed by methods already described. The value of the entire issue of bonds is merely the sum of the values of the individual bonds. It will be shown that the value of the entire issue of bonds can often be found more efficiently than by summing the individual bond values, however.

In some cases, the bonds to be redeemed on each successive redemption date are not known in advance but are chosen randomly. The value of any one bond is impossible to determine in advance with certainty, since its redemption date depends upon chance. However, the value of the entire issue of bonds can be determined with certainty.

Of course, values for any one bond can be determined on the same basis as that used for callable bonds in Section 6.7. Also, the yield rate actually realized after redemption can be determined.

The valuation of an issue of serial bonds can most efficiently be performed using Makeham's formula

$$P = K + \frac{g}{i}(C-K). \tag{6.4}$$

Assume that the serial bonds are redeemable at m different redemption dates. Let the purchase price, redemption value, and present value of the redemption value for the first redemption date be denoted by P_1, C_1, and K_1; for the second redemption date by P_2, C_2, and K_2; and so forth until the last redemption date when we have P_m, C_m, and K_m. Thus we have

$$P_1 = K_1 + \frac{g}{i}(C_1 - K_1)$$

$$P_2 = K_2 + \frac{g}{i}(C_2 - K_2)$$

$$\vdots \qquad \vdots$$

$$P_m = K_m + \frac{g}{i}(C_m - K_m)$$

and summing, we obtain

$$P' = K' + \frac{g}{i}(C' - K') \tag{6.26}$$

where

$$P' = \sum_{t=1}^{m} P_t \qquad C' = \sum_{t=1}^{m} C_t \qquad K' = \sum_{t=1}^{m} K_t .$$

Thus, the price of an entire issue of serial bonds is denoted by P' and is given by formula (6.26). This formula is usually more efficient than a summation of the prices of each individual bond, since C' and K' are often quite simple to obtain. The sum C' is merely the sum of the redemption values for the entire issue of bonds, a figure readily obtainable. The sum K' is of simple form if the bonds are redeemed according to a systematic pattern at regular intervals. In this case, K' is some form of annuity for which a simple expression is possible. Example 6.10 illustrates this technique.

Example 6.10 Find the price of a \$1000 issue of 5 1/4% bonds with annual coupons which will be redeemed in 10 equal annual installments at the end of the 11th through the 20th years from the issue date at 105. The bonds are bought to yield 7% effective.

In this example we have:

$$\begin{aligned}
F &= 100 \\
C &= 105 \\
r &= .0525 \\
g &= \frac{100}{105}(.0525) = .05 \\
i &= .07 \\
C' &= 1050 \\
K' &= 105\left(v^{11} + v^{12} + \cdots + v^{20}\right) \\
&= 105\left(a_{\overline{20}|.07} - a_{\overline{10}|.07}\right) \\
&= 105(10.59401 - 7.02358) \\
&= 374.895
\end{aligned}$$

so that the price is

$$\begin{aligned}
P' &= 374.895 + \frac{.05}{.07}(1050 - 374.895) \\
&= \$857.11.
\end{aligned}$$

6.9 SOME GENERALIZATIONS

Several generalizations of bond formulas already discussed are possible. This section will describe three of these. It should be stressed that a more general type of bond can always be handled by generalizing formula (6.1), i.e. by finding the present value of future coupons and the present value of the redemption value separately and summing the two.

The three generalizations considered in this section are: (1) yield rate and coupon rate at different frequencies, (2) coupon rate not constant, and (3) yield rate not constant.

Yield rate and coupon rate at different frequencies

The approach in this situation is analogous to that contained in Sections 4.2 and 5.5. Again, we have a two-step process:

1. Find the rate of interest, convertible at the same frequency as coupons are paid, which is equivalent to the given yield rate.

2. Using this new rate of interest do whatever calculations are required for the problem at hand using techniques covered earlier in this chapter.

This approach is illustrated in Example 6.11.

Coupon rate not constant

If the coupon rate is not constant, then the coupons constitute a varying annuity. This varying annuity can often be evaluated using the approaches developed in Sections 4.6 and 4.7. The price of the bond is then the present value of future coupons plus the present value of the redemption value. This approach is illustrated in Example 6.12.

Yield rate not constant

If the yield rate is not constant, then this change in rate must be reflected in computing the present values of future coupons and the redemption value. The present value of future coupons would be computed by using the approach developed in Section 3.8. Similarly, the present value of the redemption value would be computed by using the approach developed in Section 1.10. The price of the bond is then the present value of future coupons plus the present value of the redemption value. This approach is illustrated in Example 6.13.

Example 6.11 ***An investor is considering a number of different types of investments. The investor is unwilling to invest in any of these investments unless an annual effective yield rate of at least 7% can be achieved. One of the investments being considered is the bond in Example 6.3. Find the maximum price which this investor is willing to pay.***

The bond in Example 6.3 has the usual semiannual coupons. Thus, we must convert the 7% effective yield rate to a nominal rate convertible semiannually. We have

$$\left(1+\frac{i^{(2)}}{2}\right)^2 = 1+i = 1.07$$

or

$$i^{(2)} = 2\left[1.07^{.5}-1\right] = .06882$$

or 3.441% per half year.

The maximum price the investor is willing to pay is

$$\begin{aligned} &1050+\left[42-(1050)(.03441)\right]a_{\overline{20}|.03441} \\ &= 1050+(5.8695)(14.2886) = \$1133.87. \end{aligned}$$

Example 6.12 A corporation decides to issue an inflation-adjusted bond with a par value of $1000 and with annual coupons at the end of each year for 10 years. The initial coupon rate is 7% and each coupon is 3% greater than the preceding coupon. The bond is redeemed for $1200 at the end of 10 years. Find the price an investor should pay to produce a yield rate of 9% effective.

Using formula (4.29), the present value of future coupons is

$$70\frac{1-\left(\dfrac{1.03}{1.09}\right)^{10}}{.09-.03} = 504.368.$$

The present value of the redemption value is

$$1200(1.09)^{-10} = 506.893.$$

Thus, the price of the bond is

$$504.368 + 506.893 = \$1011.26.$$

Example 6.13 Find the price of the bond in Example 6.3 if the yield rate is 10% convertible semiannually for the first five years and 9% convertible semiannually for the next five years.

The present value of future coupons is

$$
\begin{aligned}
&42\left[a_{\overline{10}|.05}+(1.05)^{-10}a_{\overline{10}|.045}\right]\\
&=42\left[7.7217+(.61391)(7.9127)\right]\\
&=528.334.
\end{aligned}
$$

The present value of the redemption value is

$$1050(1.05)^{-10}(1.045)^{-10}=415.082.$$

Thus, the price of the bond is 528.334 + 415.082 = \$943.42. The price is higher than in Example 6.3, as would be expected, since the yield rate is lower for the final five years in the term of the bond.

6.10 OTHER SECURITIES

The preceding sections have been devoted to a discussion of redeemable bonds. This section is concerned with the other two other types of securities introduced in Section 6.2: (1) preferred stock and perpetual bonds, and (2) common stock.

Preferred stock and perpetual bonds

Preferred stock and perpetual bonds are similar in that they both are types of fixed-income securities without fixed redemption dates. Thus, the price must be equal to the present value of future dividends or coupons forever, i.e. the dividends or coupons form a perpetuity. The version of formula (6.1) for the situation would be

$$P=\frac{Fr}{i} \tag{6.27}$$

using a direct application of formula (3.18).

The reader should be aware that some preferred stock is issued with a redemption date. Such preferred stock can be handled exactly like a bond, as described in the preceding sections. Also, some preferred stock is callable and can be analyzed within the framework presented in Section 6.7.

Common stock

Common stock presents a different problem, since it is not a fixed-income security, i.e. the dividends are not known in advance, nor are they level. In practice, common stock prices fluctuate widely in the stock market, often for little apparent reason.

According to one theory, common stock prices should represent the present value of future dividends. Values computed in this fashion can be characterized as being based on the *dividend discount model.* Of course, this calculation should take into account projected changes in the dividend scale.

Consider a situation in which a corporation is planning to pay a dividend of D at the end of the current period. Assume that dividends are projected to change geometrically with common ratio $1 + k$ indefinitely and that the stock is purchased to yield i per period, where $-1 < k < i$.

Then the theoretical price of the stock is obtained from formula (4.29) which gives

$$P = \frac{D}{i-k}. \tag{6.28}$$

A calculation of this type is illustrated in Example 6.14.

It is probably unrealistic to project constant percentage increases in dividends indefinitely into the future. As corporations increase in size and become more mature, the rate of growth will generally slow down. An illustration of the dividend discount model applied under these conditions is given in Example 6.15.

In practice, the most common frequency of dividend payments on both preferred and common stock in the United States is quarterly. This is in contrast to the typical semiannual frequency of coupon payments on bonds.

The quarterly frequency typical of common stock dividends leads to another complication when future dividend increases are being projected. It would be quite unusual for a corporation to increase its dividend every single quarter. A much more common pattern would be quarterly payments with increases occurring annually.

This pattern would require an adjustment to formula (6.28). Example 6.16 provides an illustration of how such an adjustment could be done.

Example 6.14 A common stock is currently earning \$4 per share and will pay \$2 per share in dividends at the end of the current year. Assuming that the earnings of the corporation increase 5% per year indefinitely and that the corporation plans to continue to pay 50% of its earnings as dividends, find the theoretical price to earn an investor an annual effective yield rate of:
(1) 10%.
(2) 8%.
(3) 6%.

1. Using formula (6.28) the present value of dividends is

$$2\left(\frac{1}{.10-.05}\right) = \$40\ .$$

Thus, the theoretical price is 10 times current earnings.

2. The present value of dividends is

$$2\left(\frac{1}{.08-.05}\right) = \$66\ 2/3\ .$$

Thus, the theoretical price is $16\ 2/3$ times current earnings.

3. The present value of dividends is

$$2\left(\frac{1}{.06-.05}\right) = \$200.$$

Thus, the theoretical price is 50 times current earnings.

Example 6.15 Rework Example 6.14 assuming that the rate of increase in earnings is 5% for the first five years, 2 1/2% for the second five years, and 0% thereafter. Assume an annual effective yield rate of 10%.

Successive applications of formula (4.29) give

$$2\left[\frac{1-\left(\frac{1.05}{1.10}\right)^5}{.10-.05}\right] + 2\frac{(1.05)^5}{(1.10)^5}\left[\frac{1-\left(\frac{1.025}{1.10}\right)^5}{.10-.025}\right] + \frac{2(1.05)^5(1.025)^5}{(1.10)^{10}}\cdot\frac{1}{.10} = \$25.72$$

which is approximately 64% of the answer obtained in Example 6.14(1) assuming level percentage increases indefinitely. In this case the theoretical price is 6.43 times current earnings.

Example 6.16. Rework Example 6.14(1) if the dividend is payable in quarterly installments at the end of each quarter, but the increases occur annually.

The $2 dividend at the end of the first year in Example 6.14 becomes a dividend of .50 at the end of each quarter. A dividend of .50 paid times t = .25, .50, .75, and 1.00 is equivalent to a dividend of

$$.50\left[(1.1)^{.75}+(1.1)^{.50}+(1.1)^{.25}+1\right]$$

$$= .50\frac{1.1-1}{(1.1)^{.25}-1} = 2.0735$$

paid at the end of the year upon accumulating each payment at the yield rate to the end of the year. The same reasoning applies to each subsequent year, since the 5% increases occur annually.

Therefore, we can apply formula (6.28) directly to get a theoretical price of

$$\frac{2.0735}{.10-.05} = \$41.47$$

This answer is slightly higher than the $40 obtained in Example 6.14(1) reflecting the earlier payment of dividends.

6.11 VALUATION OF SECURITIES

As mentioned in Section 6.1 one of the three primary questions under consideration in this chapter is the valuation of a security after it has been purchased. This issue is discussed in this section. Institutional investors, such as insurance companies and pension funds, which invest in securities must assign values to the securities which they hold for financial statements. The determination of appropriate asset values for these securities is an issue on which universal agreement does not exist.

The determination of asset values often reflects applicable accounting principles, legal restrictions, and tradition, as well as theoretical considerations. Valuation methods will often vary depending upon the situation at hand. For example, identical securities may have different reported asset values for a pension fund as compared with an insurance company. Also valuation methods will often vary depending upon the type of security being valued. For example, an appropriate method for bonds may differ from an appropriate method for common stocks.

In practice, three main approaches to the determination of asset values have developed. Each approach is subject to various refinements and modifications. All three methods are in current use for the valuation of securities in various situations.

It is not the intent of this section to give a complete description of all the modifications of the various methods, nor is it within the scope of this section to try to determine which method should be used in any given situation. Rather, the purpose of this section is to briefly acquaint the reader with these three main approaches which are encountered in practice.

Market value method

The first approach is to use *market value* as the measure of asset value. There is a school of thought which believes that market value is the only true measure of the current worth of a security. This point of view has gained strength with a number of audiences in recent years. Also, it is maintained that market value is objective and is easily understood. The reader should note that the term "market value" is being used differently in this section than in Section 6.5.

A disadvantage of market value is that it often exhibits rather marked fluctuations. This lack of stability in asset value often creates problems. For this reason modified market value methods have been developed. These methods attempt to smooth out part of the peaks and valleys in the pure market value approach. Of course, any such modified market value method introduces an element of arbitrariness and results in a loss of simplicity. A second disadvantage of market value for certain securities is that a market may not exist. An example would be a private placement of bonds or mortgages which never traded openly on the market. Creative approaches have been developed that attempt to replicate what the market value would be if a market existed.

Cost method

The second approach is to use original *cost* as a measure of asset value. For redeemable bonds an *adjusted cost* method is often used. This adjusted cost method is equivalent to the amortized value resulting from the amortization of premium or the accumulation of discount as described in Section 6.4.

The actual cost or adjusted cost of an asset is often called the *book value* of the asset, since this is the value assigned to the asset on the books of the investor. Any excess of market value over book value is termed an *unrealized capital gain*, while any excess of book value over market value is termed an *unrealized capital loss*. If an asset is sold for a price in excess of book value, the profit is termed a *realized capital gain,* while if the price is less than the book value, the loss is termed a *realized capital loss*.

Unrealized capital gains and losses on amortized bonds are sometimes ignored on the books of the investor under the theory that bonds are usually held to maturity. In periods of high interest rates book values for bonds, purchased when interest rates were lower, are substantially in excess of market values; while the opposite is true in periods of low interest rates for bonds purchased when interest rates were higher.

The distinction between unrealized and realized capital gains and losses is important, since the two may be treated differently for tax purposes. For example, in the United States realized capital gains and losses are reflected on the income tax return of an investor subject to income tax, whereas unrealized capital gains and losses are not.

Book value produces asset values which are quite stable, objective, and easily understood. Also book value produces an element of conservatism if market value is greater than book value. However, book value does tend to become an increasingly unrealistic measure of asset value if market value and book value diverge and is non-conservative if book value is greater than market value.

Present value method

The third approach can be described as a *present value method.* According to this method the asset value is equal to the present value of all future payments under the security, where the present value is taken at some appropriate rate of interest. Calculations of this type have been illustrated in this chapter for bonds, preferred stock, and common stock.

The present value method has the advantage that a whole portfolio can be valued on a consistent basis, since consistent interest rates can be used in taking all the present values. This is especially significant when interest rates are assumed in calculating values for liabilities which offset assets. Examples of this type would be insurance companies and pension funds, which assume interest rates in calculating many of their liability values. The relationship between assets and liabilities is an important issue which is discussed further in Chapter 11.

The present value method is very sensitive to the choice of interest rate used in taking present values. This can be both an advantage and a disadvantage of the method. The method is flexible, but does have a degree of arbitrariness in connection with the choice of the interest rate to use in computing present values. The present value method can produce asset values which are significantly different from either market value or book value. Also the method is less easily understood than either market value or book value.

In summary, there is no valuation method for securities which is used in all situations. The reader should be careful when encountering asset values in practical situations to ascertain the method of valuation.

APPENDIX 6

Derivation of the bond salesman's formula

We start with formula (6.2)

$$\begin{aligned} P &= C + (Fr - Ci)a_{\overline{n}|} \\ &= C + C(g - i)a_{\overline{n}|} \end{aligned} \tag{6.2}$$

Since

$$k = \frac{P - C}{C} \tag{6.23}$$

we have

$$(g - i)a_{\overline{n}|} = \frac{P - C}{C} = k$$

or

$$i = g - \frac{k}{a_{\overline{n}|}}. \tag{6.29}$$

To solve formula (6.29) for i, we can use the series expansion

$$\begin{aligned} \frac{1}{a_{\overline{n}|}} &= \frac{i}{1 - (1 + i)^{-n}} \\ &= \frac{1}{n}\left[1 + \frac{n+1}{2}i + \frac{n^2 - 1}{12}i^2 + \cdots\right]. \end{aligned}$$

If we ignore terms of higher than the first degree in i, then formula (6.29) becomes

$$\begin{aligned} i &= g - \frac{k}{a_{\overline{n}|}} \\ &\approx g - \frac{k}{n}\left[1 + \frac{n+1}{2}i\right] \end{aligned}$$

and solving for i

$$i \approx \frac{g - \dfrac{k}{n}}{1 + \dfrac{n+1}{2n} k}. \tag{6.24}$$

where all other symbols are defined in Section 6.3.

One other observation about formula (6.24) is instructive. The formula is closely related to formula (3.21)

$$i \approx \frac{2(n-k)}{k(n+1)} \tag{3.21}$$

used to approximate an unknown rate of interest to solve $a_{\overline{n}|i} = k$. Upon dividing the numerator and denominator by $2n$, formula (3.21) becomes

$$i \approx \frac{1 - \dfrac{k}{n}}{\dfrac{n+1}{2n} k}. \tag{3.21a}$$

Formula (3.21*a*) has a verbal interpretation in connection with the amortization schedule for a loan of $a_{\overline{n}|} = k$ being repaid with payments of 1 at the end of each period for n periods analogous to the verbal interpretation of formula (6.24) given in Section 6.6.

EXERCISES

6.2 Types of securities

1. Find the price which should be paid for a zero coupon bond that matures for \$1000 in 10 years to yield:
   a) 10% effective.
   b) 9% effective.
   c) Thus, a 10% reduction in the yield rate causes the price to increase by what percentage?

2. A 10-year accumulation bond with an initial par value of \$1000 earns interest of 8% compounded semiannually. Find the price to yield an investor 10% effective.

3. A 26-week T-bill is bought for \$9600 at issue and will mature for \$10,000. Find the yield rate computed as:
   a) A discount rate, using the typical method for counting days on a T-bill.
   b) An annual effective rate of interest, assuming the investment period is exactly half a year.

6.3 Price of a bond

4. A 10-year \$100 par value bond bearing a 10% coupon rate payable semiannually and redeemable at \$105 is bought to yield 8% convertible semiannually. Find the price. Verify that all four formulas produce the same answer.

5. Two \$1000 bonds redeemable at par at the end of the same period are bought to yield 4% convertible semiannually. One bond costs \$1136.78 and has a coupon rate of 5% payable semiannually. The other bond has a coupon rate of 2 1/2% payable semiannually. Find the price of the second bond.

6. A \$1000 bond with a coupon rate of 9% payable semiannually is redeemable after an unspecified number of years at \$1125. The bond is bought to yield 10% convertible semiannually. If the present value of the redemption value is \$225 at this yield rate, find the purchase price.

7. A \$1000 par value n-year bond maturing at par with \$100 annual coupons is purchased for \$1110. If $K = \$450$, find the base amount G.

8. An investor owns a \$1000 par value 10% bond with semiannual coupons. The bond will mature at par at the end of 10 years. The investor decides that an 8-year bond would be preferable. Current yield rates are 7% convertible semiannually. The investor uses the proceeds from the sale of the 10% bond to purchase a 6% bond with semiannual coupons, maturing at par at the end of 8 years. Find the par value of the 8-year bond. Answer to the nearest dollar.

9. An n-year \$1000 par value bond matures at par and has a coupon rate of 12% convertible semiannually. It is bought at a price to yield 10% convertible semiannually. If the term of the bond is doubled, the price will increase by \$50. Find the price of the n-year bond.

10. For the bond in Example 6.3, determine the following:
    a) Nominal yield, based on the par value.
    b) Nominal yield, based on the redemption value.
    c) Current yield.
    d) Yield to maturity.

6.4 Premium and discount

11. For a \$1 bond the coupon rate is 150% of the yield rate and the premium is p. For another \$1 bond with the same number of coupons and the same yield rate, the coupon rate is 75% of the yield rate. Express the price of the second bond as a function of p.

12. For a certain period a bond amortization schedule shows that the amount for amortization of premium is \$5 and that the required interest is 75% of the coupon. Find the amount of the coupon.

13. A 10-year bond with semiannual coupons is bought at a discount to yield 9% convertible semiannually. If the amount for accumulation of discount in the next-to-last coupon is \$8, find the total amount for accumulation of discount during the first four years in the bond amortization schedule.

14. A \$1000 par value five-year bond with a coupon rate of 10% payable semiannually and redeemable at par is bought to yield 12% convertible semiannually. Find the total of the interest paid column in the bond amortization schedule.

15. You are given:

    (*i*) A 10-year 8% semiannual coupon bond is purchased at a discount of *X*.
    (*ii*) A 10-year 9% semiannual coupon bond is purchased at a discount of *Y*.
    (*iii*) A 10-year 10% semiannual coupon bond is purchased at a discount of 2*X*.
    (*iv*) All bonds were purchased at the same yield rate and have par values of $1000.

    Calculate *Y*.

16. *a*) Find the book values for the bond in Table 6.2 by the straight line method.
    b) Find the book values for the bond in Table 6.3 by the straight line method.
    c) What can you conclude from a comparison of the answers in (*a*) and (*b*) with the true values from Tables 6.2 and 6.3?

6.5 Valuation between coupon payment dates

17. Arrange in increasing order of magnitude for the three interim bond price methods:
    a) Flat price.
    b) Market price (book value).

18. Find the flat price, accrued interest, and market price (book value) two months after purchase for the bond in Table 6.3. Use all three methods.

19. A $1000 bond with semiannual coupons at $i^{(2)} = 6\%$ matures at par on October 15, $Z+15$. The bond is purchased on June 28, Z to yield the investor $i^{(2)} = 7\%$. What is the purchase price? Assume simple interest between bond coupon dates and use an exact day count (see Appendix A).

6.6 Determination of yield rates

20. A $100 par value 12-year bond with 10% semiannual coupons is selling for $110. Find the yield rate convertible semiannually:

    a) Using the exact method.
    b) Using the refined version of the bond salesman's method.

21. An investor buys two 20-year bonds, each having semiannual coupons and each maturing at par. For each bond the purchase price produces the same yield rate. One bond has a par value of $500 and a coupon of $45. The other bond has a par value of $1000 and a coupon of $30. The dollar amount of premium on the first bond is twice as great as the dollar amount of discount on the second bond. Find the yield rate convertible semiannually.

22. A \$100 bond with annual coupons is redeemable at par at the end of 15 years. At a purchase price of \$92 the yield rate is exactly 1% more than the coupon rate. Find the yield rate on the bond.

23. An n-year \$1000 par value bond with 4.20% annual coupons is purchased at a price to yield an annual effective rate of i. You are given:
    (*i*) If the annual coupon rate had been 5.25% instead of 4.20%, the price of the bond would have increased by \$100.
    (*ii*) At the time of purchase, the present value of all the coupon payments is equal to the present value of the bond's redemption value of \$1000.

    Calculate i.

6.7 Callable and putable bonds

24. A \$1000 par value bond has 8% semiannual coupons and is callable at the end of the 10th through the 15th years at par.
    a) Find the price to yield 6% convertible semiannually.
    b) Find the price to yield 10% convertible semiannually.
    c) If the bond in (*b*) is actually called at the end of 10 years, find the yield rate.
    d) If the bond is putable rather than callable, rework (*a*).
    e) If the bond is putable rather than callable, rework (*b*).

25. A \$1000 par value 8% bond with quarterly coupons is callable five years after issue. The bond matures for \$1000 at the end of ten years and is sold to yield a nominal rate of 6% convertible quarterly under the assumption that the bond will not be called. Find the redemption value at the end of five years that will provide the purchaser the same yield rate. Answer to the nearest dollar.

26. A \$1000 par value 4% bond with semiannual coupons matures at the end of 10 years. The bond is callable at \$1050 at the ends of years 4 through 6, at \$1025 at the ends of years 7 through 9, and at \$1000 at the end of year 10. Find the maximum price that an investor can pay and still be certain of a yield rate of 5% convertible semiannually.

27. A \$1000 par value bond with coupons at 9% payable semiannually was called for \$1100 prior to maturity. The bond was bought for \$918 immediately after a coupon payment and was held to call. The nominal yield rate convertible semiannually was 10%. Calculate the number of years the bond was held. Answer to the nearest interger.

28. A $1000 par value bond pays annual coupons of $80. The bond is redeemable at par in 30 years, but is callable any time from the end of the 10th year at $1050. Based on the desired yield rate, an investor calculates the following potential purchase prices P:

    (*i*) Assuming the bond is called at the end of the 10th year, $P = \$957$.

    (*ii*) Assuming the bond is held until maturity, $P = \$897$.

    The investor buys the bond at the highest price that guarantees the desired yield rate regardless of when the bond is called. The investor holds the bond for 20 years, after which time the bond is called. Calculate the annual yield rate the investor earns.

6.8 Serial bonds

29. A $10,000 serial bond is to be redeemed in $1000 installments of principal per half-year over the next five years. Interest at the annual rate of 12% is paid semiannually on the balance outstanding. How much should an investor pay for this bond in order to produce a yield rate of 8% convertible semiannually? Answer to the nearest dollar.

30. A $10,000 serial bond is to be redeemed in $500 installments of principal at the end of the 6th through the 25th years from the date of issue. Interest at the rate of 6% is paid annually on the balance outstanding. What is the price to yield an investor 10% effective? Answer to the nearest dollar.

31. Find an expression for the present value of a $100,000 issue of serial bonds, if it is known that the yield rate is 125% of the coupon rate and that the bonds are redeemable at par according to the following schedule:

End of Years	Amount Redeemable
5, 8, 11	$10,000
14, 17	20,000
20	30,000

All rates are semiannual. Express your answer strictly as a function of $a_{\overline{n|}}$'s for various values of n.

6.9 Some generalizations

32. The price of a $100 bond, which matures in n years for $105, has semiannual coupons of $4, and is bought to yield an effective rate i, can be expressed as

$$\frac{Av^n + B}{i^{(2)}}.$$

Find A and B.

33. A $1000 par value 20-year bond maturing at par has annual coupons of 5% for the first 10 years and 4% for the second 10 years. Find the price of the bond bought to yield 6% effective.

34. A $1000 par value 20-year bond with annual coupons and redemption value $1050 is purchased for P to yield an annual effective rate of 8.25%. The first coupon is $75. Each subsequent coupon is 3% greater than the preceding coupon. Determine P to the nearest dollar.

6.10 Other securities

35. A preferred stock pays a $10 dividend at the end of the first year, with each successive annual dividend being 5% greater than the preceding one. What level annual dividend would be equivalent if $i = 12\%$?

36. A common stock pays annual dividends at the end of each year. The earnings per share in the year just ended were $6. Earnings are assumed to grow 8% per year in the future. The percentage of earnings paid out as a dividend will be 0% for the next 5 years and 50% thereafter. Find the theoretical price of the stock to yield an investor 15% effective.

37. A common stock is purchased at a price equal to 10 times current earnings. During the next 6 years the stock pays no dividends, but earnings increase 60%. At the end of 6 years the stock is sold at a price equal to 15 times earnings. Find the effective annual yield rate earned on this investment.

38. A $100 par value 10% preferred stock with quarterly dividends is bought to yield 8% convertible quarterly into perpetuity. However, the preferred stock is actually called at the end of 10 tears at par. Find the nominal yield rate convertible quarterly that an investor would actually earn over the 10-year period.

6.11 Valuation of securities

39. Five years ago a pension fund invested $1,000,000 in corporate bonds and $1,000,000 in preferred stock. The investment in bonds was a purchase of 1000 bonds maturing in 20 years, each with a par value of $1000 and bearing annual 4% coupons. The investment in preferred stock was a purchase of 10,000 shares, each with a par value of $100 and bearing annual 6% dividends. The bonds are now selling for $900 per bond and the preferred stock is selling for $115 per share. Find the asset value for the pension fund currently, assuming that there have been no changes in the investment

portfolio over the past five years and that all investment income was withdrawn from the fund as earned, if:

a) All assets are assigned market value.

b) All assets are assigned book value.

c) Bonds are assigned book value and stocks are assigned market value.

d) All assets are valued using the present value method at a yield rate of 5% effective.

Miscellaneous problems

40. A \$100 par value 12-year bond has coupons at the annual rate of 9% payable continuously. If the bond is bought to yield force of interest δ, find the price of the bond expressed strictly as a function of δ.

41. A bond with par value 1 sells for $1 + p$ at a certain fixed yield rate. If the bond's coupon rate were halved, the price would be $1 + q$. If the bond's coupon rate were doubled, the price can be expressed as $1 + Ap + Bq$. Find A and B.

42. A corporation has an issue of bonds with annual 6% coupons maturing in five years, which are quoted at a price that yields 4% effective. It is proposed to replace this issue of bonds with an issue of 5% bonds with annual coupons. How long must the new issue run so that the bondholders will still realize 4% effective? Answer to the nearest year.

43. The interest paid during the 20th year on a 20-year \$1000 bond with annual coupons to be redeemed at par is equal to 70% of the principal adjustment during the same year. If $r = i + .03$, where r is the coupon rate and i is the yield rate, find the original price of the bond.

44. A firm has proposed the following restructuring for one of its \$1000 par value bonds. The bond presently has 10 years remaining until maturity. The coupon rate on the existing bond is 6.75% per annum paid semiannually. The current nominal semiannual yield on the bond is 7.40%. The company proposes suspending coupon payments for four years with the suspended coupon payments being repaid, with accrued interest, when the bond comes due. Accrued interest is calculated using a nominal semiannual rate of 7.40%. Calculate the market value of the restructured bond to the nearest dollar.

45. You have decided to invest in two bonds. Bond X is a n-year bond with semiannual coupons, while Bond Y is an accumulation bond redeemable in $n/2$ years. The desired yield rate is the same for both bonds. You also have the following information:

    (*i*) Bond X:

    - Par value is $1000.
    - The ratio of the semiannual bond rate to the desired semiannual yield rate, r/i, is 1.03125.
    - The present value of the redemption value is $381.50.

    (*ii*) Bond Y:

    - Redemption value is the same as the redemption value of Bond X.
    - Price to yield is $647.80.

    What is the price of Bond X to the nearest dollar?

46. *a*) Show that

$$P + i\sum_{t=0}^{n-1} B_t = n \cdot Fr + C.$$

    b) Verbally interpret the result obtained in (*a*).

47. If P is the price of a bond given by formula (6.1), show that:

    a) $\dfrac{dP}{di} = -Cv\left[g\,(Ia)_{\overline{n}|} + nv^n\right].$

    b) $\dfrac{dP}{dg} = C \cdot a_{\overline{n}|}.$

7

Yield rates

7.1 INTRODUCTION

In Chapter 7 some important extensions of results covered in the earlier chapters are developed. These extensions involve concepts and techniques that are widely used in financial calculations in practice.

The technique of discounted cash flow analysis and a more formal concept of yield rate are developed. The uniqueness of the yield rate is then considered. The use of these devices as tools for making financial decisions is stressed throughout.

Different techniques for measuring the interest return on an investment fund are developed and compared. The ramifications involved in the situation in which interest rates at the time of reinvestment differ from those prevailing at the time of initial investment are explored. Also developed is a generalization in which interest rates are a function of both the date of original investment and the time since investment.

Next, we analyze some unexpected difficulties in computing yield rates on specialized transactions known as "short sales." Finally, several important results from capital budgeting are presented which are widely used as tools for making business and financial decisions.

The reader will find that this chapter presents a number of important results for using the theory of interest in more complex "real-world" contexts than considered in the earlier chapters. Also, Chapter 7 extends the applications of the theory of interest beyond two-party borrowing and lending transactions to a broader range of business and financial transactions.

7.2 DISCOUNTED CASH FLOW ANALYSIS

In prior chapters we analyzed the present values of various types of financial transactions consisting of regular series of payments. This approach can be generalized to any pattern of payments and is termed *discounted cash flow analysis*.

Consider a situation in which an investor makes deposits or contributions into an investment of $C_0, C_1, C_2, \ldots, C_n$ at times $0, 1, 2, \ldots, n$. For convenience, we assume that these times are equally spaced. If $C_t > 0$, then there is a cash outflow from the investor into the investment at time *t*; while if $C_t < 0$, there is a cash inflow from the investment to the investor.

Sometimes it is more convenient to analyze a financial transaction in terms of withdrawals or returns from the investment rather than deposits or contributions into the investment. Thus, we can denote the returns as $R_0, R_1, R_2, \ldots, R_n$ at times $0, 1, 2, \ldots, n$. If $R_t > 0$, then there is a cash inflow from the investment to the investor at time *t*; while if $R_t < 0$, there is a cash outflow from the investor into the investment.

It is obvious that contributions and returns are equivalent concepts. The only difference is that the cash flows are in the opposite direction. Thus, we have

$$R_t = -C_t \text{ for } t = 0, 1, 2, \ldots, n. \tag{7.1}$$

Although it is not necessary to define C_t and R_t separately in this fashion, we will find it convenient to have both symbols available in developing certain formulas in this chapter.

It may happen that there is both a contribution and return at the same point in time. In this case, the two are offset against each other. For example, if we have a contribution of 5000 at time 5 and also a return of 1000 at time 5, then $C_5 = 4000$ and $R_5 = -4000$. The C_t's and the R_t's are frequently referred to as *net cash flows*. The word "net" refers to the process of offsetting any contributions and returns at the same point in time.

The reader is cautioned that the term "net cash flow," by itself, does not indicate in which direction cash flows are considered to be positive and in which direction they are considered to be negative. It is vital in any real-world application to carefully identify the designation of signs and be consistent throughout.

We have chosen the time periods such that the investment begins at time $t=0$ and ends at time $t=n$. Thus, if the investment is positive during this interval, we have $C_0>0\ (R_0<0)$ and $C_n<0\ (R_0>0)$. However, $C_t=-R_t$ may be either positive, negative, or zero for $t=1,2,\ldots,n-1$.

To illustrate these definitions, consider a ten-year investment project in which an investor contributes $10,000 at the beginning of the first year, $5000 at the beginning of the second year, and then incurs maintenance expenses of $1000 at the beginning of each remaining year thereafter. The project is expected to provide an investment return at the end of each year for the last five years of the project, starting at $8000 and increasing $1000 per year thereafter.

Table 7.1 summarizes the cash flows for this investment project. The last column contains values of R_t in order to display the net cash flows from the investment. We have chosen to work with R_t rather than C_t in this application, for reasons which will become clear as we proceed.

Table 7.1 Cash Flows for Investment Project Illustrated in Section 7.2

Year	*Contributions*	*Returns*	*Net Cash Flow* R_t
0	10,000	0	−10,000
1	5,000	0	− 5,000
2	1,000	0	− 1,000
3	1,000	0	− 1,000
4	1,000	0	− 1,000
5	1,000	0	− 1,000
6	1,000	8,000	7,000
7	1,000	9,000	8,000
8	1,000	10,000	9,000
9	1,000	11,000	10,000
10	0	12,000	12,000
Total	23,000	50,000	27,000

An investment project will be profitable to the investor if total returns exceed total contributions. For the illustrative investment project in Table 7.1 the investor contributes a total of \$23,000 and has a total return equal to \$50,000 indicating that the total profit on this investment is equal to 50,000 – 23,000 = \$27,000.

Of course, the astute reader will immediately point out that we should not be directly comparing contributions and returns made at various points in time without considering the time value of money. Rather we should be using an equation of value in which all contributions and returns are converted to values at the same comparison date.

Assume that the rate of interest per period is i. Then the *net present value* (NPV) at rate i of net cash flows by the discounted cash flow technique is denoted by $P(i)$ and is given by

$$\text{NPV} = P(i) = \sum_{t=0}^{n} v^t R_t. \tag{7.2}$$

The value of $P(i)$ can be either positive or negative, depending on i. For the investment project illustrated in Table 7.1, $P(i)$ will be positive for "low" values of i and negative for "high" values of i. The positive net cash flows during the last few years of the investment will dominate the negative net cash flows during the early years when present values are computed at a "low" rate of interest, while the opposite is true at a "high" rate of interest.

Figure 7.1 graphically illustrates the values of $P(i)$ as i changes for the investment project in Table 7.1.

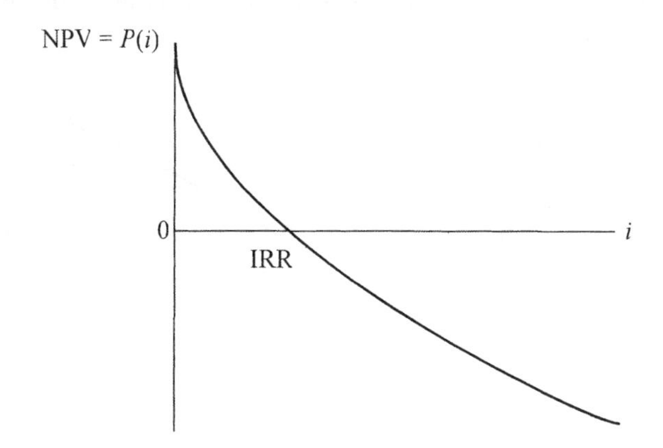

Figure 7.1 Graph of NPV = *P(i)* for the investment project in Table 7.1

A very important special case of formula (7.2) is the one in which $P(i)=0$, i.e.

$$\text{NPV} = P(i) = \sum_{t=0} v^t R_t = 0. \tag{7.3}$$

The rate of interest i which satisfies formula (7.3) is called the *yield rate* on the investment. Stated in words:

> *The yield rate is that rate of interest at which the present value of net cash flows from the investment is equal to the present value of net cash flows into the investment.*

In the business and finance literature the yield rate is often called the *internal rate of return* (IRR). The terms "yield rate" and "internal rate of return" can be used interchangeably.

Yield rates are not really a new concept; we have encountered them before. The unknown rate of interest problems in Chapters 2, 3 and 4 can be characterized as yield rate problems. Also, the loan interest rate in Chapter 5 and the yield to maturity on a bond in Chapter 6 are further examples of this concept.

In this section so far we have adopted the vantage point of the investor, i.e. lender. However, if we are dealing with two-party transactions, then we could just as easily adopt the vantage point of the borrower. If this is done, then the values of C_t and R_t change signs.

In this case, the graph of $P(i)$ would be increasing rather than decreasing. Figure 7.2 illustrates the NPV from the standpoint of the borrower for the investment project in Table 7.1. Note that Figure 7.2 is the reflection of Figure 7.1 around the x-axis.

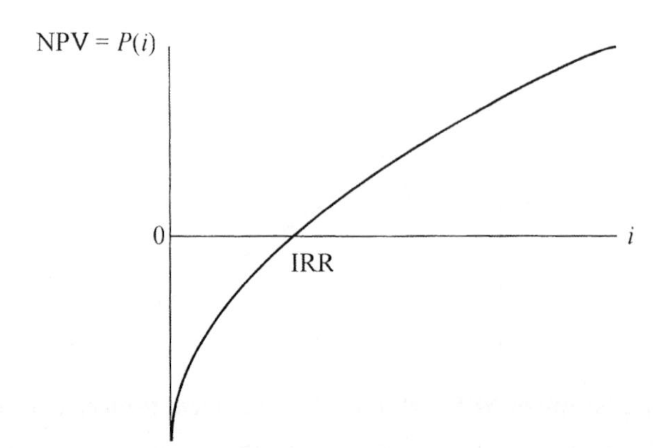

Figure 7.2 Graph of NPV = $P(i)$ from the standpoint of a borrower in a two-party transaction

However, the value of the yield rate given by formula (7.3) remains unchanged. Thus, the yield rate on a transaction is totally determined by the net cash flows defined in that transaction and their timing, and is the same from either the borrower's or lender's perspective.

Yield rates are frequently used as an index to measure how favorable or unfavorable a particular transaction may be. From the lender's perspective, the higher the yield rate the more favorable the transaction. From the borrower's perspective, the opposite is the case. Although these convenient rules will usually produce reasonable results, Section 7.3, 7.9, and 7.10 contain illustrations in which difficulties arise in using yield rates in this fashion. Sections 7.9 and 7.10 contain a more systematic discussion of methods of comparing different financial transactions.

Yield rates need not be positive. If the yield rate is zero, then the investor (lender) received no return on investment. In this case, we have total contributions equal to total returns. If the yield rate is negative, then the investor (lender) lost money on the investment. We will assume that such negative yield rates satisfy $-1 < i < 0$. It is difficult to find any practical interpretation for a situation in which $i < -1$, i.e. $1 + i < 0$.

Not all transactions are two-party transactions. For example, consider the investment project summarized in Table 7.1. Quite conceivably, the cash outflows in this project were directed to multiple parties and/or the cash inflows arose from multiple sources. If that is the case, the yield rate calculation for the investor (lender) is still valid. However, there is no single borrower on the other side of the transaction for which the same yield rate applies.

Another important consideration in using yield rates is to consider the period of time involved. For example, consider investing a sum of money under Options A and B. Option A credits 7% effective for five years, while Option B credits 6% effective for ten years. Which option should we choose as an investor?

To say that Option A is better than Option B because its yield rate is higher is naive. If we wish to invest for only five years, then the simple comparison of yield rates is valid. However, if we wish to invest for ten years, then we need to consider the rate at which we can reinvest the proceeds from Option A after the end of the first five years. Section 7.4 contains a more comprehensive treatment of reinvestment rates.

This leads to an important principle in using yield rates (IRRs) to compare alternative investments:

It is valid to use yield rates (IRRs) to compare alternative investments only if the period of investment is the same for all the alternatives.

The above definitions and formulas assume payments at equally spaced periods of time. However, the results can easily be generalized to other intervals as well.

Solving for yield rates is analogous to solving for unknown rates of interest on annuities. In fact, if the payments constitute a basic annuity, then the techniques discussed in Section 3.7 can be applied directly.

If the payments do not constitute a basic annuity, the techniques would be similar. In general, an iteration method would typically be applied to the equation of value given by formula (7.3). The easiest way to solve such problems in practice would be to utilize a financial calculator.

Financial calculators typically have two keys labeled NPV and IRR. The NPV key is used to compute net present values for various values of i using formula (7.2). Similarly, the IRR key is used to compute the internal rate of return using formula (7.3).

Financial calculators have a more general system for entering the net cash flows, i.e. R_t for $1,2,\ldots,n$ than is needed for level annuities in Chapter 3. Different values of R_t can be entered for each value of t. Usually, a streamlined system is available for situations in which the R_t values are constant throughout some portion of the range of values of t. Data entry is identical for both the NPV and the IRR calculations, and can be used for either. The data entry system varies from financial calculator to financial calculator. The reader is referred to the owner's manual, or other instructions, for the calculator being used.

Example 7.1 ***Find the yield rate (IRR) for the investment project summarized in Table 7.1.***

The equation of value is

$$1000\left(-10-5v-v^2-v^3-v^4-v^5+7v^6+8v^7+9v^8+10v^9+12v^{10}\right) = 0.$$

The yield rate (IRR) computed on a financial calculator is found to be .1296, or 12.96%.

Example 7.2 Find the effective rate which the investment under Option A must earn for the second five years to be equivalent to the investment under Option B for the entire ten years for the illustration given in this section.

Let the rate in question be denoted by i. The equation of value is

$$(1.07)^5(1+i)^5 = (1.06)^{10}$$

so that

$$i = \frac{(1.06)^2}{1.07} - 1 = .0501, \text{ or } 5.01\% .$$

Thus, if the investor expects the prevailing interest rate to be greater than 5.01% at the end of 5 years, Option A would be the better choice. Otherwise, Option B would be preferred.

7.3 UNIQUENESS OF THE YIELD RATE

Our intuition leads us to expect that the yield rate (IRR) as defined in Section 7.2 will be unique; and, in fact, in most commonly encountered financial transactions the yield rate is unique. However, transactions are occasionally encountered in which a yield rate is not unique.

As an example, consider a transaction in which a person makes payments of \$100 immediately and \$132 at the end of two years in exchange for a payment in return of \$230 at the end of one year. An equation of value for this transaction is

$$100(1+i)^2 + 132 = 230(1+i)$$

or

$$(1+i)^2 - 2.3(1+i) + 1.32 = 0.$$

Now factoring we obtain

$$\left[(1+i)-1.1\right]\left[(1+i)-1.2\right] = 0.$$

Thus, the yield rate i is equal to either 10% or 20%!

The fact that transactions exist with multiple yield rates is difficult for most people to comprehend intuitively. However, it is not surprising when we recall formula (7.3)

$$\text{NPV} = P(i) = \sum_{t=0}^{n} v^t R_t = 0. \tag{7.3}$$

Formula (7.3) is an nth degree polynomial in v and could be written as an nth degree polynomial in i by simply multiplying both sides by $(1+i)^n$. Of course, it is well-known that an nth degree polynomial has n roots (counting complex roots and roots of multiplicity m, where $m > 1$, as m roots). In the example given immediately above, we have a quadratic with two distinct positive roots for i.

Since the yield rate is widely used as a measure of the financial value of a transaction, it is important in practice to be able to ascertain whether or not a yield rate is unique.

One very common situation in which the yield rate will be unique is when all cash flows in one direction are made before the cash flows in the other direction. Stated slightly more generally, this situation is one in which the net cash flows are all of one sign for the first portion of the transaction and then have the opposite sign for the remainder of the transaction.

Stated in mathematical terms, this situation can be characterized as one in which some value of k exists, $0<k<n$, such that $R_t \leq 0$ for $t = 0, 1, 2, \ldots, k$ and $R_t \geq 0$ for $t = k+1, k+2, \ldots, n$. The financial transaction given in Table 7.1 is of this type with $n = 10$ and $k = 5$.

It can easily be shown that a yield rate in this situation will be unique. Looking at formula (7.3) as an nth degree polynomial, we see that there is only one sign change. From Descartes' rule of signs we know that there will be at most one positive real root. Since $v > 0$, then $i > -1$. Thus, the uniqueness will hold not only for positive values of i, but also for negative values of $i > -1$. This covers all values of concern, since values of $i < -1$ have no practical significance.

Descartes' rule of signs will also give us an upper bound on the number of multiple yield rates which may exist. The maximum number of yield rates is equal to the number of sign changes in the net cash flows. Of course, the actual number of yield rates may be less than the maximum.

Actually, yield rates are unique under a broader set of conditions than given above. It is possible to show that if the outstanding investment balance is positive at all points throughout the period of investment, then the yield rate will be unique.

Let B_t be the outstanding investment balance at time t where $t = 0, 1, 2, \ldots, n$. Then we have

$$B_0 = C_0 \tag{7.4}$$

and

$$B_t = B_{t-1}(1+i)+C_t \text{ for } t = 1, 2, \ldots, n. \tag{7.5}$$

Note that formula (7.5) is analogous to formulas (5.3) and (6.10) connecting successive loan balances in a loan amortization schedule and successive book values in a bond amortization schedule.

It is possible to show that if

1. $i > -1$ exists such that formula (7.3) is satisfied, and

2. For such i, $B_t > 0$ for $t = 0, 1, \ldots, n-1$,

then i is unique. The condition $i > -1$ is necessary to ensure that $1 + i$ is positive. The proof of this result is given in Appendix 7 at the end of the chapter.

Thus, if the outstanding investment balance is positive at all points throughout the period of investment, then the yield rate will be unique. However, if the outstanding investment balance ever becomes negative at any one point, then a yield rate is not necessarily unique. Figure 7.3 illustrates a hypothetical investment involving multiple yield rates.

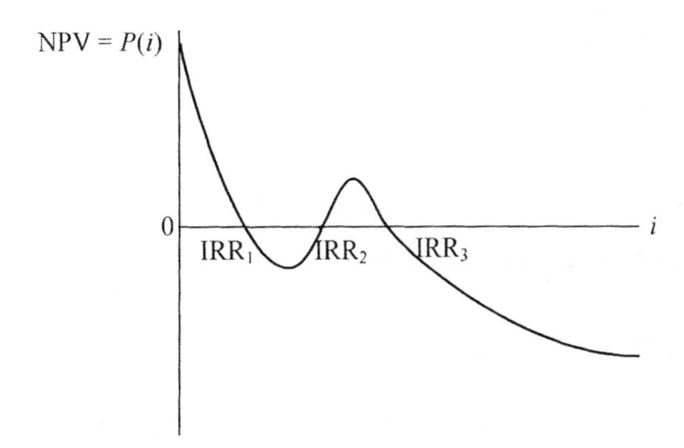

Figure 7.3 Hypothetical investment involving multiple yield rates.

The situations in which multiple yield rates can occur may strike the reader as somewhat artificial and not very realistic of typical financial transactions. Although such situations are not common, they do occur in practice. A realistic example would be an investment in a physical plant which requires major renovation expenses midway through the period of investment. The resulting sign change in net cash flows may lead to multiple yield rates.

The discussion in this section has focused on the possibility of multiple yield rates. However, it is also possible that no yield rate exists or that all yield rates are imaginary. These possibilities are illustrated in Examples 7.3 and 7.4, respectively.

***Example 7.3** A is able to borrow $1000 from B for one year at 8% effective and lend it to C for one year at 10% effective. What is A's yield rate on this transaction?*

In this example, A is able to make a $20 profit at the end of one year in exchange for no net investment at all. Thus, no finite yield rate exists. We could say the yield rate is infinite. However, such a statement would not distinguish this transaction from an even more favorable one in which A is able to lend the $1000 to a fourth party D at 12% effective.

***Example 7.4** What is the yield rate on a transaction in which a person makes payments of $100 immediately and $101 at the end of two years, in exchange for a payment of $200 at the end of one year?*

An equation of value is

$$100(1+i)^2+101 = 200(1+i)$$

or

$$100i^2 = -1.$$

Thus, the yield rates are all imaginary numbers!

7.4 REINVESTMENT RATES

So far in this book we have not directly considered the reinvestment by the lender of payments received from the borrower. This is equivalent to the implicit assumption that the lender can reinvest payments received from the borrower at a *reinvestment rate* equal to the original investment rate.

In particular, the yield rate (IRR), defined and analyzed in Section 7.2, is assumed to be level throughout the entire period of investment. Thus, all intermediate net cash flows during the period of investment are valued using this one level rate of interest. In effect, this is equivalent to saying that the reinvestment rate is not only level throughout the entire period of investment, but, in fact is equal to the yield rate (IRR).

This may not be a valid assumption in practice depending upon the particular circumstances involved. If the lender (investor) is not able to reinvest the payments from the borrower at rates as high as the original investment, then the overall yield rate considering reinvestment will be lower than the stated yield rate. On the other hand, if the lender (investor) is able to reinvest such payments at even higher rates, then the overall yield rate will be higher than that stated.

Introductory examples

Actually, we have already seen one simple example of a problem considering reinvestment rates. Example 7.2 considers the reinvestment of proceeds from Option A at the end of five years in order to make a valid comparison with Option B over the ten-year period in question. We now analyze two other situations in which reinvestment rates are directly taken into account.

First, consider the investment of 1 for n periods at rate i such that the interest is reinvested at rate j. In practice, j may be either larger or smaller than i. It is desired to find the accumulated value at the end of n periods. This situation is illustrated in Figure 7.4.

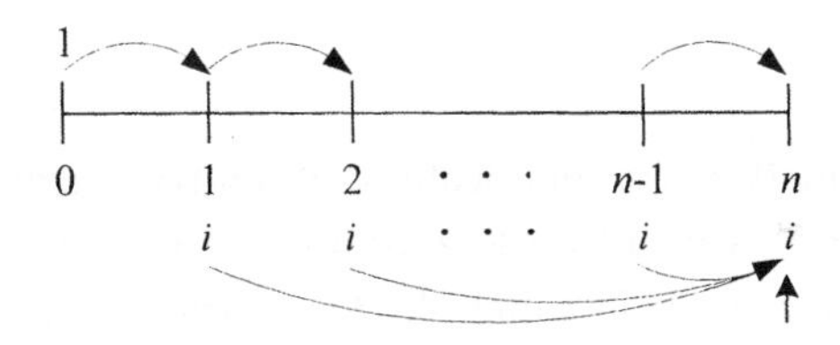

Figure 7.4 Time diagram for reinvestment rates involving an investment of 1 for *n* periods

The accumulated value at the end of n periods is equal to the principal plus the accumulated value of the interest, i.e.

$$1 + i\, s_{\overline{n}|j} \,. \tag{7.6}$$

Formula (7.6) simplifies to the familiar $(1+i)^n$ if $i = j$.

Second, consider the investment of 1 at the end of each period for n periods at rate i such that the interest is reinvested at rate j. It is desired to find the accumulated value of this annuity at the end of n periods. This situation is illustrated in Figure 7.5.

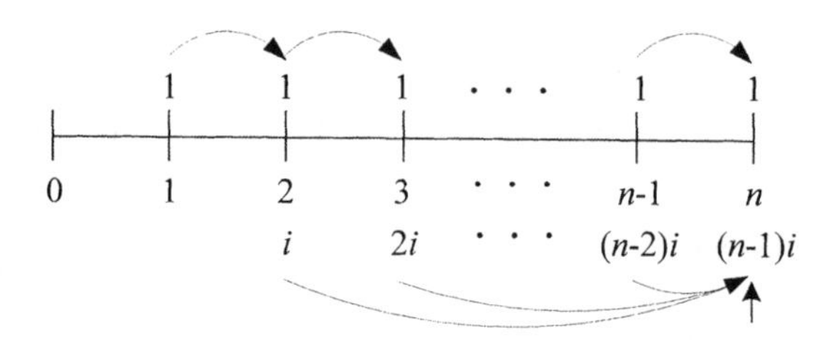

Figure 7.5 Time diagram for reinvestment rates involving an investment of 1 at the end of each period for n periods

The accumulated value of this annuity is equal to the sum of the annuity payments and the accumulated value of the interest, i.e.

$$n+i\left(Is\right)_{\overline{n-1}|j} = n+i\left(\frac{s_{\overline{n}|j}-n}{j}\right). \tag{7.7}$$

Formula (7.7) simplifies to the familiar $s_{\overline{n}|}$ if $i=j$.

Analysis for loans

We will now analyze the implication of reinvestment rates on loans as discussed in Chapter 5. Consider a loan of amount L which is repaid with level payments of R over n periods in which the loan earns a rate of interest of i per period. The basic equation of value at issue of the loan, i.e. at $t=0$ is

$$L = Ra_{\overline{n}|i}. \tag{7.8}$$

The level yields rate (IRR) is obviously i ignoring investment rates.

Now consider the position of the lender who invests the original loan amount of L and receives n periodic payments of R in return. Assume that the investor is unable to reinvest the payments of R at interest rate i as received, but can reinvest them at rate j. We wish to find an adjusted yield rate (IRR) denoted by i' which reflects the impact of a different reinvestment rate j than the loan interest rate i.

In Section 7.2 when setting up an equation of value to determine yield rates, typically the beginning of the period of investment $t=0$ is used, as in formula (7.3). However, when reinvestment rates are considered, it is usually advisable to use $t=n$, i.e. use the end of the period of investment instead.

Thus, the equation of value considering reinvestment rate j for the loan defined in formula (7.8) is

$$L(1+i')^n = Rs_{\overline{n}|j} \tag{7.9}$$

since the original loan amount accumulated to the end of the period of investment at the yield rate i' must equal the accumulated value at the same point in time of all the accumulated loan payments at reinvestment rate j. Formula (7.9) is then solved for i'.

The reader might question why the loan interest rate i does not appear in formula (7.9). It is true that i does not explicitly appear in formula (7.9). However, the yield rate i' depends on i, since i is the key determinant of the payment R necessary to repay the loan in formula (7.8).

Analysis for bonds

A similar analysis can be done for bonds. In Chapter 6 we computed the yield rate i ignoring reinvestment rates. However, investors in bonds need to consider the rates at which coupons from the bonds can be reinvested. If the investor can only reinvest the coupons at a lower rate than i, then i overstates the yield rate actually realized on the transaction taking into account reinvestment rates. However if the investor is fortunate enough to be able to reinvest the coupons at a higher rate than i, then the overall yield rate on the transaction will exceed i.

Consider the situation in which a bond is purchased for P, coupons of Fr are paid at the end of each period for n periods, the bond is redeemed for C at the end of n periods, and the coupons are reinvested at rate j. Again denoting the yield rate considering reinvestment by i' (to distinguish it from i), we would have the following equation of value quite analogous to formula (7.9)

$$P(1+i')^n = Frs_{\overline{n}|j} + C \tag{7.10}$$

since both sides represent the accumulated value of the investment at the end of n periods. An illustration of yield rates taking into account reinvestment rates is given in Example 7.7.

The effect of reinvestment rates is particularly important in analyzing callable or putable bonds, as discussed in Section 6.7. Whether or not such bonds are likely to be redeemed early is highly dependent on future price changes for the bonds, which in turn is highly dependent on changes in the level of future interest rates.

One of the reasons for the popularity of zero coupon bonds in recent years is that such bonds do not present a reinvestment risk to the investor. Since there are no coupons to reinvest, the yield rate is locked-in at the date of purchase.

Closing

The consideration of reinvestment rates in financial calculations has become increasingly important and more widely used than heretofore. This reflects the greater volatility of interest rates in recent years, as well as the increased sophistication of investors.

An important consideration to a lender (investor) is the speed of repayment by the borrower. The "faster" the rate of repayment, the more significant the reinvestment issue becomes. The "slower" the rate of repayment, the longer the initial investment rate will dominate the calculation. This phenomenon is illustrated in Example 7.6. An analytical approach to the measurement of the speed of repayment is developed in Chapter 11.

One final observation is that the results of financial calculations involving reinvestment rates are dependent upon the period of time under consideration. Thus, it is important to specify the period of time for which calculations are being made when reinvestment rates are being taken into account.

***Example 7.5** Payments of $1000 are invested at the beginning of each year for 10 years. The payments earn interest at 7% effective and the interest can be reinvested at 5% effective.*

(1) Find the amount in the fund at the end of 10 years.

(2) Find the purchase price an investor should pay to produce a yield rate of 8% effective.

1. A modification of formula (7.7) appropriate for an annuity-due is

$$n+i\,(Is)_{\overline{n}|} = n+i\left[\frac{s_{\overline{n+1}|j}-(n+1)}{j}\right].$$

Thus, the amount of the fund at the end of 10 years is

$$1000\left[10+.07\left(\frac{s_{\overline{11}|.05}-11}{.05}\right)\right] = 1000\left[10+.07\left(\frac{14.2068-11}{.05}\right)\right] = \$14,490$$

to the nearest dollar. The answer lies between $1000\ddot{s}_{\overline{10}|.05}=13,207$ and $1000\,\ddot{s}_{\overline{10}|.07}=14,784,$ as would be expected.

2. The purchase price to yield 8% effective would be the present value at time $t=0$ of the value at time $t=10,$ which is

$$14,490(1.08)^{-10} = \$6712$$

to the nearest dollar.

Example 7.6 Compare the yield rates on the three loan repayment schedules described in Example 3.3, if the repayments to the lender can be reinvested at only 7% instead of 9% as earned on the original loan.

1. The accumulated value of all payments at the end of 10 years is

$$1000(1.09)^{10} = 2367.36.$$

The yield rate i is found from the equation of value

$$1000(1+i)^{10} = 2367.36$$

which is immediately seen to be i = .09. In this case, the reinvestment risk totally disappears, since the borrower makes no payments until the end of the period of the loan.

2. The accumulated value of all payments at the end of 10 years is

$$1000+90\,s_{\overline{10}|.07} = 1000+90(13.8164) = 2243.48$$

by a direct application of formula (7.6). The yield rate i is found from the equation of value

$$1000(1+i)^{10} = 2243.48$$

which gives $i = .0842$, or 8.42%. This answer is less than the answer to case 1, since the reinvestment rate of 7% has an effect in this case.

3. The accumulated value of all payments at the end of 10 years is

$$\left(\frac{1000}{a_{\overline{10}|.09}}\right) s_{\overline{10}|.07} = (155.82)(13.8164) = 2152.88.$$

The yield rate i is found from the equation of value

$$1000(1+i)^{10} = 2152.88$$

which gives $i = .0797$, or 7.97%. This answer is less than the answer to case 2, since the repayment schedule for case 3 is "faster" than case 2 increasing the effect of the reinvestment rate on the answer even more. Note that the yield rate still exceeds 7%, as would be expected.

***Example 7.7** Assume that the coupons from the bond in Example 6.6 can be reinvested at only 6% convertible semiannually. Find the yield rate taking into account reinvestment rates.*

A direct application of formula (7.10) gives

$$90(1+i')^{20} = 4\,s_{\overline{20}|.03} + 100$$

or

$$(1+i')^{20} = \frac{(4)(26.8704) + 100}{90} = 2.30535$$

which can be solved to give $i' = .04265$. The yield rate taking into account reinvestment rates is $2(.04265) = .0853$, or 8.53%. Thus, the yield rate of 9.58% obtained in Example 6.6 drops to 8.53% if the coupons can be reinvested at only 6%.

7.5 INTEREST MEASUREMENT OF A FUND

A common requirement in practical work is the determination of the yield rate earned by an investment fund. Recall that the basic definition of an effective rate of interest given in Section 1.3 assumed that the principal remains constant throughout the period and that all the interest earned is paid at the end of the period. In practice these assumptions are often not satisfied. It is common for a fund to be incremented with new principal deposits, decremented with principal withdrawals, and incremented with interest earnings many times throughout a period, often at irregular intervals. Some method must be devised for these situations to determine reasonable effective rates of interest.

Consider finding the effective rate of interest earned by a fund over one measurement period. We make the following definitions:

A = the amount in the fund at the beginning of the period
B = the amount in the fund at the end of the period
I = the amount of interest earned during the period
C_t = the net amount of principal contributed at time t (positive or negative), where $0 \le t \le 1$
C = the total net amount of principal contributed during the period (positive or negative), i.e.

$$C = \sum_t C_t$$

${}_ai_b$ = the amount of interest earned by 1 invested at time b over the following period of length a, where $a \ge 0$, $b \ge 0$, and $a + b \le 1$

Note that in terms of the notation used in Section 7.3 $A = B_0$ and $B = B_1$. We use the alternative notation involving A and B in order to develop a formula in widespread use with its traditional notation.

The fund at the end of the period must equal the fund at the beginning of the period plus net principal contributed (positive or negative) plus interest earned, i.e.

$$B = A + C + I. \tag{7.11}$$

To be consistent with the definition of the effective rate of interest given in Section 1.3 we will assume that all the interest earned I is received at the end of the period. Then an exact equation of value for the interest earned over the period $0 \le t \le 1$ is

$$I = iA + \sum_t C_t \cdot {}_{1-t}i_t. \tag{7.12}$$

Unfortunately, formula (7.12) is not in a form which can be directly solved for i. It is necessary to find values for ${}_{1-t}i_t$. Assuming compound interest throughout the period, we have

$$_{1-t}i_t = (1+i)^{1-t} - 1 . \tag{7.13}$$

We can substitute formula (7.13) into formula (7.12) obtaining an exact equation for i. This equation can be solved by iteration. Section 7.3 guarantees that the rate found by iteration will be unique as long as the fund balance never becomes negative.

If a computer or financial calculator is not available to do the iteration, or if only approximate answers are required, it is possible to produce a simplified formula by making the assumption that

$$_{1-t}i_t \approx (1-t)\,i . \tag{7.14}$$

Formula (7.14) is a version of simple interest applied over fractional periods for this situation. We can substitute formula (7.14) into formula (7.12) and solve for i, obtaining

$$i \approx \frac{I}{A + \sum_t C_t (1-t)} . \tag{7.15}$$

The numerator of formula (7.15) is the amount of interest earned on the fund. The denominator can be interpreted as the average amount of principal invested and is often called the *exposure associated with i*. Although formula (7.15) does not produce a true effective rate of interest because of the simple interest assumption, it will generally produce results quite close to a true effective rate of interest as long as the C_t's are small in relation to A, which is often the case in practice. However, if the C_t's are not small in relation to A, then the error can become significant.

Formula (7.15) is in a form which can be directly calculated. However, the summation term in the denominator is often rather laborious. Therefore, a further simplifying assumption is often made; namely, that principal deposits and withdrawals occur uniformly throughout the period. Thus, on average, we might assume that net principal contributions occur at time $t = 1/2$. If this assumption is made, then formula (7.15) becomes

$$\begin{aligned} i &\approx \frac{I}{A + .5C} \\ &= \frac{I}{A + .5\,(B - A - I)} \qquad \text{from formula (7.11)} \end{aligned}$$

$$= \frac{2I}{A+B-I}. \tag{7.16}$$

Figure (7.6) is an illustrative time diagram for this formula.

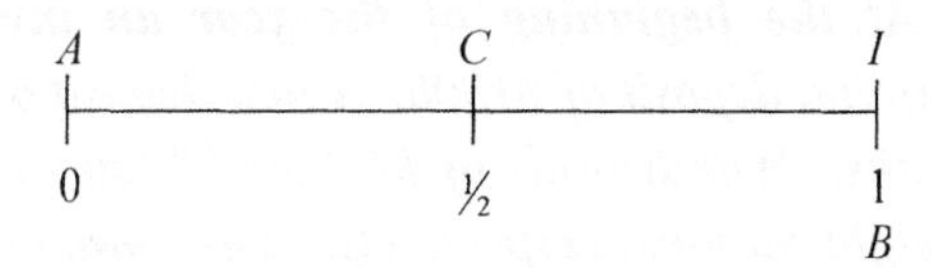

Figure 7.6 Time diagram for formula (7.16)

Formula (7.16) is an important formula which is widely used in practice to calculate approximate earned rates of interest. For example, historically it has been used to compute the yield rate on invested assets of insurance companies. It is a very convenient formula, since it involves only A, B, and I, which are all readily available. However, it should be remembered that it does assume that net principal contributions occur at time $t = 1/2$. If this assumption is not warranted, then the more exact (but still approximate) formula (7.15) should be used.

The choice of valuation methods for securities as discussed in Section 6.11 will affect computed yield rates using formula (7.16). The values of A and B are dependent upon the asset valuation methods used. Also, the value of I may vary substantially depending upon whether or not capital gains are included in I.

In some cases it is possible to develop simplified versions of formula (7.15) that will be more accurate than formula (7.16). For example, if it is known that net principal contributions occur at time k on average where $0 < k < 1$, then a generalization of formula (7.16) is given by

$$i \approx \frac{I}{kA + (1-k)B - (1-k)I}. \tag{7.17}$$

The derivation of formula (7.17) is left as an exercise. It is clear that formula (7.17) becomes formula (7.16) when $k = 1/2$. However, if we know that net principal contributions occur on April 1 on the average, then for calendar year calculations the use of formula (7.17) with $k = 1/4$ should produce superior answers to formula (7.16).

Appendix 7 at the end of the chapter contains additional material extending the discussion in this section for those readers interested in pursuing the above development in greater depth. Topics addressed are: further analysis of the simple interest assumption and interest measurement using continuous functions.

Example 7.8 ***At the beginning of the year an investment fund was established with an initial deposit of \$1000. A new deposit of \$500 was made at the end of four months. Withdrawals of \$200 and \$100 were made at the end of six months and eight months, respectively. The amount in the fund at the end of the year is \$1272. Find the approximate effective rate of interest earned by the fund during the year, using formula (7.15).***

The interest earned I is computed to be

$$1272-(1000+500-200-100) = 72.$$

Applying formula (7.15) we have

$$i \approx \frac{72}{1000+\frac{2}{3}\cdot 500-\frac{1}{2}\cdot 200-\frac{1}{3}\cdot 100} = \frac{72}{1200} = .06, \text{ or } 6\%.$$

Example 7.9 ***Find the effective rate of interest earned during a calendar year by an insurance company with the following data:***

Assets, beginning of year	***\$10,000,000***
Premium income	***1,000,000***
Net investment income	***510,000***
Policy benefits	***420,000***
Other expenses	***180,000***

We have the following:

$$\begin{aligned} A &= 10{,}000{,}000 \\ B &= 10{,}000{,}000+1{,}000{,}000+510{,}000-420{,}000-180{,}000 \\ &= 10{,}910{,}000 \\ I &= 510{,}000. \end{aligned}$$

Therefore, using formula (7.16)

$$\begin{aligned} i &\approx \frac{2(510{,}000)}{10{,}000{,}000+10{,}910{,}000-510{,}000} \\ &= .05, \text{ or } 5\% . \end{aligned}$$

7.6 TIME-WEIGHTED RATES OF INTEREST

The methods for computing the yield rate earned by an investment fund outlined in Section 7.5 are sensitive to the amounts of money invested during various subperiods when the investment experience is volatile during the year. For example, if "large" amounts happen to be invested when the earnings on the fund are "high" and "small" amounts when the earnings are "low," the overall yield rate will be quite favorable. The reverse situation will, of course, produce the opposite result.

We will demonstrate this phenomenon with an extreme illustration. Assume an investor has an investment fund in which a \$1000 investment is worth only \$500 at the end of six months, but is worth \$1000 again at the end of the year. If no principal is deposited or withdrawn during the year, then the yield rate for the entire year is obviously zero.

Now consider what happens if the investor doubles the outstanding investment at the end of six months. The original \$1000 is worth only \$500 at the end of six months, so the investor deposits another \$500 at that time. The new balance of \$1000 is then worth \$2000 at the end of the year. The equation of value for this transaction is

$$1000(1+i)+500(1+i)^{1/2} = 2000.$$

This equation can be solved as a quadratic in $(1+i)^{1/2}$, which produces the yield rate $i = .4069$, or 40.69%.

Next consider what happens if the investor halves the outstanding investment at the end of six months. The original \$1000 is worth only \$500 at the end of six months, so the investor withdraws \$250 at that time. The new balance of \$250 is then worth \$500 at the end of the year. The equation of value for this transaction is

$$1000(1+i)-250(1+i)^{1/2} = 500.$$

Again, solving the quadratic in $(1+i)^{1/2}$ produces the yield rate $i = -.2892$, or -28.92%.

It would seem that the underlying yield rate for the fund based on its actual investment performance should be zero. However, in the first illustration above the computed yield rate is considerably greater than zero because the investor deposited principal just as the investment experience was about to become very favorable. In the second illustration just the opposite happened. The investor withdrew principal which caused the yield rate to become significantly negative.

Since the amount invested clearly affects the computed yield rate, rates computed by the methods in Section 7.5 are sometimes called *dollar-weighted rates of interest.* It is important to observe that compound interest calculations as developed in previous chapters are done on this basis.

Now assume that the investment decisions for the fund are being made by an investment manager, while the decisions to deposit or withdraw principal are made by the owner of the fund. Although the dollar-weighted calculations in the above two illustrations provide an accurate measure of the actual return realized by the owner of the fund, they do not provide a good measure of the "true" performance of the investment manager, which was zero.

Such a measure is provided by an alternative basis for calculating fund yields called *time-weighted rates of interest.* In this method we consider successive subintervals of the year each time a deposit or withdrawal is made. Thus, in the illustrations given above, the yield rate for the first six months of the year is $j_1 = -50\%$ and for the second six months is $j_2 = +100\%$. We can combine these for the entire year to obtain

$$1+i = (1+j_1)(1+j_2) = (1-.5)(1+1) = 1.$$

Thus, $i = 0$ regardless of when principal is deposited or withdrawn.

We can generalize this approach as follows. Assume that m–1 principal deposits or withdrawals are made during the year at times $t_1, t_2, \ldots, t_{m-1}$. This will divide the year into m subintervals as illustrated in Figure 7.7.

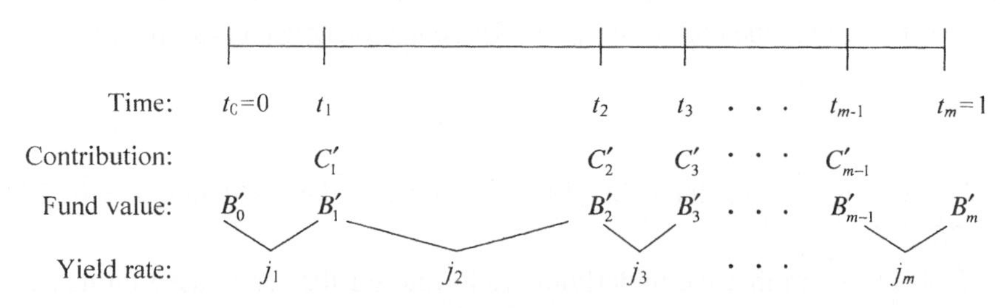

Figure 7.7 Time diagram for time-weighted rates of interest

Let the amount of the net contribution to the fund (positive or negative) at time t_k be denoted by C'_k for $k = 1, 2, \ldots, m-1$. The prime on the symbol is being used to distinguish this notation from that used earlier in the chapter, i.e. C'_k is actually equal to C_{t_k}.

Let the fund values immediately before each contribution to the fund be denoted by B'_k for $k = 1, 2, \ldots, m-1$. Also the fund value at the beginning of the year is denoted by $B'_0 = B_0$, while the fund value at the end of year is denoted by $B'_m = B_1$. Finally, let the yield rates over the m subintervals be denoted by j_k for $k = 1, 2, \ldots, m$.

The yield rates over the m subintervals by the time-weighted method are given by

$$1 + j_k = \frac{B'_k}{B'_{k-1} + C'_{k-1}}$$

or

$$j_k = \frac{B'_k}{B'_{k-1} + C'_{k-1}} - 1 \text{ for } k = 1, 2, \ldots, m. \tag{7.18}$$

In words, one plus the yield rate for each subinterval is equal to the fund balance at the end of the subinterval divided by the fund balance at the beginning of the subinterval.

The overall yield rate for the entire year is then given by

$$1 + i = (1 + j_1)(1 + j_2)\cdots(1 + j_m)$$

or

$$i = (1 + j_1)(1 + j_2)\cdots(1 + j_m) - 1. \tag{7.19}$$

The reader will note that the symbol "i" in this section has been used for both dollar-weighted values and for time-weighted values, which is a possible source of ambiguity. Sometimes dollar-weighted values are denoted by "i^{DW}" and time-weighted value are denoted by "i^{TW}" to avoid this ambiguity.

More specifically, in applications involving both types of rates, the "i" from the formulas in Section 7.5 could be labeled "i^{DW}" while the "i" in formula (7.19) could be labeled "i^{TW}".

It is important to note that yield rates computed by the time-weighted method are not consistent with an assumption of compound interest. Nevertheless, time-weighted calculations do provide better indicators of underlying investment performance than dollar-weighted calculations. However, dollar-weighted calculations provide a valid measure of the actual investment results achieved.

Example 7.10 On January 1 an investment account is worth \$100,000. On May 1 the value has increased to \$112,000 and \$30,000 of new principal is deposited. On November 1 the value has declined to \$125,000 and \$42,000 is withdrawn. On January 1 of the following year the investment account is again worth \$100,000. Compute the yield rate by:
(1) The dollar-weighted method.
(2) The time-weighted method.

Figure 7.8 illustrates the transactions involved in this example.

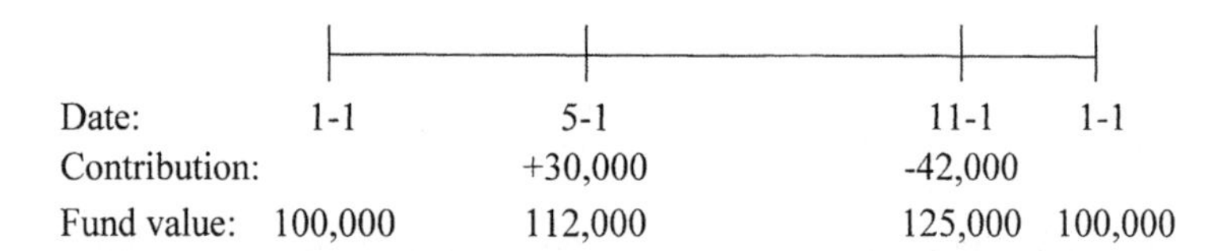

Figure 7.8 Time diagram for Example 7.10

1. The total amount of interest earned can be found from formula (7.11)

$$B = A + C + I$$

which gives

$$100,000 = 100,000 + (30,000 - 42,000) + I$$

or

$$I = 12,000.$$

We will use formula (7.15) to find the dollar-weighted rate of interest

$$i^{DW} \approx \frac{12,000}{100,000 + \frac{2}{3} \cdot 30,000 - \frac{1}{6} \cdot 42,000}$$

$$= \frac{12,000}{113,000} = .1062, \text{ or } 10.62\%.$$

A more refined answer could be obtained by using compound interest instead of formula (7.15), but solving the equation of value would require a difficult iteration. The extra effort is not worth the trouble for purposes of this example. It is important to note that the intermediate fund balances (112,000 and 125,000 in this example) do not have any effect on the answer when using the dollar-weighted method.

2. Using formulas (7.18) and (7.19) the time-weighted rate of interest is found to be

$$\begin{aligned} i^{TW} &= \left(\frac{112{,}000}{100{,}000}\right)\left(\frac{125{,}000}{142{,}000}\right)\left(\frac{100{,}000}{83{,}000}\right)-1 \\ &= (1.12)(.880282)(1.204819)-1 \\ &= .1879, \text{ or } 18.79\% . \end{aligned}$$

Thus, the time-weighted rate of interest is dramatically higher than the dollar-weighted rate of interest. The reason for this becomes evident upon analyzing the three subintervals. Investment experience was very favorable during the first four months and the last two months of the year. However, it was quite adverse during the intervening six months. Since new principal was deposited just before the experience was about to turn sour and principal was withdrawn just before the experience was about to become favorable again, the dollar-weighted calculation was quite adversely affected.

In summary, the dollar-weighted yield, 10.62%, is a measure of the actual financial results achieved by the investor. The time-weighted yield, 18.79%, is a measure of the actual performance of the investment fund independent of the amount that happens to be invested.

The reader should not think that differences of this magnitude between the two methods are typical. It took the combination of bad timing in making rather large principal deposits and withdrawals, together with highly volatile investment performance (such as could occur in a fund heavily invested in common stocks), to create such a dramatic effect. The differences between the two methods would be much smaller in the event that either the investment performance was more stable, or that principal deposits and withdrawals were smaller in relation to the fund balance, or both. In fact, in stable investment funds invested at stable interest rates, the difference between the two methods would generally be insignificant.

7.7 PORTFOLIO METHODS AND INVESTMENT YEAR METHODS

Consider the commonly-encountered situation in which an investment fund is being maintained for a number of different entities, i.e. individuals or companies. An example would be a pension fund in which each plan participant has an individual account. However, the investment fund is commingled, i.e. each account does not have its own separate group of segregated assets, but rather a pro rata share of the entire fund.

An issue arises in connection with the crediting of interest to the various accounts. Two distinctly different approaches to allocating interest to the various accounts are in common use; namely, the *portfolio method* and the *investment year method.*

Under the portfolio method an average rate based on the earnings of the entire fund is computed and credited to each account. This method is quite straightforward and simple to implement. It is a method of long-standing usage in a variety of different situations.

However, problems arise in using the portfolio method during periods of fluctuating interest rates. For example, consider a situation in which interest rates have risen significantly in the recent past. The portfolio method might produce an average rate of 6%, while new deposits might be able to earn 8% on their own. The portfolio rate is lower because the fund includes a collection of lower yielding investments made in the past. In this situation there is a significant disincentive for anyone to make new deposits to the fund, and there is also an increased incentive for withdrawals.

The investment year method was developed to address this problem by recognizing the date of investment, as well as the current date, in crediting interest. It is a method that came into vogue during the 1960s and 1970s when there was a long period of rising interest rates. The rate on new deposits under the investment year method (8% in the above example) is often called the *new money rate*.

The investment year method is obviously more complicated than the portfolio method to apply in practice. However, many financial institutions, such as banks and insurance companies, felt it necessary to utilize the investment year method to attract new deposits and discourage withdrawals during periods of rising interest rates. Of course, when interest rates decline the situation will reverse and the portfolio method will be more attractive than the investment year method.

When interest rates fluctuate a lot up and down, it becomes an interesting guessing game as to which method will produce the more favorable results.

In applying the investment year method an immediate problem arises in connection with reinvestment rates. Two general approaches to this problem have been developed in practice. Under the *declining index system*, the funds associated with a particular investment year decline as the need to reinvest the money occurs. The interest rate credited under the investment year method reflects the investment rate on the remaining assets which are dwindling.

By contrast, under the *fixed index system* the funds associated with a particular investment year remain fixed in amount. The interest rate credited under the investment year method reflects the investment rate on the original investment modified by subsequent reinvestment rates.

Another consideration in implementing the investment year method is the need to truncate the process at some point. To illustrate in the extreme, it makes little sense to attempt to maintain an investment year method for 100 years! Normally, an arbitrary period is chosen after which time the process stops and reverts to the portfolio method. For example, if the period for which the investment year method is applicable is chosen to be five years, then any funds on deposit more than five years will be credited on a portfolio basis.

In practice, what is normally done to implement the investment year method is to specify a two-dimensional table of interest rates by date of original investment and time elapsed since that date. In order to simplify the presentation, we will assume that these periods are measured in calendar years and that all deposits and withdrawals are made on January 1.

Let y be the calendar year of deposit and let m be the number of years for which the investment year method is applicable. The rate of interest credited for the tth year of investment is denoted by i_t^y for $t = 1, 2, \ldots, m$. For $t > m$ the portfolio method is applicable and interest rates vary by calendar year only. The portfolio rate of interest credited for calendar year y is denoted by i^y. This notation is a generalization of the notation developed in formula (1.4*b*) and used subsequently in Chapter 1.

Table 7.2 is an illustrative array of rates credited under the investment year method with $m = 5$. The first year in the table is calendar year z and the last year is calendar year $z + 10$.

Table 7.2 Illustration of Investment Year Method

Calendar year of original investment y	*Investment year rates* i_1^y	i_2^y	i_3^y	i_4^y	i_5^y	*Portfolio rates* i^{y+5}	*Calendar year of portfolio rate y+5*
z	8.00%	8.10%	8.10%	8.25%	8.30%	8.10%	$z+5$
$z+1$	8.25	8.25	8.40	8.50	8.50	8.35	$z+6$
$z+2$	8.50	8.70	8.75	8.90	9.00	8.60	$z+7$
$z+3$	9.00	9.00	9.10	9.10	9.20	8.85	$z+8$
$z+4$	9.00	9.10	9.20	9.30	9.40	9.10	$z+9$
$z+5$	9.25	9.35	9.50	9.55	9.60	9.35	$z+10$
$z+6$	9.50	9.50	9.60	9.70	9.70		
$z+7$	10.00	10.00	9.90	9.80			
$z+8$	10.00	9.80	9.70				
$z+9$	9.50	9.50					
$z+10$	9.00						

The pattern of interest rates for a particular year of investment follows a horizontal line to the right-hand column and then downward. For example, in Table 7.2 the solid lines are the successive interest rates credited for deposits made at the beginning of calendar year $z+2$.

The interest rates credited in any particular calendar year appear on an upward diagonal to the right. For example, in Table 7.2 the dotted lines are the various rates of interest credited in calendar year $z+7$.

Competition among investment funds often is focused on new money rates to be credited in the first year in order to entice depositors to invest in that particular fund. The new money rates appear in the column headed i_1^y and are connected by dashed lines in Table 7.2 for calendar years z through $z+10$ inclusive.

In practice, implementing an investment year method is generally more complex than may be implied by Table 7.2. One source of complexity is that investment funds often change their credited rates more frequently than annually, e.g. monthly or quarterly. Another complication is the need to handle deposits or withdrawals at any date. Typically, the credited rates are for calendar periods and the interest credited would be based on the periods for which funds are invested at the various rates.

It is also worth noting that the investment year method illustrated in Table 7.2 is probably based on the fixed index system. If the declining index system were being utilized, the rates going horizontally through the five-year period for each calendar year of original investment would be more nearly constant than in Table 7.2.

Example 7.11 ***An investment of \$1000 is made at the beginning of calendar year*** $z+4$ ***in an investment fund crediting interest according to the rates contained in Table 7.2. How much interest is credited in calendar years*** $z+7$ ***through*** $z+9$ ***inclusive?***

We can readily adapt the approach taken in formula (1.40) to compute accumulated values at varying rates of interest to this situation. The accumulated value of the investment at the beginning of calendar year $z+7$ is

$$1000(1.09)(1.091)(1.092) = 1298.60.$$

The accumulated value of the investment at the beginning of calendar year $z+10$ is

$$1000(1.09)(1.091)(1.092)(1.093)(1.094)(1.091) = 1694.09.$$

Thus, the total amount of interest credited in calendar years $z+7$ through $z+9$ is

$$1694.09 - 1298.60 = \$395.49.$$

7.8 SHORT SALES

Some investors in securities use *short sales* or *short transactions* when they think the price of a security is likely to decline. With a short sale, the sale occurs first and the purchase occurs later. Normal transactions in which the purchase comes before the sale are often called *long transactions* in this context. The phrases "going short" or "going long" are also used in connection with these transactions.

It is interesting how such a seemingly backward transaction as a short sale is possible. With a short sale the investor borrows the security from a second party and sells it in the market to a third party. At some later date the investor buys back the security in the market (hopefully at a lower price) in order to return it to the second party. The process of buying back the security is often called "covering the short."

The calculation of yield rates for short sale transactions presents some unanticipated difficulties. Consider the situation in which an investor sells a stock short for \$1000 and buys it back for \$800 at the end of one year. Clearly, a \$200 profit has been made, but what is the yield rate?

An equation of value might appear to be

$$1000(1+i) = 800.$$

However, this equation produces a yield rate of $i = -20\%$, which is clearly unreasonable since a profit has been made.

It might be tempting to try to reverse the transaction and solve the equation of value

$$800(1+i) = 1000$$

which at least gives a positive answer, i.e. $i = +25\%$. However, this answer cannot be justified either. It arises as a \$200 profit on an \$800 investment, but there never was an \$800 investment.

A third idea might be say the yield rate is $i = +20\%$ by reversing the first answer, since a short sale is a reverse transaction. However, this idea is also flawed.

If, in fact, the transaction occurs exactly as stated, the yield rate does not exist. Some might prefer to say that the yield rate is infinite, since a profit was made on no investment. This point was illustrated previously in Example 7.3.

In practice, short sales normally do not occur as just illustrated. Governmental regulations in the United States require the short seller to make a deposit of a percentage of the price, e.g. 50%, at the time the short sale is made. This deposit is called the *margin* and cannot be recovered by the short seller until the short position is covered. The required margin percentage may be changed from time to time by the Federal Reserve Board.

Thus, in the above illustration the short seller would have to deposit margin of \$500 at the time of the short sale if the margin requirement is 50%. Now the situation is such that a valid yield rate can be computed. A \$200 profit is made and \$500 was deposited over a one-year period of time, so that the yield rate is 40%.

Actually the situation is somewhat more complicated than just described. The short seller will be credited with interest on the margin deposit which will increase the yield rate somewhat. If the short seller is credited with 8% interest on the margin deposit, then the amount of interest earned will be .08(500) = 40. The yield rate taking this interest into account becomes $240/500 = 48\%$.

The astute reader may ask about interest on the proceeds of the original short sale. In the above illustration could the short seller also earn interest on the \$1000 proceeds from the short sale? The answer is no. Governmental regulations require that these proceeds remain in a non-interest bearing special account until the short position is covered at which time these funds will be used for the purchase necessary to cover the short position. Any positive residual is the profit on the transaction, while any negative residual is the loss on the transaction.

Another complication arises as the position develops a profit or loss. If the short position develops a loss, additional margin may be required prior to the position being covered. Conversely, if the position develops a profit, some of the margin may be released and can be withdrawn or used for other purposes. These types of adjustments are controlled by governmental regulation.

One other aspect of short selling is significant. If the security in question pays dividends (e.g. on stocks) or interest (e.g. on bonds), then the short seller is required to pay these to the purchaser of the security (i.e. the third party). This will serve to decrease the yield rate realized.

For example, in the above illustration, if the stock sold short pays \$60 in dividends during the year, the short seller's net profit is as follows:

Gain on short sale	+ 200
Interest on margin	+ 40
Dividends on stock	− 60
Net profit	+ 180

Now the yield rate becomes $180/500 = 36\%$. This requirement creates a significant disincentive to sell short any securities which pay a significant amount of dividends or interest.

The above example is simplified in order to illustrate the concepts and factors involved. The answer 36% is accurate only if the period of investment is exactly one year, no margin is added or subtracted during the year, and all dividends are paid exactly at the end of the year. These are somewhat artificial conditions. A more realistic illustration is given in Example 7.12.

Short selling by itself is a speculative endeavor and should not be entered into lightly. The short seller is counting on a significant decline in the value of the security in order to come out ahead. Speculative short selling is normally done over relatively brief periods, so that it is unusual for short positions to remain open for extended periods of time.

However, investment strategies have been developed that involve combinations of long and short positions in related securities which have greatly reduced risk and also have an excellent prospect to earn a reasonable return on investment. A generic name for these types of transactions is *hedging*, and many of the transactions become quite complex. In fact, on very rare occasions a situation develops in which a profit is certain. Such transactions of guaranteed profitability are called *arbitrage*. Generally, arbitrage opportunities are fleeting since market prices react quickly to eliminate such golden opportunities. Arbitrage will be discussed in more depth in Section 10.6.

Example 7.12 ***Continue the example presented in this section with the following adjustments:***

- ***The stock is bought for $850 at the end of 9 months (producing 75% of the gain in 75% of the period of investment).***
- ***The position develops enough of a profit that $60 of margin is released at the end of 6 months.***
- ***The dividends are actually $15 per quarter paid at the end of every 3 months.***

Find the annual effective yield rate the investor earns on this short sale transaction.

We first need to analyze the margin, since it will require calculations. The initial margin is $500. At the end of 6 months this will accumulate to

$$500(1.08)^{1/2} = 519.6152.$$

The margin release brings the balance to

$$519.6152 - 60 = 459.6152.$$

The ending margin balance then becomes

$$459.6152(1.08)^{1/4} = 468.54.$$

Figure 7.9 illustrates the cash flows in this transaction. Cash outflows appear above the time diagram, while cash inflows appear below.

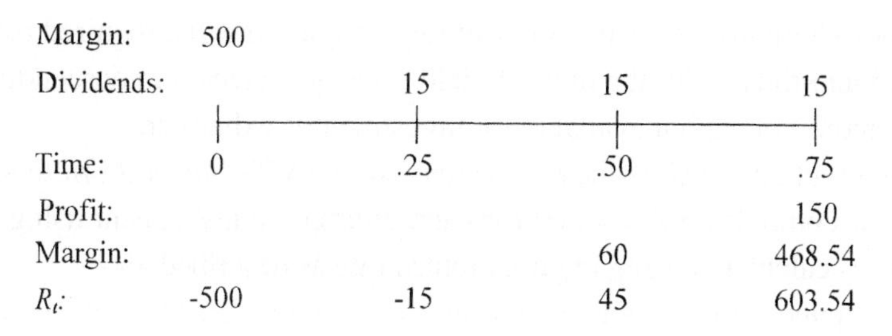

Figure 7.9 Time diagram for Example 7.12

Note that the \$1000 sale price and \$850 purchase price do not appear on the time diagram, but only the net profit of \$150 at the end of the transaction. The purchase and sale prices do not represent true cash flows in a short sale transaction.

We can solve for the quarterly yield rate j using the IRR function on a financial calculator to obtain

$$j = .082749, \text{ or } 8.2749\%.$$

The effective annual yield rate is then

$$i = (1.082749)^4 - 1 = .374, \text{ or } 37.4\%.$$

7.9 CAPITAL BUDGETING – BASIC TECHNIQUES

A problem facing both individual and corporate investors is the need to determine the amount of capital to invest and the allocation of that capital among various alternative investments. The process of making such financial decisions is often called *capital budgeting*.

In practice, two major approaches to capital budgeting are most commonly encountered. The first of these is the *yield rate method* (or *IRR method*). In this method the investor computes the yield rate (IRR) for each alternative investment using formula (7.3). The investor establishes an interest rate, which is the minimum acceptable rate of return. This rate has been given many names in the financial literature, including *required return rate, interest preference rate, opportunity cost of capital,* and *hurdle rate.* Setting the required return rate is a matter of business judgment involving considerations such as the cost of raising capital and the investor's profit objectives.

Investments with yield rates higher than the required return rate are considered further, while investments with yield rates that are lower are rejected. The various alternative investments with rates higher than the required return rate are ranked and those with the highest yield rates are selected in descending order until the amount of capital available for investment is exhausted.

The second approach is the *net present value (NPV) method.* In this method the investor computes NPV = $P(i)$ for each alternative investment using formula (7.2). $P(i)$ is calculated using required return rate as described above.

Investments with a positive $P(i)$ are considered further, while investments with a negative $P(i)$ are rejected. Capital is then allocated among those investments with a positive $P(i)$ in such a manner that the total present value of returns from the investment minus contributions to the investment is maximized. The present values are computed at the required return rate.

If a unique yield rate exists, then these two approaches will produce consistent results. In other words, investments with yield rates higher than the required return rate will have a positive $P(i)$ and conversely. However, the fact that the yield rate may not always exist and be unique has led many writers in finance to favor the net present value method over the yield rate method.

Another argument that has been advanced to favor the net present value method is that it automatically maximizes dollar returns to the investor as part of the decision process. On the other hand, the yield rate method has the appeal of using numbers that are very easy to grasp and compare. However, the use of the yield rate method does not lead directly to financial results measured in terms of dollars without making additional calculations.

The above description of capital budgeting has been viewed from the perspective of an investor (lender), which is typically the manner in which capital budgeting is applied. However, it is possible to adapt the procedure for use by a borrower. In this case, the rules for the yield rate method work in the opposite direction, i.e. a "favorable" transaction has a low yield rate while an "unfavorable" transaction has a high yield rate. On the other hand, the net present value method can be applied in the same fashion for borrowers as for lenders as long as the R_t's in formula (7.2) are from the borrower's perspective.

The discussion of capital budgeting in this section has not considered the comparative risk involved in the various alternative investments. In essence, we are assuming that risk is identical in the alternative investments being compared. Consideration of risk may well modify the decision process. For example, it is doubtful that many investors would (or should) prefer a high-risk investment with a projected yield rate of 15% to a low-risk investment with a projected yield rate of 14%. The subject of financial calculations involving risk is considered further in Section 9.8.

Example 7.13 ***Analyze the investment project given in Table 7.1 as a capital budgeting exercise.***

We know from Example 7.1 that the yield rate on this project is 12.96%. Table 7.3 tabulates the net present value, $P(i)$, at a wide range of illustrative interest rates using formula (7.2).

Table 7.3 Net Present Values for Example 7.13

Rate of interest i	*Net present value P(i)*
0%	27,000
5	12,675
10	3,695
15	– 2,046
20	– 5,778
25	– 8,236

Let us assume that an investor has a required return rate equal to 10%. Using the yield rate method the investor would accept this project for further consideration, since 12.96% > 10%. Using the net present value method the investor also would accept it, since $P(.1) = 3695 > 0$.

Now, consider an investor with a required return rate equal to 15%. Using the yield rate method the investor would reject this project since 12.96% < 15%. Using the net present value method the investor also would reject, since $P(.15) = -2046 < 0$.

It is instructive to analyze Table 7.3 graphically. These results are displayed as the solid line in Figure 7.10.

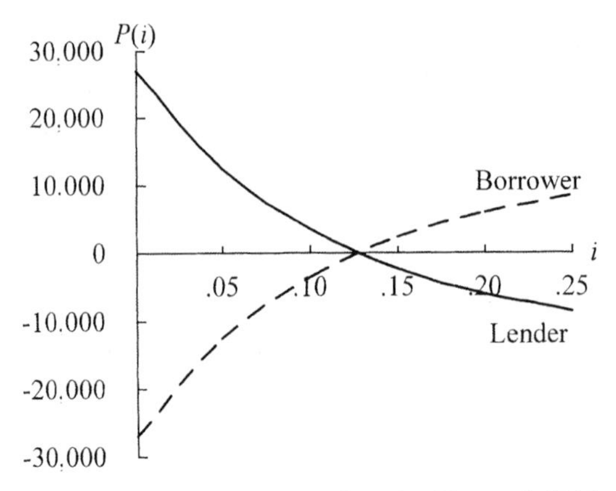

Figure 7.10 Net present values for Example 7.13

As before, we see that $P(i)$ is a decreasing function of the rate of interest. Moreover, it is positive to the left of the yield rate 12.96%, and is negative to the right. The solid line in Figure 7.10 is a typical graph for the value of a financial transaction with a unique yield rate to the investor (lender).

The reader should note that the graph for the value of a financial transaction with a unique yield rate from the borrower's side of the transaction will be an increasing function rather than decreasing. In order to illustrate this, assume that there is only one party on the borrower's side of the transaction for the project summarized in Table 7.3. The corresponding graph for the borrower is given by the dashed line in Figure 7.10. Note that positive values of $P(i)$ lie to the right of the yield rate rather than to the left and that the borrower's curve is the reflection of the lender's curve around the x-axis.

Example 7.14 Analyze the illustration given at the beginning of Section 7.3 as a capital budgeting exercise.

Figure 7.11 is a time diagram for this transaction. The two cash flows into the investment are shown at the top of the diagram and the one cash flow out of the investment is shown at the bottom.

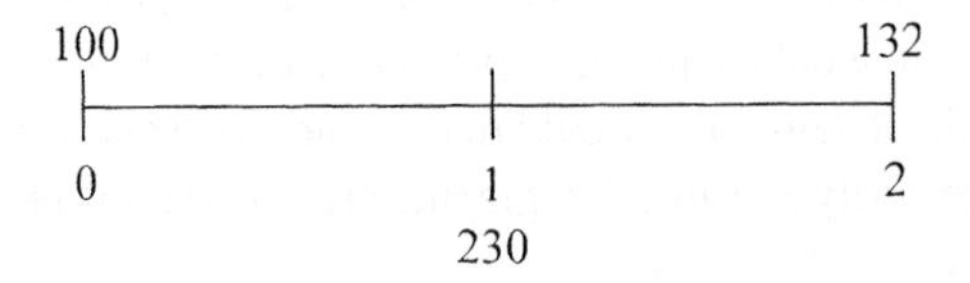

Figure 7.11 Time diagram for Example 7.14

From formula (7.2)

$$P(i) = -100 + 230v - 132v^2$$

which is shown in Section 7.3 to have two yield rates, 10% and 20%. Table 7.4 tabulates $P(i)$ at a wide range of illustrative interest rates.

Table 7.4 Net Present Values for Example 7.14

Rate of interest i	*Net present value P(i)*
0%	−2.00
5	− .68
10	0
15	+ .19
20	0
25	− .48

These results are displayed graphically in Figure 7.12. The maximum value of $P(i)$ occurs at 14.78%, but is equal to $P(i)$ at 15% to the two decimal places used in Table 7.4. The verification of this result is left as an exercise.

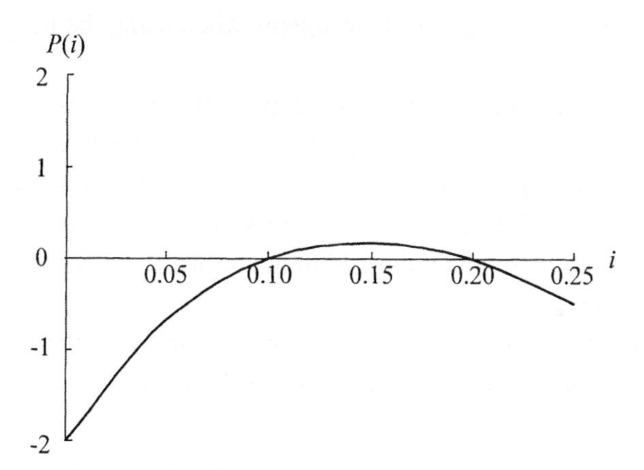

Figure 7.12 Net present values for Example 7.14

The possible non-uniqueness of the yield rate is often cited as a reason to favor the net present value method of capital budgeting over the yield rate method. However, we will now show that problems also exist in using the net present value method.

In Figure 7.12 $P(i)$ is a decreasing function in the vicinity of the 20% yield rate, which is the normal pattern from the investor's vantage point. However, $P(i)$ is an increasing function in the vicinity of the 10% yield rate. Thus, if the investor in this example requires only a 5% rate of return, the investment is a poor one since $P(i)$ is negative. However, if the lender triples the required return to 15%, the investment somehow becomes a good one since $P(i)$ is now positive! This result is illogical, showing that use of the net present value method of capital budgeting does not really solve the inherent problems when multiple yield rates exist.

7.10 CAPITAL BUGETING – OTHER TECHNIQUES

Section 7.9 discusses the basics of capital budgeting. In Section 7.10 we will supplement this discussion with the consideration of four additional techniques. The description of capital budgeting given in Sections 7.9 and 7.10 is somewhat brief and cursory. Readers interested in a more extensive treatment are referred to any of several standard textbooks in finance.

Profitability index

The first additional technique is called the *profitability index* (PI). This index is a tool to help analyze competing investments when using the net present value (NPV) method.

One of the challenges in interpreting net present values is that the size of the investment is not directly reflected. Consider two investments A and B. A has an NPV equal to 5000, while B has an NPV equal to 3000. Some readers might quickly conclude that A is the superior investment, since its NPV is higher. However, what if you were given the additional information that A is twice as big an investment as B?

The profitability index (PI) deals with this problem by standardizing the NPV to have a value calculated per unit of investment (I). Thus, the general concept is

$$\text{PI} = \frac{\text{NPV}}{\text{I}}. \qquad (7.20)$$

In the simple example above, we now see that B is actually the superior investment based on the profitability index, since

$$\frac{3000}{\text{I}} > \frac{5000}{2\text{I}} \quad \text{for any I} > 0.$$

The simple definition of the profitability index given in formula (7.20) will work fine as long as the entire investment (I) is made at inception, i.e. a time $t=0$. However, a problem develops if subsequent contributions are required after inception, as in Table 5.1. Therefore, we need to develop a more general profitability index (PI) to handle such situations.

Since the profitability index is a ratio, we will not be able to offset contributions and returns made at the same point in time and turn them into net cash flows as we have done throughout Chapter 7 up to this point.

Let C_t' be contributions into the investment and R_t' be returns form the investment at time t for $t=0,1,\ldots,n$. Primes appear on the two symbols to remind us not to offset contributions and returns made at the same point in time against each other.

By way of example, in Table 7.1 the "Contributions" column could be labeled C_t', while the "Returns" column could be labeled R_t'. The calculation of the profitability index for the investment in Table 7.1 will be left as an exercise.

We now define the profitability index (PI) as the ratio at inception of the present value of the returns to the present value of the contributions, i.e.

$$\text{PI} = \frac{\sum_{t=0}^{n} v^t R_t'}{\sum_{t=0}^{n} v^t C_t'} \tag{7.21}$$

The required return rate should be used in computing the two present values to be consistent with the original calculation of net present value. As an interesting observation, note that if the internal rate of return (IRR) is used to compute the two present values, then $\text{PI}=1$ by definition.

The profitability index is a useful tool when an investor has multiple possible investments, all of which meet the investor's standard of acceptability, but does not have enough capital to fund them all. This index, should help the investor achieve "the biggest bang for the buck" among the various alternatives.

Payback period

The second additional technique is called the *payback period*, which many investors like to consider as an alternative measure in capital budgeting. In its simplest formulation this measure answers the simple, yet powerful, question: "How long does it take to get my money back?"

This technique is clearly much less sophisticated than either the IRR or NPV methods and can easily produce suboptimal results. Nevertheless, it has an appeal to many investors who simply do not want to be "in the hole" for too long a period of time on their investment, regardless of how attractive the IRR or NPV may be.

For this measure we can revert back to the regular (unprimed) symbols. A formula for determining the payback period is to find the minimum k for which

$$\sum_{t=0}^{k} R_t \geq 0. \tag{7.22}$$

An obvious criticism of the basic payback period as defined in formula (7.22) is that it ignores the time value of money. As a result, a more sophisticated discounted payback period method has been developed and is defined as the minimum k for which

$$\sum_{t=0}^{k} v^t R_t \geq 0. \tag{7.23}$$

The present value is usually computed using the required return rate in the NPV method.

If the investment has a positive NPV at the required return rate, then $k < n$, when using this method. If the investment has a negative NPV at the required return rate, then the investment never "breaks even" using this method. Finally if the $\text{NPV} = 0$, which means the IRR is being used in computing the present value, then $k = n$.

Modified Internal Rate of Return (MIRR)

The third additional technique is the *modified internal rate of return* (*MIRR*) *method*. This technique has been developed as one approach to circumvent the problems created by multiple yield rates.

In the MIRR method, we first calculate the present value at inception of the contributions into the investment as a prescribed interest rate j. Typically, j would be the investor's required return rate.

In effect, the investor is "prefunding" the future cash outflows, i.e. a fund equal to the present value of the future cash outflows is being computed out of which these future cash outflows could be paid. Whether or not such a fund is actually established by the investor is irrelevant to the validity of the calculation. This present value is then equated to the present value at rate i of the returns, or future cash inflows from the investment. The rate i is called the modified internal rate of return (MIRR) and will be unique.

For this method we again need the new primed symbols defined above. We have

$$\sum_{t=0}^{n}(1+j)^{-t}\,C_t' = \sum_{t=0}^{n}(1+i)^{-t}\,R_t' \tag{7.24}$$

which we can solve for a unique i, the MIRR. If $i > j$, the required return rate, then presumably this would be an attractive investment. If $i < j$, then presumably it would not be.

Mixed Projects

The fourth, and final, additional technique is the *mixed project method.* This is a more sophisticated technique for circumventing multiple yield rates than the MIRR method described immediately above.

In Section 7.3 we showed that if the outstanding investment balance is positive throughout the period of investment, then the yield rate will be unique. We can generalize this result and define a *pure investment project* as one in which $B_t \geq 0$ for $t = 0, 1, 2, \ldots, n$. A pure investment project is one in which the investor has money invested in the project throughout the period of investment.

We now switch to the perspective of a borrower and define a *pure financing project* as one in which $B_t \leq 0$ for $t = 0, 1, 2, \ldots, n$. A pure financing project is one in which the investor owes money to the project throughout the period of investment. Thus, the investor has actually become a borrower in this case.

Multiple yield rates can arise when some outstanding balances are positive and others are negative during the period of investment. We will call such a project a *mixed project,* since the investor is a "net lender" during some portions of the period of investment and a "net borrower" during other portions.

This more general model is based on the premise that a different rate of interest should be used during those portions of the period of investment during which the investor is in lender status than the rate used during those portions in borrower status. The *project return rate* is denoted by r and is the required return rate during those portions of the period of investment during which the investor is in lender status, i.e. the investment balance $B_t \geq 0$. The *project financing rate* is denoted by f and is the required return rate during those portions of the period of investment during which the investor is in borrower status, i.e. the investment balance $B_t \leq 0$.

Typically, r will be greater than f, since an astute investor will have a higher required return rate as a lender than as a borrower. However, the mathematical development does not require that $r > f$.

We generalize the approach used in developing formulas (7.4) and (7.5) to fit this situation. The initial fund balance is

$$B_0 = C_0 . \tag{7.25}$$

Successive fund balances are developed as a recursion formula

$$B_t = B_{t-1}(1+r) + C_t, \text{ if } B_{t-1} \geq 0 \tag{7.26a}$$

or

$$B_t = B_{t-1}(1+f) + C_t, \text{ if } B_{t-1} < 0 \tag{7.26b}$$

for $t = 1, 2, \ldots, n$. The ending fund balance is a polynomial in r and f of the form

$$B_n = C_0(1+r)^{m_0}(1+f)^{n-m_0} + C_1(1+r)^{m_1}(1+f)^{n-m_1-1} + \cdots + C_n \tag{7.27}$$

where the m_j's are integers such that $n \geq m_0 \geq m_1 \geq \ldots \geq m_n \geq 0$. In formula (7.27) m_j is the total number of periods from time j to time n for which interest rate r is used, with rate f being used for the remainder of the periods.

If $r = f$, formulas (7.25) through (7.27) simplify to the standard case discussed in Section 7.3. Recall that $B_n = 0$ at the yield rate. If $r \neq f$, the concept of yield rate can still be utilized. However, in this more general case the yield rate is not a single number, but rather a functional relationship between r and f. In other words, for a given value of f, if a value of r can be found such that $B_n = 0$, then r and f are a yield rate pair for the transaction. A transaction for which yield rates exist will typically have an infinite number of r, f pairs and a functional relationship between r and f can be found.

The above constitutes a generalization of the yield rate method of capital budgeting. It is also possible to generalize the net present value method. Recall that formula (7.2) defining net present value is based on R_t's which are the negatives of the C_t's used above. Thus, positive values of net present value correspond to negative values of B_n, and conversely. The fact that negative values of B_n are favorable to the investor can be interpreted as reflecting the fact that a negative investment balance at the end of the investment period is, in effect, a positive balance to the investor.

Example 7.15 Compute the profitability index for an investment of $1000 which returns of $250 at the end of each year for five years. Assume that the annual required return rate is equal to 7%.

Formula (7.20) will work for this example, since the entire investment is made at inception. We have

$$\text{PI} = \frac{250a_{\overline{5}|.07}}{1000} = \frac{(250)(4.1002)}{1000} = 1.02505.$$

Obtaining $\text{PI} > 1$ indicates that the IRR for an annuity which pays 250 per year for five years in exchange of a $1000 initial deposit is greater than 7%. This can be readily confirmed using the techniques of Section 3.7. The equation of value is

$$250a_{\overline{5}|j} = 1000$$

or

$$a_{\overline{5}|j} = 4.$$

Solving this equation as an unknown rate of interest problem for a level annuity on a financial calculator, we obtain $j = .0793$, or 7.93%, which indeed exceeds 7%.

Example 7.16 Compute the following two payback periods for the investment in Table 7.1:
(1) The undiscounted payback period.
(2) The discounted payback period, using a required return rate of 9% per annum.

1. Summing the R_t column in Table 7.1 using formula (7.22) we have

$$\sum_{t=0}^{7} R_t = -4000 \text{ and } \sum_{t=0}^{8} R_t = 5000.$$

Thus, the undiscounted payback period is 8 years.

2. We now use the NPV feature on a financial calculator and formula (7.23) to obtain

$$\sum_{t=0}^{8} (1.09)^{-t} R_t = -4492 \text{ and } \sum_{t=0}^{9} (1.09)^{-t} R_t = 112.$$

Thus, the discounted payback period, using a required return rate of 9%, is 9 years.

The investment given in Table 7.1 is a good example of an attractive investment which some investors might reject anyway. Their reasoning might go something like this:

> "Yes, I know that this is an attractive investment, since my required return rate is 9% and this investment has a yield (IRR) of 12.96%. However, it is a 10-year investment which does not even break-even until 8 years into the investment on an undiscounted basis, or 9 years on a discounted basis. That is simply too long for me to wait to get my money back, even though the overall yield is attractive."

***Example 7.17** Consider the investment in Section 7.3 which has two yield rates (IRR's) equal to 10% or 20%. Find the investor's MIRR if the required return rate is 12%.*

Applying formula (7.24) directly we have

$$100 + 132(1.12)^{-2} = 230(1+i)^{-1}$$

which simplifies to

$$205.22959 = 230(1+i)^{-1}$$

or

$$1+i = \frac{230}{205.22959} = 1.1207$$

Thus, the (unique) MIRR is equal to .1207 or 12.07%. Since the MIRR exceeds the required return of 12% (just barely), this investment could receive further consideration.

***Example 7.18** An investor is required to make a contribution of $1600 immediately and $10,000 at the end of two years in exchange for receiving $10,000 at the end of one year.*
(1) Find the yield rates, if r = f.
(2) Express r as a function of f, if r and f are a yield rate pair.
(3) Would the investor accept or reject the transaction if r = 70% and f = 30%?
(4) Rework (3) if f = 50%.

1. Let $i = r = f$. The equation of value is

$$1600(1+i)^2 + 10{,}000 = 10{,}000(1+i).$$

This is a quadratic whose two roots are

$$i = .25, \text{ or } 25\%$$

and

$$i = 4, \text{ or } 400\%.$$

Thus, we have a transaction with multiple yield rates.

2. The investment balance is positive for the first year and negative for the second year. Thus, interest rate r is applicable for the first year and f is applicable for the second year. We have:

$$\begin{aligned} B_0 &= 1600 \\ B_1 &= 1600(1+r) - 10{,}000 \\ B_2 &= \left[1600(1+r) - 10{,}000\right](1+f) + 10{,}000 = 0. \end{aligned}$$

This defines a functional relationship between r and f. Solving for r as a function of f

$$\begin{aligned} 1 + r &= \frac{10{,}000}{1600}\left(1 - \frac{1}{1+f}\right) \\ r &= 6.25\left(1 - \frac{1}{1+f}\right) - 1 \\ &= 5.25 - \frac{6.25}{1+f}. \end{aligned}$$

Some illustrative values of r and f are given in Table 7.5.

Table 7.5 Project Rates for Example 7.18

Financing rate f	*Return rate r*
25%	25%
100	212.5
150	275
200	317
300	369
400	400

Note that $r = f$ at the two yield rates which would be expected. Also, note that $r > f$ between the two yield rates, which is the normal relationship. However, outside this range $r < f$. Finally, note that r increases as f increases.

3. Using formulas (7.25) through (7.27) we have:

$$\begin{aligned} B_0 &= C_o = 1600 \\ B_1 &= B_0(1+r)+C_1 \\ &= 1600(1.7)-10{,}000 = -7280 \\ B_2 &= B_1(1+f)+C_2 \\ &= (-7280)(1.3)+10{,}000 = 536. \end{aligned}$$

Since $B_2 > 0$, the investor rejects this transaction.

4. Following the same approach used immediately above, B_0 and B_1 are unchanged. The new ending balance is

$$B_2 = (-7280)(1.5)+10{,}000 = -920.$$

Since $B_2 < 0$, the investor accepts this transaction.

It is instructive to consider why (4) is accepted and (3) is rejected. The only difference between the two examples is in the borrowing required return rate f. If the maximum rate at which the investor is willing to borrow is 30%, the transaction should be rejected. However, if the investor is willing to borrow at rates up to 50%, then the transaction should be accepted.

APPENDIX 7

Uniqueness of the yield rate

We wish to prove the following result from Section 7.3. If

1. $i > -1$ exists such that formula (7.3) is satisfied, and
2. For such i, $B_t > 0$ for $t = 0, 1, \ldots, n-1$,

then i is unique. The condition $i > -1$ is necessary to ensure that $1+i$ is positive.

Now rewrite formula (7.3) as

$$C_0(1+i)^n + C_1(1+i)^{n-1} + \cdots + C_{n-1}(1+i) + C_n = 0.$$

We know that

$$\begin{aligned}
B_0 &= & C_0 &> 0 \\
B_1 &= B_0(1+i) &+ C_1 &> 0 \\
B_2 &= B_1(1+i) &+ C_2 &> 0 \\
&\vdots & \vdots & \\
B_{n-1} &= B_{n-2}(1+i) &+ C_{n-1} &> 0 \\
B_n &= B_{n-1}(1+i) &+ C_n &= 0.
\end{aligned}$$

By successive substitution in the above equations we have

$$B_n = C_0(1+i)^n + C_1(1+i)^{n-1} + \cdots + C_{n-1}(1+i) + C_n = 0. \tag{7.28}$$

This is the expected result, since the investment is exactly terminated at the end of n periods. Note that $C_0 > 0$ and $C_n < 0$, but that C_t for $t = 1, 2, \ldots, n-1$ may be either positive, negative, or zero.

To prove the uniqueness of i, let $j > i$ be another yield rate. Let the outstanding investment at time t for interest rate j be denoted by B_t'. Then we have

$$\begin{array}{lclclclclcl}
B'_0 & = & & & C_0 & = & & & C_0 & = & B_0 \\
B'_1 & = & B'_0(1+j) & + & C_1 & > & B_0(1+i) & + & C_1 & = & B_1 \\
B'_2 & = & B'_1(1+j) & + & C_2 & > & B_1(1+i) & + & C_2 & = & B_2 \\
\cdot & & & & & & \cdot & & & & \cdot \\
\cdot & & & & & & \cdot & & & & \cdot \\
\cdot & & & & & & \cdot & & & & \cdot \\
B'_{n-1} & = & B'_{n-2}(1+i) & + & C_{n-1} & > & B_{n-2}(1+i) & + & C_{n-1} & = & B_{n-1} \\
B'_n & = & B'_{n-1}(1+i) & + & C_n & > & B_{n-1}(1+i) & + & C_n & = & B_n = 0.
\end{array}$$

But this is a contradiction, since B'_n must equal 0 if j is a yield rate. Thus j cannot be greater than i. The proof for $-1 < j < 1$ can be obtained by just switching the roles of i and j. This establishes the uniqueness of i.

Further analysis of the simple interest assumption in Section 7.5

Formula (7.14) initially appears to be the same as simple interest as defined in Section 1.4. However, it can be shown that the two are not equivalent by considering the form of δ_t under each assumption.

As defined in Section 1.4, the accumulation function for simple interest is given by

$$a(t) = 1+ti. \tag{1.5}$$

This is equivalent to the assumption that

$${}_t i_0 = ti. \tag{7.29}$$

An expression for δ_t under this assumption is given by formula (1.35)

$$\delta_t = \frac{i}{1+ti}. \tag{1.35}$$

For the version of simple interest defined by formula (7.14) we have

$$e^{\int_t^1 \delta_r dr} = 1 + {}_{1-t}i_t = 1+(1-t)i$$

or

$$\int_t^1 \delta_r dr = \ln\left[1+(1-t)i\right]$$

and differentiating with respect to t

$$\delta_t = \frac{i}{1+(1-t)i} \quad \text{for } 0 \le t \le 1 . \tag{7.30}$$

Clearly formulas (1.35) and (7.30) are not equivalent; in fact, they are equal only for $t = 1/2$. Moreover, it should be noted that formula (1.35) is a decreasing function of t, while formula (7.30) is an increasing function of t.

Interest measurement using continuous functions

It is possible to develop analogous results for funds in which payments are being made continuously. Let B_t be the outstanding fund balance at time t, $0 \le t \le n$, and assume that contributions (positive or negative) are being made continuously at exact time t at the rate of C_t per period. Then a generalized version of formula (7.28) is given by

$$B_n = B_0(1+i)^n + \int_0^n C_t (1+i)^{n-t}\, dt . \tag{7.31}$$

In essence, formula (7.31) says that the fund balance at the end of n measurement periods is equal to the beginning fund balance accumulated with interest for n periods, plus the accumulated value of all the intervening payments (positive or negative) in the amount of $C_t dt$ accumulated with interest to the end of the n periods.

An even more general formula can be obtained by also allowing the force of interest to vary continuously. A generalized version of formula (7.31) would then be given by

$$B_n = B_0 e^{\int_0^n \delta_s ds} + \int_0^n C_t e^{\int_t^n \delta_s ds}\, dt. \tag{7.32}$$

The following differential equation is associated with formula (7.32)

$$\frac{d}{dt} B_t = \delta_t B_t + C_t. \tag{7.33}$$

Formula (7.33) has an interesting verbal interpretation. The left-hand side is the instantaneous rate of change in the fund balance at time t. The right-hand side attributes this instantaneous rate of change to two factors: (1) interest at force δ_t on the fund balance B_t, plus (2) the rate of contribution (positive or negative) to the fund at exact time t.

EXERCISES

7.2 Discounted cash flow analysis

1. A ten-year investment project requires an initial investment of \$100,000 at inception and maintenance expenses at the beginning of each year. The maintenance expense for the first year is \$3000, and is anticipated to increase 6% each year thereafter. Projected annual returns from the project are \$30,000 at the end of the first year decreasing 4% per year thereafter. Find R_6 to the nearest dollar.

2. An investor enters into an agreement to contribute \$7000 immediately and \$1000 at the end of two years in exchange for the receipt of \$4000 at the end of one year and \$5500 at the end of three years. Find:

   a) $P(.09)$.

   b) $P(.10)$.

3. The internal rate of return for an investment in which C_0 = \$3000, C_1 = \$1000, R_1 = \$2000, and R_2 = \$4000 can be expressed as $1/n$. Find n.

4. ABC Manufacturing decides to build a new plant. The plant will cost \$2 million immediately and is expected to have a useful life of 10 years. At the end of 5 years a major renovation expense of \$$X$ will be required to install new technology. The plant will produce level returns of \$300,000 at the end of each year for the first 5 years and double that at the end of each year for the second 5 years. Find the maximum value of X that ABC could pay that would still produce an internal rate of return on its investment of at least 12%.

5. Project P requires an investment of \$4000 at time 0. The investment pays \$2000 at time 1 and \$4000 at time 2. Project Q requires an investment of \$$X$ at time 2. The investment pays \$2000 at time 0 and \$4000 at time 1. Using the net present value method at an effective interest rate of 10%, the net present values of the two projects are equal. Calculate X.

6. The ABC Real Estate Development Corporation has just obtained a 10-year development project with the following projected net cash flows (NCFs):

Time	NCF = R_i	Time	NCF = R_i
0	-7,900,000	6	910,000
1	1,400,000	7	900,000
2	1,100,000	8	900,000
3	1,000,000	9	450,000
4	1,000,000	10	10,000,000
5	1,000,000		

   a) Calculate $P(.15)$, i.e. the net present value (NPV) at 15%.

   b) Find the internal rate of return (IRR).

7.3 Uniqueness of the yield rate

7. *a*) In Exercise 2 what is the maximum number of possible yield rates using Descartes' rule of signs?

   b) From the two answers it is apparent that a yield rate exists between 9% and 10%. Is this rate unique?

   c) Explain your answer to (*b*).

8. Payments of $100 now and $108.15 two years from now are equivalent to a payment of $208 one year from now at either rate i or j. Find the absolute difference of the two rates.

9. A project has the following cash flow stream:

Time	Net Cash Flow
0	1000
1	A
2	B

   Determine A and B such that the project will simultaneously have yield rates of 20% and 40%.

7.4 Reinvestment rates

10. An investor makes a single deposit of $10,000 into Fund A for 10 years which earns a 6% effective rate of interest payable directly to the investor each year. During the first 5 years, the interest payments can only be reinvested into Fund B which earns 4% effective over the entire 10-year period. During the second 5 years, the interest payments can only be reinvested into Fund C which earns 5% effective.
    a) Find the total accumulated value in Funds A, B, and C combined at the end of 10 years. Answer to the nearest dollar.
    b) Find the overall yield rate achieved by the investor.

11. It is desired to accumulate a fund of $1000 at the end of 10 years by equal deposits at the beginning of each year. If the deposits earn interest at 8% effective but the interest can be reinvested at only 4% effective, show that the deposit necessary is

$$\frac{1000}{2s_{\overline{11}|.04} - 12}$$

12. A loan of $10,000 is being repaid with payments of $1000 at the end of each year for 20 years. If each payment is immediately reinvested at 5% effective, find the effective annual rate of interest earned over the 20-year period.

13. An investor purchases a five-year financial instrument having the following features:
    (*i*) The investor receives payments of $1000 at the end of each year for five years.
    (*ii*) These payments earn interest at an effective rate of 4% per annum. At the end of the year, this interest is reinvested at the effective rate of 3% per annum.

    Find the purchase price to the investor to produce a yield rate of 4%. Answer to the nearest dollar.

14. A $100 par value 12-year bond with 10% semiannual coupons is selling for $110. If the coupons can only be reinvested at 7% convertible semiannually, compute the overall yield rate achieved by a bond purchaser over the 12-year period.

15. A buys a 10-year $1000 par value 6% bond with semiannual coupons. The price assumes a nominal yield of 6% compounded semiannually. As A receives each coupon payment, it is immediately put into an account earning interest at an annual effective rate of i. At the end of 10 years, immediately after receipt of the final coupon payment and the redemption value of the bond, A has earned an annual effective yield of 7% on the investment in the bond. Calculate i.

16. You invest \$300 into a bank account at the beginning of each year for 20 years. The account pays out interest at the end of every year at an annual effective interest rate of $i\%$. The interest is reinvested at an annual effective rate of $(i/2)\%$. The yield rate on the entire investment over the 20 year period is 8% effective. Determine i.

17. A new partnership takes out a loan of \$25,000 to finance the initial costs of starting their own business. The original loan with Lender #1 is for four years, carries an annual effective interest rate of 8%, and will be repaid by the amortization method. Lender #1 places no restrictions on early repayment of the loan. During the next year interest rates decline substantially. At the end of the first year, the partnership completely repays the loan to Lender #1 and refinances the loan with Lender #2. Lender #1 is only able to reinvest the proceeds from the early repayment at 6% effective for the following three years. Determine Lender #1's overall level yield rate for the four years arising from their issuing this loan to the partnership.

18. An investor pays \$100,000 today for a 4-year investment that returns cash flows of \$50,000 at the ends of years 2, 3, and 4. Each cash flow can be reinvested at 8% when it is received. Calculate $P(.1)$, i.e. the net present value (NPV) of this investment, reflecting reinvestment rates, evaluated at 10% over the 4-year period. Answer to the nearest dollar.

7.5 Interest measurement of a fund

19. A fund earning 4% annual interest has a balance of \$1000 at the beginning of the year. If \$200 is added to the fund at the end of three months and if \$300 is withdrawn from the fund at the end of nine months, find the ending balance using the simple interest approximation.

20. An investment account earning 6% is established with an initial balance at the beginning of the year of \$10,000. There are new deposits of \$1800 made at the end of 2 months and another \$900 made at the end of 8 months. In addition, there is a withdrawal of \$$K$ made at the end of 6 months. The fund balance at the end of the year is \$10,636. Determine K to the nearest dollar using the simple interest approximation.

21. An insurance company earned a simple rate of interest of 8% over the last calendar year based on the following information:

Assets, beginning of year	25,000,000
Sales revenue	X
Net investment income	2,000,000
Salaries paid	2,000,000
Other expenses paid	750,000

All cash flows occur at the middle of the year. Calculate the effective yield rate.

22. *a*) Under the assumption that ${}_{1-t}i_t = (1-t)i$, find an expression for ${}_t i_0$.
    b) Under the assumption that ${}_t i_0 = ti$, find an expression for ${}_{1-t}i_t$.

23. Derive formula (7.17).

7.6 Time-weighted rates of interest

24. In Example 7.10 assume that May 1 is changed to June 1 and November 1 is changed to October 1.
    a) Would the yield rate change when computed by the dollar-weighted method?
    b) Would the yield rate change when computed by the time-weighted method?

25. Deposits of \$1000 are made into an investment fund at time 0 and time 1. The fund balance is \$1200 at time 1 and \$2200 at time 2.
    a) Compute the annual effective yield rate computed by a dollar-weighted calculation.
    b) Compute the annual effective yield rate which is equivalent to that produced by a time-weighted calculation.

26. You invest \$2000 at time $t=0$ and an additional \$1000 at time $t = ½$. At time $t=1$ you have \$3200 in your account. Find the amount that would have to be in your account at time $t = ½$, if the time-weighted rate of return over the year is exactly .02 (i.e. 2 percentage points) higher than the dollar-weighted rate of return. Assume simple interest in calculating the dollar-weighted return.

27. You invest \$2000 at time $t=0$ and an additional \$1000 at time $t = ½$. At time $t = ½$ you have \$2120 in your account and at time $t=1$ you have \$3213.60 in your account.
    a) Find the dollar-weighted rate of return on this investment. Do not use the simple interest approximation for fractional periods.
    b) Find the time-weighted rate of return on this investment.

28. An investor deposits 50 in an investment account on January 1. The following summarizes the activity in the account during the year:

Date	Value Immediately Before Deposit	Deposit
March 15	40	20
June 1	80	80
October 1	175	75

On June 30 the value of the account is 157.50. On December 31 the value of the account is X. Using the time-weighted method, the equivalent annual yield during the first 6 months is equal to the time-weighted annual yield during the entire 1-year period. Calculate X.

29. You are given the following information about an investment account:

Date	Value Immediately Before Deposit	Deposit
January 1	10	
July 1	12	X
December 31	X	

Over the year, the time-weighted return is 0%, and the dollar-weighted return is Y. Calculate Y.

30. Let A be the fund balance on January 1, B the balance on June 30, and C the balance on December 31.
   a) If there are no deposits or withdrawals, show that yield rates computed by the dollar-weighted method and the time-weighted method are both equal to $(C - A)/A$.
   b) If there was a single deposit of D immediately after the June 30 balance was calculated, find expressions for the dollar-weighted and time-weighted yield rates.
   c) Rework (*b*) if the deposit occurred immediately before the June 30 balance was calculated.
   d) Verbally interpret the fact that the dollar-weighted yield rates in (*b*) and (*c*) are equal.
   e) Show that the time-weighted yield rate in (*b*) is greater than in (*c*).

7.7 Portfolio methods and investment year methods

31. Use the interest rates displayed in Table 7.2 to find the dollar amount of interest which \$10,000 invested at time $z+1$ will earn over the 3rd through the 6th years of investment inclusive.

32. Find $\ddot{s}_{\overline{5|}}$ from the data in Table 7.2 assuming the first payment is made in calendar year $z+3$.

33. A person deposits \$1000 on January 1, $z+6$ earning interest at the rates given in Table 7.2. Let the following be the accumulated value of the \$1000 on January 1, $z+9$:

   P: under the investment year method
   Q: under the portfolio yield method
   R: where the balance is withdrawn at the end of every year and is reinvested at the new money rate

   Determine the ranking of *P*, *Q*, and *R*.

34. The following table shows the annual effective interest rates being credited by an investment account, by calendar year of investment. The investment year method is applicable for the first three years, after which a portfolio rate is used.

Calendar Year of Investment	Investment Year Rates			Calendar Year of Portfolio Rate	Portfolio Rate
	i_1	i_2	i_3		
z	10%	10%	$j\%$	$z+3$	8%
$z+1$	12%	5%	10%	$z+4$	$(j-1)\%$
$z+2$	8%	$(j-2)\%$	12%	$z+5$	6%
$z+3$	9%	11%	6%	$z+6$	9%
$z+4$	7%	7%	10%	$z+7$	10%

An investment of 100 is made at the beginning of calendar years z, $z+1$, and $z+2$. The total amount of interest credited by the fund during the year $z+3$ is equal to 28.40. Calculate j.

35. It is known that $1+i_t^y = (1.08 + .005t)^{1+.01y}$ for $t=1, 2, 3, 4, 5$ and $y=0, 1, 2, \ldots, 10$. If \$1000 is invested for three years beginning in year $y=5$, find the equivalent level effective rate of interest.

36. An investment year method is defined by creating an accumulation function which is a function of two variables. Let $a(s,t)$ be the accumulated value at time t of an original investment of one unit at time s, where $0 \le s \le t$.
    a) Express $\delta_{s,t}$ in terms of $a(s,t)$.
    b) Express $a(s,t)$ in terms of $\delta_{s,t}$.
    c) Express $a(s,t)$ in terms of $a(s)$ and $a(t)$ for the portfolio method.
    d) Find $a(0,t)$ assuming a level effective rate of interest i.
    e) Find $a(t,t)$.

7.8 Short sales

37. In the illustration in this section the yield rate is 36% when the margin is 50% and we consider both interest on margin and payment of dividends. If the margin requirement is m, where $0<m\le 1$, derive a general formula for the yield rate as a function of m.

38. On January 1, Z you sold a stock short for 50 with a margin requirement of 80%. On December 31, Z, the stock paid a dividend of 2, and an interest amount of 4 was credited to the margin account. On January 1, $Z+1$ you covered the short sale at a price of X, earning a 20% return. Calculate X.

39. You sell a stock short with a current price of \$25,000 and buy it back for X at the end of one year. Governmental regulations require the short seller to deposit margin of 40% at the time of short sale. The prevailing interest rate is 8% effective and you earn a 25% yield rate on the transaction. Calculate X.

40. A and B sell Stocks A and B, respectively, short each for a price of \$1000. For both investors, the margin requirement is 50%, and interest on the margin is credited at an annual effective rate of 6%. A buys back Stock A one year later at a price of P. At the end of the year, Stock A paid a dividend of X. B also buys back Stock B after one year at a price of $P-25$. At the end of the year Stock B paid a dividend of $2X$. Both investors earned an annual effective yield rate of 21% on their short sales. Calculate P.

41. Example 7.12 had an annual yield rate of 37.4% in comparison to the 36% obtained earlier in the section. Explain the factor(s) leading to a slightly higher yield rate in the more refined calculation illustrated in Example 7.12.

7.9 Capital budgeting - basic techniques

42. If an investor's interest preference rate is 12%, should the investment in Exercise 2 be accepted or rejected?

43. A used car can be purchased for \$5000 cash or for \$2400 down and \$1500 at the end of each of the next two years. Should a purchaser with an interest preference rate of 10% pay cash or finance the car?

44. *a*) Draw a graph of $P(i)$ for Example 7.4.
    b) What can you conclude about the graph of $P(i)$ when all yield rates are imaginary?

45. A borrower needs \$800. The funds can be obtained in two ways:
    (*i*) By promising to pay \$900 at the end of the period.
    (*ii*) By borrowing \$1000 and repaying \$1125 at the end of the period.
    If the interest preference rate for the period is 10%, which option should be chosen?

46. Verify that the maximum value of $P(i)$ in Example 7.14 occurs at 14.78%.

7.10 Capital budgeting - other techniques

47. Compute the profitability index for the project in Table 7.1 if $i=10\%$.

48. Recompute the MIRR in Example 7.17 if the required return rate is 8%. Should the project be accepted or rejected based on this calculation?

49. Considering the same investment as in Example 7.17, find the project financing rate f corresponding to a project return rate $r = 15\%$.

50. The cash flows for the first five years of a ten-year investment period are as follows:

t	C_t
0	1000
1	2000
2	-4000
3	3000
4	-4000
5	5000

If $r = 15\%$ and $f = 10\%$, find B_5 to the nearest dollar.

Miscellaneous problems

51. An investor borrows an amount at an annual effective interest rate of 5% and will repay all interest and principal in a lump sum at the end of 10 years. The investor uses the amount borrowed to purchase a $1000 par value 10-year bond with 8% semiannual coupons bought to yield 6% convertible semiannually. All coupon payments are reinvested at a nominal rate of 4% convertible semiannually. Calculate the net gain to the investor at the end of 10 years after the loan is repaid.

52. The proceeds from a life insurance policy are left on deposit, with interest credited at the end of each year. The beneficiary makes withdrawals from the fund at the end of each year t, for $t = 1, 2, \ldots, 10$. At the minimum interest rate of 3% guaranteed in the policy, the equal annual withdrawal would be $1000. However, the insurer credits interest at the rate of 4% for the first four years and 5% for the next six years. The actual amount withdrawn at the end of year t is

$$W_t = \frac{F_t}{\ddot{a}_{\overline{11-t}|.03}}$$

where F_t is the amount of the fund, including interest, prior to the withdrawal. Calculate W_{10} to the nearest dollar.

53. An investment fund had a balance on January 1 of \$273,000 and a balance on December 31 of \$372,000. The amount of interest earned during the year was \$18,000 and the computed yield rate on the fund was 6%. What was the average date for contributions to and withdrawals from the fund?

54. An investment fund is started with an initial deposit of 1 at time 0. New deposits are made continuously at the annual rate $1 + t$ at time t over the next n years. The force of interest at time t is given by $\delta_t = (1+t)^{-1}$. Find the accumulated value in the fund at the end of n years.

8

Practical applications

8.1 INTRODUCTION

Chapter 8 contains several practical applications of the theory of interest not previously discussed. Sections 8.2 through 8.5 cover the area of consumer credit, including a discussion of "truth in lending" requirements. Special sections are devoted to two major areas of consumer credit; namely, real estate mortgages and automobile financing, including a discussion of leasing.

Section 8.6 and 8.7 deal with topics involved in the financial analysis of investments in fixed assets that have not previously been discussed. Section 8.6 introduces the reader to various depreciation methods which are in common usage. Section 8.7 discusses a type of financial analysis known as capitalized cost, a concept related to capital budgeting which was discussed in Sections 7.9 and 7.10.

Finally, Section 8.8 provides an overview of the wide variety of modern financial instruments which are in existence today. This material is of considerable value in introducing the reader on a non-technical level to a number of investment vehicles that may be unfamiliar. It also provides the foundation for further analytical development in succeeding chapters.

Each of the sections in Chapter 8 is relatively self-contained and does not significantly depend on results from the other sections. Thus, readers who are interested in only selected topics in this chapter, but not the chapter's entirety, will find the subsections of interest to be quite usable on their own.

8.2 TRUTH IN LENDING

In 1968 the United States Congress enacted the Consumer Credit Protection Act. Title I of this law is widely known as the "Truth in Lending Act" (15 USC 1601).

The primary purpose of this law is to require lenders to provide fair and accurate disclosure of the terms of consumer loans to borrowers. The law does not attempt to control the amount which lenders may charge on loans, but only to require proper disclosure. Also, the law applies only to consumer loans, and not business loans.

The law requires the disclosure of two key financial values; namely, the *finance charge* and the *annual percentage rate* (often called the "APR"). The former is designed to express the amount of interest to be charged over the term of the loan in dollars, while the latter expresses the interest to be paid as an annual rate. In addition to these two financial values, a number of additional disclosures in narrative form are required.

At the time a loan is taken out, the borrower may incur certain charges in connection with obtaining the loan. Examples of such charges would be points (to be defined in Section 8.4), other loan fees, service charges, credit report fees, and premiums for credit insurance.

The finance charge, as defined in the Truth in Lending Act, includes all interest charges. Moreover, it also includes some, but not necessarily all, of the additional charges cited in the preceding paragraph. Detailed regulations have been released by the Federal Reserve Board, the federal agency responsible for administering the Truth in Lending Act, which define items that must be included in the finance charge and those that do not have to be included.

It is specified that the annual percentage rate is to be computed by the *actuarial method.* This method is defined on a basis compatible with compound interest theory as developed in this book. Using the actuarial method leads to a subdivision of payments between principal and interest which is consistent with the loan amortization schedule discussed in Section 5.3.

One interesting aspect of the annual percentage rate (APR) is that it is quoted as a nominal rate convertible at the frequency with which payments are being made, rather than as an effective rate. For example, two loans might both quote "APR = 12%," but if one is repaid with monthly installments and the other is repaid with quarterly installments, the two rates are not equivalent. Thus, annual percentage rates on various loans cannot validly be compared directly unless they are all at the same frequency. The length of the payment interval is called the *unit period* in the law.

Truth in lending requirements make a distinction between open end credit and closed end credit. Examples of *open end credit* are a revolving charge account or a credit card. For open end credit the finance charge need only be disclosed each period as it is computed. The annual percentage rate is merely the nominal annual rate being charged on the outstanding loan balances. For example, if a credit card company charges interest each month at 1.75% on the outstanding balance, it must quote "APR = 21%."

An example of *closed end credit* is the typical loan that is repaid with installments. In order to illustrate the application of truth in lending with a standard loan transaction, we make the following definitions:

L = original loan balance after the down payment
K = finance charge
R = installment payment
m = number of payments per year
n = total number of payments in the term of the loan
i = annual percentage rate (APR)
j = rate of interest per payment period

The installment payment is given by

$$R = \frac{L+K}{n}. \tag{8.1}$$

Since the present value of installment payments must equal the original amount of the loan, we have the equation of value

$$Ra_{\overline{n}|j} = L \tag{8.2}$$

which is solved for j. The annual percentage rate is then

$$i = mj. \tag{8.3}$$

More complex loans might involve multiple payments from the lender to the borrower, called *advances*, at various points. Also the installment payments by the borrower may not be level or made at the same frequency. Such cases are handled by using formula (7.3)

$$P(j) = \sum_{t=0}^{n} v^t R_t = 0 \tag{7.3}$$

where $v = (1+j)^{-1}$. In applying formula (7.3) it must be remembered that all advances from the lender have one sign, while all payments by the borrower have the opposite sign.

For these more complex loans, the results in Section 7.3 showed that yield rates may not be unique if the outstanding loan balance changes sign somewhere during the term of the loan. The truth in lending procedures recognize this problem, but do not adequately deal with it. Fortunately, the damage is not great, since such situations are infrequent for consumer loans.

Truth in lending attributes non-unique yield rates to the existence of multiple advances. Its method of resolving the problem is to substitute one advance for the multiple advances, where the one advance is computed by the method of equated time as defined in Section 2.4. However, as we demonstrated in Section 2.4, use of the method of equated time introduces a bias in the answer. Furthermore, multiple yield rates can exist even if there is only one advance, a possibility not recognized by truth in lending.

The annual percentage rate disclosed to the borrower on a closed-end transaction assumes that the loan will be repaid according to the schedule established at the inception of the loan. However, many borrowers repay loans more quickly, either by paying off the outstanding loan balance in one lump sum or by refinancing the outstanding loan balance. Refinancing a loan is essentially equivalent to taking out a new loan.

When a loan is repaid early, a portion of the original finance charge, usually called the *unearned finance charge*, is credited to the borrower. The word "unearned" is used to reflect the fact that the lender has not yet "earned" the interest from the date of repayment to the end of the original term of the loan. The methods by which the unearned finance charge is typically computed will be discussed in Section 8.5. In some cases the computation is not done on a basis consistent with the computation of the original annual percentage rate. In such cases the rate of interest actually incurred by the borrower will differ from the original annual percentage rate quoted at the inception of the loan.

Some loans involve various types of prepayment penalties in the event the loan is repaid ahead of schedule. Under truth in lending such provisions must be disclosed in narrative fashion. However, they are not reflected in the annual percentage rate. In such cases the borrower will be credited with a value less than the unearned finance charge. In the extreme case, the borrower would not receive any credit at all, i.e. the lender would retain the entire finance charge. Thus, a borrower who repays a loan early and is charged a prepayment penalty will actually incur a rate of interest in excess of the quoted annual percentage rate.

The above brief discussion is intended to give the reader a general appreciation of the Truth in Lending Act and its application under typical conditions. However, the discussion is far from complete. Readers interested in learning more details about truth in lending are referred to "Regulation Z Truth in Lending" published by the Federal Reserve Board (12 CFR 226).

Some historical perspective on the computation of interest rates on loans is instructive. Until the early 1800s the most common method was the *Merchant's Rule*, which is essentially equivalent to simple interest. The Merchant's Rule worked satisfactorily for short-term loans, but produced illogical results for longer-term loans.

The issue reached the courts in Virginia in 1795. The landmark Ross v. Pleasants case involved a dramatic result. The roles of the debtor and creditor were reversed when the Merchant's Rule was applied over an extended period of time. Needless to say, the original creditor who became a debtor was none too pleased at this turn of events!

The issue was finally resolved by the United States Supreme Court in the decision on Story v. Livingston (38 U.S. 359) 1839. The court decided that payments by the borrower should first be applied to pay any accrued interest, with any excess being applied to reduce the outstanding loan balance. This decision is consistent with the loan amortization schedule developed in Section 5.3 and with compound interest theory. In recognition of this Supreme Court decision, the above procedure for dividing installment payments between interest and principal is often called the *United States Rule*, a term used in contrast to the Merchant's Rule.

The following is an extract from the decision in the Story v. Livingston case written by Mr. Justice Wayne:

> "The correct rule in general is that the creditor shall calculate interest whenever a payment is made. To this interest the payment is first to be applied; and if it exceed the interest due, the balance is to be applied to diminish the principal. If the payment fall short of the interest, the balance of interest is not to be added to the principal, so as to produce interest. Thus rule is equally applicable whether the debt be one which expressly draws interest, or one in which interest is given in the name of damages."

Two aspects of this decision are worthy of comment. First, the United States Rule will result in a compounding of interest whenever an installment payment is made. If installment payments are made at a regular frequency, then interest will be convertible at the same regular frequency as payments are made. However, if installment payments are made at an irregular frequency, then the United States Rule produces the rather odd result that the rate of interest quoted is convertible at the same irregular frequency as payments are made. This result is illustrated in Example 8.2.

Second, it is often said that the United States Rule and the actuarial method are equivalent. Under most circumstances, they are equivalent. However, the United States Rule is not consistent with the actuarial method when a payment is made that is insufficient to cover the accrued interest. Under the United States Rule any such deficiency is not added to the outstanding loan balance to accrue additional interest. However, under the actuarial method, which is consistent with compound interest theory, any such deficiency must be capitalized, i.e. added to the outstanding loan balance to accrue additional interest.

As mentioned briefly in Section 2.7, in recent years financial institutions have started referring to the yield rate on deposits as the *annual percentage yield* (often called the "APY"). Since the term APY is so similar to the term APR and is in widespread use, it is important to discuss the difference between these two terms.

First of all, it should be noted that APY is not a term defined in the Truth in Lending Act, which requires disclosure of the APR. The Truth in Lending Act only applies when the consumer is a borrower, not when the consumer is a lender (investor).

The relationship between APR and APY is a direct application of Chapter 1. The APR is a nominal rate of interest convertible at the same frequency as loan payments are being made. The APY is a true effective rate of interest. Thus, if we denote APY by i', then formula (8.3) would become

$$i' = (1+j)^m - 1. \tag{8.4}$$

It is interesting to observe a ramification of how this works in practice. When consumers are borrowers, they are looking for a low rate on their loans. The APR quoted will be lower than the equivalent APY. However, when consumers are lenders, they are looking for a high rate on their deposits. The APY quoted will be higher than the equivalent APR. Financial institutions are not oblivious to such consumer perceptions.

Example 8.1 Find the annual percentage rate (APR) on a consumer loan of $1000 which is repaid with monthly installments of $90 at the end of each month for one year.

The finance charge is equal to

$$K = (12)(90) - 1000 = 80.$$

The monthly rate j is determined from an application of formula (8.2)

$$90a_{\overline{12}|j} = 1000$$

or

$$a_{\overline{12}|j} = 11.1111.$$

An answer can be obtained solving for an unknown rate of interest on a level annuity as discussed in Section 3.7. Using a financial calculator, we obtain $j = .012043$, so that the $\text{APR} = 12j = .1445$, or 14.45%.

Prior to the passage of the Truth in Lending Act, this type of loan arrangement was frequently called an "8% add-on," since the finance charge for one year was 8% of the loan amount. This misleading statement implied a much lower rate of interest than the true rate given by the APR. It was this type of widespread misrepresentation that led to the enactment of truth in lending.

Example 8.2 A borrower takes out a loan of $1000 at 10% interest for 12 months. If the borrower repays $200 at the end of 3 months and $300 at the end of 8 months, find how much must be repaid at the end of 12 months:
(1) Using a true effective rate of interest.
(2) Using the Merchant's Rule (simple interest).
(3) Using the United States Rule.

1. The equation of value for the final payment is

$$1000(1.1)-200(1.1)^{3/4}-300(1.1)^{1/3} = \$575.50.$$

2. The equation of value for the final payment is

$$1000(1.1)-200(1.075)-300(1.03333) = \$575.00.$$

3. At the end of three months, the accrued interest is

$$1000(.10)(1/4) = 25.00.$$

Thus, 25.00 is applied to interest and 175.00 is applied to principal, reducing the outstanding balance to 825.00. At the end of eight months, the accrued interest is

$$825.00(.10)(5/12) = 34.38.$$

Thus, 34.38 is applied to interest and 265.62 is applied to principal, reducing the outstanding balance to 559.38. At the end of 12 months, the outstanding balance is

$$559.38[1+(.10)(1/3)] = 578.03.$$

It should be noted that the United States Rule does not assume either 10% effective or 10% nominal convertible with any regular frequency, but rather assumes 10% with conversions at the end of three and eight months. This example illustrates one unusual feature of the United States Rule.

8.3 AUTOMOBILE FINANCING

One particularly important type of consumer financing decision involves the purchase or leasing of an automobile. In Section 8.3 we will examine the basics of both automobile loans and leases. We will also discuss "buy or lease" decisions more generally.

Automobile loans

The most common way for a consumer to finance the purchase of an automobile is simply to take out a loan. Such loans typically involve level payments over a fixed term and thus follow the principles of Chapters 3 and 5. Moreover, automobile loans are a type of consumer credit covered by the Truth in Lending Act. Therefore, Section 8.2 applies directly to automobile loans.

Although automobile loans do not involve new concepts, there are certain unique attributes of such loans worthy of discussion. The starting point is clearly the purchase price of the new automobile. This value is often subject to negotiation between the buyer (consumer) and the seller (automobile dealer).

Frequently complicating the negotiation is the fact that many buyers intend to trade-in a used automobile. This value is also subject to negotiation. In effect, the net purchase price is the difference between the purchase price of the new vehicle and the *trade-in allowance* for the used vehicle. It does the buyer little good to negotiate an extra \$2000 in price concessions from the dealer on the purchase price of the new vehicle only to discover later that the trade-in allowance was \$3000 lower than could have been obtained elsewhere!

Further complicating the analysis is the fact that the automobile dealer may offer other promotional incentives such as a *cash back*. This is a cash payment from the seller to the buyer which can either be used to reduce the loan or taken in cash. However, the other terms of the loan may differ depending on how the "cash back" is utilized.

Some buyers also wish to finance ancillary items such as taxes, license and registration fees, service agreements, and any other miscellaneous charges. Other buyers would rather pay for such items up front to keep the loan amount and payments lower.

Once all the above items are determined, the buyer will usually make a *down payment* toward the purchase price. The net of all these additions and subtractions to the original purchase price of the automobile is computed and the balance becomes the initial amount of the loan.

The loan may be obtained from either the automobile dealer or from some other lender. The *term* (length) of the loan may vary (typically 36 to 60 months), as well as the interest rate charged on the loan. The interest rate on the loan may vary depending on such items as whether or not there is a "cash back", how large the down payment is, and how long the term of the loan is.

It is important that buyers shopping for an automobile loan make a valid "apples to apples" comparison of competing loan offers. Too often, buyers simply look at the size of the monthly payment, or the APR, and do not perform a complete and accurate comparison of competing offers.

One interesting phenomenon that occurs with some automobile loans is that the outstanding loan balance can exceed the market value of the automobile during the life of the loan. This may be difficult to visualize since the market value of the automobile exceeds the outstanding loan balance both at the beginning and end of the loan.

The reason for this possibility is that these two values behave differently between the beginning and end of the loan. As we saw in Chapter 5, in a loan amortization schedule the outstanding loan balance declines more slowly at the beginning of the loan and then more rapidly toward the end. The market value of an automobile behaves exactly in the opposite fashion. Figure 8.1 should help the reader visualize this phenomenon.

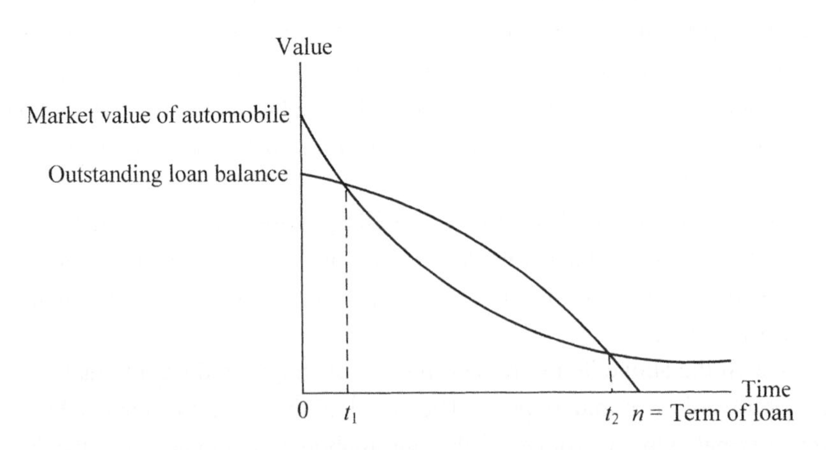

Figure 8.1 Loan balance exceeds market value between t_1 and t_2

The decline in the market value over time is often called *depreciation*. Section 8.6 presents a more detailed discussion of depreciation. A picturesque phrase often used to describe the situation illustrated in Figure 8.1 between times t_1 and t_2 is that the loan is *upside down.*

Automobile leases

In recent years *leasing* has emerged as a popular alternative for automobile financing. Under a leasing arrangement the *lessee* (automobile user) agrees to make a series of monthly payments during the term of the lease (typically 24 to 48 months). At the end of the lease the lessee returns the automobile to the *lessor* (automobile owner and lease financer). The lessee has the option to buy the automobile at that point. More frequently, the lessee will simply "walk away" and buy or lease another (newer) automobile.

Leasing has developed its own specialized terminology. We have already seen two new terms in the preceding paragraph. Several additional new terms follow:

- *Money factor* – the implicit finance charge (interest cost) for the use of the lender's capital that is tied up in the automobile.
- *Residual value* – the depreciated value of the automobile at lease expiration.
- *Gross capitalized cost* – the value of the automobile at lease inception plus any ancillary items to be capitalized and amortized over the term of the lease, such as taxes, license and registration fees, service agreements, and any other miscellaneous charges.
- *Capitalized cost reduction* – any "down payment" by the lessee or other credit available to reduce the gross capitalized cost.
- *Adjusted capitalized cost* – gross capitalized cost minus any capitalized cost reductions, the capital amount on which the lease is based.

There are a number of fees, penalties, and extra charges that may be associated with leasing agreements. Some fees of automobile ownership, such as license and registration fees are identical between buying and leasing. Sales taxes in most jurisdictions are levied only on lease payments rather than on the entire price of the automobile, as is the case with buying. This differential, by itself, will favor leasing over buying.

However, the other fees, penalties, and extra charges involved in leasing will generally be significantly greater for leasing than for buying and more than offset the sales tax advantage of leasing. The following is a list of the most common and significant, of such items:

- *Early termination penalty* – a significant penalty for early termination of the lease.
- *Mileage restriction fee* – a mileage restriction charge at the expiration of the lease for mileage which exceeds the maximum allowable under the lease (typically 10,000 to 15,000 miles per year).
- *Excess wear and tear fee* – another variable charge at the expiration of the lease for excessive wear and tear on the vehicle.
- *Lease acquisition fee* – a possible fee at lease inception to compensate the lessor for the expenses of obtaining the vehicle and processing the lease application.
- *Lease disposal fee* – a possible fee at lease expiration to compensate the lessor for the expense of dealing with the automobile which has been returned.
- *Security deposit* – typically one extra lease payment paid in advance, but refundable at lease expiration.

The monthly lease payment has two components: a *depreciation charge* and a *finance charge*. The depreciation charge compensates the lessor for the decline in market value of the automobile during the term of the lease. The finance charge compensates the lessor for the use of the lessor's capital used to buy the automobile that was tied up during the term of the lease.

We can utilize a net present value (NPV) analysis, as discussed in Section 7.2, as an analytical tool that a lessor might utilize to determine the monthly lease payment. The reader should note that the following analysis considers only the depreciation charge and the finance charge. It does not consider the fees, penalties, and extra charges discussed immediately above, which are handled separately.

The following symbols will be used in this analysis:

R = monthly lease payment
n = term of the lease in months
B_0 = price of the automobile at lease inception
B_n = residual value of an automobile at lease expiration
D = $B_0 - B_n$, depreciation of the automobile during the lease
i = money factor, expressed as a monthly rate

Figure 8.2 illustrates this transaction form the lessor's standpoint:

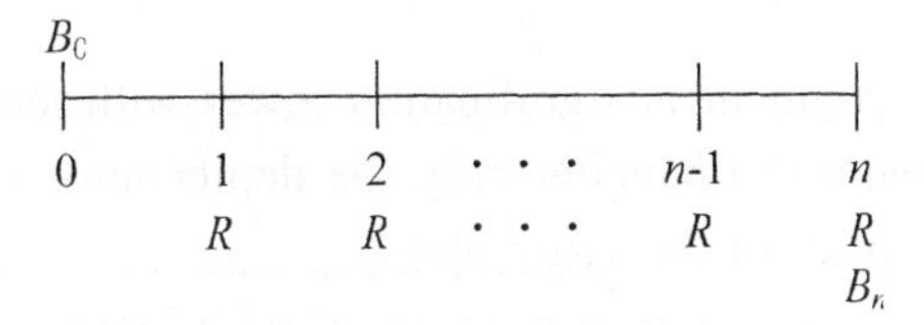

Figure 8.2 Time diagram for a lease

The reader will note that this transaction has the same structure as a bond from Chapter 6.

An equation of value using the basic formula for bond valuation is

$$B_0 = Ra_{\overline{n}|} + B_n v^n. \tag{8.5}$$

Formula (8.5) can be solved for R to give

$$\begin{aligned} R &= \frac{B_0 - B_n v^n}{a_{\overline{n}|}} \\ &= \frac{B_0(1-v^n)+(B_0-B_n)v^n}{a_{\overline{n}|}} \\ &= B_0 i + \frac{D}{s_{\overline{n}|}}. \end{aligned} \tag{8.6}$$

The first term in formula (8.6) is the finance charge, while the second term is the depreciation charge. The reader should verbally justify formula (8.6) using the general reasoning involving sinking funds presented in Section 5.4.

Leases are not subject to the Truth in Lending Act, since they are not loans. However, in 1976 the United States Congress enacted a parallel law known as the Consumer Leasing Act (15 USC 1667). This law is administered by the same governmental agencies as truth in lending and is supported by Regulation M, a regulation parallel to truth in lending's Regulation Z.

The Consumer Lending Act standardizes terminology and disclosures required in leasing agreements. As with consumer loans covered by truth in lending, the Act does not control the amount which lessors may charge on leases, but only addresses required disclosures.

Leasing has significant advantages and disadvantages in comparison with loan financing. The advantages are as follows:

1. The monthly payment is significantly lower with leasing. The reason is that the payment is financing only the depreciation over the lease term, not the entire price of the automobile.
2. The capitalized cost reduction required with leasing is usually less than the down payment required with loan financing.
3. The lessee does not have to bother with the sale, trade-in, or other disposal of the used vehicle at the expiration of the lease.
4. The lessee has the benefit of driving a new automobile every few years with a succession of leases.

The disadvantages are as follows:

1. Fees, penalties, and extra charges are higher with leasing.
2. Leasing is relatively inflexible to changing circumstances during the term of the lease with its early termination penalties, mileage restriction fees, and excess wear and tear fees.
3. The money factor in leasing tends to be higher than interest rates on automobile loans.
4. Over a longer period of time, successive leasing tends to be more expensive than successive purchases, if the purchased vehicles are kept for periods longer than the leases.

Leasing in general

"Buy or lease" decisions are not limited to automobiles, but occur in many other areas of economic activity and involve individuals, businesses, and governments. Such decisions can be analyzed as net present values (NPVs) using formula (7.2).

Since only the purchase of some fixed asset is being analyzed, the NPVs will all be negative. In other words, there will be no cash inflows to offset the cash outflows. Presumably, any cash inflows will be identical for both buying and leasing, and this will not affect the "buy or lease" decision.

Therefore, the decision criterion would be to choose the alternative with the least negative NPV. An illustration of this type of analysis is given in Example 8.5.

Example 8.3 A purchaser of a new automobile needs to finance $10,000 of the purchase price. The dealer offers two options for financing the loan with monthly payments over four years. Under Option A the APR is 9%. Under Option B the dealer offers a "cash back" of $600 and an APR of 12%. Which option is the most attractive to the purchaser, assuming the "cash back" is used to reduce the amount of the loan?

Under Option A the monthly payment is

$$R^A = \frac{10,000}{a_{\overline{48}|.0075}} = \frac{10,000}{40.1848} = \$248.85.$$

Under Option B the monthly payment is

$$R^B = \frac{9400}{a_{\overline{48}|.01}} = \frac{9400}{37.9740} = \$247.54.$$

Thus, the purchaser should accept Option B with its slightly lower monthly payment.

However, note that this analysis assumes the purchaser uses the "cash back" to reduce the amount of the loan under Option B, which is equivalent to investing $600 at 12% convertible monthly. If the purchaser takes the "cash back" and does not invest it at a rate almost as high as 12%, then Option A would have been the better choice. Since the monthly payments are so nearly equal under the two options, clearly the "break-even" rate at which the two options would be exactly equivalent is very close to 12%.

Example 8.4 ***A consumer is interested in leasing a new automobile costing $20,000 for 36 months. The automobile is expected to be worth $10,500 at the expiration of the lease. The lease uses a money factor of 0.5% per month (an annual rate of 6% convertible monthly) to compute the monthly lease payment. The lease also has a lease acquisition fee of $400 and a lease disposal fee of $250.***

(1) Find the monthly lease payment, if the lessor uses formula (8.6).

(2) Find the yield rate (IRR) which the lessee is actually paying for this lease considering fees at inception and expiration of the lease.

1. We have

$$\begin{aligned} n &= 36 \\ B_0 &= 20{,}000 \\ B_{36} &= 10{,}500 \\ D &= 9500 \\ \text{and} \quad i &= .005. \end{aligned}$$

Formula (8.6) gives

$$\begin{aligned} R &= (20{,}000)(.005) + \frac{9500}{s_{\overline{36}|.005}} \\ &= 100 + \frac{9500}{39.3361} = \$341.51. \end{aligned}$$

Thus, the lessee pays a total of 36(341.51) = $12,294.36 for the use of an automobile which loses $9,500 in value over 36 months. In effect, this could be interpreted as paying a total finance charge of 12,294.36 – 9,500 = $2,794.36 over the term of the lease.

2. The equation of value would be a modified version of formula (8.5)

$$20{,}000 = 341.51 a_{\overline{36}|j} + 400 + (10{,}500 + 250) v_j^{36}$$

which simplifies to

$$19{,}600 = 341.51 a_{\overline{36}|j} + 10{,}750 v_j^{36}.$$

Solving for j using the IRR functionality on a financial calculator gives $j = .006188$, or .6188%, per month. Expressed as an annual rate this is $12j = .0743$, or 7.43%, convertible monthly. Comparing this value with the 6% rate used to determine the monthly lease payment, gives insight into the effect of the lease acquisition fee and the lease disposal fee.

If the consumer could obtain an automobile loan with an APR significantly less than 7.43%, then a loan might be an attractive alternative. However, the consumer would likely need to make a significant down payment to obtain automobile loan at a favorable rate. Also, the monthly payment on the loan would be substantially larger than the monthly payment on the lease, since it is financing the entire price of the automobile and not just the depreciation. Finally, at lease expiration the consumer will own a used automobile and will be faced with the decision of what to do with it.

Example 8.5 ***A company is considering the acquisition of new equipment for $800,000. The equipment is estimated to be worth $100,000 at the end of six years when it will need to be replaced. Maintenance costs will be $8000 per month. The company could lease the equipment for $24,000 per month and the lessor would pay the maintenance costs. If the required return rate for the company is 12% convertible monthly, determine whether the company should buy or lease the equipment.***

First, we will analyze the "buy" alternative. The NPV is

$$\begin{aligned} & -800{,}000 - 8000a_{\overline{72}|.01} + 100{,}000(1.01)^{-72} \\ = & -800{,}000 - 409{,}203 + 48{,}850 \\ = & -1{,}160{,}353. \end{aligned}$$

Second, we will analyze the "lease" alternative. The NPV is

$$-24{,}000a_{\overline{72}|.01} = -1{,}227{,}609.$$

Thus, the better decision is to buy the equipment, since this option has the higher (i.e. less negative) NPV.

Presumably, there will be substantial cash inflows to the company during the six-year period which will make the acquisition of this equipment a profitable business decision. However, these cash inflows are identical for either alternative and do not affect the "buy or lease" decision.

8.4 REAL ESTATE MORTGAGES

Another particularly important type of loan is the real estate mortgage. The amount borrowed is typically quite large, being the largest single indebtedness for most families. Also, the term of real estate mortgages is quite long, with 15 to 30 years being typical.

The requirements of truth in lending apply to non-business related real estate mortgages just as they apply to other consumer loans. However, there are some particular features that have developed in connection with real estate mortgages worthy of discussion. In view of their importance, a separate section is being devoted to the consideration of such loans.

In view of the magnitude of the payments typically required on real estate mortgages, the payment frequency is almost always on a monthly basis. Payment dates are generally established on the first day of each calendar month. When the inception date of a mortgage loan is other than the first day of a calendar month, simple interest on the amount of the loan is charged to the borrower from the date of inception through the end of the calendar month. Generally the computation basis is actual/365, as defined in Section 2.6. No principal is repaid during the fractional period and a normal loan amortization based on the full loan amount commences on the first day of the following calendar month.

The date on which the title to the real estate legally transfers from the seller to the buyer is called the *settlement date*. This date is generally the inception date of the loan as well.

On real estate mortgages there are a number of additional expenses and fees which are charged at the settlement date. The largest fee is usually the loan origination fee. This fee is usually quoted in terms of points, where one *point* is 1% of the original amount of the loan. Thus, on a $100,000 mortgage loan, a buyer who is charged 2 points must pay $2000 to obtain the mortgage. Typically, there are also a variety of other fees covering items such as a credit report, appraisal, survey, document preparation, title examination, recording fees, tax stamps, etc.

Under truth in lending, some of these charges must be reflected in the calculation of the annual percentage rate (APR), and others do not have to be reflected. Thus, the annual percentage rate quoted under truth in lending will be higher than the stated rate on the loan. This latter rate is used to determine the monthly payment and to construct the amortization schedule. However, the annual percentage rate will usually not reflect all the expenses charged to the borrower at settlement.

The following procedure is used in computing the finance charge and the annual percentage rate required by truth in lending on a real estate mortgage. We define L, K, R, n, i, and j as in Section 8.2 and set $m = 12$. We then make the following additional definitions:

Q = expenses at settlement that must be reflected in the APR
L^* = amount financed for truth in lending purposes, i.e. reflecting Q
j' = monthly rate of interest on the loan
i' = quoted annual rate of interest on the loan

We now have the following relationships. The quoted annual rate of interest on the loan is

$$i' = 12j'. \tag{8.7}$$

The monthly payment on the loan is

$$R = \frac{L}{a_{\overline{n}|j'}}. \tag{8.8}$$

The amount financed for truth in lending purposes is the amount of the loan less the expenses at settlement that must be reflected, i.e.

$$L^* = L - Q. \tag{8.9}$$

The finance charge is equal to the difference between the total payments to be made and the amount financed for truth in lending purposes, i.e.

$$K = nR - L^*. \tag{8.10}$$

To obtain the rate of interest per month for truth in lending we solve the following equation for j

$$R\,a_{\overline{n}|j} = L^*. \tag{8.11}$$

Finally, the annual percentage rate (APR) for truth in lending is

$$i = 12j. \tag{8.12}$$

The loan amortization schedules illustrated in Chapter 5 involved loans with relatively short terms. The reader will find it instructive to examine an illustrative

30-year amortization schedule for a real estate mortgage contained in Appendix B. The early payments are almost entirely interest, while the ending payments are almost entirely principal. Many people find it frustrating to buy a home, make payments for several years, and then find that the outstanding loan balance on their real estate mortgage has declined relatively little.

In recent years a new type of mortgage loan has appeared, the *adjustable rate mortgage* (ARM). This term is in contrast to the traditional mortgage, which is often called a *fixed rate mortgage.* Under the adjustable rate mortgage the rate of interest charged on the loan can be periodically adjusted upward or downward by the lender under certain conditions and subject to certain restrictions.

The motivating factor for the development of the adjustable rate mortgage is the fact that lenders are willing to provide such mortgages at lower initial rates of interest than on traditional fixed rate mortgages. This reaction by lenders is understandable, since lenders are making firm commitments on the rate of interest to be charged on fixed rate mortgages over periods ranging from 15 to 30 years. In periods of rising interest rates lenders will be locked into fixed rate portfolios with yield rates well below prevailing market rates. On the other hand, in periods of falling interest rates borrowers will be able to refinance their loans at the lower rates.

From the borrower's perspective the adjustable rate mortgage may be attractive, since the initial rate of interest and the initial monthly payment are lower than with a fixed rate mortgage. Moreover, if interest rates fall, the monthly payment may be adjusted even lower.

However, there is a significant risk with an adjustable rate mortgage that rates of interest and monthly payments will increase and exceed those that would have existed had a fixed rate mortgage been chosen originally. Thus, with a fixed rate mortgage the risk associated with interest rate fluctuations is borne by the lender, whereas with adjustable rate mortgages much of that risk is shifted to the borrower.

The interval at which the lender can adjust the interest rate on an adjustable rate mortgage is called the *adjustment period.* This interval can be monthly, or less frequently such as every one to three years.

The interest rates on an adjustable rate mortgage are usually tied by formula to an *index rate.* This prevents the potential abuse of the lender making arbitrary upward adjustments in the interest rate even if prevailing market rates would not justify such increases. One example of a possible index rate is the yield on Treasury securities of a specified maturity. A second example would be an index rate based on the interest rates being paid to depositors in order to secure funds to lend by a broad cross section of institutional lenders. The interest rate on an adjustable rate mortgage is computed as the index rate plus a fixed *margin*, where the margin is defined by the original mortgage agreement. The reader will note that the word "margin" is yet another term with multiple meanings.

Most adjustable rate mortgages have limitations on the amount of increase in the interest rate and/or payments which are called *caps*. One type of cap is the *interest rate cap*. This type of cap places a limit on the amount of any periodic increase in the interest rate, or a limit on the total increase over the life of the loan, or both. A second type of cap is the *payment cap*. This type of cap places a percentage limit on the dollar increase in monthly payment that can occur at any one adjustment date.

One interesting aspect of a payment cap is that it does not necessarily impose a comparable limitation on the amount of the increase in the interest rate being charged. Thus, it is possible that the revised payment would not be enough to pay interest on the loan resulting in negative amortization, i.e. an increase in the outstanding loan balance. Negative amortization was first discussed in Section 5.6. Needless to say, the attractiveness of adjustable rate mortgages to borrowers evaporates rapidly in the event negative amortization occurs.

As might be expected, there are special truth in lending requirements for adjustable rate mortgages. Significant narrative disclosure is required, including a document entitled "Consumer Handbook on Adjustable Rate Mortgages" published by the Federal Reserve Board and the Federal Home Loan Bank Board. However, the determination of the annual percentage rate is based on the initial loan rate. Thus, the annual percentage rate for an adjustable rate mortgage will not numerically convey the effect of future interest rate changes.

A number of other types of real estate mortgages have also appeared in recent years. The following is a brief introduction to some of these. However, the descriptions are quite brief and the list is not complete. Additional information on the variety of real estate mortgages in existence can be obtained from any major real estate firm or mortgage company.

1. *Graduated payment mortgage* – This is a fixed or adjustable rate mortgage under which payments increase for a stated period of time, such as five years, and then become level. It is designed to appeal to young homeowners beginning careers who expect their incomes to increase rapidly in the next few years. Negative amortization is common with such mortgages.

2. *Interest only mortgage* – This is a fixed or adjustable rate mortgage on which payments for an initial period, typically five to seven years, pay only interest on the loan. At the end of the initial period, the borrower can refinance, pay of the mortgage, or start a regular payment schedule which will amortize principal as will pay interest. Negative amortization is avoided, but no principal is amortized during the initial period and mortgage payments may rise substantially thereafter.

3. *Option adjustable rate mortgage (Option ARM)* – This is a type of adjustable rate mortgage which offers the borrower a range of possible payments on each payment date. Payments can range from some defined minimum (perhaps even low enough to cause negative amortization for that month) all the way up to some defined maximum (typically a payment that, if continued, would completely amortize the loan over its remaining term). The appeal of this type of mortgage is the flexibility it offers to borrowers on each payment date.

4. *Shared appreciation mortgage* – This is a fixed rate mortgage which carries a lower rate of interest than a regular fixed rate mortgage. In exchange for the lower rate of interest, the borrower agrees to share some of the price appreciation on the underlying property with the lender. This type of mortgage has become relatively uncommon.

5. *"Wraparound" mortgage* – This is a fixed rate mortgage which requires that an existing *assumable* mortgage exist on the underlying property. An "assumable" mortgage is one which can be transferred from the prior owner to the new owner. If the original mortgage carries a lower rate of interest than is currently available, then the combination of the original mortgage and the new "wraparound" mortgage will have a lower total cost to the new owner than a new mortgage for the entire amount. However, the "wraparound" mortgage is of limited utility since most mortgages today are not assumable.

6. *Reverse annuity mortgage* – This is a fixed or adjustable rate mortgage in which the homeowner receives an annuity from the *equity* in the property. "Equity" is the difference between the value of the property and the outstanding loan balance on the mortgage. This type of mortgage is designed

to appeal to older homeowners who have large equities in their homes, but need income for retirement purposes. Of course, the outstanding loan balance increases under such an arrangement, which many retirees find unattractive. However, many reverse annuity mortgages do have a lifetime guarantee that the homeowners can continue to live in the home to remove any concern that the homeowners will lose their home by using up all the equity they have in it.

Characterizing the terms of real estate mortgages as periods of time ranging from 15 to 30 years may be misleading in one respect. The large majority of mortgages are paid off early and never continue for their full term. There are several different reasons why this happens.

First, many mortgages are refinanced when prevailing interest rates favor taking out a new mortgage rather than continuing the existing one. Second, when the property is sold, typically the existing mortgage is paid off in full at settlement. Third, some mortgages are simply paid off early by borrowers who have accumulated sufficient funds to do so.

This phenomenon creates a challenge for lenders, since they really do not know how rapidly the mortgages they issue will be repaid. The rate of early payoff of mortgage balances is called *prepayment speed*. When prevailing interest rates rise, prepayment speeds slow down, since continuing existing mortgages looks relatively more attractive. Conversely, when prevailing interest rates fall, prepayment speeds increase, since refinancing with new mortgages looks relatively more attractive.

Institutional lenders have developed sophisticated models to better understand the dynamics of anticipated prepayment behavior on the mortgages they issue. Prepayment speeds not only will vary significantly with changes in prevailing interest rates, but will also vary significantly among different types of mortgages.

***Example 8.6** A family purchases a house for $150,000. They agree to put 20% down and finance the balance with a 30-year fixed rate mortgage at 9.9%. In order to secure this loan they must pay 2 points at settlement. In additional there are $800 of other charges at settlement. Of the total charges at settlement 1 1/2 points and half of the other charges must be reflected in the APR. The house is purchased on July 12. Develop the calculations required at settlement as described in this section.*

The amount of the down payment is .2(150,000) = 30,000, so that the initial amount of the loan is

$$L = 150{,}000 - 30{,}000 = 120{,}000.$$

We then compute the interest for the rest of July. The daily interest charge is

$$\frac{.099\,(120{,}000)}{365} = 32.5479.$$

There are 20 days from July 12 through July 31 inclusive, so the amount of interest is

$$20(32.5479) = 650.96.$$

This amount must be paid on July 12 at settlement, despite the fact that it would be more appropriate under interest theory to pay it at the end of July. Of course, the requirement to pay it at settlement favors the lender.

We have $i' = .099$, so that $j' = .099/12 = .00825$. Thus, the monthly payment on the loan is

$$R = \frac{120{,}000}{a_{\overline{360}|.00825}} = 1044.23.$$

The first regular payment is made on September 1 (not August 1).

The charges at settlement are 2 points plus 800, i.e. .02(120,000) + 800 = 3200. Of these charges 1 1/2 points plus 400 must be reflected in the APR, i.e.

$$Q = .015(120{,}000) + 400 = 2200.$$

Thus, the amount financed for truth in lending purposes is

$$L^* = 120{,}000 - 2200 = 117{,}800.$$

The finance charge is equal to the total payments less the amount financed, i.e.

$$\begin{aligned} K &= (360)(1044.23) - 117{,}800 \\ &= 375{,}922.80 - 117{,}800 = 258{,}122.80 \end{aligned}$$

Note that the total payments over 30 years are more than three times the amount of the loan! The effect of compound interest over long periods of time is truly dramatic.

Finally, we need to compute the APR. From formula (8.11) we have

$$1044.23 a_{\overline{360}|j} = 117{,}800.$$

We can use a financial calculator and solve this equation as an unknown rate of interest problem, as described in Section 3.7. We find that $j = .008433$. Thus, the APR is

$$\text{APR} = i = 12(.008433) = .1012, \text{ or } 10.12\%.$$

The APR is greater than 9.9%, as expected.

Example 8.7 A borrower takes out a 30-year adjustable rate mortgage for $65,000. The interest rate for the first year is 8%. If the interest rate increases to 10% for the second year, find the increase in the monthly payment.

The monthly payment for the first year is

$$\frac{65{,}000}{a_{\overline{360}|.08/12}} = \frac{65{,}000}{136.2835} = 476.95\,.$$

The outstanding loan balance after one year is

$$476.95\,a_{\overline{348}|.08/12} = 476.95(135.1450) = 64{,}457.42\,.$$

The revised monthly payment for the second year is

$$\frac{64{,}457.42}{a_{\overline{348}|.10/12}} = \frac{64{,}457.42}{113.3174} = 568.82\,.$$

Thus, the increase in the monthly payment is

$$568.82 - 476.95 = \$91.87$$

which is an increase of 19.3%.

8.5 APPROXIMATE METHODS

The calculation of an exact annual percentage rate (APR) involves an iteration and thus requires a financial calculator for an efficient solution. Several approximate methods for calculating the unknown rate of interest on installment loans have been developed. These methods do not utilize any interest functions and can be calculated directly.

Although these methods are not as important as they were in the days before the development of financial calculators, they still have educational and conceptual value. Moreover, they are useful in providing the background necessary for computing the unearned finance charge defined in Section 8.2 and for the various depreciation methods to be considered in Section 8.6. Finally, one of these approximate methods has such a high level of accuracy that it has value in other situations.

Nevertheless, the reader should consider this section optional reading. It is included as a reference for readers interested in exploring such methods.

We will examine four such approximate methods. All of these methods are similar in that they replace the true division of the installment payments between principal and interest with an arbitrary division between principal and interest. It is assumed that the amount of principal invested during each mth of a year is invested at rate i/m for that mth of a year. Thus, if we denote the outstanding loan balance at time t/m by $B_{t/m}$, we have

$$\frac{i}{m}\sum_{t=0}^{n-1} B_{t/m} = K$$

or

$$i = \frac{mK}{\sum_{t=0}^{n-1} B_{t/m}}. \tag{8.13}$$

The derivation of formula (8.13) reflects the fact that the finance charge K must equal the sum of the amounts of interest earned during each mth of a year on the outstanding loan balances for those periods. The various methods differ only in the arbitrary division of installment payments between principal and interest, which will be reflected in the denominator of formula (8.13).

Maximum yield method

The first method is often called the *maximum yield method*, since it produces larger answers than any of the other methods. The value of i produced by this method is labeled i^{max}. This method assumes that all installment payments are applied entirely to principal until it is fully paid and thereafter are applied entirely to interest. We also assume that the finance charge is less than one installment payment, i.e.

$$K < \frac{L+K}{n}.$$

This latter assumption leads to the result that all installment payments except part of the last one are used for principal repayment.

With these assumptions Table 8.1 is a modified amortization schedule for this method. The reader should verify the entries in Table 8.1 and note the various relationships in the table.

We now need to sum the outstanding loan balance column to evaluate formula (8.13)

$$\sum_{t=0}^{n-1} B_{t/m} = Ln - \frac{L+K}{n} \cdot \frac{(n-1)n}{2}$$

so that

$$i^{max} = \frac{mK}{Ln - (L+K)\frac{n-1}{2}}$$

$$= \frac{2mK}{L(n+1) - K(n-1)}. \tag{8.14}$$

Table 8.1 Amortization Schedule Using the Maximum Yield Method

Period	*Payment amount*	*Interest paid*	*Principal repaid*	*Outstanding loan balance*
0				L
$\frac{1}{m}$	$\frac{L+K}{n}$	0	$\frac{L+K}{n}$	$L - \frac{L+K}{n}$
$\frac{2}{m}$	$\frac{L+K}{n}$	0	$\frac{L+K}{n}$	$L - 2\frac{L+K}{n}$
.	.	.	.	.
.	.	.	.	.
.	.	.	.	.
$\frac{n-1}{m}$	$\frac{L+K}{n}$	0	$\frac{L+K}{n}$	$L - (n-1)\frac{L+K}{n}$
$\frac{n}{m}$	$\frac{L+K}{n}$	K	$\frac{L+K}{n} - K$	0
Total	$L+K$	K	L	

It is interesting to note that formula (8.14) can be derived by an alternative argument which assumes simple interest throughout the life of the loan. This alternative derivation is left as an exercise. Also left as an exercise is the derivation of a more general formula for the case in which the finance charge is larger than one installment payment.

Minimum yield method

The second method is often called the *minimum yield method*, since it produces smaller answers than any of the other methods. The value of i produced by this method is labeled i^{min}. This method assumes that all installment payments are applied entirely to interest until it is fully paid and thereafter are applied entirely to principal. Again we assume that the finance charge is less than one installment payment, so that the first payment is at least enough to pay the entire amount of interest. Table 8.2 is a modified amortization schedule for this method. The reader should verify the entries in Table 8.2 and note the various relationships in the table.

We now need to sum the outstanding loan balance column to evaluate formula (8.13)

$$\sum_{t=0}^{n-1} B_{t/m} = \frac{L+K}{n} \cdot \frac{n(n+1)}{2} - K$$

so that

$$i^{min} = \frac{mK}{(L+K)\dfrac{n+1}{2} - K} = \frac{2mK}{L(n+1)+K(n-1)}. \qquad (8.15)$$

Again, the derivation of a more general formula for the case in which the finance charges is larger than one installment payment is left as an exercise.

Table 8.2 Amortization Schedule Using the Minimum Yield Method

Period	*Payment amount*	*Interest paid*	*Principal repaid*	*Outstanding loan balance*
0				$(n)\frac{L+K}{n}-K=L$
$\frac{1}{m}$	$\frac{L+K}{n}$	K	$\frac{L+K}{n}-K$	$(n-1)\frac{L+K}{n}$
$\frac{2}{m}$	$\frac{L+K}{n}$	0	$\frac{L+K}{n}$	$(n-2)\frac{L+K}{n}$
.	.	.	.	.
.	.	.	.	.
.	.	.	.	.
$\frac{n-1}{m}$	$\frac{L+K}{n}$	0	$\frac{L+K}{n}$	$\frac{L+K}{n}$
$\frac{n}{m}$	$\frac{L+K}{n}$	0	$\frac{L+K}{n}$	0
Total	$L+K$	K	L	

The maximum and minimum yield methods have been justifiably criticized, since they do not reflect the fact that each installment payment is partially principal and partially interest. The other two methods do reflect this fact.

Constant ratio method

The third, and simplest, method is the *constant ratio method.* The value of i produced by this method is labeled i^{cr}. This method assumes that a constant percentage of each installment is principal and that a constant percentage is interest. Table 8.3 is a modified amortization schedule for this method. The reader should verify the entries in Table 8.3 and note the various relationships in the table.

We now need to sum the outstanding loan balance column to evaluate formula (8.13)

$$\sum_{t=0}^{n-1} B_{t/m} = L\cdot\frac{n(n+1)}{2n}$$

so that

$$i^{cr} = \frac{mK}{L\cdot\frac{n+1}{2}} = \frac{2mK}{L(n+1)}. \tag{8.16}$$

Table 8.3 Amortization Schedule Using the Constant Ratio Method

Period	*Payment amount*	*Interest paid*	*Principal repaid*	*Outstanding loan balance*
0				$\frac{n}{n}L=L$
$\frac{1}{m}$	$\frac{L+K}{n}$	$\frac{K}{n}$	$\frac{L}{n}$	$\frac{n-1}{n}L$
$\frac{2}{m}$	$\frac{L+K}{n}$	$\frac{K}{n}$	$\frac{L}{n}$	$\frac{n-2}{n}L$
.	.	.	.	.
.	.	.	.	.
.	.	.	.	.
$\frac{n-1}{m}$	$\frac{L+K}{n}$	$\frac{K}{n}$	$\frac{L}{n}$	$\frac{1}{n}L$
$\frac{n}{m}$	$\frac{L+K}{n}$	$\frac{K}{n}$	$\frac{L}{n}$	0
Total	$L+K$	K	L	

It is interesting to note that formula (8.16) can be derived by an alternative argument. The amount of interest per year is mK/n. The average outstanding loan balance can be found by averaging the outstanding loan balances during the first period and the last period, i.e.

$$\frac{1}{2}\cdot L\cdot\frac{n}{n}+\frac{1}{2}\cdot L\cdot\frac{1}{n} = L\cdot\frac{n+1}{2n}.$$

The rate of interest is computed as the annual amount of interest divided by the average outstanding loan balance, i.e.

$$i^{cr} = \frac{m \cdot \frac{K}{n}}{L \cdot \frac{n+1}{2n}}$$

$$= \frac{2mK}{L(n+1)}. \tag{8.16}$$

The two methods are equivalent, since the outstanding loan balance is linear under these assumptions.

On occasion an even simpler version of the constant ratio method is encountered in which the average outstanding loan balance is taken to be the average of the beginning balance and the ending balance, i.e.

$$\frac{1}{2} \cdot L + \frac{1}{2} \cdot 0 = \frac{1}{2} \cdot L.$$

With this assumption the rate of interest is

$$i^{cr'} = \frac{2mK}{Ln}. \tag{8.17}$$

where the prime denotes this variation of the constant ratio method.

Formula (8.17) replaces the term $(n+1)/2n$ with $1/2$. The reader should note that the relationship between formulas (8.16) and (8.17) is quite analogous to the relationship between formulas (6.24) and (6.25), the two versions of the bond salesman's formula. In general, formula (8.17) produces less accurate results than formula (8.16).

Direct ratio method

The fourth method is the *direct ratio method.* The value of i produced by this method is labeled i^{dr}. This method uses an approximate division into principal and interest which is closest to the exact division by the actuarial method. In the true amortization schedule the interest paid column decreases over time while the principal repaid column increases. The direct ratio method reflects this pattern while none of the other approximate methods do. In general, the direct ratio method will produce more accurate results than the other approximate methods.

The direct ratio method can best be illustrated by example. Consider a one-year loan repaid with 12 monthly installments. The sum of the positive integers from 1 through 12 is 78. The direct ratio method assumes that the interest paid is 12/78 of the finance charge in the first month, 11/78 in the second month, . . . , 1/78 in the last month. This decreasing pattern of interest payments will produce a corresponding increasing pattern of principal repayments. The direct ratio method is often called the *rule of 78*, despite the fact that the number 78 is valid only for a term of 12 months.

Table 8.4 is a modified amortization schedule for this method. We define S_r to be the sum of the first r positive integers, i.e.

$$S_r = 1+2+\cdots+r = \frac{r(r+1)}{2}. \tag{8.18}$$

The reader should verify the entries in Table 8.4 and note the various relationships in the table.

Table 8.4 Amortization Schedule Using the Direct Ratio Method

Period	*Payment amount*	*Interest paid*	*Principal repaid*	*Outstanding loan balance*
0				$(n)\frac{L+K}{n} - K\cdot\frac{S_n}{S_n} = L$
$\frac{1}{m}$	$\frac{L+K}{n}$	$K\cdot\frac{n}{S_n}$	$\frac{L+K}{n} - K\cdot\frac{n}{S_n}$	$(n-1)\frac{L+K}{n} - K\cdot\frac{S_n-1}{S_n}$
$\frac{2}{m}$	$\frac{L+K}{n}$	$K\cdot\frac{n-1}{S_n}$	$\frac{L+K}{n} - K\cdot\frac{n-1}{S_n}$	$(n-2)\frac{L+K}{n} - K\cdot\frac{S_n-2}{S_n}$
. . .	. . .	. . .	. . .	. . .
$\frac{n-1}{m}$	$\frac{L+K}{n}$	$K\cdot\frac{2}{S_n}$	$\frac{L+K}{n} - K\cdot\frac{2}{S_n}$	$\frac{L+K}{n} - K\cdot\frac{S_1}{S_n}$
$\frac{n}{m}$	$\frac{L+K}{n}$	$K\cdot\frac{1}{S_n}$	$\frac{L+K}{n} - K\cdot\frac{1}{S_n}$	0
Total	$L+K$	K	L	

We now need to sum the outstanding loan balance column to evaluate formula (8.13). Before we can do this it is necessary to find the sum of S_r as r ranges from 1 to n. We have

$$\begin{aligned}\sum_{r=1}^{n} S_r &= \sum_{r=1}^{n} \frac{r(r+1)}{2} = \frac{1}{2}\sum_{r=1}^{n}\left(r^2+r\right)\\ &= \frac{1}{2}\left[\frac{1}{6}n(n+1)(2n+1)+\frac{1}{2}n(n+1)\right]\\ &= \frac{1}{6}n(n+1)(n+2).\end{aligned}$$

Using this result we have

$$\sum_{t=0}^{n-1} B_{t/m} = \frac{L+K}{n}\cdot\frac{n(n+1)}{2} - K\frac{\frac{1}{6}n(n+1)(n+2)}{\frac{1}{2}n(n+1)}$$

so that

$$\begin{aligned}i^{dr} &= \frac{mK}{(L+K)\frac{n+1}{2} - K\frac{n+2}{3}}\\ &= \frac{mK}{\frac{1}{6}\left[3(L+K)(n+1)-2K(n+2)\right]}\\ &= \frac{mK}{\frac{1}{6}\left[3L(n+1)+K(n-1)\right]}\\ &= \frac{2mK}{L(n+1)+\frac{1}{3}K(n-1)}. \qquad (8.19)\end{aligned}$$

Formula (8.19) produces surprisingly accurate answers. Table 8.5 compares the results under a variety of circumstances. In no case do the two methods produce different results to the nearest quarter percent. In fact, only for long-term loans with high interest rates do the results differ by more than 0.1%.

Table 8.5 Comparison of Exact APRs and Approximate Values Using Formula (8.19)

Frequency	*Term*	*Finance charge*	*Formula (8.16) approximate i*	*APR exact i*
Monthly	6 months	2 %	6.82 %	6.82 %
"	"	4	13.58	13.58
"	"	6	20.28	20.29
"	1 year	4	7.30	7.31
"	"	8	14.44	14.45
"	"	12	21.43	21.45
"	2 years	8	7.50	7.50
"	"	16	14.64	14.67
"	"	24	21.46	21.58
"	5 years	20	7.39	7.42
"	"	40	13.94	14.12
"	"	60	19.78	20.32
Quarterly	1 year	8	12.60	12.60
"	2 years	16	13.66	13.69
"	5 years	40	13.60	13.77

In Section 8.2 calculation of the unearned finance charge on loans which are repaid early was discussed. There are two methods in widespread use. The first is based on an exact application of the actuarial method. The second is based on the rule of 78. It will be shown in Example 8.9 that the use of the rule of 78 favors the lender. The reader should be careful not to confuse this application of the rule of 78 with the derivation of formula (8.19). Two entirely different situations are involved.

Example 8.8 Find the rate of interest on the loan in Example 8.1:
(1) By the maximum yield method.
(2) By the minimum yield method.
(3) By the constant ratio method.
(4) By the direct ratio method (rule of 78).

1. Using formula (8.14)

$$i^{max} = \frac{(2)(12)(80)}{(1000)(13)-(80)(11)} = .1584, \text{ or } 15.84\%.$$

2. Using formula (8.15)

$$i^{min} = \frac{(2)(12)(80)}{(1000)(13)+(80)(11)} = .1383, \text{ or } 13.83\%.$$

3. Using formula (8.16)

$$i^{cr} = \frac{(2)(12)(80)}{(1000)(13)} = .1477, \text{ or } 14.77\%.$$

4. Using formula (8.19)

$$i^{dr} = \frac{(2)(12)(80)}{(1000)(13)+\frac{1}{3}(80)(11)} = .1444, \text{ or } 14.44\%.$$

The exact answer produced by the actuarial method was found to be 14.45% in Example 8.1. The direct ratio method produces an answer closer to that obtained by the actuarial method than do any of the other approximate methods; and, in fact, it achieves a remarkable level of accuracy.

***Example 8.9** Compute the unearned finance charge recovered by the borrower for the consumer loan in Example 8.1 if the loan is repaid in full after six regular installments are made:*
(1) Using the actuarial method.
(2) Using the rule of 78.

1. The outstanding loan balance at the end of six months, prospectively, is

$$90\, a_{\overline{6}|.012043} = 517.95.$$

The total that would have been paid over the final six months on the original payment schedule is

$$6 \cdot 90 = 540.00.$$

Thus, the unearned finance charge is

$$540.00 - 517.95 = \$22.05.$$

2. Using the rule of 78, we have $S_6 = 21$ and $S_{12} = 78$. The total finance charge is \$80. Thus, the unearned finance charge is

$$\frac{21}{78} \cdot 80 = \$21.54.$$

Thus, the rule of 78 produces a smaller unearned finance charge than does the actuarial method. Borrowers who repay their loans early and receive a credit based on the rule of 78 are treated less favorably than if the actuarial method had been used. Truth in lending does not prohibit the use of the rule of 78 in this fashion, and both methods are used in practice.

8.6 DEPRECIATION METHODS

An important application of the theory of interest lies in the financial analysis of *fixed assets*. Such assets have a useful life of more than one year. Examples of fixed assets would be plant, equipment, real estate, and automobiles. Fixed assets result from expenditures by individuals and firms for business and investment purposes.

We make the following definitions:

n = number of interest conversion periods in the term under consideration
A = value of the asset at the beginning of the n periods
S = salvage value of the asset at the end of the n periods (S need not to be positive)
R = level periodic return after expenses from the asset
i = yield rate on the investment per interest conversion period
j = sinking fund rate of interest per interest conversion period

If $A = S$, i.e. if the asset neither increases nor decreases in value through time, then the yield rate each period is the periodic net return divided by the value of the asset, i.e.

$$i = \frac{R}{A}. \tag{8.20}$$

In general $A \neq S$, since the asset value will change through time. If $A < S$, the asset is known as an *appreciating asset*; while if $A > S$, the asset is known as a *depreciating asset*. An example of the former might be real estate, and an example of the latter would be an automobile. We will generally be concerned with depreciating assets, although many of our results can be used for either.

If $A \neq S$, then formula (8.20) is invalid, since it fails to recognize that the asset value is changing. In this case it is necessary in our analysis to replace the capital by means of a sinking fund, so that the fundamental equation of value from the principles of Section 5.4 is

$$R = Ai + \frac{A-S}{s_{\overline{n}|j}}. \tag{8.21}$$

If $A = S$, then formula (8.21) reduces to formula (8.20). In practice it is often assumed that $i = j$, especially if no sinking fund is actually established. Formula (8.21) is not restricted to $A > S$ but is also valid for $A < S$.

The reader should note that formula (8.21) is identical to formula (8.6) in the subsection of Section 8.3 addressing automobile leases. The only difference is in the notation used.

The reader should also note the similarity between the above discussion and the analysis of bonds in Chapter 6. A bond bought at a discount is analogous to an appreciating asset, while a bond bought at a premium is analogous to a depreciating asset. In fact, formula (8.21) is valid for bonds, noting that A plays the role of the price, S the redemption value, and R the coupon.

As mentioned in Section 8.3 the decline in the value over time of a depreciating asset is termed *depreciation*. This depreciation is largely due to physical deterioration and obsolescence. Sound accounting practice dictates that the value of the asset must be written down over time on the books of the investor. The value of the asset on the books of the investor at any point in time is called the *book value* at that time, and the amount by which the book value is decreased over each period is called the *depreciation charge* for that period.

In practice there are several methods of calculating book values and depreciation charges. In addition to accounting considerations, another important factor in the choice of a depreciation method is the tax code. Depreciation charges are deductible as a business expense for income tax purposes, as long as certain requirements are met. The rules involving depreciation for tax purposes in the United States have changed on several occasions and are beyond the scope of this book. However, we do want to analyze various methods in widespread use. We will examine four such methods.

Let B_t be the book value of the asset at the end of the tth period, $0 \le t \le n$. Clearly $B_0 = A$ and $B_n = S$. Let D_t be the depreciation charge for the tth period, $t = 1, 2, \ldots, n$. Then we have

$$D_t = B_{t-1} - B_t. \tag{8.22}$$

Sinking fund method

The first method is the *sinking fund method* or the *compound interest method.* This method is consistent with formula (8.21). The book value at any time must equal the initial value of the asset less the amount in the sinking fund, i.e.

$$B_t = A - \left(\frac{A-S}{s_{\overline{n}|j}}\right) s_{\overline{t}|j}. \tag{8.23}$$

Note that formula (8.23) produces the proper values for B_0 and B_n. Then the depreciation charge is

$$\begin{aligned} D_t &= B_{t-1} - B_t \\ &= \left[A - \left(\frac{A-S}{s_{\overline{n}|j}}\right) s_{\overline{t-1}|j}\right] - \left[A - \left(\frac{A-S}{s_{\overline{n}|j}}\right) s_{\overline{t}|j}\right] \\ &= \left(\frac{A-S}{s_{\overline{n}|j}}\right)\left(s_{\overline{t}|j} - s_{\overline{t-1}|j}\right) \\ &= \left(\frac{A-S}{s_{\overline{n}|j}}\right)(1+j)^{t-1}. \end{aligned} \tag{8.24}$$

It is evident from formula (8.24) that the sinking fund method produces depreciation charges which increase over the life of the asset. This may or may not be a reasonable pattern of depreciation charges, depending upon the nature of the asset. For example, it may produce a reasonable pattern of depreciation charges for an office building which depreciates slowly at first and then more rapidly later on. It probably would not produce a reasonable pattern of depreciation charges for an automobile.

However, it should be stressed that the choice of depreciation method often is not motivated by an analysis of which method produces the most realistic book values for the asset. A more important consideration for many individuals and business firms is to use an allowable method that is most favorable from a tax perspective. An individual or business firm that wants to have high tax deductions in the early years of the life of the asset would not select the sinking fund method.

It should not be thought that the sinking fund method actually requires the use of a sinking fund. It is merely a method of calculating book values and depreciation charges. A sinking fund may or may not actually be accumulated to replace the loss of capital.

Straight line method

The second, and simplest, method is the *straight line method.* This method is widely used in practice because of its simplicity. In this method the depreciation charge is constant, so that

$$D_t = \frac{A-S}{n}. \tag{8.25}$$

As a result the book values are linear

$$B_t = \left(1 - \frac{t}{n}\right)A + \frac{t}{n}S. \tag{8.26}$$

Note that formula (8.26) produces the proper values for B_0 and B_n. It is interesting to note that the straight-line method is a special case of the sinking-fund method in which $j = 0$.

Declining balance method

The third method is the *declining balance method*, the *constant percentage method*, or the *compound discount method.* This method produces depreciation charges which decrease throughout the life of the asset, as opposed to the sinking fund method in which they increase and the straight line method in which they are constant.

The declining balance method is characterized by the fact that the depreciation charge is a constant percentage of the book value at the beginning of the period, i.e.

$$D_t = d \cdot B_{t-1}. \tag{8.27}$$

Now $D_t = B_{t-1} - B_t$, so that

$$B_t = B_{t-1}(1-d)$$

Since this is true for all $t = 1, 2, \ldots, n$, we have

$$
\begin{aligned}
B_0 &= & &A \\
B_1 &= B_0(1-d) &= &A(1-d) \\
B_2 &= B_1(1-d) &= &A(1-d)^2 \\
B_3 &= B_2(1-d) &= &A(1-d)^3 \\
&\vdots & &\vdots \\
B_t &= B_{t-1}(1-d) &= &A(1-d)^t \\
&\vdots & &\vdots \\
B_n &= B_{n-1}(1-d) &= &A(1-d)^n = S.
\end{aligned} \tag{8.28}
$$

Since A and S are given, d can be found by

$$
\begin{aligned}
A(1-d)^n &= S \\
(1-d)^n &= \frac{S}{A} \\
1-d &= \left(\frac{S}{A}\right)^{\frac{1}{n}} \\
d &= 1-\left(\frac{S}{A}\right)^{\frac{1}{n}}.
\end{aligned} \tag{8.29}
$$

The name "compound discount method" is evident from formula (8.28), in which d can be interpreted as a rate of discount. It should be noted that this method assumes that S is positive. If S is zero or negative, the method breaks down.

A common variation of the declining balance method is to use a factor d different than the one defined in formula (8.29). The factor used is based on some multiple of the straight line rate, such as 125%, 150%, or 200%. Typically this factor is applied to the full value of A in the first year, ignoring S. We label this factor d', and it is defined by

$$d' = \frac{k}{n} \tag{8.30}$$

where k is the percentage of the straight-line method used, e.g. 1.25, 1.5, or 2.

The depreciation schedule then continues by the declining balance method using this revised factor. However, the asset is not depreciated below S, so that the depreciation charge in the final line of the depreciation schedule is an arbitrary value that exactly brings the book value to S. This variation of the declining balance method is illustrated in Example 8.11.

Sum of the years digits method

The fourth method is the *sum of the years digits method.* This method is based on the rule of 78 and also produces depreciation charges which decrease throughout the life of the asset. The reasoning involved in this method is similar to the reasoning involved in the direct ratio method of calculating yields on installment loans described in Section 8.5.

As before, let S_r be the sum of the first r positive integers

$$S_r = 1+2+\cdots+r = \frac{r(r+1)}{2}. \tag{8.18}$$

The depreciation charges progress as follows:

$$D_1 = \frac{n}{S_n}(A-S)$$

$$D_2 = \frac{n-1}{S_n}(A-S)$$

$$\vdots$$

$$D_t = \frac{n-t+1}{S_n}(A-S) \tag{8.31}$$

$$\vdots$$

$$D_n = \frac{1}{S_n}(A-S).$$

The sum of the depreciation charges equals $A - S$, as it must. The book value is given by

$$
\begin{aligned}
B_t &= A - \sum_{r=1}^{t} D_r \\
&= S + \sum_{r=t+1}^{n} D_r, \text{ since } \sum_{r=1}^{n} D_r = A - S \\
&= S + \frac{S_{n-t}}{S_n}(A - S). \qquad (8.32)
\end{aligned}
$$

Depletion

Depletion refers to the exhaustion of a supply of natural resources, such as coal and oil. Mathematically it is similar to depreciation in the sense that a coal mine or an oil field is a depreciating asset as the supplies of coal or oil are extracted. The above methods of calculating depreciation charges could also be used in calculating *depletion charges.*

Example 8.10 A machine costs \$10,000, will last for five years, and will have a salvage value of \$1000 at the end of the five years. Calculate the book values and depreciation charges:
(1) Using the sinking fund method where $j = .05$.
(2) Using the straight line method.
(3) Using the declining balance method.
(4) Using the sum of the years digits method.

1. Using formulas (8.23) and (8.24) we have

$$\frac{A - S}{s_{\overline{n}|}} = \frac{9000}{s_{\overline{5}|}} = 1628.775$$

and

t	D_t	B_t
0		10,000
1	1,629	8,371
2	1,710	6,661
3	1,796	4,865
4	1,886	2,979
5	1,979	1,000

2. Using formulas (8.25) and (8.26) we have

t	D_t	B_t
0		10,000
1	1,800	8,200
2	1,800	6,400
3	1,800	4,600
4	1,800	2,800
5	1,800	1,000

3. Using formula (8.29) we obtain

$$d = 1-(.1)^{.2} = 1-.631 = .369$$

and using formulas (8.27) and (8.28) we have

t	D_t	B_t
0		10,000
1	3,690	6,310
2	2,328	3,982
3	1,470	2,512
4	927	1,585
5	585	1,000

4. Using formulas (8.31) and (8.32) we have

t	D_t	B_t
0		10,000
1	3,000	7,000
2	2,400	4,600
3	1,800	2,800
4	1,200	1,600
5	600	1,000

Example 8.11 Rework Example 8.10 using the 200% declining balance method.

Using formula (8.30), we have

$$d' = \frac{2}{5} = .4.$$

This is easily confirmed by general reasoning. Under the straight line method over five years the depreciation factor would be 20% per year (ignoring salvage value). The 200% declining balance factor must be twice that amount, i.e. 40%.

Using formulas (8.27) and (8.28) we have

t	D_t	B_t
0		10,000
1	4,000	6,000
2	2,400	3,600
3	1,440	2,160
4	864	1,296
5	296	1,000

Note that $D_5 = 296$ is an arbitrary amount needed to make $B_5 = 1000$ exactly.

8.7 CAPITALIZED COST

This section discusses another type of analysis used in connection with fixed assets. An issue of considerable importance in practice is the comparison of the costs of alternative possible fixed assets. There are three costs involved in owning a fixed asset:

1. Loss of interest on the original purchase price, since that money could have been invested elsewhere at interest.
2. Depreciation expense.
3. Maintenance expense.

The *periodic charge* of an asset is defined to be the cost per period of owning the asset. If we let H be the periodic charge and M be the periodic maintenance expense, then the fundamental equation of value is

$$H = Ai + \frac{A-S}{s_{\overline{n|}j}} + M \tag{8.33}$$

where A and S retain their definitions from Section 8.6. Formula (8.33) is quite analogous to formulas (8.6) and (8.21). The term Ai is the loss of interest on the original purchase price. The term $\frac{A-S}{s_{\overline{n|}j}}$ is the periodic depreciation expense. The term M is the periodic maintenance expense. Note that in formula (8.21) the term M is not needed, since R is net of expenses.

The *capitalized cost* of an asset is defined to be the present value of the periodic charges forever, i.e. the present value of a perpetuity for the amount of the periodic charge. The capitalized cost can be looked upon as the present value of maintaining an identical asset in operation indefinitely. Denoting the capitalized cost by K, we have

$$K = \frac{H}{i} = A + \frac{A-S}{is_{\overline{n|}j}} + \frac{M}{i}. \tag{8.34}$$

In making comparisons of alternate possible assets either the periodic charge or the capitalized cost may be used.

One complication is that different assets used in production may produce output at different rates per unit of time. In these cases it is necessary to divide by the number of items produced per unit of time in order to standardize the comparison. For example, assume that machine 1 produces U_1 items per unit of time and that machine 2 produces U_2 items per unit of time. Then machine 1 and machine 2 would be equivalent if

$$\frac{A_1 i + \dfrac{A_1 - S_1}{s_{\overline{n_1|}j}} + M_1}{U_1} = \frac{A_2 i + \dfrac{A_2 - S_2}{s_{\overline{n_2|}j}} + M_2}{U_2} \tag{8.35}$$

where all symbols with subscript 1 pertain to machine 1 and similarly for machine 2.

In many cases it will be assumed that $i = j$. If this assumption is made, then formula (8.35) becomes

$$\frac{\dfrac{A_1}{a_{\overline{n_1}|}} - \dfrac{S_1}{s_{\overline{n_1}|}} + M_1}{U_1} = \frac{\dfrac{A_2}{a_{\overline{n_2}|}} - \dfrac{S_2}{s_{\overline{n_2}|}} + M_2}{U_2}. \tag{8.36}$$

Another complication is that inflation was ignored in the above development. A more sophisticated analysis might recognize inflation. Assume that the rate of inflation is r per period. The fixed asset has cost A and salvage value S over the first n periods. It might be assumed that for the second n-year period the cost is $A(1+r)^n$ and the salvage value is $S(1+r)^n$. This process could be continued for each subsequent n-period cycle. It might also be assumed that the maintenance cost M increases by a factor of $1+r$ each period. The recognition of inflation in financial calculations is discussed further in Section 9.4.

It is also instructive to relate the concept of capitalized cost to the concept of capital budgeting discussed in Sections 7.9 and 7.10. As illustrated above in formulas (8.35) and (8.36), capitalized cost can be used to compare alternative investments. Thus, capitalized cost analysis constitutes one possible approach to capital budgeting.

***Example 8.12** Machine 1 sells for $100,000, has an annual maintenance expense of $2500, and has a life of 25 years with a salvage value of $2000. Machine 2 has an annual maintenance expense of $5000 and a life of 20 years with no salvage value. Assuming an effective rate of interest of 5%, find the price of Machine 2 so that a buyer is indifferent between the two machines if Machine 2 produces output three times as fast as Machine 1.*

Using formula (8.36), we have

$$\frac{100{,}000}{a_{\overline{25}|}} - \frac{2000}{s_{\overline{25}|}} + 2500 = \frac{1}{3}\left(\frac{A_2}{a_{\overline{20}|}} + 5000\right)$$

$$\begin{aligned} A_2 &= \{3[100{,}000(.070952) - 2000(.020952) + 2500] - 5000\}12.4622 \\ &= \$294{,}854, \text{ or } \$295{,}000 \end{aligned}$$

to the nearest $1000.

Example 8.13 ***A telephone company uses telephone poles costing $100 apiece. These poles last 14 years. How much per pole would the company be justified in spending on a preservative to lengthen the life of the poles to 22 years? Assume that the poles do not have salvage value, that the annual maintenance expense of either type of pole is equivalent, and that the effective rate of interest is 4%.***

Using formula (8.36) we have

$$\frac{100}{a_{\overline{14}|}} = \frac{100+x}{a_{\overline{22}|}}$$

$$\begin{aligned} x &= 100\left(\frac{a_{\overline{22}|}}{a_{\overline{14}|}} - 1\right) \\ &= 100\left(\frac{14.4511}{10.5631} - 1\right) \\ &= \$36.81. \end{aligned}$$

8.8 MODERN FINANCIAL INSTRUMENTS

There was a time when the universe of financial instruments used for investment purposes was little more extensive than already discussed in this book, i.e. bonds, preferred stock, common stock, and real estate mortgages. However, since the 1970s there has been a virtual explosion of new and creative financial instruments.

In this section we briefly introduce the reader to a number of the more significant financial instruments which have been developed. This listing is not exhaustive, nor are the descriptions complete. Readers who are interested in more information are referred to any of several standard textbooks on finance or securities. Also, most brokerage firms, banks, insurance companies and other financial institutions have brochures and other literature with pertinent information about these instruments.

Finally, the material in this section is descriptive, not analytical, since the purpose is to familiarize the reader with the nature of these instruments. Many of them can be analyzed with principles developed in the earlier chapters of this book. Also, there is further analysis involving certain of them in succeeding chapters. Finally, some of them involve analysis which goes beyond the scope of this book.

It is interesting to observe that we have already discussed certain securities with features akin to some of the financial instruments to be discussed in this section. For example, in Chapter 6 we discussed callable bonds and convertible bonds. The former provide an option to the bond issuer (borrower) to redeem or not redeem the bond in the future depending upon conditions at that time. The latter provides an option in the future to the bond holder (lender) to convert or not convert the bond into common stock, again depending on whether or not such action is advantageous.

Money market funds

Money market funds provide an investor a secure investment with high liquidity and an attractive yield. *Liquidity* is the ability to quickly turn an investment into cash, ideally without significant loss of principal. Many money market funds even provide check-writing facilities, making such accounts virtually equivalent to checking accounts crediting attractive rates of interest.

The investments made by the typical money market fund are in a variety of short-term, fixed-income instruments issued either by the government or by firms in the private sector. Since all the investments are in short-term instruments, the rate credited on a money market fund fluctuates frequently with movements in short-term interest rates.

Since money market funds generally allow withdrawals on demand without penalty, they are attractive to investors as a place to "park" funds while considering other investment possibilities. Many brokerage firms routinely provide *sweep accounts*, in which all available non-investment funds are automatically "swept" into a money market fund.

Certificates of deposit

Certificates of deposit (CDs) are an investment instrument issued by banks which provide a specified rate of interest for a fixed period of time, typically 90 days to 5 years. Rates of interest credited on larger CDs (e.g. $25,000 and above) may be higher than on CDs below than this amount.

CDs offer more stability in yield rates than money market funds, since the rate of interest paid is fixed rather than variable. However, there is a sacrifice of liquidity, since many CDs have a penalty for early withdrawal. One means an investor may be able to use to avoid such a penalty is sell the CD to another investor in the secondary market, although this may be difficult to do in practice.

CDs do not fluctuate in value with movements in the level of interest rates, as would be the case with a bond portfolio. Also, investments in CDs in the United States are guaranteed by the Federal Deposit Insurance Corporation (FDIC), a federal agency, up to a maximum of $100,000.

Guaranteed investment contracts

Guaranteed investment contracts (GICs) are investment instruments issued by insurance companies to large investors such as pension funds. They are similar to CDs in that they guarantee principal and interest over a stated period of time, for periods from one to as long as five years. As a result, their market value does not fluctuate with movements in the level of interest rates.

However, some GICs are more flexible than CDs in allowing certain additional deposits and withdrawals after issue. Withdrawals from GICs prior to maturity are often restricted only to benefit payments that are not discretionary. GICs often have other features typical of insurance contracts, such as annuity purchase options when the GIC is being used for the investment of a pension fund.

GICs usually pay higher rates of interest than CDs, closely matching yields on Treasury securities. However, GICs are not insured by the FDIC.

In order to compete with the insurance companies, banks have developed a very analogous instrument called the *bank investment contract* (BIC). Account balances in BICs are insured up to a maximum of $100,000 by the FDIC.

Recent years have witnessed the development of a variety of similar instruments with features move complex than the basic GICs and BICs described above. These instruments are often referred to as *stable value products.*

Mutual funds

Mutual funds are pooled investment accounts in which the individual investor buys shares. Their primary advantage is to offer a greater degree of diversification than individuals could achieve on their own.

Originally, mutual funds were primarily invested in common stocks. More recently, mutual funds offering a broader array of other investment options (e.g. bonds and other fixed income instruments) have appeared. Even within the traditional category of common stock mutual funds, considerable variation exists among various funds in their relative emphases on various types of common stocks.

Mutual funds can be categorized in a number of different ways. *Open-end funds* issue and redeem shares each day and do not have a fixed number of outstanding shares. They are priced daily at *net asset value* (NAV) based on the market value of the entire portfolio. *Closed-end funds* have a fixed number of outstanding shares and trade on one of the stock exchanges. Their price can change moment to moment and also may vary (sometimes substantially) from the NAV of the underlying stocks in the portfolio.

Index funds are designed to follow one of a number of different indices of stock market prices. Their appeal is a low expense ratio. *Actively managed funds* consist of individual stocks which are selected by the investment manager(s) according to their own investment criteria. The investment managers attempt to "beat the index" most closely aligned with their approach. The expense ratios for these funds are significantly higher, reflecting the costs of "active management."

Growth funds concentrate on stocks of companies expected to grow rapidly. Dividends are low to non-existent for many of these companies. *Value funds* concentrate on slower growing companies that pay significantly higher dividends. They also attempt to find stocks which the investment managers believe are "undervalued" compared to their true worth.

Sector funds (or *specialty funds*) invest in stocks within certain industries. Examples would be: energy, healthcare, real estate, and utilities. Geography can also be a categorization for many funds. Such terms as *domestic funds*, *international funds*, *emerging market funds*, and *single-country funds* are frequently encountered.

Bond funds may concentrate on bonds with short-term, intermediate-term, or long-term maturities. They may also focus on different quality levels, ranging from funds exclusively investing in United States Treasury securities, all the way to high-yield (or "junk bond") funds at the other end of the spectrum. Municipal bond funds and international bond funds are other types of specialized bond funds encountered.

In short, mutual funds can probably be found that concentrate on just about any subset of securities for which there is sufficient customer demand.

Mortgage backed securities

Mortgage backed securities (MBS) are securities created out of a defined pool of real estate mortgages. Investors receive periodic payments consisting of both principal and interest. The rate at which principal is repaid is variable depending on the rate at which the underlying mortgages are paid off. MBS are often called *pass-throughs*, since payments of interest and principal by borrowers directly "pass through" to the owners of these securities.

MBS provide a means by which individuals and companies can readily invest in a diversified pool of real estate mortgages as investors. They are issued by three governmentally owned or chartered corporations holding large numbers of mortgages. The three corporations are as follows:

1. The Government National Mortgage Association (GNMA) issues MBS called "Ginnie Maes." GNMA is owned by the U. S. Government and payment of principal and interest is guaranteed by the full faith and credit of the U. S. Government.

2. The Federal Home Loan Mortgage Corporation (FHLMC) issues MBS called "Freddie Macs." FHLMC is chartered by the U. S. Government and the corporation (but not the government) guarantees payment of principal and interest.

3. The Federal National Mortgage Association (FNMA) issues MBS called "Fannie Maes." FNMA is chartered by the U. S. Government and the corporation (but not the government) guarantees payment of principal and interest.

Collateralized mortgage obligations

Collateralized mortgage obligations (CMOs) are a newer type of financial instrument designed to improve upon the traditional MBS. CMOs involve the same type of investment in real estate mortgages as MBS, but involve complex structuring of the portfolios into different segments called "tranches" designed to have differing characteristics.

CMOs do not have a specific maturity date and are sold on a basis which quotes their "average life." The average life is the average amount of time that each dollar of principal is expected to be outstanding, assuming a reasonable prepayment schedule for the mortgages in the pool. CMOs are structured with a wide range in average life in order to provide more choice to the investor. Different tranches also have risk characteristics that may vary significantly form the other tranches.

CMOs typically offer higher yields than corporate bonds in order to compensate for the uncertainly of their repayment schedule and the attendant reinvestment risk. CMOs typically make payments monthly rather than semiannually as with bonds. CMOs are quite liquid, since there is an active market in existing issues. Prices in the market for existing CMOs vary inversely with prevailing interest rates, similarly to bond prices.

In recent years, *collateralized debt obligations* (CDOs) have appeared. These financial instruments are similar to CMOs, except that a broader range of debt instruments than real estate mortgages are utilized.

Options

The reader has already been briefly introduced to options in Section 6.7 with the discussion of callable and putable bonds. These are bonds issued with "embedded options" as part of their structure. In this section we will discuss options more generally.

Options are financial instruments which give the owner the right to buy or sell a security on a future date at a fixed price, called the *exercise price* or *strike price*. There are two types of options: calls and puts. A *call* gives the owner the right to purchase the security at the exercise price, while a *put* gives the owner the right to sell the security at the exercise price. With European options the exercise of the option must occur on a fixed date at which time the option expires. With American options the exercise can occur on any future date through the expiry date.

Investors can either buy or sell options. Thus, if an investor thinks the security price is likely to rise, then a call should be purchased or a put should be sold. Conversely, if an investor thinks the security price is likely to fall, then a put should be purchased or a call should be sold.

There are two primary motivations for buying or selling options, which are at opposite ends of the spectrum. One motivation is speculation. Option prices are highly volatile, which leads to a large potential for profit and a large risk of loss. For example, consider a security selling at $50 with a call option to buy the security at $45. The option is worth at least $5 (it will sell for more than $5 prior to expiry). If the security increases in price to $55 the option is worth at least $10. Thus, a 10% increase in the price of the underlying security leads approximately to a 100% increase in the value of the option. This effect is called *leverage.*

The second motivation is quite the opposite. Options offer great flexibility in developing hedging strategies to reduce investment risk. Hedging was introduced briefly in Section 7.8 in the discussion of short sales. Many of the option hedging investment strategies have become quite complex, and require computer analysis to implement effectively.

Originally, options were offered only on common stock. However, more recently options have been developed on other securities, including bonds. There are even options on future interest rates. Options have become standardized and trade on several different stock exchanges.

A *warrant* is a type of security that preceded the development of standardized calls and puts. A warrant functions very similarly to a call, only it can be issued with more distant expiry dates than are available on calls. There are other legal differences as well, since warrants are issued by the firm issuing the underlying security, while the firm typically has no connection with the options on its securities. As an instructive insight, a convertible bond is conceptually equivalent to the combination of a regular bond and a warrant in one package. Options will be discussed in more depth in Chapter 13.

Futures

Futures are a type of contract in which the investor agree to buy or sell an asset at a specified future date. The price is fixed at issue, but payment does not occur until the expiry of the contract, called the *delivery date.* Futures originated in the commodities markets. However, in recent years futures markets have developed for a variety of financial assets such as bonds, foreign currencies, and stock market indexes.

The current price of an asset is often called the *spot price*, while the price at the delivery date of the futures contract is often called the *futures price*. If an investor wants to buy a security, there are two choices. The first is to buy it immediately at the *spot price*. The second is to buy a futures contract. Under such a contract the futures price does not need to be paid until the delivery date, at which time it must be paid regardless of the market (spot) price at that time. In this latter case, the investor can earn interest on the purchase price during the period of deferral until it is paid at the delivery date. However, the investor will not receive any dividends or interest that the security pays during this period.

Forwards

Forwards are conceptually very similar to futures. The primary difference is that futures contracts are standardized and sold in active markets. Forward contracts are tailor-made between two parties and are not actively traded in open markets.

Forward contracts have been used in two areas primarily. The first area is to protect a firm against fluctuation in foreign currency exchange rates. Many banks are willing to buy and sell forward currency for periods of up to one year or longer.

The second area is to lock-in future interest rates. For example, a firm in need of borrowing a substantial amount of money in six months can buy a forward contract from a bank to lock-in the rate immediately. This type of contract provides protection against increases in interest rates over the next six months. Of course, if instead interest rates decline, the firm will be stuck with borrowing money at rates above market rates at the end of six months.

Swaps

Swaps are exchanges of two similar financial quantities which behave differently. One example is the *currency swap* in which a borrower agrees to swap loan repayments in one currency and agrees to make them in a different currency. Whether this swap is favorable to the borrower or not depends on the behavior of exchange rates over the remainder of the loan.

A second example is the *interest rate swap.* Commercial loans are set up on two bases, either as fixed rate loans or floating rate loans. A *fixed rate loan* has a predetermined rate and is equivalent to loans considered previously in this book. A *floating rate loan* has a rate that varies according to some external index of interest rates in the financial markets. An interest rate swap is the exchange of an agreement to pay interest on one basis for an agreement to pay interest on the other basis.

A commercial loan as described above, which is unsecured and open-ended up to some maximum limit, is called a *line of credit.* Under a line of credit the firm can borrow and repay whenever it wants, subject only to the maximum limit.

Derivatives

The last four financial instruments discussed, i.e. options, futures, forwards, and swaps, are all examples of *derivative instruments.* The value of such instruments depends on other financial values in the marketplace. These instruments are not primary instruments in the sense that they represent ownership or indebtedness in anything directly. Rather they represent instruments whose value is determined by other values, such as security prices, interest rates, and currency exchange rates.

EXERCISES

8.2 Truth in lending

1. A discount electronics store advertises the following financing arrangement:

   We don't offer you confusing interest rates. We'll just divide your total cost by 10 and you can pay us that amount each month for a year.

   The first payment is due on the date of sale and the remaining eleven payments at monthly intervals thereafter. Calculate the effective annual interest rate the store's customers are paying on their loans.

2. A finance company uses a carrying charge of 12% of the loan for 18-month loans repaid with monthly payments. Find the APR paid by the borrowers.

3. A finance company requires monthly repayments of \$7.66 at the end of each month for 16 months per \$100 of initial loan. Find the APY earned by the finance company on these loans.

4. A loan of \$12,000 is to be repaid in one year according to one of the following arrangements:

   A - \$1000 payable at the end of each month in addition to a finance charge of \$1000 payable when the loan is approved.

   B - Repayment at the end of each month according to an amortization schedule with $i^{(12)} = 12\%$.

   a) Find the difference in the amount of interest paid under options A and B.

   b) Find the APR for Option A .

   c) Find the APR for Option B.

5. A borrower visits three banks to obtain quotes on a car loan repayable with 24 monthly installments. The first bank quotes a monthly payment of X based on a total carrying charge equal to the product of the initial balance, the number of years to repay, and 6.5%. The second bank quotes a monthly payment of Y based on an annual effective interest rate of 12.6%. The third bank quotes a monthly payment of Z based on an interest rate of 12% convertible monthly. Rank the values of X, Y, and Z.

6. A loan of \$8000 at an interest rate of 12% per annum is to be repaid with three payments:

   (*i*) A payment of \$2000 at the end of 3 months.

   (*ii*) A payment of \$4000 at the end of 9 months.

   (*iii*) A payment of \$$X$ at the end of 12 months.

   Find X:

   a) Using the United States Rule.

   b) Using the Merchant's Rule.

7. A borrows \$10,000 for two years at an effective rate of interest of 10%. A agrees to pay interest at the end of each year and to repay the principal at the end of two years. At the end of one year A is able to pay only \$500. Find the amount necessary to completely repay the loan at the end of two years:

   a) Using the actuarial method.

   b) Using the United States Rule.

8. A borrower deposits \$200 immediately for the guarantee to be able to borrow \$1000 at the end of one year. The borrower must repay the \$1000 at the end of two years.

   a) Find the two positive yield rates for this transaction.

   b) Truth in lending does not resolve this situation since there is only one advance. Compute the APR using the method of equated time on the payments rather than on the advances.

9. The tables promulgated under truth in lending for handling irregular transactions define three terms as follows:

   A - number of regular payments.

   B - equivalent single payment point (exact, not by the method of equated time)

   C - finance charge per \$1000 of payment (related to payments by the borrower, not to advances).

   Show that the following series of identities is valid:

$$A - a_{\overline{n}|} = A - A(1+i)^{-B} = C\left(\frac{A}{1000}\right).$$

8.3 Automobile financing

10. The purchase price of a new automobile is \$10,000. The dealer offers a promotional incentive of a \$1000 cash back and two options for financing the loan with monthly payments over four years. Under Option A the APR is 9% and the cash back is used to reduce the amount of the loan. Under Option B the APR is 10% and the purchaser gets the cash back. If the cash back is invested by the buyer, what annual effective interest rate must be earned for Option B to be equivalent to Option A .

11. There are two financing offers for a $20,000 automobile with monthly payments over two years. Under Option A, the trade-in allowance is $4000 and the APR is 0%. Under Option B, the trade-in allowance is $4500 and the APR is 3.49%.

    a) If there is no down payment, which offer is more attractive?

    b) What is the down payment necessary to make the two offers equivalent? Answer to the nearest dollar.

12. A car dealer offers to sell a car for $15,000. The current car loan rate is 12% per annum compounded monthly. As an inducement, the dealer offers 100% financing at an effective annual interest rate of 5%. The loan is to be repaid in equal installments at the end of each month over a four-year period. Calculate the cost to the dealer of this inducement. Answer to the nearest dollar.

13. A and B each finance $20,000 of the purchase price of two new automobiles. A finances the loan with monthly payments over four years, while B finances the loan with monthly payments over two years. Both APRs are 7%. After one year, the car depreciates to $15,000.

    a) Compare the market value of the car after one year and the two loan balances to the nearest dollar.

    b) What is the cost to the nearest dollar for the one-year use of the car (present value) for each person calculated at a rate of 6% convertible monthly, if A and B both sell their cars after one year? Answers to the nearest dollar.

14. A consumer wants to lease a new automobile costing $20,000 for 24 months. The value of the automobile is $16,000 after one year and $13,000 after two years. The lease uses a money factor of 0.5% per month. The lease also has a lease acquisition fee of $300, a lease disposal fee of $200, and an early termination penalty of $600.

    a) Find the monthly lease payment, if the lessor uses formula (8.6).

    b) Find the yield rate which the lessee is actually paying for this lease considering fees if the lease expires as expected.

    c) Find the yield rate which the lessee is actually paying for this lease, if the lease is terminated at the end of the first year.

15. In Example 8.4, if there is a security deposit that is one extra lease payment paid in advance but refundable at lease expiration, find the nominal yield rate convertible monthly which the lessee is actually paying for this lease considering fees and the deposit.

16. A company is considering the possibility of acquiring new computer equipment for \$400,000. The salvage value is estimated to be \$50,000 at the end of the six-year life of the equipment. Maintenance costs will be \$4000 per month, payable at the end of each month. The company could lease the equipment for \$12,000 per month, payable at the end of each month. Under the lease agreement, the lessor would pay the maintenance costs. The company can earn 12% convertible monthly on its capital.

    a) Calculate the NPV of the "buy" option.

    b) Calculate the NPV of the "lease" option.

    c) Which option should be chosen?

8.4 Real estate mortgages

17. A family purchases a house for \$160,000. They agree to put 25% down and finance the balance with a 30-year fixed rate mortgage at 9%. In order to secure this loan they must pay 2 points at settlement. They go to settlement on September 16.

    a) Find the total amount of interest paid during the first calendar year of the mortgage, if $1\ 1/2$ points are deemed to be interest and the family makes payments on the first day of each month.

    b) Find the APR on the mortgage loan, assuming that the other 1/2 point and all other closing costs do not have to be reflected in the APR.

18. A 15-year mortgage has monthly payments of \$1000 with interest convertible monthly. At the end of each month, the borrower makes a \$1000 payment. In addition to the regular monthly payment, the borrower makes an additional payment equal to the amount of principal that would have been repaid in the next regular monthly payment. Under this arrangement the loan will be completely repaid after 90 payments. Show that the amount of interest saved over the life of the loan is equal to

$$90{,}000 - 1000\frac{\ddot{a}_{\overline{180|}}}{s_{\overline{2|}}}$$

where the annuity symbols are computed at the monthly rate of interest on the loan.

19. A builder took out a $2,000,000 construction loan disbursed in three installments. The first installment of $1,000,000 is disbursed immediately and this is followed by two $500,000 installments at six month intervals. The interest on the loan is calculated at a rate of 15% convertible semiannually and accumulated to the end of the second year. At that time, the loan and accumulated interest will be replaced by a 30-year mortgage at 12% convertible monthly. The amount of the monthly mortgage payment for the first five years will be one-half of the payment for the sixth and later years. The first monthly mortgage payment is due exactly two years after the initial disbursement of the construction loan. Find the amount of the 12th mortgage payment. Answer to the nearest dollar.

20. A $100,000 loan is to be repaid by 30 equal payments at the end of each year. Interest on the loan is at 8% effective. In addition to the annual payments, the borrower must pay an origination fee at the time the loan is made. This fee is 2% of the loan but does not reduce the loan balance. When the second payment is due, the borrower pays the remaining loan balance in full. Determine the yield to the lender considering the origination fee and the early pay-off of the loan.

21. A 10-year adjustable rate mortgage loan is being repaid with quarterly installments of $1000 based upon an initial interest rate of 12% convertible quarterly. Immediately after the 12th payment the interest rate is increased to 14% convertible quarterly. The quarterly installments remain at $1000. Calculate the loan balance immediately after the 24th payment. Answer to the nearest dollar.

22. A 30-year graduated payment mortgage of $100,000 is to repaid with annual payments at the end of each year. Each payment for the first five years is 5% greater than for the preceding year, while each payment thereafter is equal to the payment at the end of five years. Interest on the loan is at 9% effective.
    a) Find the initial payment at the end of the first year. Answer to the nearest dollar.
    b) Does negative amortization occur on this loan?

23. A family purchases a house for $120,000 and agrees to put 15% down. They are able to assume an existing 30-year 8% mortgage with annual payments originally issued for $60,000 exactly 10 years ago. They take out a new "wraparound" mortgage with annual payments at an interest rate of 10% which will be fully repaid at the same time as the assumed mortgage. Find the total annual mortgage payment required to purchase this house. Answer to the nearest dollar.

24. A retiring couple owns a house with $100,000 on which there is no indebtedness. They take out a reverse annuity mortgage at 12% convertible monthly which will pay them $500 per month in extra retirement income. If the house appreciates in value 6% per year, find their equity in the house at the end of five years. Answer to the nearest dollar.

8.5 Approximate methods

25. A $1200 loan with a finance charge of $108 is to be repaid in 12 equal monthly installments. Find the outstanding loan balances immediately after the fourth payment using:
    a) Maximum yield method.
    b) Minimum yield method.
    c) Constant ratio method.
    d) Direct ratio method.

26. An installment loan over a nine-month period is being repaid by the direct ratio method. If the amount of interest in the second payment is $20, find the amount of interest in the eighth payment.

27. An installment loan of $690 is being repaid with six monthly payments of $50 each followed by six monthly payments of $75 each. Use the constant ratio method to approximate the rate of interest on the loan.

28. If an installment loan has a yield rate of 20% using the maximum yield method and a yield rate of 12.5% using the minimum yield method, find the yield rate under the direct ratio method.

29. A loan is to be repaid with five annual payments of P at an effective annual interest rate of i. The loan is amortized by the direct ratio method. A second loan is also to be repaid with five annual payments of P, but is to be amortized by the actuarial method at an effective interest rate of 5%. The balances outstanding at the end of two years for the two loans are equal. Find $a_{\overline{5}|\,i}$.

30. Derive formula (8.14) by assuming simple interest.

31. Show that i^{cr} is the harmonic mean of i^{max} and i^{min}.

32. Show that if it takes $r > 1$ payments to cover the finance charge:
    a) The maximum yield formula becomes

$$\frac{2mnK}{2n(n-r+1)L-(n-r)(n-r+1)(L+K)}.$$

    b) The minimum yield formula becomes

$$\frac{2mnK}{2nrL+(n-r)(n-r+1)(L+K)}.$$

8.6 Depreciation methods

33. *a*) An asset is being depreciated over a 10-year period. It has no salvage value at the end of the 10 years, i.e. $S = 0$. If the depreciation charge in the third year is \$1000, find the depreciation charge in the ninth year:
    (1) By the sinking fund method, assuming $j = .05$.
    (2) By the straight line method.
    (3) By the sum of the years digits method.
    Why can the declining balance method not be used?
    b) Find the original value of the asset in each of the above three cases.

34. A corporation buys a new machine for \$2000. It has an expected useful life of 10 years, and a salvage value of \$400. The machine is depreciated using the sinking fund method and an annual effective rate of i. Depreciation is taken at the end of each year for the 10-year period. The present value of the depreciation charges over the 10-year period is \$1000 at the annual effective rate i. Calculate i.

35. A copier costs X and will have a salvage value of Y after n years.
    (*i*) Using the straight line method, the annual depreciation expense is \$1000.
    (*ii*) Using the sum of the years digits method, the depreciation expense in year 3 is 800.
    (*iii*) Using the declining balance method, the depreciation expense is 33.125% of the book value at the beginning of the year.
    Calculate X.

36. A manufacturer buys a machine for \$20,000. The manufacturer estimates that the machine will last 15 years. It will be depreciated using the constant percentage method with an annual depreciation rate of 20%. At the end of each year, the manufacturer deposits an amount into a fund that pays 6% annually. Each deposit is equal to the depreciation expense for that year. How much money will the manufacturer have accumulated in the fund at the end of 15 years? Answer to the nearest dollar.

37. A machine is purchased for $5000 and has a salvage value of S at the end of 10 years. The machine is depreciated using the sum of the years digits method. At the end of year 4, the machine has a book value of $2218. At that time, the depreciation method is changed to the straight-line method for the remaining years. Determine the new depreciation charge for year 8.

38. Two machines, purchased at the same time, are to be depreciated over 20 years. Machine I, which was purchased for $40,000, is depreciated by the sum of the years digits method to its salvage value of $5000. Machine II, which was also purchased for $40,000, is depreciated by the sinking fund method at $j = 3\ 1/2\%$ to its salvage value of S. At the end of the 18th year, the book value of each machine is the same. Find S. Answer to the nearest dollar.

39. A piece of equipment that was purchased for $15,000 will have a salvage value of $2000 after 15 years. Its book value has been determined by depreciation in accordance with the compound interest method, using an interest rate of 5% per annum. At the end of the 10th year, the depreciation method is changed to the straight line method for the remaining 5 years. Determine the book value at the end of the 12th year. Answer to the nearest dollar.

40. A company buys two machines. Both machines are expected to last 14 years, and each has a salvage value of $1050. Machine A costs $2450, while Machine B costs $$Y$. The depreciation method used for Machine A is the straight line method, while the depreciation method used for Machine B is the sum of the years digits method. The present value of the depreciation charges made at the end of each year for Machines A and B are equal. If the effective rate of interest is 10%, calculate Y.

41. Assume that book values of an asset are continuous functions of t. Find an expression for that value of t at which the excess of B_t by the straight line method over B_t by the constant percentage method is a maximum.

8.7 Capitalized cost

42. A machine sells for $10,000 and has a salvage value of $1000 at the end of 10 years. The annual maintenance expense of the machine is $500. Assuming 5% interest:
    a) Calculate the periodic charge of the asset.
    b) Calculate the capitalized cost of the asset. Answer to the nearest dollar.

43. Machine 1 sells for \$1000 with a salvage value of \$50 at the end of nine years. Machine 2 sells for \$1100 with a salvage value of \$200 at the end of nine years. At what rate of interest would a purchaser be indifferent between the two machines? Assume equal maintenance expenses for the two machines.

44. Plastic trays last 8 years and cost \$20 each. Metal trays last 24 years and cost \$$X$ each. Trays are needed for 48 years, and inflation will increase the cost of the trays 5% per year. At 10.25% interest, determine X so that the buyer is indifferent between purchasing plastic or metal trays.

45. Rework Example 8.13 assuming that the cost of poles is expected to increase by 2% per year indefinitely into the future.

46. A construction firm buys \$1000 worth of lumber. Find the maximum amount the firm would be willing to pay to treat the lumber to extend its life from 10 to 15 years if the salvage value in either case is \$50. The effective rate of interest is 3 1/2%.

47. Machine 1 sells for \$100,000, has an annual maintenance expense for the first year of \$3000, and has a useful life of 20 years with no salvage value. Machine 2 has an annual maintenance expense for the first year of \$10,000 and has a useful life of 15 years with no salvage value. It is anticipated that the cost of the machines and the annual maintenance expenses will increase by 4% per year indefinitely into the future. Machine 2 produces output twice as fast as Machine 1. Maintenance expenses are paid at the beginning of each year. Assuming the effective rate of interest is 8%, find the price of Machine 2 at which a buyer would be indifferent between the two machines. Answer to the nearest \$100.

48. You are trying to determine the initial purchase price of a certain physical asset. You have been able to determine the following:
    - (*i*) Asset is 6 years old.
    - (*ii*) Asset is depreciated using the sinking fund method, with an annual effective rate of 9%.
    - (*iii*) Book value of the asset after 6 years is \$55,216.36.
    - (*iv*) The loss of interest on the original purchase price is at an annual effective rate of 9%.
    - (*v*) Annual cost of the asset is \$11,749.22.
    - (*vi*) Annual maintenance cost of the asset is \$3000.

    What was the original purchase price of the asset to the nearest dollar?

9

More advanced financial analysis

9.1 INTRODUCTION

In prior chapters the existence of interest and its magnitude are largely taken as givens. These earlier chapters deal with financial calculations involving interest under a variety of situations. In large measure, the focus is on mathematically analyzing actual past transactions, or future transactions for which certainty is assumed to prevail.

In Chapters 9-13 more fundamental questions are posed which take the reader into the world of economics and finance. One fundamental question is what determines the level of interest rates, both in general and in any particular situation? A related question, which is important in making financial calculations involving the future, is what interest rate should be assumed in making such calculations?

The emphasis on the future is inherent in any present value calculation. Using present values is fundamental for financial analysis and decision making involving future events. Yet we know that the future brings with it considerable uncertainty. The use of interest in calculations involving future events requires a somewhat different perspective than the use of interest in calculations made solely to record accurately the transactions of the past.

This emphasis on using interest in calculations being made for financial analysis and decision making involving the future is not entirely new, of course. For example, the discussion of discounted cash flow analysis, yield rates, and net present value calculations in Chapter 7 involves such a perspective. Chapters 9-13 will build on this foundation and extend it significantly.

Interest rates based on actual past experience are often called *ex post rates.* By way of contrast, rates expected to occur in the future are called *ex ante rates.* A question of considerable significance is the extent to which the former are useful in estimating the latter. Interest rates in existence at the present time are often called *current* or *market rates.*

Chapter 9 also directly discusses five other factors which may affect certain calculations involving interest in real-world applications. These are:

1. Inflation
2. Expenses
3. Taxes
4. Currency exchange rates
5. Risk and uncertainty

A separate section is devoted to each.

9.2 AN ECONOMIC RATIONALE FOR INTEREST

The payment of interest by borrowers to lenders is such a pervasive aspect of contemporary economic life that we take the existence of interest for granted. It is difficult to imagine an economy functioning without interest.

However, the reader may be surprised to learn that interest has not always been an automatic aspect of economic activity. In fact, throughout much of recorded history interest has been condemned by numerous philosophers, religions, and famous authors.

A steady stream of Greek and Roman philosophers denounced the charging of interest as unproductive and immoral, including Plato, Aristotle, Cato, Cicero, Seneca, and Plutarch. Much more recently, Karl Marx argued that interest is exploitative and results from paying workers less than their just wage. Thus, interest has not existed in certain Marxist and communistic societies.

Organized religions have not always looked favorably on lenders charging interest on loans. Traditional Jewish law forbids the charging of interest by one Jew to another Jew. There are a number of such references throughout the Torah, and Old Testament. In much of the Islamic world today interest is banned as being in violation of the Qur'an. In the 13th Century, St. Thomas Aquinas, a leading Christian theologian, argued eloquently that charging interest is morally wrong. As a result, throughout the Middle Ages all interest was banned as *usury* by the Catholic Church. Today "usury" refers only to "excessive" interest.

In the United States usury laws exist at the state level. As a result, there are significant differences from state to state as to the level at which rates of interest become usurious. Also, there is considerable variation as to the applicability and the level of interest rates to which usury laws apply for different types of loans. Finally, there are some types of loans completely exempt from state usury laws.

Interest has not fared much better in literature throughout the centuries. In the 14th Century, Dante in *The Divine Comedy* places usurers in the inner ring of the seventh circle of hell, below even suicides. In the early 17th Century, Shakespeare found it necessary for Shylock, a rich money lender, to forsake usury before he could be redeemed in *The Merchant of Venice*. Even as late as the 19th Century in Charles Dickens' classic holiday fable *A Christmas Carol*, we find Ebenezer Scrooge's business enterprise to be, of course, money lending.

In Section 1.1 we defined interest as a form of rent that the borrower pays to the lender to compensate for the loss of use of the capital by the lender while it is loaned to the borrower. It is instructive to look more deeply into why such rent should be paid. A number of different theories have been advanced as reasons for the existence of interest. However, they fall into two broad categories, one for the supply side of the transaction and one for the demand side.

On the supply side, the primary issue is *time preference*. Most individuals and business firms exhibit a strong preference to have access to dollars today rather than an equal number of dollars tomorrow. Dollars today can be utilized to meet immediate needs. Dollars tomorrow can only be used to meet deferred needs in an uncertain future. Interest is then the price that is sufficient to cause individuals and firms to overcome their time preference to retain dollars today and be willing to lend them. Even individuals and firms with a strong recognition of the need for future dollars can easily move current dollars into the future by saving and investing.

On the demand side, the primary issue is the *productivity of capital*. Virtually all business firms need capital on which to operate successfully. Some of this capital generally comes from borrowing. In the long run, the firm will be successful only if the return on capital employed is greater than the cost of borrowing. Of course, not all borrowing is done by firms, but much is also done by individuals and the government. Admittedly, a portion of this borrowing is used to finance current consumption. However, a portion of it is also in some sense being invested, e.g. individuals borrowing to purchase homes and to finance college educations, and the government borrowing to build infrastructure such as roads and airports. In the end, a healthy economy requires that a substantial portion of money being borrowed be invested productively.

Although these two major theories are quite different, they are in no way incompatible. In fact, quite the contrary, they serve to reinforce each other.

The above discussion barely scratches the surface of some of the economic, or even psychological and philosophical, theories attempting to explain the existence of interest. However, the above discussion is sufficient for the purposes of this book. Curious readers who would like to explore this area more completely are encouraged to refer to relevant literature in economics and finance.

9.3 DETERMINANTS OF THE LEVEL OF INTEREST RATES

Section 9.2 provides a rationale for the existence of interest. However, there was little in that analysis that sheds light on the level of interest rates that exist at various points in time.

If we examine interest rates existing in the past, we discover that great variation has occurred over time. In 1945 the average yield on Treasury bills was 0.33%. In 1981 the same security had an average yield of 14.71%. In August 1980 the prime rate (to be defined later in this section) was 11%. By December 1980 it was 21.5%. What can explain variations of this magnitude?

In looking at the level of interest rates it is necessary to distinguish between two types of variation. The first type of variation is general and pertains to the overall level of interest rates prevailing in the market. The second type of variation is specific and pertains to the level of the interest rate on a particular transaction.

Basic economic theory would suggest that rates of interest, like other prices, are established by supply and demand. If the demand for funds to borrow is strong in relation to the availability of funds, interest rates will rise. Conversely, if the demand for funds to borrow is weak in relation to the availability of funds, interest rates will fall. It sounds simple, but in practice there are a large number of factors that come together in complex ways to determine rates of interest.

The following is a list of major factors which have an influence on the level of the rate of interest. The list is not exhaustive, but it does include most of the major determinants.

1. *The underlying "pure" rate of interest*
   Most economic and financial theorists believe that there is an underlying "pure" rate of interest as a base which is related to long-term productivity growth in the economy. This rate would prevail on a risk-free investment if there were no inflation. This rate has proven to be relatively stable over many decades. In the United States this rate has typically been in the range of 2% to 3%.

2. *Inflation*
   Experience has shown that inflation has a significant effect on the rate of interest. This factor is discussed in more detail in Section 9.4.

3. *Risk and uncertainty*
   Experience has also shown that risk and uncertainty have a significant effect of the rate of interest. This factor is discussed in more detail in Section 9.8.

4. *Length of investment*
   There will normally be differences between market rates of interest on short-term and long-term loans and investments, all other things being equal. This phenomenon is discussed in more detail in Chapter 10.

5. *Quality of information*
   In finance theory "efficient" markets are defined as those in which all buyers and sellers (in this context borrowers and lenders) possess the same information. Aberrations in the rate of interest are more likely to exist in "inefficient" markets. In the modern computer-information age, markets tend to be more efficient than in the past. However, certain market rigidities remain which can affect the rate of interest.

6. *Legal restrictions*
   Some rates of interest are regulated by the government. For example, the 1945 rate mentioned earlier in the section resulted from price controls during World War II. In the United States there has been a trend toward deregulation in recent years, so that this has become a less significant factor than in the past. Nevertheless some rates of interest still are subject to some degree of regulation.

7. *Governmental policy*
   The federal government has a major influence on the level of interest rates through its monetary and fiscal policy. One major factor control is the ability of the Federal Reserve Board to adjust the supply of money in the economy. A second factor is the policy of the Federal Reserve Board to set short-term interest rates on loans within the banking system. Finally, a third factor is the level of governmental deficit or surplus which affects the demand side of the credit market significantly.

8. *Random fluctuation*
   In addition to all the above, the movement of interest rates over time also shows random fluctuations. Chapter 12 introduces stochastic approaches to interest.

At any particular point in time there is a vast array of interest rates being used in the myriad of financial transactions involving interest. However, a few key short-term rates are widely watched as bellwethers of movements in interest rates. Three such key rates are:

1. *Prime rate* – The base rate used on high-grade corporate loans by major banks. Many loan rates are indexed to the prime rate.

2. *Federal funds rate* – The rate on reserves traded among commercial banks for overnight use. This rate changes daily and provides day-to-day information about interest rate movements.

3. *Discount rate* – The rate charged to member banks on loans by the Federal Reserve. Changes in this rate signal significant monetary policy adjustments

by the Federal Reserve Board and are likely to have widespread effect on other short-term rates, including those defined immediately above.

There is no single key indicator of long-term rates that is as widely cited as the above rates. The yields on Treasury bonds with a term of ten or more years are probably the most widely used indicator of movements in long-term rates. The relationship between short-term and long-term rates of interest is discussed further in Chapter 10.

A term which is often used in connection with interest rate movements is *basis point*. One hundred basis points is equal to one percent. Thus, if a particular interest rate rises from 7% to 7.25%, many in the financial community would say that "the rate went up by 25 basis points."

Another term which the reader may encounter in practical applications is *spread*. This term is used in comparing two different interest rates, one of them often being that applicable to Treasury securities. For example, if the yield rate on Treasury securities maturing in five years is 6.25% and the yield rate on some other financial instrument is 7.50%, a phrase that might be heard is "the spread over five-year Treasuries is 125 basis points."

9.4 RECOGNITION OF INFLATION

There is considerable evidence that rates of interest are positively correlated with rates of inflation, i.e. that over time the two will tend to move in the same direction. This phenomenon certainly seems reasonable on the surface of it. Inflation represents loss of purchasing power over time. Lenders will therefore demand higher rates of interest than they otherwise would to compensate for the loss of value in their capital. Similarly, borrowers will be willing to pay higher rates of interest (albeit reluctantly), since they will be able to pay off their loans in "cheaper" dollars.

Actually we need to sharpen the above discussion somewhat. It might be thought that the relationship would be between the current rate of interest and the current rate of inflation. However, the prevailing view among economists who have researched this phenomenon is that the relationship is actually between the current rate of interest and the *expected* rate of inflation rather than the *current* rate of inflation. Unfortunately, this makes the relationship more difficult to measure empirically, since expected rates of inflation cannot directly be measured objectively. Nevertheless, despite the difficulty of precisely measuring such expectations, the evidence clearly indicates that such a relationship does exist.

The rate of interest eliminating inflation is often called the *real rate of interest* and is denoted by i'. The actual rate of interest in the market is often called the *nominal rate of interest* and is denoted by i. We use the letter "i" without superscript since this is the familiar rate of interest we have been using throughout this book. The reader should note that the use of the word "nominal" in this context is different than two other meanings in Sections 1.8 and 6.3, which is an unfortunate source of ambiguity.

We will denote the rate of inflation by r and for the time being we assume it to be constant. Then the equation which relates all the above is

$$1+i = (1+i')(1+r) \tag{9.1}$$

where $r>0$ and $i>i'>0$, assuming the rate of inflation is positive.

If we solve for i, we obtain

$$i = i'+r+i'r. \tag{9.2}$$

Thus, the nominal rate of interest is equal to the real rate of interest plus the rate of inflation plus the product of the two. Since the cross product term is typically small, many people tend to ignore it and conveniently think of the nominal rate of interest as just the sum of the real of interest and the rate of inflation.

We can also solve for i', which gives

$$1+i' = \frac{1+i}{1+r} \tag{9.3a}$$

or

$$i' = \frac{i-r}{1+r}. \tag{9.3b}$$

According to the theory outlined above, i' will be relatively stable over time. However, i and r will tend to move up and down together. The above relationships are not precise. The real rate i' is not totally constant over time, nor is the correlation between i and r exact either. Also, we have the dual problems of measurement and time lags, since r should be the expected rate of inflation. Thus, these formulas should not be thought of as exact relationships, but rather as convenient rules of thumb.

Nevertheless, formula (9.3*a*) is quite useful in performing calculations involving rates of inflation. For example, assume that we wish to find the present value of a series of payments at the end of each period for n periods in which the base payment amount at time 0 is R, but each payment is indexed to reflect inflation. If r is the periodic rate of inflation and i is the periodic rate of interest, then using the right-hand side of formula (9.3*a*) the present value of this series of payments is

$$R\left[\frac{1+r}{1+i}+\frac{(1+r)^2}{(1+i)^2}+\cdots+\frac{(1+r)^n}{(1+i)^n}\right] = R(1+r)\frac{1-\left(\frac{1+r}{1+i}\right)^n}{i-r} \tag{9.4}$$

by applying formula (4.29) with an adjustment factor of $1+r$.

However, if we use the left-hand side of formula (9.3*a*) the formulation of the problem becomes

$$R\left[\frac{1}{1+i'}+\frac{1}{(1+i')^2}+\cdots+\frac{1}{(1+i')^n}\right] = Ra_{\overline{n}|\,i'}\ . \tag{9.5}$$

Formulas (9.4) and (9.5) produce the same numerical answer and have an important verbal interpretation. Formula (9.4) represents the present value of the payments *including* inflation computed at the *nominal* rate of interest. However, in formula (9.5) this is seen to equal the present value of the payments *excluding* inflation computed at the *real* rate of interest.

The above verbal interpretation really provides more general guidance in computing present values of future payments in practical situations as follows:

1. If future payments are not affected by inflation, then discount at the nominal rate of interest.

2. If future payments are adjusted to reflect the rate of inflation and the adjustment is reflected in the payment amount, then also discount at the nominal rate of interest.

3. If future payments are adjusted to reflect the rate of inflation but the adjustment is not reflected in the payment amount, the correct procedure is to discount at the real rate of interest.

The above discussion involves a present value analysis. It is also instructive to consider inflation in connection with accumulated values. Consider the common situation in which an investor invests A dollars for n periods at interest rate i. The value of this investment in "nominal dollars" at the end of n periods is

$$A(1+i)^n . \tag{9.6}$$

However, how much is this investment really worth at that future date? If the rate of inflation is r, then the purchasing power of this investment at the end of n periods is

$$A \frac{(1+i)^n}{(1+r)^n} = A(1+i')^n . \tag{9.7}$$

Thus, the value of this investment in "real dollars" is lower, since $i > i'$. Many investors would find it quite enlightening to analyze their investment programs in terms of "real" results as well as "nominal" results, rather than considering only the latter.

In the above discussion, there has been the implicit assumption that $i > r$, i.e. that the nominal rate of interest is greater than the rate of inflation. In general, this relationship will hold, particularly over significant periods of time.

However, in some cases, for at least some investors, this may not be the case. Such a result is most likely to occur during periods of high inflation. For example, in the United States during 1979-1981 the rate of inflation, as measured by the *Consumer Price Index* (CPI), which is probably the most widely used index of inflation, was in "double digits" (i.e. over 10%). Yet during this same period of time billions of dollars were invested in savings accounts at rates of interest in the 7% range. For all those investors, the "nominal value" of their savings was increasing, but the "real value" was declining.

Investors (lenders) seeking direct protection against future inflation have few choices and must look to government bonds. Borrowers in the private sector are simply unwilling to underwrite the uncertain cost of providing future inflation protection on an unlimited basis.

Government bonds indexed to inflation have been available in the United Kingdom and Canada for a number of years, but did not become widely available in the United States until 1997. In that year the U.S. Department of Treasury launched the Treasury Inflation Protection Securities (TIPS) program. TIPS were briefly introduced in Section 6.2.

TIPS are a new type of security in which both the maturity value and coupons are adjusted for future changes in the CPI. TIPS trade in the bond market as do "regular" Treasury bonds. The stated coupon rate is substantially less than that for otherwise comparable "regular" Treasury bonds since the stated coupon will be adjusted for changes in the CPI.

The principal amount of the bond (original face amount adjusted by CPI changes) is calculated each period. The coupon for that period is then computed as the fixed coupon rate times the adjusted principal amount at that time. The maturity value of the bond is the adjusted principal amount at the maturity date of the bond.

TIPS have several attractive properties. First, they provide a new investment vehicle for investors seeking true inflation protection. Second, they provide better market-based information on future inflation expectations. Third, they provide additional incentive for the Federal government to control inflation since it will reduce the cost of servicing debt on these bonds.

Example 9.1** **An insurance company is making annual payments under the settlement provisions of a personal injury lawsuit. A payment of $24,000 has just been made and ten more payments are due. Future payments are indexed to the Consumer Price Index which is assumed to increase at 5% per year. Find the present value of the remaining obligation if the rate of interest assumed is 8%.

In this example the nominal rate of interest $i = .08$, while the rate of inflation $r = .05$. Thus, from formula (9.3*b*) the real rate of interest is

$$i' = \frac{.08 - .05}{1 + .05} = .028571.$$

In practice, many people think of the real rate of interest as the difference between the nominal rate of interest and the rate of inflation, i.e. as $i \approx .08 - .05 = .03$. Although this is an easy rule of thumb, it does consistently overstate the correct value somewhat.

Using formula (9.4) the present value is computed to be

$$24{,}000(1.05)\,\frac{1 - \left(\dfrac{1.05}{1.08}\right)^{10}}{.08 - .05} = \$206{,}226$$

to the nearest dollar.

If we use formula (9.5), we obtain

$$24,000\, a_{\overline{10|}.028571} = 24,000 \frac{1-(1.028571)^{-10}}{.028571} = \$206,226$$

to the nearest dollar. This numerically illustrates the equivalency of the two approaches given by formulas (9.4) and (9.5).

***Example 9.2** A two-year TIPS bond is issued with an annual coupon rate of 3.4% payable semiannually. The CPI progression during the life of the bond is as follows:*

Time	*CPI*
0	*225.0*
0.5	*229.7*
1	*234.1*
1.5	*240.4*
2	*246.6*

Find the amount of the four coupons and the maturity value for a bond issued in the amount of $10,000.

The CPI values are used to compute an *index ratio* by dividing the CPI value at time t by the value at time 0. Table 9.1 displays the results. The four coupons are displayed in the last column. The maturity value of the bond is $10,960.00.

Table 9.1 Bond Payment Schedule for a 2-Year TIPS Bond

Time	*CPI*	*Index ratio*	*Principal amount*	*Coupon amount*
0	225.0		10,000.00	
1	229.7	1.020889	10,208.89	173.55
2	234.1	1.040444	10,404.44	176.88
3	240.4	1.068444	10,684.44	181.64
4	246.6	1.096000	10,960.00	186.32

The line of the table for time $t = 1$ is computed as

$$\text{Index ratio} = \frac{229.7}{225.0} = 1.020889$$

$$\text{Principal amount} = 10{,}000(1.020889)$$
$$= 10{,}208.89$$

$$\text{Coupon amount} = 10{,}208.89\left(\frac{.034}{2}\right)$$
$$= 173.55$$

Each succeeding line in the table is computed similarly.

9.5 CONSIDERATION OF EXPENSES

A factor which may have significant implications for financial calculations of the type discussed in this book is the treatment of expenses. Some rates of interest are quoted net of expenses and others are not. In the latter case, the apparent financial results arising from the effects of interest on borrowers and/or lenders may be materially affected by the expenses incurred.

The variety of situations in which expenses are a significant concern is too vast to cover comprehensively in this section. A few commonly encountered situations, both at an individual level and at an institutional level, will be presented. The reader is encouraged always to consider how expenses may affect financial results when applying the material in this book to "real-world" situations.

Consumer borrowing

The impact of expenses incurred at the time consumers take out loans was previously discussed in Section 8.2, 8.3, and 8.4. Sometimes the interest rate charged by the lender on such loans covers all expenses; sometimes it does not. When it does not, the expenses may or may not be fully reflected in the annual percentage rate (APR) disclosure.

A particularly good example is the real estate mortgage. As discussed in Section 8.4, there typically are several different types of expenses involved in obtaining a real estate mortgage that are not included in the basic interest rate on the mortgage loan itself. Some of these expenses are reflected in the APR, but others are not. Governmental regulations prescribe which expenses must be reflected and which need not be reflected.

Additional fees and penalties after loan inception may also occur. For example, nearly all loans have fees and penalties associated with late and delinquent payments by the borrower. Going in the opposite direction, most lenders permit accelerated or early repayment of the loan without penalty. However, some loan agreements may impose a fee or penalty for early repayment.

Personal investing

Some investment options not directly involving expenses do exist for individual investors. Examples would be savings accounts or certificates of deposit (CDs) offered by banks, credit unions, and other financial institutions. Of course, the interest rate being offered is significantly lower than the rate that the financial institution can earn on the money permitting the financial institution to cover their expenses and earn a profit.

However, costs may arise after inception. For example, certificates of deposit generally have penalties for early withdrawal. This was discussed previously in Section 2.7.

Another example of a "no expense" investment is a debt issued by the federal government. The United States Treasury Department has developed a program called "Treasury Direct" in which individual investors can buy Treasury securities in relatively small amounts over the internet at no expense.

Despite these examples, most investment options for individual investors do involve expenses. For example, consider the investment in securities, i.e. bonds and stocks, of the type discussed in Chapter 6. Typically, such securities are bought and sold through a brokerage account. Commissions or other fees would typically be charged on the purchase and sale of such securities. In the case of bonds, it should be noted that generally no expenses are charged when a bond is redeemed or matures.

When commissions or other fees are charged in buying and selling securities, the actual yield rate realized by the investor will be reduced. This yield rate could be determined by increasing the purchase price by any expenses at purchase and decreasing the sale price by any expenses at sale.

As discussed in Section 8.8, mutual funds have become a popular investment vehicle for many individual investors. The expense structure with a mutual fund differs from individual securities described above. Typically a mutual fund charges an asset-based fee, often called an *expense ratio*, as a percentage of the value of the investor's balance in the fund.

The net effect is to reduce the investor's return by the amount the expense ratio. For example, if a mutual fund earns 7.5% over a one-year period, but the annual expense ratio is 1.5%, the investor actually earns only 6% over the year.

Expense ratios on mutual funds are typically assessed on a daily basis. Also, the total expense ratio, and its decomposition into components, must be fully disclosed in a *prospectus* made available at initial purchase and periodically thereafter.

Institutional borrowing

Institutional borrowing by corporations and governmental entities involves much larger amounts of money than consumer borrowing. There are a variety of mechanisms and lenders involved in providing the source of funds for such borrowing.

Short-term borrowing typically involves other institutional lenders and individual investors are usually not significantly involved in financing such borrowing. However, long-term borrowing, particularly for larger amounts, is often implemented by an issuance of bonds of the type discussed in Chapter 6.

Institutional borrowing with a bond issuance is a major undertaking. No one lender has the capacity, nor the willingness, to finance such a large borrowing. As a result, the debt will be financed by hundreds, even thousands, of institutional and individual investors who become the bondholders.

The process of actually issuing the bonds and marketing them to the initial bondholders is a complex process called *underwriting* and is done by *investment bankers*. Once the initial underwriting is complete, the bonds trade in the bond market as securities and the principles discussed in Chapter 6 apply.

However, the expenses involved in the initial underwriting are substantial. The net effect is that the bond issuer (borrower) receives less proceeds than the amount of debt incurred. For example, if the underwriting cost of issuing $50 million in new bonds is 8%, the institutional borrower will only receive $46 million, but will have $50 million of new indebtedness to ultimately repay.

Institutional investing

Institutions, such as corporations, may invest in the equity (stock) or debt (bonds) of other institutions. Such investing may occur in open markets with publicly traded securities or as *private placements* with an institution-to-institution transaction. Since these types of transactions involve large amounts of money and sophisticated parties, the transaction expenses tend to be quite low on a relative basis. Moreover, no new principles are really involved in such transactions.

Another type of institutional investing involves financial institutions, such as banks, insurance companies and other investment companies. Investing for such financial institutions is a business, not a passive activity as it might be for a non-financial institution. As such, expenses will be incurred to generate various types of revenue. It is important that these expenses be properly allocated and offset against various sources of revenue, so that an accurate picture emerges of the net investment income being earned by the various investment activities of the firm.

Summary

The above examples are far from comprehensive and should be considered illustrative of the variety of issues that emerge when considering expenses in financial transactions. However, they should be sufficient to sensitize the reader to consider the possible impact of expenses when applying the principles in this book to real-world situations.

Example 9.3 Consider the two-year bond illustrated in Table 6.2 with 8% coupons paid semiannually bought to yield 6% convertible semiannually. If the commission to buy this bond is \$12, find the yield rate the investor will actually achieve. Assume the bond is held to maturity.

The price computed in Section 6.4 is 1037.17. With the commission the investor will actually pay

$$1037.17 + 12.00 = 1049.17$$

for the bond.

The yield to maturity reflecting the commission will be the solution for i of the following equation of value

$$1049.17 = 40a_{\overline{4}|i} + 1000(1+i)^{-4}.$$

This equation of value can be solved using either the bond functionality or the IRR functionality on a financial calculator to give $i = .02687$. Thus, the yield to maturity reflecting commission expense is

$$2(.02687) = .0537, \text{ or } 5.37\%$$

convertible semiannually. This compares with the yield to maturity of 6% not considering expenses.

Note that no commission is charged when the bond matures. However, if the bond were to be sold prior to maturity, a second commission would be incurred.

Since commissions are one-time costs, their impact is spread over the length of time the bond is held. For a short-term bond, as in this example, the reduction in the yield rate is substantial. For a longer-term bond, the reduction in the yield rate would be significantly lower if the bond is held to maturity.

***Example 9.4** An investor age 35 deposits $10,000 in the mutual fund described in this section which is expected to earn 7.5% effective and has a expense ratio of 1.5%. The investor intends to leave the money on deposit until age 65 as a retirement fund. Determine the percentage reduction in the expected retirement accumulation attributable to the expense ratio.*

If there were no expense ratio, the expected retirement accumulation would be

$$10{,}000(1.075)^{30} = 87{,}549.55.$$

However, with the expense ratio, the expected retirement accumulation actually becomes

$$10{,}000(1.06)^{30} = 57{,}434.91.$$

The percentage reduction in the annual return due to expenses is

$$\frac{7.5-6.0}{7.5} = .20, \text{ or } 20\%.$$

However, the percentage reduction in the expected retirement accumulation actually becomes

$$\frac{87{,}549.55-57{,}434.91}{87{,}549.55} = .344, \text{ or } 34.4\% \text{ !}$$

This illustrates the dramatic impact which even seemingly small expense ratios like 1.5% can produce over long periods of time. This phenomenon is attributable to the compounding of expense ratios over an extended period.

Thus transaction-based expenses, as in Example 9.3, have their greatest impact over short periods of time, while asset-based expenses, as in Example 9.4, have their greatest impact over long periods of time.

Example 9.5 Assume that the $50 million dollar bond issue described in this section has a 15-year term, 6% coupon rate payable semiannually, matures at par, and is issued at par. Determine the impact of the 8% underwriting expense at bond issuance on the overall interest cost to the corporation of issuing the bonds.

The semiannual coupon payments are

$$.03(50{,}000{,}000) = 1{,}500{,}000.$$

Thus, an equation of value at issue is

$$46{,}000{,}000 = 1{,}500{,}000 a_{\overline{30|}\,i} + 50{,}000{,}000(1+i)^{-30}.$$

This equation of value can be solved using either the bond functionality or the IRR functionality on a financial calculator to give $i = .03431$. Thus, the interest cost to the corporation reflecting underwriting expense is

$$2(.03431) = .0686, \text{ or } 6.86\%.$$

convertible semiannually. This compares with the coupon cost of 6% convertible semiannually not considering underwriting expense.

Example 9.6 In Example 7.9 an audit discovers that $20,000 of investment-related expenses were inadvertently classified as other expenses. Recalculate the effective rate of interest earned.

The values $A = 10{,}000{,}000$ and $B = 10{,}910{,}000$ are unchanged, but net investment income should have been

$$I = 510{,}000 - 20{,}000 = 490{,}000.$$

The revised rate of interest earned using formula (7.16) becomes

$$i = \frac{2(490{,}000)}{10{,}000{,}000 + 10{,}910{,}000 - 490{,}000} = .0480, \text{ or } 4.8\% .$$

9.6 EFFECT OF TAXES

Another factor which may affect financial calculations involving interest is the effect of taxes; more specifically, income taxes. We will attempt to address the effect of taxes as generically as we can, but the effect of taxes may well differ significantly from situation to situation and from political jurisdiction to political jurisdiction. Again, the context for this discussion will be significantly shaped by the federal income tax structure in the United States.

Consider first a situation in which an investor (lender) can invest money at a completely tax-free rate. Thus, if \$1000 is invested at time $t = 0$ at 8% effective for one year, the investor will earn .08(1000) or \$80 in interest at the end of the year, for an ending balance of \$1080. The yield rate (IRR) for the year is obviously $i = .08$, or 8%.

Now assume that the interest income is taxed at a rate of 25%. The investor pays a tax of .25(80) = \$20 at the end of the year producing a net ending balance of 1080 – 20 = \$1060. The after-tax yield rate (IRR) for the year becomes $i = .06$, or 6%.

In general, let i^b be the before-tax rate of interest, i^a the after-tax rate of interest, and t the tax rate. Then we have

$$i^a = (1-t)i^b. \tag{9.8}$$

If the tax rate stays level for n years and if interest is taxed each year as it is earned, then the after-tax accumulated value is given by

$$a(n) = (1+i^a)^n = \left[1+(1-t)i^b\right]^n. \tag{9.9}$$

The after-tax yield rate (IRR) over the n-year period is simply $i = i^a$. This type of result is quite typical and would apply when interest income is taxable as ordinary (i.e. fully taxable) income.

We now turn to a more complex example. An excellent and useful application is provided by a retirement planning illustration. The basic principles just described can be adapted and generalized to fit a variety of situations that face individuals accumulating money for retirement.

This variety is attributable to the complex structure of the federal income tax system in the United States. In particular, in retirement planning, depending upon the circumstances:

1. Contributions may be made:
    - With after-tax dollars.
    - With before-tax dollars.

2. Investment income may be:
    - Taxed as it is earned.
    - Taxed, but on a deferred basis.
    - Not taxed at all, i.e. tax-exempt.

3. Retirement income withdrawals may be:
    - Taxed as taken
    - Not taxed at all, i.e. tax-exempt.

4. Different types or segments of income may be taxed differently:
    - Some investment income may be taxed as ordinary income, while some may be taxed as capital gains income at a lower rate.
    - Taxation may vary depending upon source, e.g. investment income, employer contributions, or employee contributions.
    - Even when ordinary income tax applies, the tax bracket structure may result in different tax rates applying to different segments of income.

It is impractical to illustrate all the combinations that can occur in practice. However, some commonly-encountered situations will be illustrated in Examples 9.7 and 9.8.

Present values are similar, but somewhat more subtle. Let us reverse the simple example given above. The present value at time $t = 0$ of the before-tax accumulation of \$1080 at time $t = 1$, calculated at a before-tax rate of interest of 8%, is equal to \$1000. Similarly, the present value of at time $t = 0$ of the after-tax accumulation of \$1060 at time $t = 1$, calculated at an after-tax rate of interest of 6%, is also equal to \$1000.

Therefore, it would appear to be consistent either to discount before-tax cash flows at a before-tax rate of interest, or after-tax cash flows at an after-tax rate of interest. By implication, it would be inconsistent to mix before-tax and after-tax values in one calculation.

However, some unexpected complexities and pitfalls arise with transactions involving multiple payments made at different points in time. Present values computed on an after-tax basis may not easily be reconciled with present values computed on a before tax basis in some circumstances.

An important application involving present values is provided by the internal rate of return (IRR) and net present value (NPV) analysis presented in Section 7.2. Discounted cash flow analysis on an after-tax basis is widely used in making business decisions in practice.

Some of the complexities and pitfalls involved in making such present value calculations are illustrated in Examples 9.9 and 9.10.

***Example 9.7** A retirement contribution of \$10,000 is made as a part of a financial plan. The money will be invested for 20 years at which time it will be withdrawn in one lump-sum for retirement. It is assumed that the investment will earn 8% effective over the entire 20-year period. It is also assumed that the income tax rate is a level 25% over the entire period. Find the after-tax accumulation and yield rate (IRR) achieved under the following tax situations:*

(1) No taxes are incurred.

(2) All investment income is fully taxed as it is earned.

(3) Contributions are deductible when made and taxes are deferred until the funds are withdrawn.

(4) Contributions are not deductible when made and taxes are deferred until the funds are withdrawn.

(5) Contributions are not deductible when made and no taxes are incurred thereafter.

1. This is the baseline result if there were no taxes at all. The accumulated value is

$$10{,}000(1.08)^{20} = 46{,}610$$

and the yield rate (IRR), is

$$i = .08, \text{ or } 8\%.$$

2. This is the result for normal investing with no tax preferences. We can directly apply formula (9.9) to obtain the after-tax accumulated value as

$$10{,}000\left[1+(1-.25)(.08)\right]^{20} = 10{,}000(1.06)^{20} = \$32{,}071.$$

The after-tax yield rate (IRR), is

$$i = .06, \text{ or } 6\%.$$

3. This is the result for the typical 401(k) plan or for a fully deductible regular IRA (individual retirement account). Financially, the $10,000 contribution only costs the investor 10,000 (1–.25) = 7,500, since 25% of it is, in effect, financed by the government. The before-tax accumulated value is

$$10{,}000(1.08)^{20} = 46{,}610,$$

but since the entire amount is subject to taxes, the after-tax accumulated value becomes

$$10{,}000(1.08)^{20}(.75) = 34{,}957.$$

The after-tax yield rate (IRR) achieved can be obtained from the equation of value

$$7500(1+i)^{20} = 34{,}957$$

which gives

$$i = .08, \text{ or } 8\%.$$

Interestingly, the same after-tax yield rate (IRR) is achieved as if there were no taxes at all!

Some readers may be troubled by this result. Although it does appear that the investor earned the same yield rate (IRR) as in case (1), the investor ended up with less money at retirement. However, remember that the investor essentially invested only $7500 rather than $10,000.

It is important to note that if the investor could invest

$$\frac{10{,}000}{.75} = 13{,}333,$$

the net out-of-pocket cost at inception would be $10,000. If this amount is invested, then the after-tax accumulation at retirement would be

$$13{,}333(1.08)^{20}(.75) = \$46{,}610,$$

exactly the same answer as in case (1).

4. This is the result for a non-deductible IRA (which applies to investors with incomes above a specified threshold). Since the contribution is not deductible, the taxes at the end of 20 years are computed only on the growth, not on the entire accumulated value. Thus the after-tax accumulated value is

$$\begin{aligned} &10{,}000\left\{1+.75\left[(1.08)^{20}-1\right]\right\} \\ &= 10{,}000\left\{.75(1.08)^{20}+.25\right\} \\ &= \$37{,}457. \end{aligned}$$

The after-tax yield rate (IRR) achieved can be obtained from the equation of value

$$10{,}000(1+i)^{20} = 37{,}457$$

which can solved to give

$$i = .0683, \quad \text{or} \quad 6.83\%.$$

As expected, the yield rate (IRR) is more favorable than case (2), but less favorable than case (3).

5. This is the result for a Roth IRA. The results are identical to those in case (1). Thus, the accumulated value is

$$10{,}000(1.08)^{20} = \$46{,}610$$

and the yield rate (IRR) is

$$i = .08, \quad \text{or} \quad 8\%.$$

Note that the results for the regular IRA in case (3) and the Roth IRA in case (5) are financially equivalent. The only difference is that taxes with the regular IRA are paid at the end of the 20 years, while taxes with the Roth IRA are, in effect, paid at the beginning.

Example 9.8 Rework Example 9.7 (2) if half the investment income each year is taxed at 25% and the other half is taxed at 15%.

This example illustrates a common situation in which some investment income is ordinary income, taxed at the regular rate, and some is capital gains income taxed at a lower rate. We can generalize formula (9.8) to obtain

$$\begin{aligned} i^a &= (1-.25)(.5)(.08)+(1-.15)(.5)(.08) \\ &= .064. \end{aligned}$$

Thus, the after-tax accumulated value is

$$10{,}000(1.064)^{20} = 34{,}581$$

and the after-tax yield rate (IRR) is

$$.064, \text{ or } 6.4\%.$$

***Example 9.9** An investor contributes $1000 immediately in exchange for payments of $600 at the end of one year and $720 at the end of two years.*

(1) Find the before-tax yield rate (IRR).

(2) Find the after-tax yield rate (IRR), if all contributions are tax deductible and all returns are fully taxable. The income tax rate is 25%.

1. We can apply the results from Section 7.2 directly. Formula (7.3) gives the equation of value

$$-1000 + 600(1+i)^{-1} + 720(1+i)^{-2} = 0$$

and solving the quadratic, we find that the before-tax yield rate (IRR) is

$$i^b = .20, \quad \text{or} \quad 20\%.$$

2. In this case all dollar amounts become 75% of the amounts above, so that the equation of value is

$$-750 + 450(1+i)^{-1} + 540(1+i)^{-2} = 0.$$

Solving the quadratic, the after-tax yield rate (IRR) is still

$$i^a = .20, \quad \text{or} \quad 20\%.$$

The reader will probably find this result surprising and counter-intuitive. However, it is mathematically evident why this is the case, since all dollar amounts are reduced proportionally.

***Example 9.10** Under the theory that after-tax payments should be discounted at an after-tax yield rate (IRR), find the net present value (NPV) in Example 9.9 at this after-tax rate.*

Formula (9.8) gives an after-tax yield rate equal to

$$i^a = (1-.25)(.20) = .15.$$

Formula (7.2) then gives the (NPV) as

$$\begin{aligned} \text{NPV} &= P(.15) = -750+450(1.15)^{-1}+540(1.15)^{-2} \\ &= 49.62. \end{aligned}$$

The NPV is positive reflecting the fact that we are computing present values at 15%, when the IRR = 20%. However, an intuitive interpretation of this answer is not immediately evident.

Examples 9.9 and 9.10 indicate that computing present values before and after taxes, when multiple payments at different points in time are involved, raises challenging issues of interpretation.

9.7 CURRENCY EXCHANGE RATES

Yet another factor which may affect financial calculations involving interest is the effect of foreign currency exchange rates. Such calculations historically have been of little interest to the large majority of borrowers and lenders, whose financial transactions all involved domestic activities within one country. However, much has changed in recent years to make this topic relevant to a much larger audience.

Perhaps a historical note would be helpful. Throughout much of history foreign currency exchange rates were tightly controlled by governments. Also, there were many difficulties and complexities involved in borrowing or lending across international borders. Thus, this activity was largely confined to large, sophisticated, international institutions.

These impediments to making financial transactions in foreign countries have dramatically lessened in recent years. Since the early 1970s most economically developed countries have deregulated currency exchange rates and permitted their currency's value to be determined in open international markets. Second, the computer revolution has greatly facilitated the movement of funds across international borders.

Today, the vast majority of currencies in the economically developed countries actively trade in international currency markets and their values can fluctuate moment to moment based upon supply and demand. Also, every day billions of dollars routinely cross international borders at the click of a computer key.

We will assume that the risks of investing in various countries are identical. For example, investments could be in governmental debt of various countries for which the default risk is assumed to be zero. Section 9.8 addresses financial calculations in which risk and uncertainty are considered. The results in that section can be applied to foreign currency transactions in which differing levels of risk exist.

The purpose of Section 9.7 is to explore the relationship between interest rates and currency exchange rates. In free markets, economic theory suggests that an equilibrium condition called *interest rate parity* will exist. If different levels of interest rates exist between Country A and Country B on comparable investments, then there must be an expectation for changes in currency exchange rates to maintain equilibrium.

We will now develop an algebraic expression that will hold under interest rate parity. We will first need some definitions of new symbols. Let:

i^d = current domestic interest rate
i^f = current foreign interest rate
e^c = current exchange rate
e^e = expected future exchange rate
r = expected return on foreign investment

Before proceeding further, some observations are in order:

1. Exchange rates are relative between two different currencies. There is no absolute standard against which all currencies are measured. Thus, there are as many different exchange rates as there are pairs of currencies of interest.

2. The exchange rate e expresses 1 unit of domestic currency in terms of a foreign currency. For example, let the domestic currency be the U.S. dollar (\$) and the foreign currency be the European euro (€). If the currency markets price €1 to be worth \$1.25, then the correct way to express e is

$$e = .80,$$

$$\text{i.e. } \$1 = €1/1.25 = €.80.$$

3. For convenience, we will assume a one-year investment period. However, our results can easily be generalized to other periods.

We can invest $1 today in a domestic investment for one year and then convert the ending balance into foreign currency. In this case we will have

$$\left(1+i^d\right)e^e$$

in foreign value at the end of one year. Alternatively, we can convert the $1 into foreign currency immediately and then invest directly in a foreign investment. In this case, we will have

$$\left(1+i^f\right)e^c$$

in foreign value at the end of one year.

Under interest rate parity, these two values will be equal, i.e.

$$\left(1+i^d\right)e^e = \left(1+i^f\right)e^c \qquad (9.10)$$

which we can express as

$$1+i^d = \left(1+i^f\right)\frac{e^c}{e^e}. \qquad (9.11)$$

We can solve for our expected return on the investment r, by setting $r=i^d$ in formula (9.11) and solve for r to obtain

$$r = \left(1+i^f\right)\frac{e^c}{e^e}-1. \qquad (9.12)$$

If any three of the four values in formulas (9.10) through (9.12) are known, then we can solve for the fourth to establish interest rate parity.

Example 9.11 Governmentally-insured one-year certificate of deposits (CDs) yield 3.35% in the United States and 2.31% in Japan. The current exchange rate is 107.88 Japanese yen (¥) per dollar. Find the expected exchange rate one year from today under interest rate parity.

We are given:

$$i^d = .0335$$
$$i^f = .0231$$
$$e^c = 107.88.$$

Solving formula (9.10) for e^e we obtain

$$e^e = \frac{1+i^f}{1+i^d}e^c = \frac{1.0231}{1.0335}(107.88)$$
$$= 106.79 \text{ yen per dollar.}$$

It is instructive to confirm this answer. If a U.S. investor invests \$10,000 in a U.S. CD, at the end of one year the investor will have

$$10,000(1.0335) = \$10,335.$$

If, instead, the U.S. investor invests \$10,000 in a Japanese CD, at the end of one year the investor will have

$$10,000(107.88)(1.0231) = ¥\,1,103,720$$

If this investor converts this balance back to dollars, and the exchange rate actually does equal 106.79 at then end of one year, then the investor will have

$$\frac{1,103,720}{106.79} = \$10,335.$$

Thus, at an expected exchange rate in one year of 106.79 the investor is indifferent between the two investments. If the exchange rate is higher than 106.79, the investor will come out better by investing in the U.S. Conversely, if the exchange rate is lower than 106.79, the investor will come out better by investing in Japan.

9.8 REFLECTING RISK AND UNCERTAINTY

In previous chapters of this book when considering future payments we have implicitly assumed that the payments are of known amount and are certain to be paid at known points in time. The analysis then proceeds from that point. In some financial calculations involving interest this level of exactness prevails, e.g. buying a Treasury security and holding it to maturity. However, in other situations there are one or more elements of risk and uncertainty.

In this book we will use the terms "risk" and "uncertainty" interchangeably. However, in the accounting literature a distinction has sometimes been drawn. In that context "risk" is the subset of uncertainty that can be quantified. Risk may then be used in preparing entries for financial statements under some conditions, while unquantifiable uncertainty is not reflected. We are not making such a distinction in this book, but the reader may encounter the distinction elsewhere.

The level of risk and uncertainty rises substantially when discounted cash flow analysis is applied to analyze general business and financial transactions involving estimated future receipts and/or disbursements at various points of time. However, even within the narrower universe of well-defined borrowing and lending transactions, significant risk and uncertainty exists. Examples would be the risk of default in payments, the possibility of prepayments or refinancing of mortgage loans, the risk associated with reinvestment rates, and uncertain redemption dates on callable bonds.

There are two categories of risk which affect the market value of investments such as bonds and mortgage loans. The first is *market risk*, which is the risk of future price changes arising from changes in the rate of interest. As we saw in previous chapters, market prices for such investments change inversely with changes in the prevailing level of interest rates.

The second is *credit risk* and arises from the possibility of default in the future. For example, consider two bonds A and B which are identical in terms of coupons, redemption value, and maturity (redemption) date. Bond A is issued by the United States Treasury, while Bond B is a high-risk corporate bond. Clearly, Bond B will sell in the market for substantially less than Bond A because of the risk of default. Thus, the computed yield to maturity rate for Bond B will be significantly greater than for Bond A reflecting its lower price. For this reason high-risk bonds are often called *high-yield bonds*.

Thus, in valuing bonds, if the risk of default is translated into a change in the computed yield rate it will cause a significant increase in that yield rate. However, a yield rate computed on this basis is somewhat misleading to a potential investor. It will only materialize if, in fact, all the payments are made on schedule by the borrower. On the other hand, if default does occur, then substantial losses will actually be realized.

We will demonstrate these concepts with a simple illustration. Consider a $1000 one-year bond with 8% annual coupons maturing at par. If the prevailing yield rate in the market for risk-free investments is 8% and the market believes this bond has no risk of default, then the bond will sell for $1000.

The reader might inquire at this point how a "risk-free" rate of interest can be determined. In the United States yields on Treasury securities are considered to be risk-free. All other investments are assumed to carry some risk of default.

Now consider an otherwise identical bond on which there is a significant risk of default. Assume that this bond is selling in the market for \$940. The \$60 difference in price compensates the purchaser of the bond for the risk of default.

If we compute the yield rate on this bond ignoring the probability of default, we have the following equation of value

$$940 = \frac{1080}{1+i}$$

which gives $i = .1489$, or 14.89%. The excess of this rate over the risk-free rate, i.e. $14.89\% - 8\% = 6.89\%$, is often called the *risk premium* in the interest rate. In general, the greater the risk in an investment the higher the risk premium.

This computed yield rate is somewhat misleading, however. After the fact, for this one bond the yield rate will actually turn out to be 14.89% if no default occurs. However, if total default occurs, the actual realized yield rate will be -100%. If partial default occurs, the realized yield rate will be somewhere in between.

We might be interested in knowing the probability of default which is implicit in the purchase of this high-risk bond. We define the *expected present value* (EPV) of a future payment as its present value multiplied by the probability of payment. We can compute the implicit probability of payment, denoted by p, as

$$940 = p\,\frac{1080}{1.08}$$

which gives $p = .94$. Thus, we have an implicit probability of default equal to .06. Note that the present value is computed at the risk-free rate of 8%.

The above analysis is valid as far as it goes, but it needs refinement. It is quite unlikely that bond purchasers would be willing to pay \$940 for this bond if they really think that the probability of default is as high as .06. Why would investors buy a high-risk investment with an expected yield rate of only 8% when they could buy a risk-free investment with the same yield rate?

Thus, a more reasonable interpretation of a price like \$940 for such a high-risk bond is that the \$60 price differential partially represents the probability of default and partially represents a higher return to the purchaser as compensation for the assumption of risk.

Let us assume that investors think that assumption of this level of risk is worth an extra 3% in the yield rate, i.e. 11% instead of 8%. Then, the implicit probability of payment p can be determined from

$$940 = p\,\frac{1080}{1.11}$$

which gives $p = .9661$. Thus, the implicit probability of default is .0339. It is obvious that this answer is not unique and that other combinations of yield rates and probabilities of default would also produce a price equal to $940.

The above analysis considers one bond bought in isolation. Now consider a diversified portfolio of bonds all of which are similar to the above bond, so that the law of large numbers applies. If the actual rate of default on the portfolio turns out to be .0339, then the yield rate on the entire portfolio will be 11%. Of course, in reality the rate of default will not be exactly .0339 but will follow a probability distribution of some type. The results of mathematical statistics can then be applied to make probability statements about various possible yield rates to be expected on the overall portfolio. This will be illustrated in Example 9.13.

Now, let us turn this illustration around and look at it another way. Assume we want to quantify the risk factor separately from the interest rate. Thus, if the market price of the bond is $940 and the risk-free rate of interest is 8%, then the value at the end of the year would be $940(1.08) = 1015.20$. This way of quantifying risk adjusts the expected payoff downward from 1080 to 1015.20 to reflect risk, but then computes present values at the risk-free rate of interest.

This second approach illustrates an error that is sometimes made in financial analysis. One way of quantifying risk is to adjust the interest rate. A second way of quantifying risk is to adjust the payment amount. These are two different, but both valid, ways of quantifying risk. The mistake that is sometimes made is to do both, i.e. lower the expected payoff and raise the interest rate. This procedure is flawed, since it "double counts" the risk involved.

We now generalize these results to more complex situations involving multiple payments. Consider a series of future payments $R_1, R_2, \ldots, R_n$ that are made at times $1, 2, \ldots, n$. For example, on a 10-year $1000 bond with 8% annual coupons, we have $R_1 = R_2 = \cdots = R_9 = 80$ and $R_{10} = 1080$. Assume that the probabilities of payment are $p_1, p_2, \ldots, p_n$, respectively. Then the expected present value (EPV) of this series of payments is given by

$$\text{EPV} = \sum_{t=1}^{n} R_t\,(1+i)^{-t}\,p_t \tag{9.13}$$

where i is an appropriate rate of interest reflecting the risk involved as discussed above.

Formula (9.13) involves three key values: (1) the expected present value EPV, (2) the yield rate i, and (3) a set of probabilities of payment p_t for $t=1, 2, \ldots, n$. Situations arise in practice in which we know two of these values and wish to determine the third.

One obvious complication is that there are many patterns of probabilities p_t that might be used. One assumption that is often made in connection with default risk is to assume that the probability of default is constant during each period. Let this constant probability of default during one period be denoted by q. The corresponding probability of non-default is then $p=1-q$. Under these assumptions, the probability that the tth payment will be made is

$$p_t = p^t \tag{9.14}$$

since non-default must occur in each of the first t intervals for the tth payment to be made. Under this simplifying assumption, formula (9.13) becomes

$$\text{EPV} = \sum_{t=1}^{n} R_t \left(\frac{p}{1+i} \right)^t \tag{9.15}$$

which is much easier to apply than the more general formula (9.13). Of course, other patterns of the probabilities of payment p_t are possible and formula (9.13) would be utilized for these more complex cases.

We now consider the computation of expected present values for a series of future payments more generally. These are three major categories of risk that might be applicable in any particular situation:

1. Probability of the payments.
2. Amount of the payments.
3. Timing of the payments.

The analysis of default risk above falls into the first category. That is the primary risk with which we are concerned in this section. For investments such as mortgage loans and bonds the amount and timing of payments would appear to be well-defined, and thus there would not seem to be any risk involved in the second and third categories.

However, in fact, risk in these categories does exist. As one example, mortgage loan prepayments together with reinvestment rate considerations constitute a significant timing risk. As a second example, a callable bond with variable call premiums depending on the redemption date involves both amount and timing risk.

When we move beyond the realm of normal borrowing and lending transactions and seek to analyze more general business and financial transactions involving estimated future receipts and/or disbursements at various points in time, all three of these risks are important considerations. The actuarial literature is rich with this type of analysis, much of which goes beyond the scope of this book.

One important observation is that although putting a risk premium in the interest rate may be an appropriate method of dealing with default risk, it is not necessarily an appropriate method of dealing with other types of risk.

For example, consider two investments A and B, each of which will pay an estimated $1000 at the end of each year for 20 years. Investment A has relatively low risk and present values are computed at 10%. Investment B has relatively high risk and present values are computed at 20%. Table 9.2 compares the present values of the first payment and the last payment on each basis rounded to the nearest dollar.

Table 9.2 Comparison of Present Values Using a Risk-Adjusted Rate of Interest

	Present value of 1000 paid at end of	
Investment	*Year 1*	*Year 20*
A	909	149
B	833	26
Ratio B/A	92%	17%

Thus, for the payment at the end of year 1, the ratio of B's present value to A's present value is 92%. However, at the end of year 20, the ratio is 17%. This may be reasonable if the greater risk in B is due to the probability of default which increases over time. However, this may not be reasonable if the greater risk in B is due to some other factor such as a higher variance in payment amounts that applies throughout the 20-year period.

It is important to caution the reader against making a common mistake in connection with risk premiums in the interest rate. Based on the analysis in this section it would appear that reflecting risk in the rate of interest will increase the rate. This is certainly true in valuing assets, since the use of a higher rate of interest produces lower present values.

However, just the opposite occurs with liabilities. In this case a risk-adjusted rate of interest would be lower than the risk-free rate of interest, not higher. This point has not always been recognized correctly in the accounting and finance literature, since there has been much more attention paid to risk analysis for assets than for liabilities.

In order to illustrate this phenomenon, consider two insurance companies A and B, both of which wish to sell a portfolio of liabilities consisting of commitments to make payments in the future. The two portfolios have equal expected present values. However, portfolio A has relatively low risk, while portfolio B has relatively high risk. Clearly, company B will have to pay more than company A in order to have some third party assume the portfolio of liabilities. If this higher price is quantified in the interest rate, it would mean using a lower rate of interest in computing the present value of the liabilities for company B than for company A.

One final observation is to note that we have not dealt with reinvestment rate risk in this section. This is a very important risk, but it is addressed elsewhere in this book.

***Example 9.12** The prevailing yield rate for risk-free 10-year bonds is 9% effective. A $1000 10-year bond with annual coupons is issued on which the coupon rate is 9%.*

(1) Find the price an investor would be willing to pay if the probability of default each year is .005 and if the investor requires a yield rate of 11% in compensation for the risk of default.

(2) Find the risk premium in the interest rate in this transaction.

1. If the bond were risk-free, it would obviously sell at par, i.e. the price would be \$1000. We can utilize formula (9.15) to find the price

$$90\left[\frac{.995}{1.11}+\left(\frac{.995}{1.11}\right)^2+\cdots+\left(\frac{.995}{1.11}\right)^{10}\right]+1000\left(\frac{.995}{1.11}\right)^{10} = \$852.825$$

upon summing the geometric progression.

2. We have the following equation of value to determine the yield rate on the bond

$$852.825 = 90a_{\overline{10|}\,i} + 1000(1+i)^{-10}.$$

We can use either the IRR functionality or the bond functionality on a financial calculator to obtain the yield rate $i = 11.56\%$. Thus, the risk premium in the interest rate is 11.56% - 9% = 2.56%. It is instructive to note that the risk premium is approximately equal to the difference between the two interest rates, i.e. 11% minus 9%, plus the default rate, 0.5%.

Example 9.13 Consider the illustration in this section in which a \$1000 one-year 8% bond selling for \$940 bought at a yield rate of 11% has an implicit probability of default equal to .0339. Assume that a diversified portfolio of 500 such bonds is purchased. Use the normal distribution to find a 95% confidence interval for the average probability of default in the portfolio.

The standard deviation for the probability of default is equal to

$$\sigma_p = \sqrt{\frac{pq}{n}} = \sqrt{\frac{(.0339)(.9661)}{500}} = .0081.$$

Thus, the 95% confidence interval using the normal distribution is

$$\mu_p \pm 1.96\,\sigma_p = .0339 \pm 1.96(.0081)$$

or (.0180, .0498). When translated into yield rates, the confidence interval becomes (9.17%, 12.83%). Readers desiring a brief statistical review are referred to Appendix D.

9.9 INTEREST RATE ASSUMPTIONS

Within the realm of standard borrowing and lending transactions the rate of interest involved is typically specified or implied by the provisions of the transaction. For example, loan rates on mortgages and yield to maturity rates on bonds are either known or can readily be determined. The same can be said of other borrowing and lending transactions we have discussed in this book.

However, as we have also seen, the use of discounted cash flow analysis is a powerful analytical and decision-making tool with applicability going well beyond borrowing and lending transactions. In particular, the discussion of capital budgeting, net present value, and internal rate of return in Chapter 7 was motivated by the need to analyze more general business and financial transactions involving estimated future receipts and/or disbursements at various points of time.

This type of analysis is widely used in the field of actuarial science in which present value analysis of future contingent events is a fundamental activity. Another area in which this type of analysis is becoming increasingly important is in the field of accounting. An increasing number of values appearing on financial statements are based on present value calculations. Many other examples could also be cited illustrating the importance of discounted cash flow analysis in financial analysis and decision making.

In using discounted cash flow analysis for these types of more complex situations, the decision maker must resolve three basic ingredients listed in Section 9.8:

1. Probability of the payments.
2. Amount of the payments.
3. Timing of the payments.

However, once these are resolved a key issue remains; namely, what interest rate (or rates) should be used in doing the present value calculations?

In this section we will list a number of considerations that may influence, or even determine, this choice. We do not attempt to arrive at what the decision should be in any particular set of circumstances. Such determinations are beyond the scope of this book. Rather, our purpose is to convey to the reader the large number of options which exist and some of the considerations involved.

1. Should the rate be a real rate or a nominal rate, i.e. how should inflation be reflected? This issue was discussed in Section 9.4.

2. Should the rate be a risk-free rate or a risk-adjusted rate? This issue was discussed in Section 9.8.

3. Should the rate be level or should it reflect the term structure of interest rates? This issue will be addressed in Chapter 10. Alternatively, should the rate vary according to some other pattern motivated by factors other than the yield curve?

4. Should the rate be based on "best estimates" or should it have some level of conservatism? If the latter, then how much conservatism is warranted? Furthermore, is the level of conservatism determined by the degree of uncertainty, i.e. variance, in results or is it based on other considerations?

5. Should the rate be based on a case-by-case determination for each particular situation or should grouping and averaging be used in some fashion that would apply across an entire class?

6. Should the rate be "before-tax" or "after-tax"? This issue was discussed in Section 9.6.

The above six points address some of the primary considerations involved in selecting an interest rate for a particular present value calculation. The following five points list some of the commonly used techniques by which the rate is selected.

1. *New transaction rate* – This is a rate that would be applicable for a new transaction "at the margin." In the case of borrowing, this is the rate that would have to be paid on new indebtedness. In the case of lending, this is the rate that could be earned on a newly invested asset. The new transaction rate is sometimes called the *opportunity rate*.

2. *Average transaction rate* – This is the average rate on a portfolio of similar assets or liabilities. In the case of borrowing, this is the average rate being paid on outstanding indebtedness. In the case of lending, this is the average rate being earned on invested assets. This latter rate is quite analogous, and often identical, to that produced by the "portfolio method" described in Section 7.7.

3. *Settlement rate* – This is the market rate that would be applicable if the series of payments in question were bought or sold today. In some cases, this rate is relatively easy to determine, since there is an active market for the payments in question. However, in other cases a ready market may not exist, in which case the determination of the rate on this basis may be difficult.

4. *Rates that associate assets and liabilities* – This basis looks at related assets and liabilities in determining the applicable rate and does not consider an asset or liability in isolation. This is an important type of analysis and will be discussed further in Chapter 11.

5. *Specified rates* – In this case a rate external to both the entity involved and the particular transaction in question is used. One example would be a rate prescribed by legislation or regulation. A second example would be a rate based on some external index, such as the prime rate or the rate on Treasury securities with a particular maturity.

EXERCISES

9.4 Recognition of inflation

1. The nominal rate of interest is 8% and the rate of inflation is 5%. A single deposit is invested for 10 years. Let:

   A = value of the investment at the end of 10 years measured in "constant dollars," i.e. in dollars valued at time 0.

   B = value of the investment at the end of 10 years computed at the real rate of interest.

   Find the ratio A/B.

2. Rework Exercise 1 assuming equal level deposits at the beginning of each year during the 10-year period instead of a single deposit.

3. Money is invested for five years in a savings account earning 7% effective. If the rate of inflation is 10%, find the percentage of purchasing power lost during the period of investment.

4. From the standpoint of the lender, mortgages involve investing dollars today and receiving dollars back in the future. Due to the effects of inflation over time, the lender will be paid back in "cheaper" dollars in the future. Consider a 15-year 7% mortgage that can be repaid with 15 annual payments of $18,000. Find the adjusted total amount paid by the borrower over this 15-year period in "real" dollars, if the annual rate of inflation over this 15-year period is 3.2%. Answer to the nearest dollar.

5. You deposit X in an account today in order to fund your retirement. You would like to receive payments of 50 per year, in real terms, at the end of each year for a total of 12 years, with the first payment occurring seven years from now. The inflation rate will be 0.0% for the next 6 years and 1.2% per annum thereafter. The annual effective rate of return is 6.3%. Calculate X to the nearest dollar.

6. For a potential project, you are given:

   (*i*) Initial investment at time 0 is $10,000.

   (*ii*) Net cash flows are projected as $2000 at times 1 through 8.

   (*iii*) Inflation is at a constant annual rate of 3.5%.

   (*iv*) The real interest rate is at a constant annual rate of 4.0%.

   Calculate the profitability index.

7. A 2-year TIPS bond with a coupon rate of 5% payable annually is issued with a par value of \$10,000. The purchase price of the bond is \$10,500. The inflation rates experienced during the next two years are 4% and 5%.

   a) Find the amount of the two coupons and the maturity value.

   b) Find the nominal and real yield rates.

8. You are given two \$1000 par value 5-year bonds A and B with 4% annual coupons maturing at par. Bond A is a regular bond and Bond B is a TIPS bond. The purchase price of Bond A is \$950. Assume the annual inflation rate in the next five years is 5%. Calculate the price of Bond B so that the two bonds will have the same yield rate.

9. An employee has just retired after working exactly 25 years for one employer. The employee was hired at \$10,000 per year and received annual pay raises of 4%. The employee is eligible to receive a pension based on salary computed on one of three bases as specified below.
   a) Find the final salary.
   b) Find the average salary over the final five years of employment.
   c) Find the average salary over the entire working career.

10. A business buys a \$240,000 building on which a \$40,000 down payment is made. The business plans to obtain a 10-year mortgage with annual payments. A mortgage company offers two options:

    A - A standard mortgage with a 10% effective rate of interest.

    B - A shared appreciation mortgage with an 8% effective rate of interest in exchange for 50% of the price appreciation over the next 10 years in the building.

    The business estimates that the building will increase in value by 3% per year. Determine the option which should be chosen if the analysis is based on an effective rate of interest equal to:
    a) 8%.
    b) 10%.

9.5 Consideration of expenses

11. Rework Example 9.3 when the bond term is three years instead of two years and other conditions are not changed. Compare the two yield rates.

12. A invests $900 in a five-year bond with a 6% annual coupon rate. The bond matures for its par value of $1000. The commission to buy this bond is $10 and no commission is charged when the bond matures. However, if the bond is sold prior to maturity, another commission of $10 would be paid by the seller. One year later, A wants to sell this bond and still obtain the same yield rate as before. Determine the price at which the bond must sell for A to achieve this yield rate.

13. Rework Example 9.4 if the deposit is withdrawn at age 70 instead of 65 and other conditions are not changed. Compare the two percentage reductions.

14. An amount of $10,000 is deposited for 10 years in a mutual fund which is expected to earn 8% effective and has an annual expense ratio of 2%. Assume half of the expenses can be invested at the end of each year by the mutual fund company in another account at an annual rate of 9%. Calculate the accumulated value in this other account at the end of 10 years.

15. A mutual fund returns 7.5% over a one-year period, and the annual expense ratio is 1.5%. In reality, the expense ratio on this mutual fund is assessed on a daily basis. Calculate the nominal daily expense ratio for this mutual fund.

16. A corporation issues $10 million of bonds at par with a 10-year term and 6% annual coupon rate. The underwriting cost of issuing the bonds is split into two equal parts at the beginning of the first and second years. The overall interest cost to the corporation of issuing the bonds is 7%. Find the amount of underwriting cost each year to the nearest $1000.

9.6 Effect of taxes

17. A worker invests a sum of money for 20 years for retirement in a fund earning 8% effective. Interest income is subject to a 25% income tax rate. On Basis A the money accumulates tax-free and is subject to income tax at the end of the period of investment. On Basis B the interest income is subject to income tax each year as it is earned. Find the ratio of the after-tax accumulation on Basis A to the after-tax accumulation on Basis B.

18. A company has a asset with a depreciation basis of $100,000 which will be depreciated according to the following schedule:

Year	Percent
1	33.33
2	44.45
3	14.81
4	7.41

The depreciation charge at the end of each year is tax deductible. The marginal tax rate is 35% and the pretax borrowing rate is 12%. Calculate the present value of the tax deductions created by the depreciation schedule. Answer to the nearest dollar.

19. A five-year 10% bond with semiannual coupons and maturity value at par of $700 is purchased for $670. The income tax rate is a level 25% over the entire period.

    a) Find the before-tax effective yield rate.

    b) Find the after-tax effective yield rate, if all investment income is fully taxed as it is earned.

20. The current stock price of a firm is $97.78 and a dividend of $10 is payable at the end of the year. The estimated stock price of the firm is $102.50 in one year. Assume the tax rate on dividend income is 40% and on capital gains is 20%. Find the before-tax and after-tax yield rates for the stock over the next year.

21. A loan of $10,000 is amortized by equal annual payments for 30 years at an effective annual interest rate of 5%. The income tax rate is level at 25%. Assume the tax on the interest earned is based on the amortization schedule.

    a) Determine the income tax in the 10th year.

    b) Determine the total income taxes over the life of the loan.

    c) Calculate the present value of the after-tax payments using the before-tax yield rate. Answer to the nearest dollar.

22. A agrees to repay a loan of $10,000 over 30 years at an effective annual interest rate of 5%. Interest payments are made annually and a sinking fund is built up with 30 equal payments at the end of each year. Interest on the sinking fund is 4% compounded annually. The income tax rate is 25%. Interest on the loan is not tax deductible, but interest income is taxable. Calculate the total cost of the loan to A reflecting both interest and taxes. Answer to the nearest dollar.

23. You deposit \$240, \$200 and \$300 in an account at the beginning of each of the next three years. The account accumulates to \$800 after taxes at the beginning of the third year. Assume all taxes are paid at the beginning of the third year. If the income tax rate is 25%, calculate the before-tax yield rate.

24. A company needs a new machine and can either buy it for \$250,000 or lease it. After a "buy or lease" analysis, the company decides to lease. The lease terms require the company to make six annual payments at the beginning of every year of \$62,000. The company pays no taxes. However, the lessor pays income tax at 35%. The lessor can depreciate the machine linearly for tax purposes over five years, which results in taxes on the depreciation charge being credited back to the lessor each year. The machine will have no residual value at the end of year 5. The interest rate is 8%.

    a) What is the NPV of the lease for the company?

    b) What is the NPV of the lease for the lessor?

9.7 Currency exchange rates

25. You are given that one-year U.S. bonds yield 7.5%, one-year Japanese bonds yield 4.9%, and the current nominal exchange rate is 118 yen per dollar. Assuming interest rate parity, what is the expected exchange rate one year from now?

26. Suppose that over the past year, the nominal exchange rate increased from 1.25 Swiss francs per U.S. dollar to 1.50. Further suppose that over this period the U.S. inflation rate was 3% and the Swiss rate was 2%. What is the change in the real exchange rate?

27. The following table shows interest rates and exchange rates for the U.S. dollar and the Philippine peso. The current exchange rate is 56.46 pesos = \$1. Complete the missing entries:

	1 Month	3 Months	1 Year
Dollar interest rate (annually compounded)	1.0	1.0	
Peso interest rate (annually compounded)	9.42		9.32
Expected future exchange rate		57.61	60.99

28. Suppose that two-year interest rates are 3.65% in the U.S. and .06% in Japan. The current exchange rate is 120.7 yen per dollar. Suppose that one year later interest rates are 3% in both countries, while the value of the yen has appreciated to 115 yen per dollar.

    a) A person from the U.S. invested in a U.S. two-year zero-coupon bond at the start of the period and sold it after one year. What was the return?

    b) A person from Japan bought dollars, invested them in the two-year U.S. zero-coupon bond, and then sold it after one year. What was the return?

29. The forecasted cash flows of a project in millions of euros are as follows:

C_0	C_1	C_2	C_3	C_4	C_5
-80	10	20	23	27	25

The current exchange rate is $1.2 = €1. The interest rate in the U.S. is 8% and the euro interest rate is 6%.

a) Calculate the NPV of the euro cash flows.

b) What are the dollar cash flows from the project?

c) Calculate the NPV of the dollar cash flows.

9.8 Reflecting risk and uncertainty

30. Compute the effective yield rate on a mortgage recovery following default in which the lender recovers 40% of the default amount at the end of 1 year after default and 50% at the end of 2 years after default. The other 10% is a complete loss.

31. Ten years ago an investor made a $10,000 investment in a business venture which returned $1500 at the end of each year. Just after the current payment, the venture fails and the $10,000 investment is lost. The annual proceeds were invested in a fund earning 8% effective. Find the yield rate the investor realizes on this investment.

32. Find the price of a $1000 par value 10-year bond with 8% annual coupons bought to yield 12% effective. It is assumed a certainty that the coupons will be paid when due, but it is assumed that the probability the borrower will repay the principal is only .98, i.e. there is a 2% chance of complete default at maturity. Assume that an appropriate price is given by the expected present value of payments by the borrower.

33. An investment is made such that the probability is 90% that \$1000 will be received at the end of one year and 10% that nothing will be received. The effective rate of interest is 25%.
    a) Find the mean of the present value of this investment, i.e. its EPV.
    b) Find the standard deviation of the present value of this investment.
    c) Find the risk premium in the interest rate.

34. A 20-year \$1000 bond with annual coupons of \$87.50 sells at a price to yield 9.5%. If the risk-free rate of interest is equal to 8.75%, find the implied level annual probability of default.

35. *a)* Show that formula (9.15) can be expressed as

$$\text{EPV} = \sum_{t=1}^{n} R_t e^{-ct} e^{-\delta t}.$$

    b) What is the risk premium in the force of interest? This quantity is sometimes called the *force of default*.
    c) What is the annual probability of default?
    d) What is the probability of default anytime during the *n* periods?

36. A mortgage company issues \$1,000,000 in two-year mortgages which carry an effective rate of interest of 8%. The mortgages will be repaid with equal payments of principal at the end of each of the two years in addition to any interest then due. The borrowers may prepay the mortgages at the end of the first year without penalty. The effective rate of interest at the end of one year is equally likely to be either 6% or 10%. The mortgage company can reinvest all proceeds received at the end of the first year at this rate for the second year. It is assumed that borrowers will exercise any option to prepay to their advantage. The probability of default is zero.
    a) Find the expected accumulated value of these mortgages to the mortgage company at the end of two years.
    b) Find the standard deviation of the accumulated value in (*a*).
    c) Find the expected yield rate to the mortgage company in issuing these mortgages.
    d) Justify from general reasoning that the answer in (*c*) is less than 8%.

37. A 15-year mortgage has level annual payments at the end of each year and carries an interest rate of 12% effective. The annual probability of default is 1%. The expected present value of the payments for this mortgage is $150,000 under these conditions.
    a) Find the expected present value if the annual probability of default doubles. Answer to the nearest $100.
    b) Rework (*a*), if the expected present value is also revalued at 14% effective in view of the extra risk.

38. An investor buys a $1000 10% callable bond with annual coupons. The bond will mature at par at the end of ten years but may be called at $1050 at the end of five years. The investor can reinvest any proceeds received over the next ten years at 7% effective. The investor paid $1100 for the bond. Compute the investor's overall expected yield rate on this investment over the next ten years, if it is assumed that the probability the bond will be called is .25.

10

The term structure of interest rates

10.1 INTRODUCTION

In most of the applications of the theory of interest discussed in Chapters 1 - 9 we have assumed one level interest rate is applicable throughout the period of investment. In particular, the "yield to maturity" on a bond discussed in Chapter 6 and the more general "internal rate of return" discussed in Chapter 7 are level rates of interest.

However, astute readers who have looked at a variety of financial instruments (such as certificates of deposit, mortgage loans, and bonds) of different terms have probably noticed that short-term and long-term rates of interest frequently differ. The phenomenon in which rates of interest differ depending on the term of otherwise identical financial instruments is called the *term structure of interest rates.*

In this chapter we will explore some of the ramifications of this phenomenon. As a result, more sophisticated models are developed for performing financial calculations involving the term structure of interest rates rather than a level yield rate. One of the most fertile areas of application for this new theory will be for bond valuation.

In this chapter we will also develop certain relationships among different financial instruments which must prevail for consistency. If these relationships do not hold, then arbitrage opportunities exist. "Arbitrage" was defined and briefly described in Section 7.8. That brief description will be expanded in this chapter.

The basic theory and relationships involving the term structure of interest rates are developed using discrete functions. However, in Section 10.7 we will develop a continuous model consistent with the earlier discrete development. The continuous model has both conceptual and practical applications.

10.2 YIELD CURVES

In Section 10.1 we defined the "term structure of interest rates" as the relationship between rates of interest and the term of the investment. The graph that displays this relationship is often called a *yield curve*.

Figure 10.1 displays a hypothetical yield curve showing the relationship between the effective rate of interest and the term of the investment.

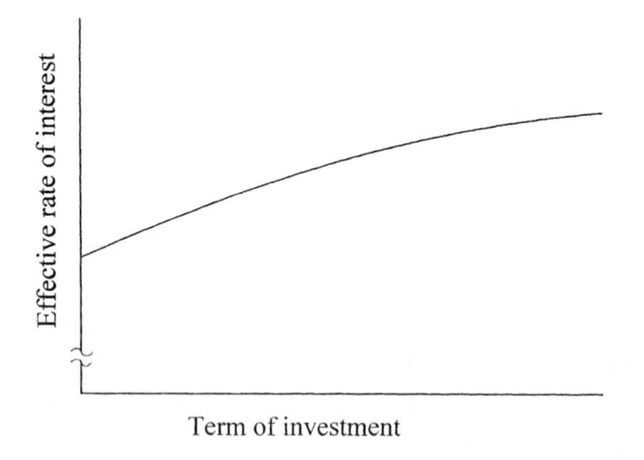

Figure 10.1 Normal yield curve

When rates increase with the length of investment period as in Figure 10.1 it is said that "the yield curve has a positive slope." Such a yield curve is often called a *normal yield curve*, since most of the time yield curves have this shape.

Several theories have been advanced to try to explain why this upward sloping pattern of interest rates typically develops in the market. The first theory is the *expectations theory*. According to this theory, a higher percentage of individuals and business firms have an expectation that interest rates will rise in the future than the percentage which expect them to fall.

The second theory is the *liquidity preference theory*. According to this theory, individuals and firms prefer to invest for short periods rather than for long periods so that they will have early access to their funds, i.e. to remain "liquid." An increase in the rate of interest for longer-term investments is necessary to induce investors to commit their funds for longer periods of time. In essence, this theory is a generalization of the time preference theory of interest discussed in Section 9.2.

The third theory is the *inflation premium theory*. According to this theory, investors feel a significant amount of uncertainty about future rates of inflation and thus will demand higher rates of interest on longer-term investments. As we saw in Section 9.4, higher rates of inflation lead to higher rates of interest, which will depress market values of investments such as mortgages and bonds. Long-term asset values are affected more than short-term asset values by such movements in interest rates.

Of course, in free markets exceptions will occasionally occur. In some cases short-term rates will exceed long-term rates. Such situations are characterized as having an *inverted yield curve*. Figure 10.2 displays a hypothetical inverted yield curve.

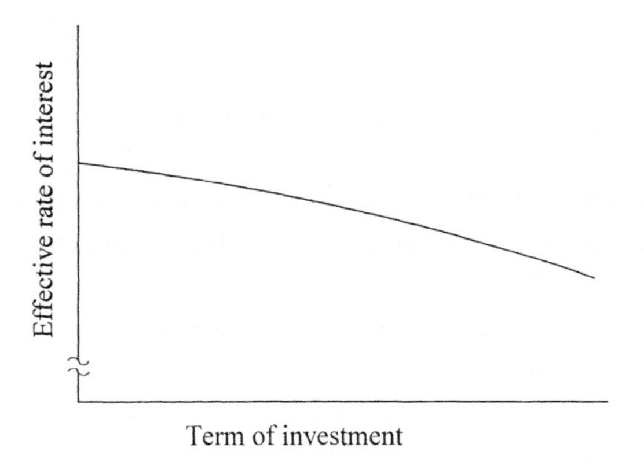

Figure 10.2 Inverted yield curve

One explanation advanced to explain inverted yield curves is the relationship between the Federal Reserve Board and the bond market. Short-term interest rates are heavily influenced by the policies of the Federal Reserve Board, which may be setting high short-term rates to fight current inflation or to remove excess liquidity from the economy. Long-term rates are essentially determined by supply and demand in the bond market and may be lower due to expectations of lower inflation rates in the future, or the possibility of an economic slowdown or recession. Other theories could undoubtedly be developed by economists to explain inverted yield curves.

Another pattern, sometimes encountered is a *flat yield curve*, at least over a major portion of the term structure. Figure 10.3 displays a hypothetical flat yield curve. Flat yield curves are typically not completely level over all terms but they would have no pronounced slope over any major portion of the term structure.

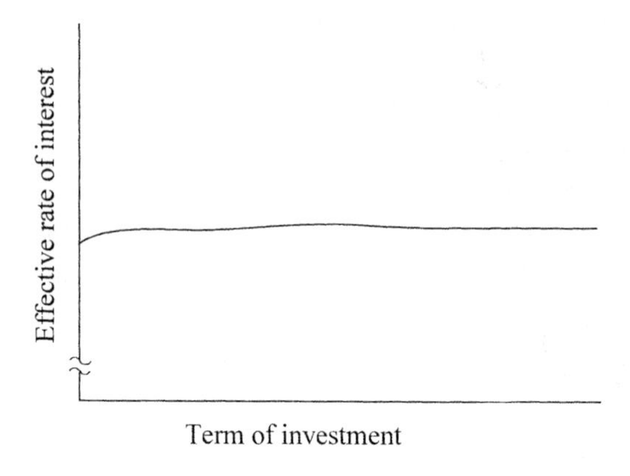

Figure 10.3 Flat yield curve

Flat yield curves may occur in periods of stability in which investors do not expect dramatic changes in the economy, investment markets, or future inflation rates.

Sometimes yield curves may not be monotonically increasing, decreasing, or level. For example, they may have a hump, or a dip, over some portion of the term structure. Another pattern occasionally encountered is a yield curve which is basically flat over much of term structure, but has a positive or negative slope on one end or the other. Other patterns also occur.

The shape of the yield curve does not usually change much on a daily basis, but it can significantly change over a period of weeks and months. For example, in August 2000 the yield curve was distinctly inverted; it became relatively flat in October 2000; and by March 2001 it had a distinctly positive slope.

The reader may wonder how a yield curve can be determined. The most basic yield curve is determined by the yields on zero coupon bonds of varying terms backed by the United States Treasury. These securities actively trade as Treasury STRIPS and were discussed in Section 6.2.

This type of yield curve is not unique and other yield curves can be constructed. For example, a yield curve based on corporate bonds might be constructed. Such a yield curve would lie above the Treasury yield curve, since yields for all terms are higher on corporate bonds than on Treasury bonds.

The difference between the yield on a non-Treasury bond and on an otherwise identical Treasury bond is often called the *spread over Treasuries*. If the spread over Treasuries is constant over all terms, then the yield curve for the securities in question would be parallel to the Treasury yield curve. However, if the spread over Treasuries is not constant over all terms, then the shape will be somewhat different than the Treasury yield curve.

There are some other technical issues that arise in constructing yield curves. First, is the interest conversion period. One way to construct them is to base everything on an annual effective rate of interest, as in Figures 10.1-10.3. However, the reader should be alert to yield curves constructed on a different basis. For example, coupon bonds typically have semiannual coupons and yield rates, and this frequency may be encountered in yield curves determined from coupon bond yields.

Second, yield curves based on the maturity dates of coupon bonds may be encountered. However, this is not an accurate process for coupon bonds. A 10-year zero coupon bond does have a term of 10 years. However, a 10-year coupon bond does not, because of the coupons paid at earlier points in time than 10 years. A 10-year coupon bond is actually a "shorter" security than 10 years. This important point is analyzed more completely in Section 10.4 and in Chapter 11.

Third, yield curves are typically displayed as continuous, as in Figures 10.1-10.3. However, actual market yields on zero coupon bonds exist only at discrete points, so that some type of interpolation is needed to obtain a continuous curve.

10.3 SPOT RATES

The interest rates on the yield curve are often called *spot rates.* This term is somewhat analogous to the term "spot price" defined in Section 8.8 in the discussion of futures. The spot rate for a term of length is t is denoted by s_t. Note that s_t is expressed as an annual effective rate for any value of t.

Spot rates offer a more sophisticated way of calculating net present value (NPV) and the internal rate of return (IRR) than that presented in Section 7.2. One criticism that has been advanced of NPV and the IRR, as defined in Section 7.2, is that they ignore the term structure of interest rates. Rather they use one interest rate regardless of the length of the transaction. Thus, from this perspective, the NPV and IRR calculations involve a complex averaging of many different spot rates from the yield curve.

Consider formula (7.2) for computing the net present value of a series of future payments (positive or negative)

$$\text{NPV} = P(i) = \sum_{t=0}^{n} v^t R_t . \tag{7.2}$$

Formula (7.2) is based on a single rate of interest i.

Another procedure that could be used is to discount each payment by its associated spot rate. Thus, a generalized version of formula (7.2) is given by

$$\text{NPV} = P(s) = \sum_{t=0}^{n} (1+s_t)^{-t} R_t . \tag{10.1}$$

We use the symbol $P(s)$ to denote the fact that the net present value is based on a series of spot rates s_t. We are using s_t to denote spot rates rather than i_t to avoid ambiguity with other meanings attached to the symbol i_t in earlier chapters.

The reader should note the similarity of formula (10.1) to formula (3.24). The use of spot rates is one important application of computing annuity values with varying rates of interest as discussed in Section 3.8.

It is often claimed that present values computed in this fashion better represent economic reality than do constant yield rates. For example, consider two 10-year bonds A and B. Bond A has 5% annual coupons while Bond B has 10% annual coupons. Assume both are priced at the same yield to maturity.

Our prior analysis would indicate that an investor should be indifferent between the two bonds, since the two yield rates are equal.

However, if we compute revised values based on spot rates we will find that equality no longer holds. This happens because the incidence of payments differs. Bond A pays relatively less prior to maturity while Bond B pays relatively more. Thus, Bond A is a slightly longer term investment than Bond B and this will be reflected when the computation is based on different spot rates from the yield curve. Bond values computed using spot rates will be analyzed in more detail in Section 10.4.

Example 10.1 ***You are given the following selected values from a yield curve:***

Term	*Spot rate*
1 year	*7.00 %*
2 years	*8.00*
3 years	*8.75*
4 years	*9.25*
5 years	*9.50*

(1) Find the present value of payments of \$1000 at the end of each year for five years using these spot rates.

(2) What level yield rate would produce an equivalent value?

1. The present value of the payments using formula (10.1) is

$$1000\left[(1.07)^{-1}+(1.08)^{-2}+(1.0875)^{-3}+(1.0925)^{-4}+(1.095)^{-5}\right] = \$3906.63.$$

2. The level yield rate is found by solving

$$a_{\overline{5}|i} = 3.90663.$$

If we solve this unknown rate of interest problem using the techniques discussed in Section 3.7, we obtain

$$i = .0883, \text{ or } 8.83\%.$$

As expected, the level yield rate lies well within the range of spot rates, i.e. $[.07, .095]$. Thus, we could characterize the level yield rate (IRR) as a type of average of the related spot rates over the term of the annuity.

10.4 RELATIONSHIP WITH BOND YIELDS

The purpose of this section is to examine the relationship of spot rates to the level bond yield to maturity discussed in Chapter 6. This section extends the analysis of Section 10.3 to this important relationship.

Recall that the price of a bond at a level yield rate, using the basic formula, is given by formula (6.1)

$$P = Fra_{\overline{n}|} + Cv^n \tag{6.1}$$

where all interest functions are calculated at the yield to maturity rate i.

We can generalize this formula to a calculation involving spot rates using the approach taken in formula (10.1) as follows:

$$P = Fr\sum_{t=1}^{n}(1+s_t)^{-t} + C(1+s_n)^{-n}. \tag{10.2}$$

How will the price of the bond computed by formula (10.2) compare with that computed by formula (6.1)? According to modern finance theory, these two prices must be equal. This is sometimes called the *Law of One Price*.

The concept is that a coupon bond can be decomposed into a series of zero coupon bonds, each of which can be valued precisely using its associated spot rate. The Law of One Price says that in efficient markets a security must have one price regardless of how the security is constructed. If it does not, then an arbitrage opportunity exists. "Arbitrage" will be discussed in Section 10.6.

Thus, if the Law of One Price holds, the bond must sell at a level yield rate which will establish an equality with the series of n payments, each valued as a separate zero coupon bond, as given by formula (10.2).

Looking at this relationship in reverse, it is also possible to determine a set of spot rates given a set of coupon bond prices at each of the durations for which a spot rate is to be determined. The technique for doing this is sometimes called the *bootstrap method.*

For ease of discussion we will use annual coupon bonds. However, the technique can easily be generalized to other coupon payment frequencies, such as semiannual.

Let P_t be the price of a t-year coupon bond. The bootstrap method is a recursive technique as follows:

1. Use P_1 to determine s_1.
2. Use P_2 and s_1 to determine s_2.
3. Use P_3, s_1, and s_2 to determine s_3.
4. Continue this process to generate as many spot rates as desired (assuming that bond prices are available for each required term).

In step 1 there is only one coupon paid at the time the bond matures, which gives

$$P_1 = \frac{Fr+C}{1+s_1}$$

which can be solved for s_1.

In step 2, we have

$$P_2 = \frac{Fr}{1+s_1} + \frac{Fr+C}{(1+s_2)^2}$$

which can be solved for s_2 using the value of s_1 from step 1.

In step 3, we have

$$P_3 = \frac{Fr}{1+s_1} + \frac{Fr}{(1+s_2)^2} + \frac{Fr+C}{(1+s_3)^3}$$

which can be solved for s_3 using the values of s_1 from step 1 and s_2 from step 2.

This process can be continued for as many periods as we have bond prices available. In general, in step k we have

$$P_k = \frac{Fr}{1+s_1} + \frac{Fr}{(1+s_2)^2} + \cdots + \frac{Fr}{(1+s_{k-1})^{k-1}} + \frac{Fr+C}{(1+s_k)^k}. \qquad (10.3)$$

Formula (10.3) is solved for s_k at each step in the process.

Note that the above formulas appear to imply that we must have a set of bond prices with the same coupon for each bond. However, the bootstrap technique is more general than this. For example, the coupon (Fr) in step 3 could be different than the coupon (Fr) in step 2. The technique still works, since P_k will accurately reflect whatever coupon is paid on the bond of term k.

Another topic relating spot rates and bond yields is the concept of *at-par yield*. This is another measure of bond yield that measures the hypothetical yield rate, based on the spot rates, that would cause a bond to have a yield rate equal to its coupon rate. As we know from Chapter 6, such a bond would sell "at par."

We can derive an expression for the at-par yield rate based on the spot rates. Consider a standard \$1 bond on which $F = C = 1$ and $r = g$. We know that P also is equal to 1. Thus, from equation (10.2) we have

$$1 = r\sum_{t=1}^{n}(1+s_t)^{-t} + (1+s_n)^{-n}$$

and solving for the at-par yield rate r we have

$$r = \frac{1 - (1+s_n)^{-n}}{\sum_{t=1}^{n}(1+s_t)^{-t}}. \tag{10.4}$$

Note that the r in formula (10.4) is a function of n, so that we could write the at-par yield rate as r_n to specify the term of the bond to which it would apply.

What useful information does the at-par yield rate convey? When an institutional borrower issues a new release of bonds, it may want the bonds originally to be issued at, or very near, par value. Releasing a new bond issue that immediately has a significant premium or discount may not be desirable. The at-par yield rate based on the spot rates at issue for the type of bond involved would provide the desired coupon rate on the bond.

Example 10.2 ***Bond A is a two-year bond maturing for \$1000 with 10% annual coupons. Bond B is a two-year bond maturing for \$1000 with 5% annual coupons. The current term structure is defined by***

$$s_t = .05 + .02t \quad for \quad t = 0,1,2.$$

(1) Find the price of Bond A.
(2) Find the yield to maturity of Bond A.
(3) Find the price of Bond B.
(4) Find the yield to maturity of Bond B.
(5) Explain the difference between the answers to (2) and (4).

1. We have spot rates

$$s_1 = .07 \quad \text{and} \quad s_2 = .09.$$

The coupon on Bond A is

$$Fr_A = 1000(.10) = 100.$$

Thus, the price of Bond A will be

$$P_A = \frac{100}{1.07} + \frac{1100}{(1.09)^2} = \$1019.31.$$

The bond sells at a premium, as expected.

2. The level yield to maturity rate is the value of i_A that satisfies the equation of value

$$1019.31 = 100(1+i_A)^{-1} + 1100(1+i_A)^{-2}.$$

Solving this quadratic for i_A, we obtain

$$i_A = .0890, \quad \text{or} \quad 8.90\%.$$

3. The coupon on Bond B is

$$Fr_B = 1000(.05) = 50.$$

Thus, the price of Bond B will be

$$P_B = \frac{50}{1.07} + \frac{1050}{(1.09)^2} = \$930.49.$$

The bond sells at a discount, as expected.

4. The level yield to maturity rate is the value of i_B that satisfies the equation of value

$$930.49 = 50(1+i_B)^{-1} + 1050(1+i_B)^{-2}.$$

Solving this quadratic for i_B, we obtain

$$i_B = .0895, \quad \text{or} \quad 8.95\%.$$

5. Bond A has 10% coupons and thus is a slightly "shorter" bond than Bond B with 5% coupons. With a normal (increasing) yield curve, as we have in this example, the

yield on the "shorter" bond, i.e. 8.90%, will be less than the yield on the "longer" bond, i.e. 8.95%.

The difference is not great because the term of both bonds is so short. Thus, the two-year spot rate of 9% dominates both calculations. However, the pattern is clear and will exist whenever there is a normal (increasing) yield curve.

It is important to note that if the yield curve is inverted, then the opposite pattern would exist. In that case, the "shorter" bond would sell at a higher yield rate than the "longer" bond. This phenomenon is explored in the exercises.

Example 10.3 Find the at-par yield rate for the bond in Example 10.2.

Applying formula (10.4), we calculate the at-par yield rate to be

$$r = \frac{1 - (1.09)^{-2}}{(1.07)^{-1} + (1.09)^{-2}}$$
$$= .0891, \quad \text{or} \quad 8.91\%.$$

Thus, if a bond issuer wanted to issue a new two-year bond to sell initially at par, it should set the coupon rate at 8.91%.

Example 10.4 You are given the following prices of \$1000 par value bonds with 10% annual coupons:

Term	***Price***
1 year	***1028.04***
2 years	***1036.53***
3 years	***1034.47***

Find the spot rates for t = 1, 2, 3 that are implied by these bond prices.

We will demonstrate the bootstrap method, as described in this section. First, we consider the one-year bond, which gives

$$P_1 = 1028.04 = \frac{1100}{1+s_1}$$

and solving for s_1, we have

$$s_1 = .0700, \quad \text{or} \quad 7.00\%.$$

Next, we consider the two-year bond, which gives

$$P_2 = 1036.53 = \frac{100}{1+s_1} + \frac{1100}{(1+s_2)^2}$$

$$= \frac{100}{1.07} + \frac{1100}{(1+s_2)^2}$$

and solving for s_2, we have

$$s_2 = .0800, \quad \text{or} \quad 8.00\%.$$

Finally, we consider the three-year bond, which gives

$$P_3 = 1034.47 = \frac{100}{1+s_1} + \frac{100}{(1+s_2)^2} + \frac{1100}{(1+s_3)^3}$$

$$= \frac{100}{1.07} + \frac{100}{(1.08)^2} + \frac{1100}{(1+s_3)^3}$$

and solving for s_3, we have

$$s_3 = .0875, \quad \text{or} \quad 8.75\%.$$

Thus, the spot rates consistent with these bond prices are as follows:

t	s_t
1	.0700
2	.0800
3	.0875

10.5 FORWARD RATES

Another type of interest rate is the *forward rate*. This is an expected spot rate which will come into play in the future. A set of current spot rates will imply a set of forward rates.

In order to illustrate this concept, consider a business firm that needs to borrow a sizable amount of money for two years. The one-year spot rate is 7% and the two-year spot rate is 8%. The firm has two options. The first option is to borrow for two years at the two-year spot rate of 8%. The second option is to borrow for one year at the one-year spot rate of 7% and then borrow for the second year at the one-year spot rate in effect a year later. This one-year spot rate for the second year is called a "forward rate."

We will now analyze the two options. Let the forward rate be denoted by f. The firm will then be indifferent between the two options if

$$(1.08)^2 = (1.07)(1+f)$$

which can be solved to give $f = .0901$, or 9.01%. Thus, if the firm expects the forward rate to be greater than 9.01%, it should use the first option to borrow. However, if the firm expects the forward rate to be less than 9.01%, it should use the second option.

We now approach the subject more generally. Let f_t be 1-year forward rate which comes existence at time t and covers the interval from time t to time $t+1$. The notation for forward rates differs from the notation for spot rates. The subscript t for the spot rate s_t denotes an effective interest rate by the end of the period over which it applies. The subscript t for the forward rate f_t denotes an effective interest rate by the beginning of the period to which it applies.

Also, note that the forward rate f_0 is a one-year spot rate, i.e.

$$f_0 = s_1. \tag{10.5}$$

Thus applying this notation to the two-year example given above, we have

$$\begin{aligned} s_1 &= .0700 \\ s_2 &= .0800 \\ f_0 &= .0700 \\ f_1 &= .0901. \end{aligned}$$

We now consider forward rates further into the future. We can accumulate 1 for n years into the future at the n-year spot rate. However, we can also express this value by accumulating 1 for $n-1$ years at the $(n-1)$-year spot rate and then for one additional year at the $(n-1)$-year forward rate. This gives the relationship

$$(1+s_n)^n = (1+s_{n-1})^{n-1}(1+f_{n-1}). \tag{10.6}$$

Note that formula (10.5) is a special case of formula (10.6) when $n = 1$. We can solve formula (10.6) for f_{n-1}, which gives

$$f_{n-1} = \frac{(1+s_n)^n}{(1+s_{n-1})^{n-1}} - 1. \tag{10.7}$$

Thus, we can readily determine one-year forward rates from a set of spot rates.

Next, we can express an n-year spot rate in terms of a set of n one-year forward rates as follows

$$(1+s_n)^n = (1+f_0)(1+f_1)\ldots(1+f_{n-1}). \tag{10.8}$$

This formula can be derived by applying formula (10.7) n times in succession at times 0, 1, 2..., $n - 1$. Finally, formula (10.8) can be solved for s_n to give

$$s_n = \left[(1+f_0)(1+f_1)\ldots(1+f_{n-1})\right]^{\frac{1}{n}} - 1 \tag{10.9}$$

which directly expresses the n-year spot in terms of n one-year forward rates.

It is also possible to define forward rates over periods other than one year. Let ${}_mf_t$ be the m-year forward rate which applies over the period from time t to time $t + m$. For example, a forward rate of interest between 3 and 8 years from the present would be denoted by ${}_5f_3$. In essence, this forward rate could be characterized as an expected 3-year deferred 5-year spot rate.

Obviously, ${}_1f_t$ is the same as f_t. Thus, ${}_mf_t$ is the general notation for forward rates and we merely suppress the subscript m when $m = 1$.

We can develop a general formula for ${}_mf_t$ by considering an investment for $t + m$ years in two segments. The first segment runs from time 0 to time t, while the second segment runs from time t to time $t + m$. We then have

$$(1+s_{t+m})^{t+m} = (1+s_t)^t(1+{}_mf_t)^m. \tag{10.10}$$

Figure 10.4 clarifies the reasoning involved in formula (10.10). Also, note that formula (10.6) is a special case of formula (10.10) in which $t = n - 1$ and $m = 1$.

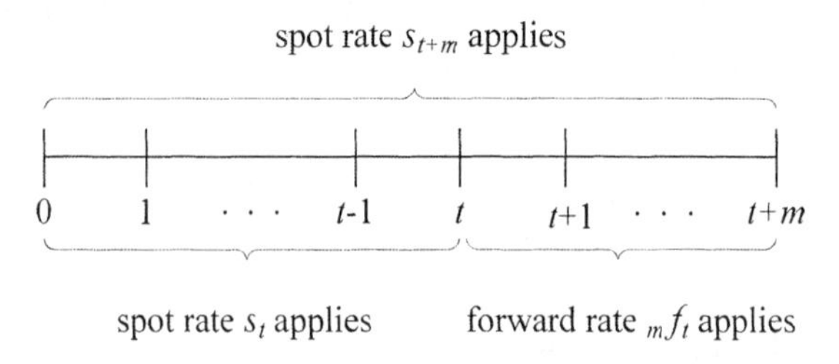

Figure 10.4 Illustration of general forward rate ${}_m f_t$

Example 10.5 Determine all one-year forward rates that can be determined using the spot rates given in Example 10.1.

We are given:

$$\begin{aligned} s_1 &= .0700 \\ s_2 &= .0800 \\ s_3 &= .0875 \\ s_4 &= .0925 \\ s_5 &= .0950 \end{aligned}$$

Applying formulas (10.5) and (10.7) successively, we have

$$\begin{aligned}
f_0 &= s_1 && = .0700 \\
f_1 &= \frac{(1+s_2)^2}{1+s_1} - 1 = \frac{(1.08)^2}{1.07} - 1 && = .0901 \\
f_2 &= \frac{(1+s_3)^3}{(1+s_2)^2} - 1 = \frac{(1.0875)^3}{(1.08)^2} - 1 && = .1027 \\
f_3 &= \frac{(1+s_4)^4}{(1+s_3)^3} - 1 = \frac{(1.0925)^4}{(1.0875)^3} - 1 && = .1076 \\
f_4 &= \frac{(1+s_5)^5}{(1+s_4)^4} - 1 = \frac{(1.095)^5}{(1.0925)^4} - 1 && = .1051.
\end{aligned}$$

Note that formula (10.8) could be used to check this answer. We have

$$(1+s_5)^5 = (1.095)^5 = 1.5742$$

and

$$\begin{aligned}&(1+f_0)(1+f_1)(1+f_2)(1+f_3)(1+f_4)\\ &= (1.07000)(1.09009)(1.10266)(1.10764)(1.10506)\\ &= 1.5742\end{aligned}$$

producing the same accumulated value at the end of five years. (Note that one extra decimal place of accuracy is used for the forward rates to avoid an accumulation of roundoff error.)

Example 10.6 Reverse Example 10.5 by assuming that the forward rates are given and you are asked to find the implied spot rates.

In this situation we can apply formulas (10.5) and (10.9) successively to obtain

$$\begin{aligned}
s_1 &= f_0 = .0700\\
s_2 &= \left[(1+f_0)(1+f_1)\right]^{\frac{1}{2}}-1\\
&= \left[(1.07)(1.09009)\right]^{\frac{1}{2}}-1\\
&= (1.1663963)^{\frac{1}{2}}-1 = .0800\\
s_3 &= \left[(1+f_0)(1+f_1)(1+f_2)\right]^{\frac{1}{3}}-1\\
&= \left[(1.1663963)(1.10266)\right]^{\frac{1}{3}}-1\\
&= (1.2861385)^{\frac{1}{3}}-1 = .0875\\
s_4 &= \left[(1+f_0)(1+f_1)(1+f_2)(1+f_3)\right]^{\frac{1}{4}}-1\\
&= \left[(1.2861385)(1.10764)\right]^{\frac{1}{4}}-1\\
&= (1.4245785)^{\frac{1}{4}}-1 = .0925\\
s_5 &= \left[(1+f_0)(1+f_1)(1+f_2)(1+f_3)(1+f_4)\right]^{\frac{1}{5}}-1\\
&= \left[(1.4245785)(1.10506)\right]^{\frac{1}{5}}-1\\
&= (1.5742447)^{\frac{1}{5}}-1 = .0950.
\end{aligned}$$

The reader should note and validate that the above calculations are equivalent to applying formula (10.6) successively as a recursion formula.

Example 10.7 Using the spot rates given in Example 10.5 calculate $_3f_2$.

In this example we are asked to find a 3-year forward rate that comes into effect 2 years from now. Applying formula (10.10) with $t = 2$ and $m = 3$ we have

$$(1+s_5)^5 = (1+s_2)^2(1+{}_3f_2)^3$$

or

$$(1.095)^5 = (1.08)^2(1+{}_3f_2)^3$$

and solving for $_3f_2$ we have

$$_3f_2 = \left[\frac{(1.095)^5}{(1.08)^2}\right]^{\frac{1}{3}} - 1 = .1051.$$

Example 10.8 Rework Example 10.4 to generate forward rates rather than spot rates from a set of bond prices.

We can adapt the bootstrap technique to generate forward rates directly without first calculating spot rates. First, we consider the one-year bond, which gives

$$P_1 = 1028.04 = \frac{1100}{1+f_0}$$

and solving for f_0, we have

$$f_0 = .07000.$$

Next, we consider the two-year bond, which gives

$$\begin{aligned} P_2 = 1036.53 &= \frac{100}{1+f_0} + \frac{1100}{(1+f_0)(1+f_1)} \\ &= \frac{100}{1.07} + \frac{1100}{(1.07)(1+f_1)} \end{aligned}$$

and solving for f_1, we have

$$f_1 = .0901.$$

Finally, we consider the three-year bond, which gives

$$\begin{aligned} P_3 = 1034.47 &= \frac{100}{1+f_0} + \frac{100}{(1+f_0)(1+f_1)} + \frac{1100}{(1+f_0)(1+f_1)(1+f_2)} \\ &= \frac{100}{1.07} + \frac{100}{(1.07)(1.09009)} + \frac{1100}{(1.07)(1.09009)(1+f_2)} \end{aligned}$$

and solving for f_2, we have

$$f_2 = .1027.$$

Thus the forward rates consistent with these bond prices are as follows:

t	f_t
0	.0700
1	.0901
2	.1027

(Again note that one extra decimal place of accuracy is used for the forward rates to avoid an accumulation of roundoff error.)

Example 10.9 Find the present value of the remaining payments in the annuity given in Example 10.1 immediately after two payments have been made. The forward rates at that time are expected to be 1% higher for all periods than the current spot rates.

The comparison date for this calculation is at the end of two years. At that time there are three remaining annuity payments to be made. The expected forward rates are the current spot rates for 1, 2, and 3 years (not for 3, 4, and 5 years) each increased by 1%. Thus, the remaining present value is

$$1000\left[(1.08)^{-1} + (1.09)^{-2} + (1.0975)^{-3}\right] = \$2524.07.$$

10.6 ARBITRAGE

In Sections 10.3 through 10.5 we developed various relationships among spot rates, forward rates, level yield rates, and bond prices that must exist for consistency. Section 10.1 indicated that if these relationships do not hold, then an arbitrage opportunity is present.

"Arbitrage" was first introduced in Section 7.8 in the discussion on short sales. In this section we will extend that discussion with a more detailed analysis, as well as an illustration.

A more precise definition of arbitrage is the following:

Arbitrage is an investment strategy in which a certain profit can be made with no risk of loss.

The primary method by which this could be achieved, if it is possible at all, involves the simultaneous purchase and sale of related securities which are mispriced, i.e. are not priced consistently.

If arbitrage were really possible, it would imply that an investor could "get something for nothing," or a "free lunch." Modern finance theory has shown that arbitrage opportunities should not exist in "efficient" markets, i.e. in free markets with multiple buyers and sellers, easy execution of trades, and readily available information to all market participants. For arbitrage opportunities to exist, there would need to be some degree of "inefficiency" in the market for some reason.

The basic concept of arbitrage is to look for related securities for which the relationships developed earlier in this chapter do not hold. If the price of a security is too high based on these relationships, the security is said to be *overvalued.* Similarly, if the price is too low, the security is said to be *undervalued.*

The arbitrage technique is simultaneously to buy the security which is undervalued and sell short the related security which is overvalued. These transactions taken together will secure a certain profit with no net cash outflow ever required. This will be illustrated in Example 10.10.

Before readers get "stars in their eyes" about getting rich quick using arbitrage, they might want to consider the following points:

- Even if an arbitrage opportunity were to exist, the amount of mispricing is likely to be quite small.

- Any such mispricing is likely to be fleeting and may well disappear before the required trades could be executed.

- Buying and selling securities involves transaction costs which might negate any miniscule arbitrage gain actually achieved.

- Short selling involves margin requirements and other restrictions which also could eliminate any arbitrage gains achieved.

However, there are large, sophisticated institutional investors and money managers who attempt to secure arbitrage profits. These investors engage in very large volumes with razor-thin transaction fees. The constantly monitor prices in markets on a global basis by computer to identify mispriced securities. If they identify any mispriced securities, they are able to execute trades electronically with practically no time lag.

One type of institutional entity engaging in such activity is the *hedge fund.* A hedge fund is similar to a mutual fund, but caters only to investors with high income and net worth. Hedge funds have fewer regulatory restrictions than regular mutual funds, since they are open only to sophisticated, wealthy individual investors, presumably needing less governmental protection.

As indicated in Section 7.8, a generic name for simultaneously buying and short selling related securities to reduce risk is "hedging," which gives "hedge funds" their name. Many investors, both large and small, use hedging techniques to reduce risk. However, precious few of them are able to reduce risk completely to zero, which is what true arbitrage requires. Almost always in real life, some residual risk remains with even the most sophisticated hedging strategies.

Example 10.10 Consider the two-year $1000 bond with 10% annual coupons in Example 10.4 which should sell for $1036.53 if the one-year spot rate is 7% and the two-year spot rate is 8%.

(1) If the bond actually sells for $1040, develop an arbitrage strategy that guarantees a certain profit. Determine the amount of that profit and when it is realized. Assume that there are no transaction fees and no margin requirements on short sales.

(2) Rework (1) if the bond actually sells for $1030.

1. As shown in Section 10.4, the Law of One Price shows how to replicate the two-year bond with two zero-coupon bonds. The arbitrage transaction is as follows:

   - Since the coupon bond is overvalued, sell it short for 1040.
   - Buy a one-year zero coupon bond for 100/1.07 = 93.46. This bond will mature for 100 in one year and the proceeds will be used to pay the coupon then due, since the investor is short the bond.
   - Buy a two-year zero coupon bond for $1100/(1.08)^2$ = 943.07. This bond will mature for 1100 in two years and the proceeds will be used to pay the coupon and maturity value then due.

The investor receives 1040 and pays 93.46 + 943.07 = 1036.53, all at time 0. There are no further net cash flows at times 1 and 2, since the cash inflows and outflows exactly match. The investor realizes an arbitrage profit of 1040 - 1036.53 = $ 3.47 at time 0.

2. In this case everything is reversed:

- Since the coupon bond is undervalued, buy it for 1030.
- Sell short a one-year zero coupon bond for 93.46. Use the 100 coupon on the coupon bond to settle the 100 short position on the zero coupon bond at time 1.
- Sell short a two-year zero coupon bond for 943.07. Use the 100 coupon and the 1000 maturity value on the coupon bond to settle the 1100 short position on the zero coupon bond at time 2.

The investor realizes an arbitrage profit of 1036.53 - 1030 = $6.53 at time 0. Again, all cash inflows and outflows at times 1 and 2 exactly match.

10.7 A CONTINUOUS MODEL

The term structure of interest rates developed in this chapter has been based on a series of spot rates at discrete points in time. We have used annual effective rates for simplicity in illustrating the concepts and relationships involved. Extension to discrete time periods other than annual is straightforward.

However, since yield curves rarely are completely flat, it would seem that a continuous model for the term structure might be useful. Figures 10.1 and 10.2 graphically illustrate a normal yield curve, and an inverted yield curve, respectively. These graphs clearly suggest the appropriateness of a continuous model providing a spot rate for any point in time in the future.

Let λ_t be a continuously compounded spot rate over the interval from time 0 to t. Note that λ_t changes as t changes, but that λ_t is level over the interval from time 0 to t once t is chosen. The level spot rate, an effective rate of interest over the same interval, is s_t.

We have the following relationship using the relationship between the effective rate of interest and the force of interest from Chapter 1

$$a(t) = (1+s_t)^t = e^{t \cdot \lambda_t} \tag{10.11}$$

From this equation, we see that

$$e^{\lambda_t} = 1 + s_t \tag{10.12}$$

or

$$s_t = e^{\lambda_t} - 1 \tag{10.13}$$

and

$$\lambda_t = \ln(1 + s_t). \tag{10.14}$$

Formulas (10.12), (10.13) and (10.14) are analogous to formulas (1.31), (1.32), and (1.33), respectively.

We now want to relate λ_t to δ_t, the force of interest underlying the spot rates which is not level over the interval from 0 to t. Combining formulas (10.11) and (1.27) we have

$$a(t) = e^{t \cdot \lambda_t} = e^{\int_0^t \delta_r dr}, \tag{10.15}$$

so that

$$t \cdot \lambda_t = \int_0^t \delta_r dr \tag{10.16}$$

leading to

$$\lambda_t = \frac{1}{t} \int_0^t \delta_r dr. \tag{10.17}$$

Formula (10.17) is interesting, since it shows that λ_t is a continuous average of the varying force of interest over the interval from 0 to t.

It is important to note that conceptually δ_t is an instantaneous forward rate at time t, since it applies only at that one point in time. This clearly distinguishes δ_t from λ_t, which conceptually is an instantaneous level spot rate over the interval form 0 to t. From this perspective, formula (10.16) is seen to be the continuous analogue to formula (10.9), the discrete formula expressing s_n as a function of f_t for $t = 0, 1, \ldots, n-1$.

If we differentiate formula (10.16) with respect to t, we obtain

$$\lambda_t + t\frac{d\lambda_t}{dt} = \delta_t. \tag{10.18}$$

This formula leads to the following observations:

1. Normal yield curve

$$\frac{d\lambda_t}{dt} > 0, \quad \text{so that} \quad \delta_t > \lambda_t.$$

2. Inverted yield curve

$$\frac{d\lambda_t}{dt} < 0, \quad \text{so that} \quad \delta_t < \lambda_t .$$

3. Flat yield curve

$$\frac{d\lambda_t}{dt} = 0, \quad \text{so that} \quad \delta_t = \lambda_t$$

and, in fact, δ_t and λ_t are not only equal, but are also constant for all t.

In summary, formula (10.17) can be used to find a continuous spot rate λ_t if the continuous forward rate δ_t is given. Alternatively, formula (10.18) can be used to find a continuous forward rate δ_t if the continuous spot rate λ_t is given. Moreover, formula (10.13) can be used to convert the continuous spot rate to a discrete spot rate, at which point the identities in prior sections of the chapter become available.

Example 10.11 ***A continuous yield curve is defined by***

$$\lambda_t = .05 + .006t - .0003t^2 \quad \textbf{for} \quad 0 \le t \le 10$$

Determine the following values:

(1) δ_t **for** $0 \le t \le 10$.

(2) s_3.

(3) ${}_2f_3$.

1. From formula (10.18) we have

$$\begin{aligned}\delta_t &= \lambda_t + t\frac{d\lambda_t}{dt} \\ &= \left(.05 + .006t - .0003t^2\right) + t\left(.006 - .0006t\right) \\ &= .05 + .012t - .0009t^2 \quad \text{for} \quad 0 \le t \le 10.\end{aligned}$$

2. Applying formula (10.13) with $t = 3$ we have

$$\begin{aligned}s_3 &= e^{\lambda_3} - 1 \\ &= e^{\left[.05 + .006(3) - .0003(3)^2\right]} \\ &= e^{.0653} - 1 = .06748.\end{aligned}$$

3. First, using formula (10.13) again with $t = 5$ we have

$$\begin{aligned} s_5 &= e^{\lambda_5} - 1 \\ &= e^{\left[.05+.006(5)-(.0003)(5)^2\right]} - 1 \\ &= e^{.0725} - 1 = .07519. \end{aligned}$$

Now applying formula (10.10) with $t = 3$ and $m = 2$, we have

$$(1+s_5)^5 = (1+s_3)^3(1+{}_2f_3)^2$$

or

$$(1.07519)^5 = (1.06748)^3(1+{}_2f_3)^2$$

and solving for ${}_2f_3$ we have

$${}_2f_3 = \left[\frac{(1.07519)^5}{(1.06748)^3}\right]^{\frac{1}{2}} - 1 = .0869.$$

EXERCISES

10.3 Spot rates

1. *a*) Rework Example 10.1(1) if the yield curve is inverted as follows:

Term	Spot rate
1 year	9.50%
2 years	9.25%
3 years	8.75%
4 years	8.00%
5 years	7.00%

   b) Explain the relative magnitude of the answers to (*a*) above and to Example 10.1(*a*).

2. The spot rate of interest is defined by $s_t = .1(.9)^t$ for $t = 1, 2, 3, 4, 5$. Find the present value of a 5-year annuity-due in which the first payment is equal to \$1000, and each subsequent payment increases by 5% of the immediately preceding payment.

3. A yield curve is defined by the equation:

$$s_k = .09 + .002k - .0005k^2 \text{ for } 0 \le k \le 4.$$

   a) Describe the shape of the yield curve for $0 \le k \le 2$.
   b) Describe the shape of the yield curve for $2 \le k \le 4$.

4. Find the value of $\ddot{s}_{\overline{5}|}$ 1using spot rates of interest in which the spot rates in Example 10.1 apply for the first year and the entire yield curve shifts downward by .25% for each year thereafter through the end of the five-year period.

5. A invests \$10,000 in a four-year zero coupon bond using the yield curve given in Example 10.1. If the rate of inflation is 5% per annum for the first two years and 4% per annum for the second two years, find the accumulated value in "constant dollars" (i.e. in real terms) of A's investment at the end of four years.

10.4 Relationship with bond yields

6. Consider the bonds in Example 10.2 from a different vantage point. Assume an investor has the choice of buying one 10% bond (Bond A) or two 5% bonds (Bond B). Either choice will produce an identical flow of coupons.
   a) Find the difference in the amounts originally invested.
   b) Find the difference in the payouts when the bonds mature.
   c) Verify that (*b*) is the accumulated value of (*a*) at the spot rate of interest for the term of the bonds.

7. A 6-year bond with 6% annual coupons has a yield rate of 12% effective. A 6-year bond with 10% annual coupons has a yield rate of 8% effective. Find the 6-year spot rate.

8. The current term structure is defined by $s_t = .06 + .01t$ for $t = 0, 1, 2, 3$.
   a) Calculate the at-par yield rate for a two-year bond.
   b) Calculate the at-par yield rate for a three-year bond.
   c) Explain the difference between the two at-par yield rates.

9. You are given a $1000 three-year bond with annual 6% coupons. The annual spot rates are the same as in Exercise 8.
   a) Determine whether it is a premium or a discount bond using the at-par yield rate in Exercise 8.
   b) Calculate the amount of premium or discount.

10. You are given the following prices of $1000 par value bonds with 10% annual coupons. The price of a 3-year bond is $1030, the price of a 4-year bond is $1035, and the price of a 5-year bond is $1037. The 3-year spot rate is 8% and the 6-year spot rate is 7%. Find the:
    a) 4-year spot rates.
    b) 5-year spot rates.
    c) Price of a 6-year bond.

11. You are given that a bond has a par value of \$1000, a term to maturity of 3 years, and a coupon rate of 6% payable annually. You are also given the following yield curve:

Term	Annual spot interest rates
1	7%
2	8%
3	9%

   a) Calculate the value of the bond.
   b) Calculate the annual effective yield rate for the bond if the bond is sold at a price equal to its par value.

12. Bonds 1, 2, and 3 all have annual coupons and mature in 1, 2, and 3 years, respectively. However, the coupon amounts are unknown. The effective yield rate on all three bonds in 8%. Find the spot rates s_1, s_2, and s_3.

13. The current term structure is as follows: $s_1 = 6\%$, $s_2 = 8\%$, and $s_3 = X\%$. A 3-year bond with a 8% annual coupon rate has an effective yield rate equal to 9%. Find *X*.

14. Rework Example 10.2 using the inverted yield curve

$$s_t = .09 - .02t \quad \text{for} \quad t = 0, 1, 2.$$

Verify that the relationship between the yield rates on the two bonds goes in the opposite direction than in Example 10.2.

10.5 Forward rates

15. Based on the yield curve given in Example 10.1, find the following expected forward rates:
   a) 1-year deferred 2-year forward rate.
   b) 2-year deferred 3-year forward rate.

16. Consider the forward interest rates defined by the following equation:

$$f_k = .09 + .002k - .002k^2 \quad \text{for } k = 0, 1, 2, 3, 4.$$

   a) Find the 4-year spot rate.
   b) Find the 2-year deferred 3-year forward rate.

17. The term structure is defined by $s_t = .05 + .005t$ for t = 1, 2, 3, 4. A three-year annuity-immediate will be issued one year from now with annual payments of \$1000. Using the appropriate forward rates, calculate the present value of this annuity one year from now.

18. Rework Example 10.5 to generate forward rates f_3, f_4 and ${}_2f_3$ without using 4-year and 5-year spot rates.

19. Yield rates to maturity for zero coupon bonds are currently quoted at 8.5% for one-year maturity, 9.5% for two-year maturity, and 10.5% for three-year maturity. Let i be the one-year forward rate for year two implied by the current yields of these bonds. Calculate i.

20. Consider a yield curve defined by the following equation:

$$s_k = 0.09 + 0.002k - 0.001k^2 \text{ for } k = 1, 2, 3, 4, 5.$$

where s_k is the annual effective rate of return for zero coupon bonds with maturity of k years. Let j be the one-year effective rate during year 5 that is implied by this yield curve. Calculate j.

21. You are given the following yield curve:

Term (in years)	Spot interest rate
1	5.00%
2	5.75%
3	6.25%
4	6.50%

A three-year annuity-immediate will be issued a year from now with annual payments of \$5000. Using the appropriate forward rates, calculate the present value of this annuity a year from now. Answer to the nearest dollar.

22. Evaluate $s_{\overline{5}|}$ assuming each payment is invested at the relevant forward rates implied by the spot rates given in Example 10.1.

10.6 Arbitrage

23. You are given the following prices of $500 par value bonds with 10% annual coupons:

    (*i*) One year $514.02
    (*ii*) Two years $516.00

    Determine whether arbitrage is possible with the two bonds and with zero coupon bonds using the spot rates given in Example 10.1. If arbitrage is possible, determine the amount of that profit and when it is realized. Assume that there are no transaction fees and no margin requirements on short sales.

24. The current effective yield rates for the zero coupon bonds are as follows:

    (*i*) One year 6%
    (*ii*) Two years 7%

    You are also able to borrow money at 7% effective one year from now to be repaid two years from now.

    a) Construct a transaction involving no net cash flows at times 0 and 1 that will generate a certain profit at time 2.

    b) If your initial position involves going long a security at a cost of $1000, find the arbitrage profit that will be made.

25. The current spot rates are as follows: $s_1 = 7\%$ and $s_2 = 9\%$. A 2-year bond with annual 5.5% coupons and a par value of $100 has a yield rate to maturity of 9.3%. Construct a transaction that involves the purchase or sale of exactly one of the coupon bonds and produces an arbitrage profit. Find the amount of the arbitrage profit and when it is realized.

10.7 A continuous model

26. The continuous force of interest is given as

$$\delta_t = .03 + .008t + .0018t^2 \text{ for } 0 \leq t \leq 5.$$

Find the following values:

a) λ_t for $0 \leq t \leq 5$.

b) 2-year spot rate.

c) 2-year deferred 3-year forward rate.

d) Determine the shape of the yield curve.

27. If $\lambda_t = .05 + .01t$ for $0 \le t \le 5$. Evaluate the present value of 1 to be paid at the end of 5 years.

Miscellaneous

28. An investor has \$100,000 to invest for three years. The account balance may be reinvested at the end of either the first or second years. The yield curve given in Example 10.1 applies for the first year. The entire yield curve shifts upward by 2% for the second year and another 2% for the third year. Considering all possible patterns of investment, find the minimum and maximum accumulation at the end of the three-year investment period. Answers to the nearest dollar.

29. The underlying real rate of interest, as defined in Section 9.4, is assumed to be a level 3% under all circumstances. Find the expected inflation rates for each of the next three years implied by the inflation premium theory using the yield curve given in Example 10.1.

11

Duration, convexity and immunization

11.1 INTRODUCTION

In numerous places throughout the prior chapters we have mentioned the relationship between rates of interest and the length of various financial transactions. For example, this relationship has been considered in connection with the analysis of loans and the analysis of various securities and other financial instruments, particularly bonds.

We have also considered the sensitivity of the present values of future cash flows to changes in the rate of interest. In particular, the analysis of yield rates in Chapter 7 addressed this issue at some length.

In Sections 11.2 through 11.5 we will see that these two concepts, i.e. "average length" and "interest rate sensitivity" of a series of future cash flows are closely related. We will explore this relationship more systematically and in more depth than in prior chapters.

Sections 11.6 through 11.9 will then explore a related topic; namely, the relationship between assets and liabilities, both of which involve future cash flows. The concepts and techniques developed in Sections 11.2 through 11.5 can be applied to great effect in better managing an entity's financial assets and liabilities. Such techniques can often be applied to achieve considerable reduction in financial risks arising from fluctuations in future rates of interest.

The results in this chapter can be quite useful to both individuals and firms in dealing with assets and liabilities involving future cash flows. As a result, better financial decisions involving less risk are often possible.

11.2 DURATION

The average length, or term, of a financial transaction is an important consideration in various applications discussed in prior chapters. In order to analyze this topic in more depth, we will develop indices to measure the timing of future cash flows.

The crudest index we could use is the *term to maturity*. For example, for 10-year bonds at issue the term to maturity is 10. This index would at least distinguish a 10-year from a 20-year bond, but it is of limited value. For example, it would not distinguish between two 10-year bonds, one with 5% coupons and the other with 10% coupons.

A better index is the *method of equated time* which was defined in Section 2.4. This index is computed as the weighted average of the various times of payment, where the weights are the various amounts paid. This weighted average can be interpreted as the average length of the transaction.

Let $R_1, R_2, \ldots, R_n$ be a series of cash flows occurring at times 1, 2,..., n. The method of equated time was defined in formula (2.2). If we apply this formula with the required change in notation, we obtain

$$\bar{t} = \frac{\sum_{t=1}^{n} t \cdot R_t}{\sum_{t=1}^{n} R_t}. \tag{11.1}$$

For example, consider the two bonds cited above. If the coupons are paid annually, then the average length of the 5% bond is

$$\bar{t} = \frac{1 \cdot 5 + 2 \cdot 5 + \cdots + 10 \cdot 5 + 10 \cdot 100}{5 + 5 + \cdots + 5 + 100} = 8.50.$$

Similarly, the average length of the 10% bond is

$$\bar{t} = \frac{1 \cdot 10 + 2 \cdot 10 + \cdots + 10 \cdot 10 + 10 \cdot 100}{10 + 10 + \cdots + 10 + 100} = 7.75.$$

The 5% bond has an average payment date of 8.50 years, while the 10% bond has an average payment date of 7.75 years. Thus, we could say that the 5% bond is a longer term bond than the 10% bond. This confirms the statement we made in comparing these same two bonds (labeled Bond A and Bond B, respectively) in Section 10.3.

An even better index is given by *duration*. The concept behind duration is similar to the method of equated time, except that the present value of each cash flow is used as the weight instead of the cash flow itself. The rate of interest used is typically the yield rate, or IRR. Then duration, denoted by $\bar{d}$, is given by

$$\bar{d} = \frac{\sum_{t=1}^{n} tv^t R_t}{\sum_{t=1}^{n} v^t R_t}. \tag{11.2}$$

Note that formula (11.2) assumes that the payment period and the interest conversion period coincide, for convenience. Also, note that $\bar{d}$ is a function of i.

Several special cases of formula (11.2) are of importance:

1. If $i = 0$, then $\bar{d} = \bar{t}$. This is obvious upon inspection, since formula (11.2) immediately simplifies to formula (11.1). Thus, the method of equated time is, in essence, a special case of duration which ignores interest.

2. The duration $\bar{d}$ is a decreasing function of i. A mathematical proof of this result will be given in Section 11.3. However, the result does have an important verbal interpretation. As the rate of interest increases, the terms in the numerator of formula (11.2) with the higher values of t are discounted relatively more than the terms with the lower values of t. This serves to reduce the overall weighted average value of t, i.e. $\bar{d}$.

3. If there is only one future cash flow, then $\bar{d}$ is the point in time at which that cash flow is made. This intuitively appealing result is obvious upon examining formula (11.2), since the summations in the numerator and denominator have only one term each and everything cancels except the time the cash flow occurs.

We next examine the rate of change in the present value of a series of future cash flows as the rate of interest changes. The relative rate of change in this present value is often called *interest rate sensitivity* of a set of future cash flows. Let this present value be denoted by $P(i)$, i.e.

$$P(i) = \sum_{t=1}^{n} v^t R_t = \sum_{t=1}^{n} (1+i)^{-t} R_t . \tag{11.3}$$

which is consistent with formula (7.2). We now define the *volatility* of this present value, denoted by $\bar{v}$, as

$$\bar{v} = -\frac{P'(i)}{P(i)} \tag{11.4}$$

where $\bar{v}$ is a function of i.

The reasoning behind formula (11.4) is analogous to the reasoning behind the definition of the force of discount given in Section 1.9. The term $P'(i)$ measures the instantaneous rate of change in the present value of the cash flows as the rate of interest changes. Dividing by $P(i)$ expresses this instantaneous rate of change in units independent of the size of the present value itself. The minus sign is necessary to make $\bar{v}$ positive, since $P'(i)$ is negative.

The word "volatility" seems appropriate to describe $\bar{v}$, since $\bar{v}$ is a measure of how rapidly the present value of a series of future cash flows changes as the rate of interest changes, i.e. $\bar{v}$ measures the "interest rate sensitivity" of these future cash flows.

We obtain a very interesting result if we substitute formula (11.3) into formula (11.4)

$$\begin{aligned} \bar{v} &= -\frac{P'(i)}{P(i)} \\ &= -\frac{\frac{d}{di}\sum_{t=1}^{n}(1+i)^{-t} R_t}{\sum_{t=1}^{n}(1+i)^{-t} R_t} \\ &= \frac{\sum_{t=1}^{n} t(1+i)^{-t-1} R_t}{\sum_{t=1}^{n}(1+i)^{-t} R_t} \\ &= \frac{\bar{d}}{1+i}. \end{aligned} \tag{11.5}$$

Thus, volatility is equal to duration divided by $1 + i$. In view of this close relationship, volatility is often called *modified duration*.

Regular duration is often called *Macaulay duration*, a term which clearly distinguishes it from modified duration. This term is named after F. R. Macaulay, who first introduced the concept of duration in a 1938 publication entitled *Some Theoretical Problems Suggested by the Movements of Interest Rates, Bond Yields, and Stock Prices in the United States Since 1856*.

Formula (11.5) establishes the close connection between the "average length" and the "interest rate sensitivity" of a set of future cash flows. Macaulay duration was developed by analyzing "average length," whereas modified duration was developed by analyzing "interest rate sensitivity."

The use of the word "modified" in the name of modified duration may imply to some readers that regular or Macaulay duration is the primary measure, while modified duration is a variation. However, any possible implication that modified duration is of lesser importance should not be read into the terminology. In fact, the primary consideration often is interest rate sensitivity of a set of future cash flows, and modified duration directly measures that sensitivity. It just so happens that this sensitivity is directly tied to the timing of those cash flows.

Macaulay duration and modified duration are important analytical tools in financial analysis. One very useful application lies in the consideration of reinvestment risk.

For example, consider two bonds C and D bought at the same yield rate. If Bond C has a Macaulay duration equal to 5 and Bond D has a Macaulay duration equal to 10, then, in essence, Bond D will produce this yield rate for twice as long as Bond C before we have to worry about reinvestment rates. On the other hand, Bond C is more liquid than Bond D, which may be quite important if early cash flow needs arise.

Modified duration offers a method to estimate the change in the present value of a series of future cash flows when the yield rate changes. We can rewrite formula (11.4) as

$$P'(i) = \frac{dP(i)}{di} = -P(i) \cdot \bar{v}.$$

We now let the yield rate i change to $i+h$ and we obtain the following finite approximation to the derivative

$$\frac{\Delta P}{\Delta i} = \frac{P(i+h)-P(i)}{(i+h)-i} \approx -P(i)\cdot\bar{v}$$

which simplifies to

$$P(i+h)-P(i) \approx -P(i)\cdot h\cdot\bar{v} \tag{11.6a}$$

or

$$P(i+h) \approx P(i)\left[1-h\bar{v}\right]. \tag{11.6b}$$

Formula 11.6 is based on a common application from calculus illustrated in Figure 11.1. The price on the $P(i)$ curve is approximated using the tangent line at $P(i)$.

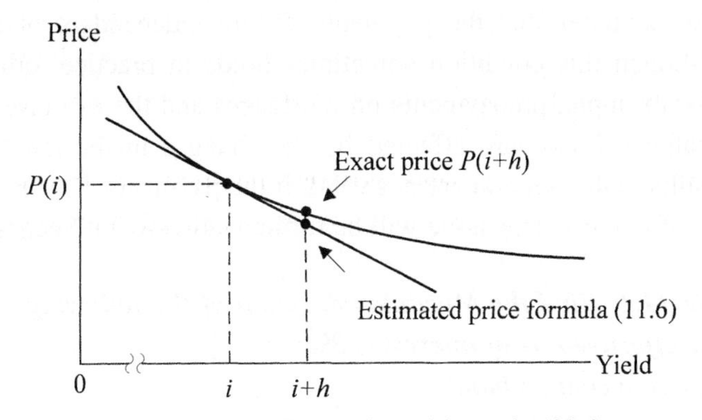

Figure 11.1 Illustration of formula (11.6)

There is another relationship between Macaulay duration and modified duration that is quite enlightening. All of the formulas above are based on the discrete yield rate *i*. Now consider what happens if the analysis is based on the continuous force of interest δ rather than *i*.

From formula (11.2) we have

$$\bar{d} = \frac{\sum_{t=1}^{n} tv^t R_t}{\sum_{t=1}^{n} v^t R_t} = \frac{\sum_{t=1}^{n} te^{-\delta t} R_t}{\sum_{t=1}^{n} e^{-\delta t} R_t}.$$

Now

$$P(\delta) = \sum_{t=1}^{n} e^{-\delta t} R_t$$

and

$$P'(\delta) = -\sum_{t=1}^{n} te^{-\delta t}R_t,$$

so that formula (11.4) becomes

$$\bar{v} = -\frac{P'(\delta)}{P(\delta)} = \frac{\sum_{t=1}^{n} te^{-\delta t}R_t}{\sum_{t=1}^{n} e^{-\delta t}R_t}.$$

Thus, $\bar{v} = \bar{d}$. In words, Macaulay duration and modified duration are equal when a force of interest is used rather than a discrete rate of interest!

One additional observation about duration is quite important. The analysis in this section assumes that the payments R_t are independent of the rate of interest. Although this condition sometimes holds in practice, other times it does not. For example, prepayments on mortgages and the exercise of the call feature on callable bonds are affected by the changes in the rate of interest. Thus, the results in this section are not valid, if the payments R_t vary depending upon the rate of interest. This issue will be further addressed in Section 11.4.

Example 11.1 Find the Macaulay duration of the following investments assuming the effective rate of interest is 8%:
(1) A 10-year zero coupon bond.
(2) A 10-year bond with 8% annual coupons.
(3) A 10-year mortgage repaid with level annual payments of principal and interest.
(4) A preferred stock paying level annual dividends into perpetuity.

1. Since only a single payment is involved, obviously $\bar{d} = 10$. Note that this answer is independent of the rate of interest being paid on the zero coupon bond. Also note that this intuitively appealing result will not hold if modified duration is used.

2. Per dollar of redemption value, formula (11.2) gives

$$\bar{d} = \frac{.08(Ia)_{\overline{10|}} + 10v^{10}}{.08\,a_{\overline{10|}} + v^{10}}$$

$$= \frac{.08(32.6872) + 10(.46319)}{.08(6.7101) + .46319}$$

$$= 7.25.$$

Thus, a 10-year bond with coupons has a shorter duration than a 10-year zero coupon bond, which should be obvious. A shortcut method exists for calculating duration of bonds selling at par which is illustrated in Exercise 39.

3. Per dollar of mortgage payment, formula (11.2) gives

$$\bar{d} = \frac{(I\,a)_{\overline{10}|}}{a_{\overline{10}|}} = \frac{32.6872}{6.7101} = 4.87\,.$$

Note that this answer is independent of the rate of interest being paid on the mortgage. That may seem surprising at first, but it does make sense upon reflection. Duration depends on the pattern of the level payments, not their amount.

Also, it is important to note that duration for a 10-year mortgage is significantly shorter than for a 10-year bond. This happens because a mortgage repays some principal in every installment but the bond repays principal only at its redemption date. (This statement is not exactly true for premium and discount bonds, but the effect is generally not large enough to invalidate the above comparison between bonds and mortgages.)

4. Per dollar of dividend, formula (11.2) gives

$$\bar{d} = \frac{(Ia)_{\overline{\infty}|}}{a_{\overline{\infty}|}} = \frac{1.08/.08^2}{1/.08} = 13.5.$$

Note that this answer is independent of the dividend rate being paid on the preferred stock. Also note that duration for preferred stock is longer than for any of the other investments. This seems reasonable, since preferred stock involves payments being made into perpetuity.

Example 11.2 Use formula (11.6) to estimate the price of the bond in Example 11.1 (2) if the yield rate rises to 9%.

We first convert the Macaulay duration of 7.2469 (carrying more decimal places) from Example 11.1 (2) to modified duration

$$\bar{v} = \frac{\bar{d}}{1+i} = \frac{7.2469}{1.08} = 6.7101.$$

Per dollar of redemption value, we know that $P(.08)=1$, since an 8% coupon bond would sell at par.

Now applying formula (11.6b), we have

$$\begin{aligned} P(.09) &\approx P(.08)\left[1-(.01)(6.7101)\right] \\ &= 1-.067101 = .9329. \end{aligned}$$

The actual price of the bond is

$$\begin{aligned} P(.09) &= .08a_{\overline{10}|.09} + (1.09)^{-10} \\ &= .08(6.41766) + .422411 \\ &= .9358, \end{aligned}$$

for an error of $.9358 - .9329 = .0029$, i.e. 29 cents on a \$100 bond.

Note that if Macaulay duration had been used, rather than modified duration, the answer would have been

$$\begin{aligned} P(.09) &\approx P(.08)\left[1-(.01)(7.2469)\right] \\ &= 1-.072469 = .9275, \end{aligned}$$

which has an error of $.9358 - .9275 = .0083$, i.e. 83 cents on a \$100 bond. Clearly, modified duration produces a more accurate answer, as would be expected.

***Example 11.3** Find the modified duration of a 10-year zero coupon bond, if present values are based on the force of interest δ.*

We have

$$P(\delta) = e^{-10\delta}$$

and

$$P'(\delta) = -10e^{-10\delta}.$$

Now applying formula (11.4), using δ instead of i, we have

$$\bar{v} = -\frac{P'(\delta)}{P(\delta)} = \frac{10e^{-10\delta}}{e^{-10\delta}} = 10.$$

However, we know that the Macaulay duration of a 10-year zero coupon bond is also equal to 10. This illustrates the result that Macaulay duration and modified duration are equal when forces of interest are used.

11.3 CONVEXITY

In Section 11.2 we considered the sensitivity of the present value of a set of cash flows $P(i)$ to changes in the rate of interest. This analysis resulted in formulas involving the first derivative $P'(i)$. A graphical representation of this analysis was given in Figure 11.1.

It is possible to obtain more accurate results by considering the second derivative $P''(i)$, in addition to the first derivative $P'(i)$. This can be accomplished by using a Taylor series expansion to second derivatives, i.e.

$$P(i+h) \approx P(i) + hP'(i) + \frac{h^2}{2}P''(i) \tag{11.7}$$

Note that formula (11.6) could have been derived in a similar matter by carrying the Taylor series expansion only as far as first derivatives.

The reader will recall that we divided $P'(i)$ by $P(i)$ in the definition of modified duration $\bar{v}$ in order to obtain a relative measure independent of the magnitude of $P(i)$. In an analogous fashion we define the *convexity* of the present value of the cash flows, denoted by $\bar{c}$, as

$$\bar{c} = \frac{P''(i)}{P(i)}. \tag{11.8}$$

The name "convexity" comes from Figure 11.1 in which the price curve is convex in shape. In effect, by considering convexity as well as modified duration, we can approximate the price $P(i+h)$ using a quadratic rather the straight line in Figure 11.1. This will significantly improve the approximation.

We can use formulas (11.7) and (11.8) to obtain a refined version of formula (11.6) as

$$P(i+h) - P(i) \approx -P(i)h\bar{v} + P(i)\frac{h^2}{2}\bar{c} \tag{11.9a}$$

or

$$P(i+h) \approx P(i)\left[1 - h\bar{v} + \frac{h^2}{2}\bar{c}\right]. \tag{11.9b}$$

In Section 11.2 we saw that modified duration $\bar{v}$ measures the interest rate sensitivity of $P(i)$. In a somewhat analogous fashion, we can show that convexity appears when we measure the interest rate sensitivity of modified duration $\bar{v}$.

Consider the rate of change of modified duration $\bar{v}$ as i changes. We have

$$\frac{d\bar{v}}{di} = \frac{d}{di}\left[-\frac{P'(i)}{P(i)}\right]$$

and differentiating the quotient, we have

$$= \frac{-P(i)P''(i) + [P'(i)]^2}{[P(i)]^2}$$

$$= \left[\frac{P'(i)}{P(i)}\right]^2 - \frac{P''(i)}{P(i)}$$

$$= \bar{v}^2 - \bar{c}. \tag{11.10}$$

Formula (11.10) directly expresses the interest rate sensitivity of modified duration as a function of modified duration itself and of convexity.

Although the above general formulas seem relatively straightforward, specific applications can become complex to evaluate in practice. In general, we have

$$P(i) = \sum_{t=1}^{n} t(1+i)^{-t} R_t \tag{11.3}$$

$$P'(i) = -\sum_{t=1}^{n} t(1+i)^{-t-1} R_t \tag{11.11}$$

and

$$P''(i) = \sum_{t=1}^{n} t(t+1)(1+i)^{-t-2} R_t. \tag{11.12}$$

We see that formula (11.11) involves the combination of a first-degree polynomial in t, a geometric progression, and the payment pattern R_t. Similarly, formula (11.12) involves the combination of a second-degree polynomial in t, a geometric progression, and the payment pattern R_t.

The standard approach which works best in practice is to use a spreadsheet application on a computer. Formulas (11.3), (11.11), and (11.12) are ideally suited for spreadsheet applications and can readily be applied to any pattern of cash flows R_t.

An alternative approach for summing the series, not requiring a computer, is available if the payment pattern R_t is level. Appendix 11 at the end of the chapter contains an algorithm from numerical analysis that can be applied in summing a series in which each term is the product of a polynomial and an exponential. This technique will be illustrated in Example 11.4 (4).

The reader may have noticed that so far in this section we have only considered convexity based on modified duration. We can also define "Macaulay convexity" using the force of interest δ rather than the rate of interest i.

We then obtain

$$P(\delta) = \sum_{t=1}^{n} e^{-\delta t} R_t \tag{11.13}$$

$$P'(\delta) = -\sum_{t=1}^{n} t e^{-\delta t} R_t \tag{11.14}$$

and

$$P''(\delta) = \sum_{t=1}^{n} t^2 e^{-\delta t} R_t . \tag{11.15}$$

Formulas (11.13), (11.14), and (11.15) are somewhat simpler versions of formulas (11.3), (11.11) and (11.12) for which Macaulay duration and modified duration would be equal. *Macaulay convexity* could then be defined as

$$\frac{P''(\delta)}{P(\delta)} = \frac{\sum_{t=1}^{n} t^2 e^{-\delta t} R_t}{\sum_{t=1}^{n} e^{-\delta t} R_t} . \tag{11.16}$$

The reader should note that the term "modified convexity," which might signify convexity based on "modified duration," is normally not used, since it cannot readily be obtained by modifying some other formula. Convexity based on modified duration is usually just called "convexity."

We obtain a very interesting result if we examine how $\bar{v} = \bar{d}$ changes as δ changes. If we differentiate $\bar{d}$ with respect to δ, we obtain

$$\begin{aligned}
\frac{d\bar{v}}{d\delta} = \frac{d\bar{d}}{d\delta} &= \frac{d}{d\delta} \frac{\sum_{t=1}^{n} t e^{-\delta t} R_t}{\sum_{t=1}^{n} e^{-\delta t} R_t} \\
&= -\frac{\left(\sum_{t=1}^{n} e^{-\delta t} R_t\right)\left(\sum_{t=1}^{n} t^2 e^{-\delta t} R_t\right) - \left(\sum_{t=1}^{n} t e^{-\delta t} R_t\right)^2}{\left(\sum_{t=1}^{n} e^{-\delta t} R_t\right)^2} \\
&= -\left[\frac{\sum_{t=1}^{n} t^2 e^{-\delta t} R_t}{\sum_{t=1}^{n} e^{-\delta t} R_t} - \left(\frac{\sum_{t=1}^{n} t e^{-\delta t} R_t}{\sum_{t=1}^{n} e^{-\delta t} R_t}\right)^2\right] \\
&= -\sigma^2
\end{aligned} \tag{11.17}$$

We adapt the notation σ^2 standing for variance from probability and statistics, and note that formula (11.17) is the negative of $E(t^2)-\left[E(t)\right]^2$ where the weights are $e^{-\delta t}R_t$. Formula (11.17) is also seen to be equivalent to formula (11.10) with $E(t^2)=\bar{c}$ and $E(t)=\bar{v}$.

Two observations are relevant:

1. Duration can be construed as a weighted mean of the time of payment of the various cash flows. Convexity then relates to the dispersion of times around that mean value.

2. This derivation demonstrates that $\bar{d}$ is a decreasing function of δ (and therefore *i*), since σ^2 is always positive. This confirms the statement made without proof in item 2 following formula (11.2) in Section 11.2.

In summary, we have provided two quite interesting conceptual interpretations involving convexity. First, convexity appears in the formula for measuring the interest rate sensitivity of duration. Second, convexity also appears in the formula for measuring the dispersion of cash flow payment times around their mean value (duration).

Moreover, on a pragmatic level, convexity is quite important in many applications. First, as we will see in Example 11.5, convexity will significantly improve approximations in comparison with those based on duration only. Second, convexity is a key component in various "immunization" strategies to be developed in Sections 11.6 through 11.9.

Example 11.4 Find the convexity of the four investments illustrated in Example 11.1.

1. We have

$$P(i) = (1+i)^{-10}$$

$$P'(i) = -10(1+i)^{-11}$$

and

$$P''(i) = (10)(11)(1+i)^{-12} = 110(1+i)^{-12},$$

so that

$$\bar{c} = \frac{P''(.08)}{P(.08)} = \frac{110(1.08)^{-12}}{(1.08)^{-10}} = 94.31.$$

2. The calculations from formulas (11.3), (11.11), and (11.12) are displayed in Table 11.1.

Table 11.1 Duration and Convexity Calculations for the Bond in Example 11.1 (2)

t	R_t	v^t	$v^t R_t$	$tv^{t+1}R_t$	$t(t+1)v^{t+2}R_t$
1	0.08	0.925926	0.074074	0.068587	0.127013
2	0.08	0.857339	0.068587	0.127013	0.352814
3	0.08	0.793832	0.063507	0.176407	0.653360
4	0.08	0.735030	0.058802	0.217787	1.008271
5	0.08	0.680583	0.054447	0.252068	1.400377
6	0.08	0.630170	0.050414	0.280075	1.815303
7	0.08	0.583490	0.046679	0.302551	2.241115
8	0.08	0.540269	0.043222	0.320159	2.667994
9	0.08	0.500249	0.040020	0.333499	3.087957
10	1.08	0.463193	0.500249	4.631935	47.177115
			1.000000	6.710081	60.531320

As a check, we have

$$\bar{v} = \frac{6.710081}{1.000000} = 6.7101$$

and

$$\bar{d} = (1+i)\bar{v} = (1.08)(6.7101) = 7.25$$

agreeing with Example 11.1 (2). The convexity is given by

$$\bar{c} = \frac{60.531320}{1.000000} = 60.53.$$

3. The calculations from formulas (11.3), (11.11), and (11.12) are displayed in Table 11.2.

Table 11.2 Duration and Convexity Calculations for the Mortgage in Example 11.1 (3)

t	R_t	v^t	$v^t R_t$	$tv^{t+1} R_t$	$t(t+1)v^{t+2} R_t$
1	1	0.925926	0.925926	0.857339	1.587664
2	1	0.857339	0.857339	1.587664	4.410179
3	1	0.793832	0.793832	2.205090	8.166998
4	1	0.735030	0.735030	2.722333	12.603393
5	1	0.680583	0.680583	3.150848	17.504712
6	1	0.630170	0.630170	3.500942	22.691293
7	1	0.583490	0.583490	3.781882	28.013942
8	1	0.540269	0.540269	4.001992	33.349931
9	1	0.500249	0.500249	4.168741	38.599457
10	1	0.463193	0.463193	4.288829	43.682513
			6.710081	30.265660	210.610084

As a check we have

$$\bar{v} = \frac{30.265660}{6.710081} = 4.5105$$

and

$$\bar{d} = (1+i)\bar{v} = (1.08)(4.5105) = 4.87$$

agreeing with Example 11.1 (3). The convexity is given by

$$\bar{c} = \frac{210.610084}{6.710081} = 31.39.$$

4. We have

$$P(i) = \sum_{t=1}^{\infty}(1+i)^{-t}$$

$$P'(i) = -\sum_{t=1}^{\infty} t(1+i)^{-t-1}$$

and

$$P''(i) = \sum_{t=1}^{\infty} t(t+1)(1+i)^{-t-2}.$$

Since the summations go to ∞ and since the payments R_t are level, we will demonstrate formula (11.32) derived in Appendix 11. We have

$$P(i) = a_{\overline{\infty|}} = \frac{1}{i} = \frac{1}{.08} = 12.50$$

and

$$P''(i) = v^2 \sum_{t=1}^{\infty} (t^2 + t) v^t .$$

Now applying formula (11.32), we have

$$\begin{aligned} f(t) &= t^2 + t \\ \Delta f(t) &= \left[(t+1)^2 + (t+1) \right] - \left[t^2 + t \right] \\ &= 2t + 2 \end{aligned}$$

and

$$\Delta^2 f(t) = \left[2(t+1) + 2 \right] - \left[2t + 2 \right] = 2 .$$

Therefore, $P''(.08) = v^2 \sum_{t=1}^{\infty} v^t f(t) = \left[\frac{v^{t-1}}{i} \left\{ 1 + \frac{\Delta}{i} + \frac{\Delta^2}{i^2} \right\} f(t) \right]_{t=\infty}^{1}$

$$\begin{aligned} &= \frac{v^2}{i} \left[(t^2 + t) + \frac{2t+2}{i} + \frac{2}{i^2} \right]_{t=\infty}^{1} \\ &= \frac{1}{.08(1.08)^2} \left[(1+1) + \frac{2+2}{.08} + \frac{2}{(.08)^2} \right] \\ &= 3906.25. \end{aligned}$$

The convexity is given by

$$\overline{c} = \frac{3906.25}{12.5} = 312.50.$$

Note that formula (11.32) could also be directly applied to solve Example 11.4(3), since the cash flows on the mortgage are level. However, it could not be directly applied without modification to solve Example 11.4 (2), since the cash flows on the bond are not level.

Example 11.5 Rework Example 11.2 to obtain a refined answer using convexity as well as modified duration.

From Example 11.2, we have $\overline{v} = 6.7101$ and from Example 11.4(2) we have $\overline{c} = 60.53$. Now applying formula (11.9b), we have

$$\begin{aligned} P(.09) &\approx P(.08)\left[1-(.01)(6.7101)+\frac{(.01)^2}{2}(60.53)\right] \\ &= 1-.067101+.003027 \\ &= .9359. \end{aligned}$$

The actual price of the bond is .9358, so using convexity as well as duration produces an approximation with an error of only .0001, i.e. 1 cent on a $100 bond. The approximate answer using duration only had an error of .0029, or 29 cents on a $100 bond.

Example 11.6 Find the Macaulay convexity of the bond given in Example 11.3.

We have

$$\begin{aligned} P(\delta) &= e^{-10\delta} \\ P'(\delta) &= -10e^{-10\delta} \end{aligned}$$

and

$$P''(\delta) = 100e^{-10\delta}.$$

Now applying formula (11.16), we see that Macaulay convexity is equal to

$$\frac{P''(\delta)}{P(\delta)} = 100.$$

Note that Macaulay convexity is equal to the square of Macaulay duration, whose value of 10 was obtained in Example 11.3. This result is not a coincidence and Macaulay convexity will always equal to the square of Macaulay duration for single payments.

Further note that this same simple relationship does not hold for modified duration and its convexity, as illustrated above in Example 11.4 (1).

11.4 INTEREST SENSITIVE CASH FLOWS

In Sections 11.2 and 11.3 we assumed that the cash flows are not affected by changes in the rate of interest. By way of contrast, *interest sensitive cash flows* are cash flows that are affected by changes in the rate of interest.

Simple examples of interest sensitive cash flows, already encountered earlier in the book, are callable bonds and prepayments on mortgages. The decision to call a bond or prepay a mortgage in the future is significantly affected by changes in future rates of interest.

A full analysis of financial instruments with interest sensitive cash flows is beyond the scope of this book. Such an analysis would require developing models that contain an appropriate functional relationship between the cash flows and the level of future rates of interest. We will not attempt to develop such models in general and will assume that prices (i.e. present values) reflecting interest sensitive cash flows are available from some source.

Effective duration is a third type of duration developed for this purpose. It is based on the price change if the rate of interest increases from its current level and the price change if the rate of interest decreases from its current level. We will work with three prices:

$P(i)$ – current price at yield rate i.
$P(i+h)$ – price if yield rate increases by h.
$P(i-h)$ – price if yield rate decreases by h.

The formulas for modified duration and convexity, both of which involve derivatives, cannot be directly applied. It will be necessary to use a finite approximation for $P'(i)$ similar to that used in the derivation of formula (11.6), i.e. $\Delta P / \Delta i$.

We then approximate $P'(i)$ by

$$P'(i) \approx \frac{P(i+h) - P(i-h)}{2h} \tag{11.18}$$

using values on both sides of $P(i)$, rather than only on one side as in the derivation of formula (11.6). This is a standard result from calculus using the slope of a secant line to approximate the slope of the tangent line.

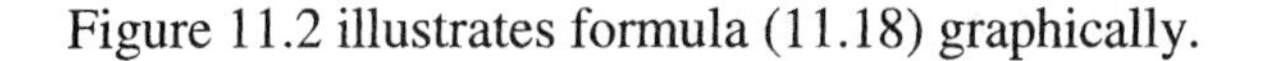

Figure 11.2 illustrates formula (11.18) graphically.

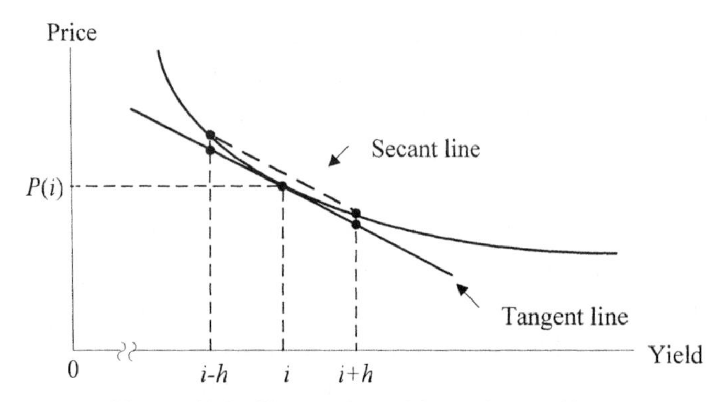

Figure 11.2 Illustration of formula (11.18)

If we combine formula (11.18) with formula (11.4) we have the following formula for "effective duration" (labeled $\bar{d}_e$):

$$\bar{d}_e \approx \frac{P(i-h)-P(i+h)}{2hP(i)} \tag{11.19}$$

In an analogous fashion, we can develop a formula for *effective convexity* (labeled $\bar{c}_e$) using a finite approximation to the second derivative, as

$$\bar{c}_e \approx \frac{P(i-h)-2P(i)+P(i+h)}{h^2P(i)}. \tag{11.20}$$

The derivation of formula (11.20) is left as an exercise.

Formula (11.6b) can be adapted and applied as

$$P(i \pm h) \approx P(i)\left[1 \mp h\bar{d}_e\right]. \tag{11.21}$$

Also, formula (11.9b) can be adapted and applied as

$$P(i \pm h) \approx P(i)\left[1 \mp h\bar{d}_e + \frac{h^2}{2}\bar{c}_e\right]. \tag{11.22}$$

Note that the signs of effective duration on the right-hand side of formulas (11.21) and (11.22) go in the opposite direction from the signs for prices on the left-hand side. However, the sign for effective convexity on the right-hand side is always positive.

If the formulas for effective duration are applied for non-interest sensitive cash flows, results very close to modified duration are obtained. However, effective duration produces significantly better results if the cash flows are interest sensitive.

Example 11.7 Consider the bond in Example 11.1(2) based on a yield rate of 8%. Assume a 1% increase and a 1% decrease in the yield rate.
(1) Calculate the effective duration.
(2) Calculate the effective convexity.

1. We have the following prices:

$$P(.09) = .08a_{\overline{10}|.09} + (1.09)^{-10} = .935823$$

and

$$P(.07) = .08a_{\overline{10}|.07} + (1.07)^{-10} = 1.070236.$$

Now applying formula (11.19) we have

$$\bar{d}_e = \frac{P(.07) - P(.09)}{2(.01)P(.08)} = \frac{1.070236 - .935823}{(2)(.01)(1)} = 6.72.$$

This value for effective duration is quite close to the modified duration of 6.71 calculated in Example 11.2. This result illustrates that effective duration is virtually the same as modified duration for non-interest sensitive cash flows.

2. Applying formula (11.20) we have

$$\bar{c}_e = \frac{P(.07) - 2P(.08) + P(.09)}{(.01)^2 P(.08)} = \frac{1.070236 - (2)(1) + .935823}{(.0001)(1)} = 60.59.$$

This value for effective convexity is quite close to the value $\bar{c} = 60.53$ calculated in Example 11.4 (2).

Example 11.8 Rework Example 11.7 if the bond is callable at the end of 5 years at par. Using the approach presented in Section 6.7, assume the bond will not be called if the rate of interest rises, but will be called if it falls.

1. We need to recompute $P(.07)$ assuming the bond will be called. We have

$$P(.07) = .08a_{\overline{5}|.07} + (1.07)^{-5}$$
$$= 1.041002.$$

Now applying formula (11.19) we have

$$\bar{d}_e = \frac{P(.07)-P(.09)}{2(.01)P(.08)} = \frac{1.041002-.935823}{(.02)(1)}$$
$$= 5.26.$$

Note that duration has "shortened" from 6.72 to 5.26 reflecting the possibility that the bond may be called early.

2. Applying formula (11.20) we have

$$\bar{c}_e = \frac{P(.07)-2P(.08)+P(.09)}{(.01)^2 P(.08)}$$
$$= \frac{1.041002-(2)(1)+.935823}{(.0001)(1)} = -231.75.$$

At first glance, this answer looks wrong, since it is negative. It is true that convexity will not be negative if cash flows are not interest sensitive. This was shown in the derivation of formula (11.17).

However, "negative convexity" is possible with interest sensitive cash flows. The convexity in this example appears to be negative. The reader is cautioned against placing high reliability on the particular value obtained, i.e. -231.75. The prices in this problem are based on the simple "yield to worst" model for callable bonds presented in Section 6.7, together with considering only a 1% increase and a 1% decrease in the rate of interest. More sophisticated models beyond the scope of this book are required for realistically modeling interest sensitive cash flows in general.

11.5 ANALYSIS OF PORTFOLIOS

In this section we will address three issues arising in practical applications of the material covered in Sections 11.2 through 11.4. No new theory is presented, but rather some important implementation issues are addressed in analyzing portfolios.

Multiple securities

In the prior sections we have presented analyses of individual securities or other financial instruments. However, in practice frequently an investment portfolio, even a relatively small one, will contain multiple securities. How should we compute the duration and convexity of the entire portfolio?

Fortunately, the answer is straightforward and easy to apply. Both duration and convexity have an "additivity property." Moreover, this property is valid for all the different types of duration and convexity measures presented earlier.

Consider a portfolio consisting of *m* different securities. Let P_j, $\bar{v}_j$, and $\bar{c}_j$ be the price (or market value), modified duration, and convexity, respectively, of the $j-th$ security where $j = 1, 2, \ldots, m$. Let P, $\bar{v}$ and $\bar{c}$ be the comparable values for the entire portfolio.

We then immediately see that

$$P = P_1 + P_2 + \ldots + P_m. \tag{11.23}$$

For modified duration, we have

$$\begin{aligned}\bar{v} &= -\frac{\frac{d}{di}P}{P} = -\frac{\frac{d}{di}(P_1 + P_2 + \ldots + P_m)}{P} \\ &= \frac{P_1}{P}\bar{v}_1 + \frac{P_2}{P}\bar{v}_2 + \ldots + \frac{P_m}{P}\bar{v}_m\end{aligned} \tag{11.24}$$

directly by applying formula (11.4) *m* times, once for each security.

In words, formula (11.24) says that the modified duration of the entire portfolio is simply the weighted average of the modified durations of each security in the portfolio, where the weights are the fraction of the entire portfolio applicable to each security.

An analogous result holds for convexity as well, i.e.

$$\bar{c} = \frac{P_1}{P}\bar{c}_1 + \frac{P_2}{P}\bar{c}_2 + \ldots + \frac{P_m}{P}\bar{c}_m \tag{11.25}$$

using the same derivation with formula (11.8) rather than formula (11.4).

Passage of time

In the prior sections we computed "snapshot" measures of duration at a beginning time $t=0$. Moreover, all future cash flows occurred on anniversary dates of $t=0$, i.e. at times $t=1, 2,\ldots, n$.

The issue now considered is how duration changes over time as the security ages. This analysis should address the value of duration at interim points between cash flow payment dates, as well as the value on the cash flow payment dates themselves.

The answer is quite simple for securities with only one future cash flow, e.g. zero coupon bonds. Macaulay duration is obviously just the remaining time interval from the date of calculation to the date of future payment. Since modified duration is proportional to Macaulay duration at any point in time, its value changes over time in a similar manner.

For the large majority of securities that have multiple future cash flows, an interesting phenomenon occurs. Basically, as time passes the security gets "shorter" and the duration decreases.

However at the time a cash flow occurs there is a discontinuity and duration spikes up since the security "lengthens" at that point. In other words, the duration is greater just after the cash flow than it was just before the cash flow.

This produces a zigzag pattern for duration that is illustrated in Figure 11.3.

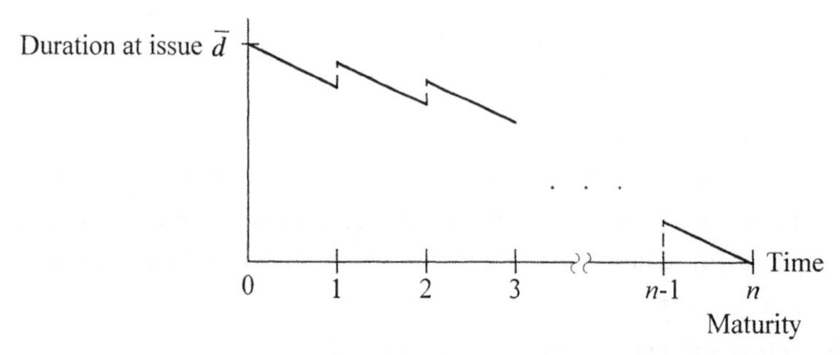

Figure 11.3 Duration behavior over time

In a portfolio, different securities have different cash flow payment dates. Therefore, the need to be able to calculate duration at any future date after issue all the way to the maturity date is evident.

Interest conversion frequency

In the prior sections we assumed that the yield rate is convertible at the same frequency as cash flows occur. This simplifies the formulas considerably and is normally done in practice for convenience.

For example, if we are working with bonds that have semiannual coupons, the yield rate is a nominal rate convertible semiannually. Similarly, if we are working with mortgages that have monthly payments, the yield rate is a nominal rate convertible monthly. In a portfolio we will typically have a mix of securities with different frequencies of future cash flows.

There may be a need to use one conversion frequency for the entire portfolio, e.g. an annual effective rate. It would seem to be a straightforward matter to convert the various nominal rates of interest to one effective rate of interest using the standard formulas in Chapter 1.

Although this is basically true, there is a need to proceed carefully. For example, many practitioners like to analyze what will happen if interest rates rise or fall by a certain amount, say 100 basis points. (The number 100 is completely arbitrary. Select any number you like.) This is the type of analysis we used for effective duration in Section 11.4.

It is important to specify clearly which interest rate you are changing in making these types of tests. For example, changing the nominal rate on a bond with semiannual coupons by 100 basis points and changing the nominal rate on a monthly mortgage by 100 basis points are not equivalent to each other. Moreover, neither is equivalent to changing the effective rate on the entire portfolio by 100 basis points.

***Example 11.9** An investment fund wants to invest $100,000 in a mix of 5-year zero coupon bonds yielding 6% and 10-year zero coupon bonds yielding 7%, such that the modified duration of the portfolio will equal 7. Find the amount that should be invested in each type of bond.*

The Macaulay duration for the 5-year bond is 5 and the modified duration is

$$\frac{5}{1.06} = 4.7169811.$$

The Macaulay duration for the 10-year bond is 10 and the modified duration is

$$\frac{10}{1.07} = 9.3457944.$$

Let X be the amount to be invested in the 5-year bond. Adapting formula (11.24), we have

$$\bar{v} = 7 = \frac{X}{100{,}000}(4.7169811) + \frac{100{,}000 - X}{100{,}000}(9.3457944).$$

Now solving for X we have

$$700{,}000 = 4.7169811X + 934{,}579.44 - 9.3457944X$$

so that

$$4.6288133X = 234{,}579.44$$

or

$$X = \$50{,}678.$$

The investment fund should invest \$50,678 in 5-year zero coupon bonds and \$49,322 in 10-year zero coupon bonds.

Example 11.10 ***A 20% one-year bond with semiannual coupons is purchased at par. Calculate the progression of Macaulay durations at quarterly intervals over the entire life of the bond.***

On the issue date $t = 0$ and

$$\bar{d} = \frac{(.50)(.10)(1.1)^{-1} + (1.00)(1.10)(1.1)^{-2}}{(.10)(1.1)^{-1} + (1.10)(1.1)^{-2}} = .955.$$

After one quarter $t = .25$ and

$$\bar{d} = \frac{(.25)(.10)(1.1)^{-.5} + (.75)(1.10)(1.1)^{-1.5}}{(.10)(1.1)^{-.5} + (1.10)(1.1)^{-1.5}} = .705.$$

After two quarters $t = .50$ just *before* the coupon is paid

$$\bar{d} = \frac{(0)(.10)(1.1)^{0} + (.50)(1.10)(1.1)^{-1}}{(.10)(1.1)^{0} + (1.10)(1.1)^{-1}} = .455.$$

After two quarters $t = .50$ just *after* the coupon is paid

$$\bar{d} = \frac{(.50)(1.10)(1.1)^{-1}}{(1.10)(1.1)^{-1}} = .500.$$

After three quarters $t = .75$ and

$$\bar{d} = \frac{(.25)(.10)(1.1)^{-.5}}{(1.10)(1.1)^{-.5}} = .250.$$

After four quarters $t = 1$ and $\bar{d} = 0$.

Note that in general the duration of the bond decreases as it ages, but also note the jump in duration at the time of the coupon payment date $t = .50$. Finally, note that these Macaulay durations can all be converted to modified durations by dividing each of the answers by 1.1.

Example 11.11 You have an investment portfolio consisting of coupon bonds with a 7% yield rate convertible semiannually and mortgages with a 6% yield rate convertible monthly. For analytical purposes you are using annual effective rates on the entire portfolio and wish to examine the effects of a 100 basis points (1%) increase and decrease in the effective rate of interest. Find the yield rates which should be used:
(1) For the bonds.
(2) For the mortgages.

1. Use B to denote bonds and we have

$$1 + i_B = \left(1 + \frac{i_B^{(2)}}{2}\right)^2 = \left(1 + \frac{.07}{2}\right)^2 = 1.071225.$$

Thus, our tests will be run at effective rates .061225 and .081225. The equivalent nominal rates for the bonds are

$$i_{BL}^{(2)} = 2\left[(1.061225)^{.5} - 1\right] = .0603, \quad \text{or} \quad 6.03\%$$

and

$$i_{BH}^{(2)} = 2\left[(1.081225)^{.5} - 1\right] = .0796, \quad \text{or} \quad 7.96\%$$

where L denotes the lower rate and H the higher rate.

2. Use M to denote mortgages and we have

$$1+i_M = \left(1+\frac{i_M^{(12)}}{12}\right)^{12} = \left(1+\frac{.06}{12}\right)^{12} = 1.061678.$$

Thus, our tests will be run at effective rates .051678 and .071678. The equivalent nominal rates for the mortgage are

$$i_{ML}^{(12)} = 12\left[(1.051678)^{\frac{1}{12}}-1\right] = .0505, \quad \text{or} \quad 5.05\%$$

and

$$i_{MH}^{(12)} = 12\left[(1.071678)^{\frac{1}{12}}-1\right] = .0694, \quad \text{or} \quad 6.94\%.$$

11.6 MATCHING ASSETS AND LIABILITIES

Until this point in the book we have largely been analyzing individual transactions. We now shift our focus and consider a whole collection of transactions. More specifically, we consider the interrelationship between assets and liabilities for some financial enterprise, such as a bank, an insurance company, or a pension fund.

The assets will generate a series of cash inflows. We label the cash inflows as $A_1, A_2, \ldots, A_n$ which are made at times $1, 2, \ldots, n$. Similarly, the liabilities will generate a series of cash outflows. These are labeled $L_1, L_2, \ldots, L_n$ and occur at times $1, 2, \ldots, n$. The issue is how to achieve an equilibrium or safe balance between these cash inflows and outflows.

Before going further with the development of the theory, let us consider the nature of the problems that can arise if such equilibrium does not exist. The primary problem is the risk of adverse effects created by changes in the level of interest rates.

We can illustrate this problem with an example. Consider a financial institution, such as a bank or an insurance company, that issues a one-year instrument with a guaranteed rate of interest, e.g. a certificate of deposit (CD) or a guaranteed investment contract (GIC). A significant risk to the financial institution exists if the assets backing these contracts are invested either "too long" or "too short."

First, consider the case in which the assets are invested "too long," e.g. in investments with duration equal to two. The financial institution is vulnerable to losses if interest rates rise. Under these conditions contract holders are likely to withdraw their funds at the end of the year. The financial institution may have to sell assets to pay these departing contract holders. However, the assets that would have to be sold have declined in value due to the rise in interest rates. Losses may be incurred as a result.

Second, consider the case in which the assets are invested "too short," e.g. in very short-term investments with duration close to zero. Now the financial institution is vulnerable to losses if interest rates fall. Since its assets are invested very short-term, its interest earnings will decline quickly and may not be sufficient to pay the guaranteed interest on the contracts at the end of the year. Thus, losses may be incurred in this case as well.

Several techniques have been developed to address this issue. We will examine some of these in Sections 11.6 through 11.9.

The first approach is *absolute matching*, which is also called *dedication*. The concept with this approach is to structure an asset portfolio in such a fashion that the cash inflow that will be generated will exactly match the cash outflow from the liabilities in every period. If this can be achieved, then the enterprise is fully protected against any movement in interest rates.

As an example, consider a pension fund which provides annuities to a closed group of pensioners with a highly predictable payout pattern. A portfolio of high-grade non-callable bonds is structured such that the cash inflow will exactly match the annuity payout in each period. Such an investment fund is often called a *dedicated bond portfolio*. If such an arrangement can be achieved, the investment manager for the pension fund can relax, put feet on desk, and read the sports pages instead of the financial section of the newspaper!

The most straightforward method for constructing a dedicated bond portfolio is to use a series of zero coupon bonds to match each of the future cash outflows. However, such an approach does restrict the available pool of investments considerably.

It is also possible to construct a dedicated bond portfolio using coupon bonds. This will greatly broaden the available pool of investments. In order to find the right amount of each type of coupon bond to purchase, it will be necessary to select coupon bonds with maturity dates matching each the of cash outflow dates and to display the cash flows from each of the bonds. Then the technique is to start at the end and match the last cash flow with the longest term bond and work backwards recursively to the first cash flow. This technique will be illustrated in Example 11.13.

***Example 11.12** Several years ago ABC Corporation entered into a 10-year lease agreement under which ABC committed to make 10 annual lease payments. The first payment was $840,000 and each payment thereafter was to be adjusted for inflation with annual 4% increases (compounded). ABC has just made its seventh lease payment and has enough extra funds on hand from an unrelated property sale that it wishes to "pre-fund" its three remaining lease payments. It decides to do so using an absolute matching strategy with zero coupon bonds. The current yield curve for zero coupon bonds shows the following rates:*

Term	*Spot Rate*
1 year	*7.00%*
2 years	*8.00%*
3 years	*8.75%*

Find the amount that ABC will need to invest to implement this strategy.

The three remaining lease payments are in the amounts:

Time	Amount
8	$840{,}000(1.04)^7 = 1{,}105{,}383$
9	$840{,}000(1.04)^8 = 1{,}149{,}598$
10	$840{,}000(1.04)^9 = 1{,}195{,}582$

The cost of the absolute matching strategy is

$$\frac{1{,}105{,}383}{1.07} + \frac{1{,}149{,}598}{(1.08)^2} + \frac{1{,}195{,}582}{(1.0875)^3} = \$2{,}948{,}253.$$

***Example 11.13** Rework Example 11.12 using coupon bonds with annual coupons. Assume that the coupon bonds all have the same yield rate as the zero coupon bonds above and that all sell at par.*

We start at the end and work backwards. We must fund the last lease payment with the last coupon and the maturity value on a 3-year bond. Per dollar of redemption value, this is 1.0875. Thus, ABC should buy

$$\frac{1{,}195{,}582}{1.0875} = 1{,}099{,}386$$

face amount of 3-year bonds. In addition to producing the right payment at time 10, this bond also produces coupons of

$$1{,}099{,}386(.0875) = 96{,}196$$

at times 8 and 9.

We next go to the 2-year bond. Per dollar of redemption value, this bond produces 1.08 at time 9. Thus, ABC should buy

$$\frac{1{,}149{,}598 - 96{,}196}{1.08} = 975{,}352$$

face amount of 2-year bonds. In addition to producing the right payment at time 9, this bond also produces a coupon of

$$975{,}372(.08) = 78{,}030$$

at time 8.

Finally, we go to the 1-year bond. Per dollar of redemption value, this bond produces 1.07 at time 1. Thus, ABC should buy

$$\frac{1{,}105{,}383 - 96{,}196 - 78{,}030}{1.07} = 870{,}240$$

face amount of 1-year bonds.

Since the bonds all sell at par, the total cost to ABC is

$$\begin{array}{r} 1{,}099{,}386 \\ 975{,}372 \\ 870{,}240 \\ \hline \$2{,}944{,}998 \end{array}$$

Actually, based on the theory developed in Chapter 10, it is not completely consistent for coupon bonds and zero coupon bonds of the same term to sell at the same yield rate. This artificial assumption was used to illustrate more simply the type of calculations needed when coupon bonds are used for absolute matching and to make an enlightening comparison.

Why is the cost using coupon bonds slightly lower than the cost using zero coupon bonds? The answer can be seen by first looking at the rental payment due at time 8. Using zero coupon bonds, this entire payment is financed with money earning 7%. However, when using coupon bonds, a small portion of it is financed with money earning 8% and another small portion with money earning 8.75%. Similarly, when using zero coupon bonds at time 9, the entire rental payment is financed with money earning 8%. However, when using coupon bonds, a small portion of it is financed with money earning 8.75%.

Table 11.3 Summary of Results for Example 11.13.

	$P=C$	CF_8	CF_9	CF_{10}
Liability CF		1,105,383	1,149,598	1,195,582
3-year bond	1,099,386	96,196	96,196	1,195,582
2-year bond	975,372	78,030	1,053,402	
1-year bond	870,240	931,157		

Table 11.3 compiles the calculations described above. The symbols "P" and "C" are standard bond symbols from Chapter 6, while "CF_t" stands for a cash flow at time t.

We end this example with one final terminology note. In the accounting literature when a company "pre-funds" a liability in this fashion, it is said to *defease* that liability. The accounting treatment for a defeased liability may be different than it is for a liability that is not defeased.

11.7 IMMUNIZATION

Immunization is another technique that has been developed to structure the assets and liabilities in a manner that would reduce or even eliminate the type of problems described in Section 11.6. In other words, the enterprise would be "immunized" against adverse effects created by changes in the level of interest rates.

This technique is more flexible than absolute matching, since it does not require exacting matching of an asset cash flow for each liability cash flow. It is frequently called *Redington immunization* in tribute to F.M. Redington who first introduced the concept of immunization in a 1952 publication entitled *Review of the Principles of Life-Office Valuations*.

Immunization starts with the assumption that the yield curve is flat. It then assumes that interest rate changes are parallel shifts up or down in that yield curve. Let the net cash flow at time t be denoted by R_t, i.e.

$$R_t = A_t - L_t \quad \text{for} \quad t = 1, 2, \ldots, n \qquad (11.26)$$

where A_t and L_t were defined in Section 11.6.

We will assume that the present value of the cash inflows from the assets is equal to the present value of the cash outflows from the liabilities. Thus, from formula (11.3) we have

$$P(i) = 0. \tag{11.27}$$

We now institute a small change in the rate of interest from i to $i+\varepsilon$. If we expand $P(i)$ as a Taylor series as far as second derivatives, we have

$$P(i+\varepsilon) = P(i) + \varepsilon P'(i) + \frac{\varepsilon^2}{2} P''(i+\xi), \quad \text{where} \quad 0<|\xi|<|\varepsilon| .$$

$P(i)$ will have a local minimum at i if two conditions hold. First, we must have

$$P'(i) = 0. \tag{11.28}$$

Note that formula (11.28) can be interpreted as requiring that modified duration of the net cash flows must equal zero. Second, we must have

$$P''(i) > 0. \tag{11.29}$$

Formula (11.29) can be interpreted as requiring that convexity of the net cash flows is greater than zero.

If $P(i)$ has a local minimum, we obtain a key result in immunization theory; namely, that small changes in the interest rate in either direction will increase the present value of net cash flows. This certainly seems to be a highly desirable result, if it can be achieved.

It is important to characterize these results verbally. The liabilities are largely determined by forces outside the control of the enterprise in question. Thus, immunization is aimed at managing the structure of the assets. The immunization strategy is to arrange the assets so that three conditions are met:

1. The present value of the cash inflows from the assets is equal to the present value of the cash outflows from the liabilities. This condition assures that the correct amount of assets are utilized to support the liabilities.

2. The modified duration of the assets is equal to the modified duration of the liabilities. This condition assures that price sensitivity to changes in interest rates is the same for the assets and the liabilities.

3. The convexity of the assets is greater than the convexity of the liabilities. When this condition is satisfied, a decrease in interest rates will cause asset values to increase by more than the increase in liability values. Conversely, an increase in interest rates will cause asset values to decrease by less than the decrease in liability values.

Condition 3 is particularly interesting. It may not be immediately clear how such a favorable result could occur. Figure 11.4 is an expansion of Figure 11.1 and graphically displays how Condition 3 could happen.

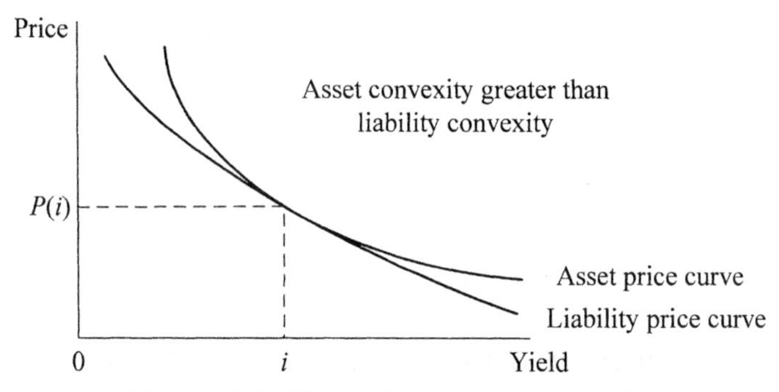

Figure 11.4 Illustration of formula (11.29)

In practice there are some difficulties and limitations in implementing an immunization strategy as described above. We list seven such problems with immunization:

1. The choice of the one interest rate i which should be used in the calculations for all assets and liabilities is not always clear. Different strategies may emerge depending upon the value of i chosen.

2. The technique is designed to work for small changes in i. There is no assurance it will continue to work for large changes in i. However, a technique has been developed, sometimes called "full immunization," which extends immunization theory so that it is applicable for large changes in i as well. The details are given in Section 11.8.

3. The yield curve is flat and the entire yield curve shifts in parallel when interest rates change. If other patterns develop, then the technique breaks down. Unfortunately, yield curves are usually not flat and shifts are often not parallel.

4. Immunization requires frequent rebalancing of portfolios to keep modified duration of assets and liabilities equal. Modified duration may change at different rates for each of the assets and for each of the liabilities as time passes.

5. Exact cash flows may not be known and may have to be estimated. For example, the liabilities may involve payments whose timing cannot be precisely determined in advance. Also, cash inflows from assets may vary because of prepayments on mortgages and the exercise of the call feature on callable bonds.

6. The convexity condition would seem to imply that a profit can be made with interest rate movements in either direction. This appears to violate a principle of finance theory which states that risk-free arbitrage does not exist for any significant period of time in efficient markets.

7. Assets may not exist in the right maturities to achieve immunization. For example, this could happen if the modified duration of the liabilities is quite long.

Despite these qualifications, the development of immunization as described above has been a large step forward in improving investment strategies. Even when immunization is not or cannot be completely implemented, partial immunization has still proven to be superior in practice to not recognizing the relationship between assets and liabilities at all.

Furthermore, the technique as described above has served as the springboard for attempts to improve the technique by eliminating or lessening the impact of the problems listed above. Considerable research and literature has been devoted to these efforts in recent years.

***Example 11.14** A owes B $1100 at the end of one year and is required to set up an investment fund in order to meet this obligation. The only investments available are a money market fund earning 10% currently with the rate changing daily and two-year zero coupon bonds also earning 10%. Develop an investment program based on immunization. Assume the effective rate of interest is equal to 10% in all calculations.*

Let X be the amount invested in the money market fund and Y be the amount invested in two-year zero coupon bonds. Then we have

$$\begin{aligned} P(i) &= X + 1.21Y(1+i)^{-2} - 1100(1+i)^{-1} \\ P'(i) &= -2.42Y(1+i)^{-3} + 1100(1+i)^{-2} \\ P''(i) &= 7.26Y(1+i)^{-4} - 2200(1+i)^{-3}. \end{aligned}$$

Formula (11.27) gives us the equation

$$P(.1) = X + Y - 1000 = 0.$$

Formula (11.28) gives us the equation

$$P'(.1) = -\frac{2Y}{1.1} + \frac{1000}{1.1} = 0.$$

This gives us two equations in two unknowns, so that we do not have the flexibility in this case to try to apply formula (11.29). Solving the two equations in two unknowns gives us $X = 500$ and $Y = 500$.

Although we could not apply formula (11.29) in developing the investment allocation, we need to test our answer for convexity. We have

$$P''(.1) = \frac{(7.26)(500)}{(1.1)^4} - \frac{2200}{(1.1)^3} = 826.45 > 0 .$$

Thus, our strategy satisfies formula (11.29) anyway, which is a happy result.

Let us test the result empirically for changes in i of 1% in either direction. We have

$$\begin{aligned} P(.10) &= 0 \\ P(.11) &= 500 + \frac{(1.21)(500)}{(1.11)^2} - \frac{1100}{1.11} = .0406 > 0 \\ P(.09) &= 500 + \frac{(1.21)(500)}{(1.09)^2} - \frac{1100}{1.09} = .0421 > 0. \end{aligned}$$

Thus, the value of $P(i)$ increases for movements of i away from i = 10% in either direction! This may seem too good to be true, but it illustrates a result that immunization is attempting to achieve.

Example 11.15 For the assets in Example 11.14 compute:
(1) Modified duration.
(2) Convexity.

1. Using the asset portion of the expressions above, we have

$$P(i) = X + 1.21Y(1+i)^{-2} = 1000.00$$

and

$$P'(i) = -2.42Y(1+i)^{-3} = -909.09$$

when evaluated at $X = 500$, $Y = 500$, and $i = .1$. Then applying formula (11.4) we have

$$\bar{v} = -\frac{P'(i)}{P(i)} = .90909.$$

Another approach is to use formula (11.5). We have the following modified durations:

Money market fund: $\bar{v} = 0$

Two-year zero coupon bonds: $\bar{v} = \frac{2}{1.1}$

The weighted average of these two values reflecting our investment allocation is

$$.5(0)+.5\left(\frac{2}{1.1}\right) = .90909.$$

As an exercise the reader will be asked to confirm that this value equals the modified duration of the liability.

2. Again, using the asset portion of the expressions above, we have

$$P''(i) = 7.26Y(1+i)^{-4} = 2479.34$$

when evaluated at $Y = 500$ and $i = .1$. Then applying formula (11.8), we have

$$\bar{c} = \frac{P''(i)}{P(i)} = 2.47934.$$

As an exercise the reader will be asked to confirm that this value is greater than the convexity of the liability.

11.8 FULL IMMUNIZATION

The immunization technique developed in Section 11.7 is designed to work for small changes in i. *Full immunization* is an extension of this technique which can be applied for changes of any magnitude in i.

Consider one liability cash outflow of L_k at time k. The concept of full immunization is to hold two assets providing cash inflows of A at time $k-a$ and B at time $k+b$, where $a>0$, $b>0$, and $a \le k$. Thus, one asset produces a cash inflow prior to the liability outflow, while the other asset produces an inflow subsequent to the liability outflow.

Assume that exactly two of the four values of A, B, a, and b are known. We will use the force of interest δ equivalent to i. From formulas (11.27) and (11.28), using time k rather than time 0 as the comparison date, we obtain

$$P(\delta) = Ae^{a\delta} + Be^{-b\delta} - L_k = 0 \tag{11.30}$$

and

$$P'(\delta) = Aae^{a\delta} - Bbe^{-b\delta} = 0. \tag{11.31}$$

The full immunization strategy is obtained by solving these two equations in two unknowns.

We now show that full immunization achieves the desired result. Consider some other force of interest δ'. We have

$$\begin{aligned} P(\delta') &= Ae^{a\delta'} + Be^{-b\delta'} - L_k \\ &= Ae^{a\delta'} + Be^{-b\delta'} - \left(Ae^{a\delta} + Be^{-b\delta}\right) \\ &= Ae^{a\delta}\left[e^{a(\delta'-\delta)} + \frac{a}{b}e^{-b(\delta'-\delta)} - \left(1+\frac{a}{b}\right)\right] \end{aligned}$$

upon substituting the formula for $P'(\delta)=0$.

Now consider the function

$$f(x) = e^{ax} + \frac{a}{b}e^{-bx} - \left(1+\frac{a}{b}\right).$$

Note that $f(0) = 0$. Differentiating, we have

$$f'(x) = a\left(e^{ax} - e^{-bx}\right)$$

from which we see that

$$\begin{aligned} f'(x) &= 0 \text{ for } x = 0 \\ f'(x) &> 0 \text{ for } x > 0 \\ f'(x) &< 0 \text{ for } x < 0. \end{aligned}$$

Thus, $f(x) > 0$ for all $x \neq 0$. From this result we see that $P(\delta') > 0$ for all $\delta' \neq \delta$. This confirms the results of full immunization.

The two equations in two unknowns may or may not have a unique solution. If the two known quantities are: (1) a, b; (2) B, b; (3) A, a; or (4) A, b; then a unique solution exists. However, for the cases: (5) a, B; and (6) A, B; a unique solution does not necessarily exist. In these latter two cases, solutions may be multiple or nonexistent.

Applying full immunization requires structuring the assets in such a way that two asset cash inflows are associated with each liability cash outflow. Frequent rebalancing of the portfolio is necessary, just as it is with regular immunization.

Example 11.16 ***Show that full immunization produces the same investment strategy as Redington immunization in Example 11.14.***

One liability cash outflow of 1100 occurs at time $k = 1$, i.e. $L_1 = 1100$. We need to offset this cash outflow with two asset inflows of A at time $k - a$ and B at time $k + b$. Based on the two assets given in the question, we will have cash inflows at times $t = 0$ and 2. Clearly, $a = 1$ and $b = 1$, since $k = 1$. Thus, exactly two of the four values A, B, a and b are known.

Formula (11.30) gives us

$$Ae^{a\delta} + Be^{-b\delta} - L_k = 0$$

or

$$A(1.1) + B(1.1)^{-1} - 1100 = 0.$$

Formula (11.31) gives us

$$Aae^{a\delta} - Bbe^{-b\delta} = 0$$

or

$$A(1.1) - B(1.1)^{-1} = 0.$$

Substituting $B(1.1)^{-1} = A(1.1)$ from the second equation into the first equation, we have

$$2A(1.1) = 1100 \quad \text{or} \quad A = 500.$$

Substituting back into the first equation, we have

$$B(1.1)^{-1} = 1100 - 500(1.1) = 550$$

so that

$$B = 550(1.1) = 605.$$

Now A is a value at time $t = 0$, and thus is the amount invested in the money market fund. However, B is a value at time $t = 2$, so the amount that should be invested in the two-year zero coupon bond at time $t = 0$ is

$$\frac{6.05}{(1.1)^2} = 500.$$

Thus, we get the same answer as Example 11.14.

11.9 A MORE GENERAL MODEL

Our last model is more general in the sense that it incorporates behavioral assumptions and thus involves probability and statistics. None of the other models in this chapter involve probability and statistics. This method is rather complicated and the full details are beyond the scope of this book. However, we will present a simple illustration of the basic concept.

Let us again focus on two types of risk from movements in the level of interest rates for a financial enterprise investing funds which are required as backing for future cash outflow commitments:

1. When interest rates fall, the risk is having to reinvest funds at lower rates of interest. This provides an incentive to invest in long-term instruments. The normal yield curve with a positive slope also provides the same incentive.

2. When interest rates rise, the risks are having to sell assets at losses and also missing the opportunity to reinvest funds at higher rates of interest. This provides an incentive to invest in short-term instruments.

The following example demonstrates an approach to balance these two conflicting motivations. Assume that a bank guarantees an effective rate of interest of 8% on two-year certificates of deposit. Funds can be withdrawn without penalty at the end of the first or second year. The bank can invest in two types of instruments only:

- One year notes yielding 8% effective.
- Two year notes yielding 8.5% effective.

This pattern reflects the normal yield curve with positive slope. Thus, we already see one new feature in this model. Classical immunization theory does not recognize the term structure of interest rates.

Let k_1 and k_2 be the amount of funds withdrawn by the holders of the CDs at the ends of years 1 and 2, respectively. The reader should be careful to note that k_1 and k_2 are amounts withdrawn, not rates of withdrawal. For each dollar deposited in the CDs we have the equation of value

$$1 = (1.08)^{-1} k_1 + (1.08)^{-2} k_2$$

which can be expressed as

$$k_2 = (1.08)^2 - 1.08k_1.$$

Explicit recognition of future withdrawal rates is a second new feature in this model.

Let p_1 and p_2 equal the proportion of funds the bank invests in one-year and two-year notes, respectively. Clearly, $p_1 + p_2 = 1$. Let f be the forward (reinvestment) rate on one-year notes in the second year. Note that in Chapter 10 this forward rate was denoted by f_1. Explicit consideration of reinvestment rates is a third new feature in this model. Finally, let A_2 equal the accumulated value of the bank's funds arising from this transaction at the end of the second year. Then we have

$$\begin{aligned} A_2 &= \left[p_1(1.08) - k_1\right](1+f) + \left[p_2(1.085)^2 - k_2\right] \\ &= \left[p_1(1.08) - k_1\right](1+f) + \left[(1-p_1)(1.085)^2 - (1.08)^2 + (1.08)k_1\right] \\ &= \left[(1.08)(1+f) - (1.085)^2\right]p_1 + k_1(.08 - f) + (1.085)^2 - (1.08)^2. \end{aligned}$$

We need to analyze the impact of fluctuations in f on the value of A_2 in order to develop a recommendation concerning the selection of p_1 (and thus p_2 also).

First, we consider the case of a decrease in interest rates. Suppose that f is equal to 7%. This will create a low rate of withdrawal by the holders of the CDs at the end of the first year, since there are incentives to leave funds in the CD. Assume the amount withdrawn k_1 is only 10 cents per dollar originally invested. We then have

$$A_2 = -.021625\,p_1 + .011825.$$

We want A_2 to be greater than 0, which will happen if $p_1 < .5468$.

Second, we consider the case of an increase in interest rates. Suppose that f is equal to 9.5%. This will create a high rate of withdrawal by the holders of the CDs at the end of the first year, since high rates are available elsewhere. Assume the amount withdrawn k_1 is 90 cents per dollar originally invested. We then have

$$A_2 = .005375\,p_1 - .002675.$$

We want A_2 to be greater than 0, which will happen if $p_1 > .4977$.

Thus, the recommended investment strategy for the bank based on these assumptions is to choose p_1 such that $.4977 < p_1 < .5468$. Since $p_2 = 1 - p_1$, the investment allocation is determined.

Application of this technique requires investment managers to make certain key assumptions which are not required in classical immunization. One key assumption is how high and how low to set the forward (reinvestment) rate in working through the two cases. A second key assumption is the level of withdrawal rates that will develop in the two cases. Unfortunately, the technique is sensitive to these assumptions, which means that relatively modest changes in the assumptions can result in significantly different allocation strategies. Nevertheless, despite this sensitivity, this model has proven to be useful in practical applications.

APPENDIX 11

Further analysis of varying annuities

In Section 11.3 in discussing convexity we encountered series whose terms are the product of a second degree polynomial and an exponential. The following algorithm is useful in summing such series.

From the subject of numerical analysis, the first difference is defined by

$$\Delta f(t) = f(t+1) - f(t).$$

Higher order differences can be developed by successively applying the above formula.

A formula for summation by parts can be derived which is analogous to integration by parts

$$\sum_{t=1}^{n} v^t f(t) = \left[\frac{v^t}{v-1} \left\{ 1 - \frac{v\Delta}{v-1} + \frac{v^2\Delta^2}{(v-1)^2} - \frac{v^3\Delta^3}{(v-1)^3} + \cdots \right\} f(t) \right]_{t=1}^{t=n+1}$$

$$= \left[\frac{v^{t-1}}{i} \left\{ 1 + \frac{\Delta}{i} + \frac{\Delta^2}{i^2} + \frac{\Delta^3}{i^3} + \cdots \right\} f(t) \right]_{t=n+1}^{t=1} \qquad (11.32)$$

This formula will give practical results whenever higher order differences past a certain point can be safely ignored. In particular, if $f(t)$ is a polynomial of degree m, then $(m+1)$th and higher differences are all zero.

Thus, this formula can be used to find the present value of varying annuities whose payments follow a polynomial.

EXERCISES

11.2 Duration

1. Show that $\lim_{i \to \infty} \bar{d}$ is equal to the point in time at which the first payment is made.

2. Find the Macaulay duration of a common stock which pays dividends at the end of each year, if it is assumed that each dividend is 4% greater than the prior dividend and the effective rate of interest is 8%.

3. Find an expression for the modified duration of $\bar{a}_{\overline{n}|}$.

4. Show that the modified duration of a perpetuity-immediate and the present value of the same perpetuity are equal.

5. Calculate the Macaulay duration of an 8-year 100 par value bond with 10% annual coupons and an effective rate of interest equal to 8%.

6. The current price of an annual coupon bond is 100. The derivative of the price of the bond with respect to the yield to maturity is −650. The yield to maturity is an effective rate of 7%.

   a) Calculate the Macaulay duration of the bond.

   b) Estimate the price of the bond using formula (11.6) when the yield rate is 8% instead of 7%.

7. You are aware that prepayments will "shorten" the average life of a mortgage. You are looking at a group of 15-year mortgages with annual installments. You are asked to compute the Macaulay duration for a 15-year mortgage which is "prepaid" immediately after the 3rd regular payment is made. The effective rate of interest on the mortgages is 6% per annum.

11.3 Convexity

8. Find the convexity of a mortgage with annual installments which is prepaid at the end of one year. The effective rate of interest is 8% on the mortgage.

9. There is a loan obligation to pay $1000 one year from today and another $1000 two years from today. Assuming the annual effective rate of interest is 10%, find the following:

   a) The Macaulay duration of this loan.

   b) The convexity of this loan.

10. If there is only one payment, then the variance σ^2 in formula (11.17) would be zero. Verbally interpret the result that $\frac{d\bar{v}}{d\delta} = 0$ in this situation.

11. A loan is to be repaid with payments of $1000 at the end of one year, $2000 at the end of two years, and $3000 at the end of three years. The effective rate of interest is 25%.

    a) Find the amount of the loan.

    b) Find the duration.

    c) Find the modified duration.

    d) Find the convexity.

12. Find the convexity of a loan repaid with equal installments over n periods if $i = 0$.

13. Find the convexity of the common stock in Exercise 2.

14. Rework Exercise 6 to obtain a refined answer using convexity as well as modified duration. The value of $\frac{d\bar{v}}{di}$ is given to be 800.

11.4 Interest sensitive cash flows

15. A 5-year $100 par value bond has 6.7% coupons payable semiannually. Its current price is $101.2606 and it is yielding 6.4% convertible semiannually. If the yield rate decreases by 0.1%, its price increases to 101.6931. If the yield rate increases by 0.1%, its price decreases to 100.8422.

    a) Calculate the effective duration of the bond.

    b) Calculate the effective convexity of the bond.

    c) Estimate the price of the bond if the yield rate increases by .75%.

16. A borrower has a loan of $100,000 repaid with level annual payments at the end of each year for 20 years at an effective interest rate of 8%. The borrower can renegotiate or prepay the loan at any time without penalty. At the time the tenth regular payment is made, if the market interest rate rises, the borrower will still repay the loan as originally scheduled. However, if it falls, the borrower will repay the loan with five level annual payments at the end of each following five years. Assume a 1% increase and a 1% decrease in the interest rate.

    a) Calculate the effective duration.

    b) Calculate the effective convexity.

17. In Example 16 apply formula (11.22) to estimate the market value of the loan at market interest rates of 7% and 9%. Answers to the nearest dollar.

18. Derive formula (11.20).

11.5 Analysis of portfolios

19. You have purchased three bonds to form a portfolio as follows:

    (*i*) Bond A has semiannual coupons at 4%, a duration of 21.46 years, and was purchased for $980.

    (*ii*) Bond B is a 15-year bond with a duration of 12.35 years and was purchased for $1015.

    (*iii*) Bond C has a duration of 16.67 years and was purchased for $1000.

    Calculate the duration of the portfolio at the time of purchase.

20. A 3-year loan at 10% effective is being repaid with level annual payments at the end of each year.

    a) Calculate the "jump" in duration at the time the first payment is made.

    b) Rework (*a*) at the time the second payment is made.

    c) Compare the answers to (*a*) and (*b*) and verbally explain the relationship.

21. A government bond fund buys a mix of 3-month Treasury bills with a stated rate of 6% and a variety of Treasury bonds with semiannual coupons. The firm is analyzing the implications if the stated yield rates on the Treasury bonds increase or decrease by 100 basis points. What rates should be used on the Treasury bills for consistency?

22. A $60,000 portfolio is constructed with $10,000 used to buy 2-year zero coupon bonds, $20,000 used to buy 5-year zero coupon bonds, and $30,000 used to buy 10-year zero coupon bonds. The yield rates on the bonds are unknown. Calculate the Macaulay convexity of the portfolio at inception.

11.6 Matching assets and liabilities

23. In Example 11.12 find the overall level yield rate (IRR) earned by ABC Corporation over the 3-year period.

24. Rework Example 11.12 if the yield curve is inverted as follows:

Term	Spot rate
1 year	8.75%
2 years	8.00%
3 years	7.00%

25. A company must pay liabilities of $1000 and $2000 at the end of years 1 and 2, respectively. The only investments available to the company are the following two zero-coupon bonds:

Maturity (years)	Effective annual yield	Par
1	10%	1000
2	12%	1000

Determine the cost to the company today to match its liabilities exactly.

26. An insurance company accepts an obligation to pay $10,000 at the end of each year for 2 years. The insurance company purchases a combination of the following two bonds at a total cost of $$X$ in order to exactly match its obligation:

    (i) 1-year 4% annual coupon bond with a yield rate of 5%.

    (ii) 2-year 6% annual coupon bond with a yield rate of 5%.

Calculate X to the nearest dollar.

27. A company must pay liabilities of $1000 due 6 months form now and $2000 due one year from now. The only investments available to the company are two bonds. Bond A is a 6-month bond with 8% nominal annual coupon rate convertible semiannually and a 6% nominal annual yield rate convertible semiannually. Bond B is a 1-year bond with 5% nominal annual coupon rate convertible semiannually and a 7% nominal annual yield rate convertible semiannually

    a) Determine the cost to the company now to match its liabilities exactly.

    b) What is the level nominal annual IRR convertible semiannually for investment in the bonds required to exactly match its liabilities?

11.7 Immunization

28. *a*) Confirm that the modified duration of the assets obtained in Example 11.15(1) is equal to the modified duration of the liability.

    b) Confirm that the convexity of the assets obtained in Example 11.15(2) is greater than the convexity of the liability.

29. *a*) In Example 11.14 assume that the investor puts $600 in the money market fund and $400 in two-year bonds. Find:

    (1) $P(.09)$

    (2) $P(.10)$

    (3) $P(.11)$

    b) Rework (*a*) assuming the investor puts $400 in the money market fund and $600 in two-year bonds.

    c) Verbally interpret the answers to (*a*) and (*b*) in comparison with the answers in Example 11.14.

30. A company owes $100 to be paid at times 2, 4, and 6. The company plans to meet the obligation with an investment program that produces asset cash flows of A_1 at time 1 and A_5 at time 5. The effective rate of interest is 10%.

    a) Determine A_1 and A_5.

    b) Does this investment program satisfy the conditions for Redington immunization?

11.8 Full immunization

31. A payment of \$10,000 is due at time 10. This obligation will be met by two payments of A at time 5 and B at time 15. The effective rate of interest is 10% and a full immunization strategy is adopted.

    a) Find A.

    b) Find B.

32. A payment of \$10,000 is due at time 10. This obligation will be met by two payments of A at time $10 - a$ and \$6000 at time 12. The effective rate of interest is 10% and a full immunization strategy is adopted.

    a) Find A.

    b) Find a.

11.9 A more general model

33. *a*) Rework the illustration in Section 11.9 if the forward rates are 7.5% and 9% instead of 7% and 9.5%, respectively.

    b) Rework the illustration in Section 11.9 if the forward rates are 6.5% and 10% instead of 7% and 9.5%, respectively.

34. *a*) Rework the illustration in Section 11.9 if $k_1 = 20$ cents and 80 cents instead of 10 cents and 90 cents, respectively.

    b) Rework the illustration in Section 11.9 if $k_1 = 0$ cents and 100 cents instead of 10 cents and 90 cents, respectively.

Miscellaneous

35. As of $12/31/z$, an insurance company has an obligation to pay \$1,000,000 on $12/31/z+4$. To fund this liability, the company purchases 4-year 5% annual coupon bonds totaling \$822,703 of par value. The company anticipates reinvestment interest rates to remain constant at 5% through $12/31/z+4$. The maturity value of the bond equals the par value. The company is testing reinvestment interest rate scenarios effective $1/1/z+1$ in which interest rates increase or decrease by ½ %. Find the insurance company's profit or loss as of $12/31/z+4$ after the liability is paid under these two scenarios.

36. A financial institution accepts a \$20,000 deposit from a customer on which it guarantees to pay 10% effective for two years. The customer expresses an intention to withdraw half the proceeds at the end of the first year. The financial institution can invest in either one-year zero coupon bonds yielding 10% or two-year zero coupon bonds yielding 11%. The institution is analyzing two options:

    A - an absolute matching strategy.

    B - investing entirely in two-year bonds to receive the higher rate.

    a) Find the profit at inception to the institution under Option A.

    b) Find the one-year forward rate on one-year bonds at which Option B would be equivalent to Option A.

37. A financial institution accepts an \$85,000 deposit from a customer on which it guarantees to pay 8% compounded annually for ten years. The only investments available to the institution are five-year zero coupon bonds and preferred stocks, both yielding 8%. The institution develops an investment policy using the following reasoning:

    (*i*) The duration of the five-year zero coupon bonds is 5.

    (*ii*) The duration of the preferred stock is 13.5 (see Example 11.1(4)).

    (*iii*) The duration of the obligation to the customer is 10.

    (*iv*) Taking the weighted average of the durations, the amount invested in five-year zero coupon bonds is chosen to be

    $$\frac{13.5-10}{13.5-5}(85,000) = \$35,000$$

    while the amount invested in preferred stock is chosen to be

    $$\frac{10-5}{13.5-5}(85,000) = \$50,000.$$

    Verify that this investment strategy is optimal under immunization theory, assuming the customer leaves the funds on deposit for the full ten-year period.

38. A financial institution has an obligation to pay \$10,000 at the end of each year for 5 years. The institution receives $10,000a_{\overline{5}|.1} = \$37,908$ in exchange for assuming this obligation. The only investments available to the institution are 1, 3, and 5-year zero coupon bonds, all yielding 10%. The institution develops an investment policy using the following reasoning:

    (*i*) The durations of the obligations are symmetrically spaced around the durations of the available investments.

    (*ii*) Thus, the money to be invested will be divided in thirds, so that \$12,636 will be invested in each of the 1, 3, and 5-year zero coupon bonds.

    Verify that this investment strategy is not optimal under immunization theory. Develop a superior investment strategy.

39. *a*) Consider a \$1 bond with annual coupons of g per year for n years. If the bond sells for par, i.e. of $g = i$ where i is the yield rate, then show that the Macaulay duration of the bond is equal to $\ddot{a}_{\overline{n}|}$ at rate $g = i$, assuming the bond is held to maturity.

    b) Use this shortcut technique for at-par bonds to confirm the answer to Example 11.1(2).

40. The following formula has appeared in the literature as an alternative to formula (11.6)

$$P(i+h) \approx P(i)\left(\frac{1+i}{1+i+h}\right)^{\bar{d}}$$

for estimating the price of a bond based on the price at another rate of interest.

a) Rework Example 11.2 using this formula.

b) Find the error in this approach.

12

Stochastic approaches to interest

12.1 INTRODUCTION

The prior chapters in this book have presented the theory of interest largely on a deterministic basis. Chapter 12 introduces the reader to some stochastic approaches to interest.

Actually, there were two areas in the prior chapters where probabilities were explicitly introduced. One area was the consideration of default probabilities in Section 9.8, and the second was the assumption regarding withdrawals from the certificate of deposit illustration in Section 11.9. Also, formula (11.17) for the derivative of duration was denoted with variance notation for ease in presentation. Finally, there was implicit recognition of risk and uncertainty in such areas as the exercise of the call provision on callable bonds and prepayment rates on mortgage loans. Nevertheless, the overall approach taken previously in the book has been largely deterministic.

In Chapter 12 we first consider the rate of interest directly as a random variable. We then provide a basic introduction to several models with a stochastic basis which have important applications in practice. Finally, we examine the widely used approach of scenario testing as a means of dealing with future uncertainty.

We assume that the reader has a basic background in mathematical statistics. The level of statistics used in this chapter is not advanced. Readers who would like a condensed refresher of the results from statistics that are used in this chapter are referred to Appendix D.

12.2 INDEPENDENT RATES OF INTEREST

We now consider the rate of interest to be a random variable. In Sections 12.2 and 12.3 we consider the case in which the rate of interest in one period is independent of the rate of interest in any other period. Starting in Section 12.4 we will remove the independence assumption and examine some models in which successive rates are correlated in some fashion.

A preliminary illustration

We will first demonstrate that expected accumulated and present values are not necessarily equal to accumulated and present values at the expected rate of interest. In order to demonstrate this possibility, consider the investment of one unit for ten years at a constant effective rate of interest which is unknown, but is equally likely to be 7%, 8%, or 9%.

Let $\bar{i}$ be the mean effective rate of interest. From elementary statistics the expected rate of interest is given by

$$\bar{i} = \mathrm{E}[i] = \frac{1}{3}[.07 + .08 + .09] = .08.$$

The expected accumulated value is given by

$$\mathrm{E}\left[(1+i)^{10}\right] = \frac{1}{3}\left[(1.07)^{10} + (1.08)^{10} + (1.09)^{10}\right] = 2.16448.$$

However, the accumulated value at the expected rate of interest is

$$(1+\bar{i})^{10} = (1.08)^{10} = 2.15892.$$

Thus, in this illustration the expected accumulated value is not equal to the accumulated value at the expected rate of interest. The rate of interest j which would produce the expected accumulated value can be determined from

$$(1+j)^{10} = 2.16448$$

which can be solved to give $j = .08028$, or 8.028%.

A similar result can also occur for present values. Assume we wish to invest an amount today sufficient to accumulate to one unit at the end of ten years and assume the same conditions described above concerning the unknown constant rate of interest.

The expected present value is given by

$$\text{E}\left[(1+i)^{-10}\right] = \frac{1}{3}\left[(1.07)^{-10} + (1.08)^{-10} + (1.09)^{-10}\right] = .46465$$

while the present value at the expected rate of interest is

$$(1+\bar{i})^{-10} = (1.08)^{-10} = .46319.$$

The rate of interest j which would produce the expected present value can be determined from

$$(1+j)^{-10} = .46465,$$

which can be solved to give $j = .07966$, or 7.966%.

Accumulated values

In the above illustrations we assumed that the uncertain rate of interest was constant over the ten-year period. We now consider the situation in which the rate of interest can vary from period to period according to some distribution which does not change over time.

We will adopt the notation used in Chapter 1 and let the rate of interest during the tth period, i.e. from time $t-1$ to t, be denoted by i_t for $t = 1, 2, \ldots, n$. The accumulated value of an investment of 1 at the end of n periods is given by formula (1.40) with a change in notation

$$a(n) = (1+i_1)(1+i_2)\cdots(1+i_n) = \prod_{t=1}^{n}(1+i_t). \tag{1.40}$$

Now assume that the i_t's are independently and identically distributed with mean $\bar{i}$. The mean of the accumulated value is given by

$$\begin{aligned} \mathrm{E}[a(n)] &= \mathrm{E}\left[\prod_{t=1}^{n}(1+i_t)\right] \\ &= \prod_{t=1}^{n}\mathrm{E}[1+i_t] \text{ from independence} \\ &= (1+\bar{i})^n. \end{aligned} \tag{12.1}$$

Note that in this case the expected accumulated value does equal the accumulated value at the expected interest rate.

We next consider the variance of the accumulated value which is

$$\begin{aligned} \mathrm{Var}[a(n)] &= \mathrm{E}[a^2(n)] - \{\mathrm{E}[a(n)]\}^2 \\ &= \mathrm{E}[a^2(n)] - (1+\bar{i})^{2n}. \end{aligned} \tag{12.2}$$

Assume that the i_t's have constant variance s^2. We then can compute the second moment about the origin of $a(n)$

$$\begin{aligned} \mathrm{E}[a^2(n)] &= \mathrm{E}\left[\prod_{t=1}^{n}(1+i_t)^2\right] \\ &= \prod_{t=1}^{n}\mathrm{E}\left[(1+i_t)^2\right] \text{ from independence} \\ &= \prod_{t=1}^{n}\mathrm{E}\left[1+2i_t+i_t^{\,2}\right] \\ &= (1+2\bar{i}+\bar{i}^2+s^2)^n. \end{aligned} \tag{12.3}$$

This result is based on the fact that for each value of t

$$\mathrm{Var}[i_t] = \mathrm{E}[i_t^2] - \{\mathrm{E}[i_t]\}^2$$

or

$$s^2 = \mathrm{E}\left[i_t^2\right] - \bar{i}^2$$

which gives

$$\mathrm{E}\left[i_t^2\right] = \bar{i}^2 + s^2 .$$

Thus, the variance of the accumulated value is given by

$$\mathrm{Var}\left[a(n)\right] = \left(1 + 2\bar{i} + \bar{i}^2 + s^2\right)^n - \left(1 + \bar{i}\right)^{2n} \tag{12.4a}$$

which can be written as

$$\mathrm{Var}\left[a(n)\right] = \left(1 + \bar{j}\right)^n - \left(1 + \bar{i}\right)^{2n} \tag{12.4b}$$

where $\bar{j} = 2\bar{i} + \bar{i}^2 + s^2$.

We now extend the above analysis involving a single payment to a level annuity. Consider an n-period annuity-due. Following the approach developed in Section 3.8 for the portfolio rate method, the accumulated value of this annuity is

$$\begin{aligned} \ddot{s}_{\overline{n|}} &= (1+i_n) + (1+i_n)(1+i_{n-1}) + \cdots + (1+i_n)(1+i_{n-1})\cdots(1+i_1) \\ &= \sum_{t=1}^{n} \prod_{s=1}^{t} (1 + i_{n-s+1}). \end{aligned} \tag{3.25}$$

The mean of $\ddot{s}_{\overline{n|}}$ can be obtained from formula (3.25) as

$$\begin{aligned} \mathrm{E}\left[\ddot{s}_{\overline{n|}}\right] &= \mathrm{E}\left[\sum_{t=1}^{n} \prod_{s=1}^{t} (1 + i_{n-s+1})\right] \\ &= \sum_{t=1}^{n} \prod_{s=1}^{t} \mathrm{E}\left[1 + i_{n-s+1}\right] \quad \text{from independence} \\ &= \sum_{t=1}^{n} \left(1 + \bar{i}\right)^t \\ &= \ddot{s}_{\overline{n|}\,\bar{i}} . \end{aligned} \tag{12.5}$$

We next seek to find the variance of $\ddot{s}_{\overline{n|}}$. The variance of a series of this form is complicated and is derived in Appendix 12 at the end of the chapter.

Define m_1^s and m_2^s to be the first and second moments of $1+i_t$ about the origin, respectively, i.e.

$$m_1^s = \mathrm{E}[1+i_t] = 1+\bar{i} \tag{12.6}$$

and

$$m_2^s = \mathrm{E}\left[(1+i_t)^2\right] = 1+\bar{j} \tag{12.7}$$

where $\bar{j}$ is defined in formula (12.4*b*). Then applying the results from Appendix 12, we have

$$\mathrm{Var}\left[\ddot{s}_{\overline{n}|}\right] = \frac{m_2^s + m_1^s}{m_2^s - m_1^s}\,\ddot{s}_{\overline{n}|\bar{j}} - \frac{2m_2^s}{m_2^s - m_1^s}\,\ddot{s}_{\overline{n}|\bar{i}} - \left(\ddot{s}_{\overline{n}|\bar{i}}\right)^2. \tag{12.8}$$

Present values

Parallel results to those above for accumulated values can also be developed for present values. However, we must be careful in the choice of interest rates to use, since in general

$$\mathrm{E}\left[\frac{1}{1+i_t}\right] \neq \frac{1}{\mathrm{E}[1+i_t]}.$$

Thus, when working with present values we must define $\bar{i}$ by

$$\mathrm{E}\left[(1+i_t)^{-1}\right] = (1+\bar{i})^{-1}.$$

It must be stressed that this value of $\bar{i}$ is different than the value of $\bar{i}$ used above for accumulated values for which $\mathrm{E}[i_t] = \bar{i}$.

Our first result is to develop a formula for the mean of the present value of a single payment analogous to formula (12.1). We have

$$\mathrm{E}\left[a^{-1}(n)\right] = (1+\bar{i})^{-n}. \tag{12.9}$$

The derivation of formula (12.9) is similar to formula (12.1) and is left as an exercise.

For the variance of the present value we have

$$\begin{aligned}\text{Var}\left[a^{-1}(n)\right] &= \text{E}\left[a^{-2}(n)\right] - \left\{\text{E}\left[a^{-1}(n)\right]\right\}^2 \\ &= \left(1+\bar{k}\right)^{-n} - \left(1+\bar{i}\right)^{-2n} \qquad (12.10)\end{aligned}$$

where $\left(1+\bar{k}\right)^{-1} = \text{E}\left[\left(1+i_t\right)^{-2}\right]$.

Unfortunately, this is as far as we can carry the development without knowing how i_t is distributed. The approach used above for finding the second moment for accumulated values will not work for present values. Evaluation of formula (12.10) will require computing the second moment based on a particular probability density function.

Now turning to the present value of an n-period annuity-immediate we have from Section 3.8

$$\begin{aligned}a_{\overline{n|}} &= \left(1+i_1\right)^{-1} + \left(1+i_1\right)^{-1}\left(1+i_2\right)^{-1} + \cdots \\ &\quad + \left(1+i_1\right)^{-1}\left(1+i_2\right)^{-1}\cdots\left(1+i_n\right)^{-1} = \sum_{t=1}^{n}\prod_{s=1}^{t}\left(1+i_s\right)^{-1}. \qquad (3.23)\end{aligned}$$

The mean of $a_{\overline{n|}}$ is the anticipated result

$$\text{E}\left[a_{\overline{n|}}\right] = a_{\overline{n|}\,\bar{i}}\,. \qquad (12.11)$$

The derivation of formula (12.11) is similar to formula (12.5) and is left as an exercise.

Finally, we consider the variance of $a_{\overline{n|}}$. Define m_1^a and m_2^a to be the first and second moments of $\left(1+i_t\right)^{-1}$ about the origin, respectively, i.e.

$$m_1^a = \text{E}\left[\left(1+i_t\right)^{-1}\right] = \left(1+\bar{i}\right)^{-1} \qquad (12.12)$$

and

$$m_2^a = \text{E}\left[\left(1+i_t\right)^{-2}\right] = \left(1+\bar{k}\right)^{-1}. \qquad (12.13)$$

Again, applying the results from Appendix 12., we have

$$\text{Var}\left[a_{\overline{n|}}\right] = \frac{m_2^a + m_1^a}{m_2^a - m_1^a}\,a_{\overline{n|}\,\bar{k}} - \frac{2m_2^a}{m_2^a - m_1^a}\,a_{\overline{n|}\,\bar{i}} - \left(a_{\overline{n|}\,\bar{i}}\right)^2. \qquad (12.14)$$

Finding numerical solutions

Thus, if we know the first and second moments of $1+i_t$ and $(1+i_t)^{-1}$, we can find the mean and variance of the accumulated value or the present value of either a single payment or a level annuity. We may choose to make an assumption about the probability density function for i_t. Unfortunately, the above formulas do not generally result in a known probability density function, even if we know the mean and the variance.

The standard approach to handle this situation in practice is to use *simulation*. The procedure is as follows:

1. Make an appropriate assumption about the probability density function for i_t and its parameters.

2. Generate a series of enough random numbers to run as many trials as desired. If m trials are desired, then mn random numbers will be necessary.

3. Using standard simulation techniques, use these random numbers to compute m sets of values for $i_1, i_2, \ldots, i_n$.

4. For each of the m sets $i_1, i_2, \ldots, i_n$ compute the required financial function, i.e. $a(n)$, $a^{-1}(n)$, $\ddot{s}_{\overline{n}|}$, $a_{\overline{n}|}$, or some other function.

5. The m outcomes can be used to develop an approximate probability density function for that financial function. Estimated probabilities for various possible outcomes can be calculated from these m outcomes.

We will not discuss the technique of simulation further, since we assume that the reader is familiar with simulation. Readers who are unfamiliar with the technique are referred to standard textbooks on the topic.

***Example 12.1** Assume that i_t is an effective rate of interest uniformly distributed on the interval [.07, .09] for t = 1, 2, and 3. For the accumulated value of an investment of 1 at the end of 3 years, find the:*
(1) Mean.
(2) Standard deviation.

1. For the uniform distribution we have

$$\mathrm{E}\left(i_t\right) = \bar{i} = \frac{a+b}{2} = \frac{.07+.09}{2} = .08.$$

A direct application of formula (12.1) gives

$$\mathrm{E}\left[a(3)\right] = (1.08)^3 = 1.25971.$$

2. For the uniform distribution we have

$$\mathrm{Var}\left[i_t\right] = s^2 = \frac{(b-a)^2}{12} = \frac{(.09-.07)^2}{12} = \frac{.0001}{3}.$$

A direct application of formula (12.4*a*) gives

$$\mathrm{Var}\left[a(3)\right] = \left[1+.16+.0064+\frac{.0001}{3}\right]^3 - (1.08)^6$$
$$= .00013605.$$

Thus, the standard deviation is $\sqrt{.00013605} = .01166$. This answer seems reasonable in relation to the maximum range of results possible, i.e.

$$(1.07)^3 = 1.22504 \text{ to } (1.09)^3 = 1.29503.$$

Example 12.2 Rework Example 12.1 for the accumulated value of an investment of 1 made at the beginning of each year for three years.

1. A direct application of formula (12.5) gives

$$\mathrm{E}\left[\ddot{s}_{\overline{3}|}\right] = \ddot{s}_{\overline{3}|.08} = 3.5061.$$

2. Applying formulas (12.6) and (12.7) we have

$$m_1^s = 1+\bar{i} = 1.08$$

and

$$m_2^s = 1+\bar{j} = 1.166433.$$

Now applying formula (12.8)

$$\text{Var}\left[\ddot{s}_{\overline{3|}}\right] = .0005603$$

so that the standard deviation is $\sqrt{.0005603} = .0237$. This answer seems reasonable in relation to the maximum range of results possible, i.e. $\ddot{s}_{\overline{3|}.07} = 3.4399$ to $\ddot{s}_{\overline{3|}.09} = 3.5731$.

12.3 THE LOGNORMAL MODEL

There is one important special case of the model developed Section 12.2 for which a usable result can be obtained analytically. Suppose that the random variable $\ln(1+i_t)$ follows a normal distribution with mean μ and variance σ^2. Then the random variable $1+i_t$ follows a lognormal distribution with parameters μ and σ^2. The mean and variance of the lognormal distribution with parameters μ and σ^2 are given by

$$\text{mean} = e^{\mu+\sigma^2/2} \tag{12.15}$$

and

$$\text{variance} = e^{2\mu+\sigma^2}\left(e^{\sigma^2}-1\right). \tag{12.16}$$

Now starting with formula (1.40), as in Section 12.2, we have

$$\ln a(n) = \sum_{t=1}^{n} \ln(1+i_t). \tag{12.17}$$

The right-hand side is the sum of n independent normal random variables each with mean μ and variance σ^2.

Since means and variances are additive when we have independent distributions, we have

$$\text{E}\left[\ln a(n)\right] = n\mu \tag{12.18}$$

and

$$\text{Var}\left[\ln a(n)\right] = n\sigma^2. \tag{12.19}$$

Now $a(n)$ itself follows a lognormal distribution whose means and variances are additive, so that we have

$$\mathrm{E}\left[a(n)\right] = e^{n\mu+n\sigma^2/2} \tag{12.20}$$

and

$$\mathrm{Var}\left[a(n)\right] = e^{2n\mu+n\sigma^2}\left(e^{n\sigma^2}-1\right). \tag{12.21}$$

We next consider present values for which we must analyze the distribution of $(1+i_t)^{-1}$. We have

$$\ln(1+i_t)^{-1} = -\ln(1+i_t)$$

which is normally distributed with mean $-\mu$ and variance σ^2.

Thus, we have the following extensions of formulas (12.18) and (12.19) for $\ln a^{-1}(n)$:

$$\mathrm{E}\left[\ln a^{-1}(n)\right] = -n\mu \tag{12.22}$$

and

$$\mathrm{Var}\left[\ln a^{-1}(n)\right] = n\sigma^2. \tag{12.23}$$

Similarly, we have the following extensions of formula (12.20) and (12.21) for $a^{-1}(n)$ itself:

$$\mathrm{E}\left[a^{-1}(n)\right] = e^{-n\mu+n\sigma^2/2} \tag{12.24}$$

and

$$\mathrm{Var}\left[a^{-1}(n)\right] = e^{-2n\mu+n\sigma^2}\left(e^{n\sigma^2}-1\right). \tag{12.25}$$

The above variance formulas for $a(n)$ and $a^{-1}(n)$, i.e. formulas (12.21) and (12.25), are rather complicated and difficult to work with. In practice, logarithms of $a(n)$ and $a^{-1}(n)$ are generally used, which allows us to use the normal distribution and work with the much simpler formulas (12.19) and (12.23) when we need variances.

With the above formulas, we are able to find moments and make probability statements about possible outcomes of $a(n)$, $a^{-1}(n)$, $\ddot{s}_{\overline{n|}}$, and $a_{\overline{n|}}$ without resorting to simulation.

Recall formula (1.33) for the force of interest

$$\delta = \ln(1+i). \tag{1.33}$$

Thus, we see that the right-hand side of formula (12.17) can be interpreted as a summation of δ's. As in Section 1.10 we define

$$\delta_{[t]} = \ln(1+i_t). \tag{12.26}$$

The bracket distinguishes $\delta_{[t]}$, which is a level force applicable over the interval $t-1$ to t, from δ_t, which is a force applicable at only the instantaneous moment t.

It would seem reasonable in some cases to assume that fluctuations in the force of interest follow a normal distribution. When this assumption is made, then the associated accumulation and discount factors, i.e. $(1+i_t)$ and $(1+i_t)^{-1}$ will follow a lognormal distribution.

Even when $1+i_t$ and $(1+i_t)^{-1}$ do not follow a lognormal distribution, it is still possible to take logarithms and use the normal distribution for large n. This is an application of the *Central Limit Theorem* in statistics. This theorem justifies the use of formulas (12.18) and (12.19) and formulas (12.22) and (12.23) as acceptable approximations for large n regardless of how $1+i_t$ and $(1+i_t)^{-1}$ are distributed. The Central Time Limit Theorem can then be used to make probability estimates and to develop confidence intervals for various outcomes. This will be illustrated in Example 12.4.

One final observation is to note that means and variances for the normal distribution are proportional to n. However, the standard deviation in proportional to $\sqrt{n}$. For example, in analyzing $\ln a(n)$, if we double n it will double the mean. However, the standard deviation will only increase by a factor of $\sqrt{2}=1.414$.

***Example 12.3** Assume that $1+i_t$ follows a lognormal distribution with $\mu=.06$ and $\sigma^2=.01$. Find the mean and standard deviation for:*

(1) $a(5)$.

(2) $\ddot{s}_{\overline{5}|}$.

(3) $a^{-1}(5)$.

(4) $a_{\overline{5}|}$.

1. <u>*Mean*</u>

From formula (12.15) we have

$$\mathrm{E}[1+i_t] = e^{.06+.005} = 1.067159.$$

Applying formula (12.1) gives us the mean

$$\mathrm{E}[a(5)] = (1.067159)^5 = 1.38403.$$

The result can also be obtained by a direct application of formula (12.20).

<u>*Standard deviation*</u>

Now $a(5)$ has a lognormal distribution with parameters 5μ and $5\sigma^2$, so that from formula (12.21)

$$\mathrm{Var}[a(5)] = e^{5(.12+.01)}\left(e^{.05}-1\right) = .098212.$$

Thus, the standard deviation is $\sqrt{.098212} = .31339$. As an exercise, the reader will be asked to confirm this answer by the alternate approach of using formula (12.4*a*).

2. <u>*Mean*</u>

From formula (12.5) we have

$$\mathrm{E}\left[\ddot{s}_{\overline{5}|}\right] = \ddot{s}_{\overline{5}|.067159} = 6.1023.$$

<u>*Standard deviation*</u>

From formula (12.8) we have

$$\mathrm{Var}\left[\ddot{s}_{\overline{5}|}\right] = .881737.$$

Thus, the standard deviation is $\sqrt{.881737} = .9390.$

3. <u>*Mean*</u>

From formula (12.15) we have

$$\mathrm{E}\left[(1+i_t)^{-1}\right] = e^{-.06+.005} = .946485.$$

Applying formula (12.9) gives us the mean

$$\mathrm{E}\left[a^{-1}(5)\right] = (.946485)^5 = .759572.$$

This result can also be obtained by a direct application of formula (12.24). Note that $(1+i)^{-1} = .946485$, so that $\bar{i} = .056541$, which is different than in parts 1 and 2 above.

Standard deviation

Now $a^{-1}(5)$ has a lognormal distribution with parameters -5μ and $5\sigma^2$, so that from formula (12.25)

$$\mathrm{Var}\left[a^{-1}(5)\right] = e^{5(-.12+.01)}\left(e^{.05}-1\right) = .029581.$$

Thus, the standard deviation is $\sqrt{.029581} = .17199$.

4. *Mean*

In part 3 above we found that $\bar{i} = .056541$. Thus, from formula (12.11) we have

$$\mathrm{E}\left[a_{\overline{5}|}\right] = a_{\overline{5}|.056541} = 4.2523.$$

Standard deviation

We have $(1+k)^{-1} = e^{-.12+.01}e^{.01} = e^{-.10} = .904837$, so that $k = .105171$. Applying formula (12.14) we have

$$\mathrm{Var}\left[a_{\overline{5}|}\right] = .383244.$$

Thus, the standard deviation is $\sqrt{.383244} = .6191$.

Example 12.4 A 35-year old has just inherited \$100,000 and wishes to invest all of it for retirement at age 65. The investment fund will earn an effective return of 4%, 7%, or 10% with the following probabilities:

$$i_t = \begin{cases} .04 & .3 \\ .07 & .4 \\ .10 & .3 \end{cases}$$

The return for each year is independent of the returns in any other year. Use the Central Limit Theorem to determine the amount that this investor will accumulate at age 65 with 95% probability.

Table 12.1 contains the calculations needed to evaluate the needed formulas in this section. Remember that after taking logarithms we are working with values that are normally distributed.

Table 12.1 Calculations for Example 12.4

Probability	$1+i_t$	$\ln(1+i_t)$	$[\ln(1+i_t)]^2$
.3	1.04	.039221	.0015383
.4	1.07	.067659	.0045777
.3	1.10	.095310	.0090840
Expected value	1.07	.067423	.0050178

The mean of $\ln(1+i_t)$ is

$$\mu = .067423$$

The variance of $\ln(1+i_t)$ is

$$\sigma^2 = .0050178 - (.067423)^2 = .0004719.$$

We have $n = 30$. Formula (12.18) gives

$$\mathrm{E}[\ln a(30)] = 30\mu = 30(.067423) = 2.02269$$

and formula (12.19) gives

$$\mathrm{Var}[\ln a(30)] = 30\sigma^2 = 30(.00047191) = .014157.$$

The value which can be achieved 95% of the time occurs at the 5th percentile. In the standard normal distribution we have

$$\Phi(-1.645) = .05.$$

Let A be the accumulated value per dollar invested and we have

$$Z = \frac{X-\mu}{\sigma} = \frac{\ln A - 2.02269}{\sqrt{.014157}} = -1.645.$$

Solving this equation we have

$$\ln A = 2.02269 - (1.645)(.118983) = 1.82696$$

or

$$A = 6.21498$$

per dollar invested. Thus, the answer is

$$100{,}000A = \$621{,}498$$

which can be accumulated at age 65 with 95% probability.

It is instructive to compare this answer with the mean accumulated value which is

$$100{,}000(1.07)^{30} = \$761{,}226.$$

12.4 TIME SERIES MODELS

In Sections 12.2 and 12.3 we assumed that the rates of interest i_t in each successive period are independent. In Sections 12.4 though 12.6 we consider some models in which this assumption is removed.

Dependent rates certainly have intuitive appeal. For example, if the rate of interest in one period is considerably higher than a long-term average rate, then it is reasonable to assume that the following period's rate is more likely to be higher than average than it is to be lower than average. The same assumption would also seem reasonable for rates lower than average.

In other words, historical experience suggests that it is more likely for rates to stay high or low for several successive periods than it is for rates to bounce around randomly above and below some average rate. This seems even more plausible when we consider the fact that the level of interest rates is somewhat tied to economic conditions and governmental policy.

There are many different models which could be constructed to reflect dependence. Several of them are beyond the scope of this book. However, we will discuss some of the simpler ones starting with time series analysis from applied statistics.

Several families of time series models have been developed. The primary models are *moving average* (MA) models, *autoregressive* (AR) models, and mixtures of the two. We will demonstrate only AR models in this section, since they are easier to apply. However, readers who have a background in time series methods should consider the application of MA models as well.

As a simple introductory illustration of the basic idea, consider the uniform distribution that was used in Examples 12.1 and 12.2. We will assume that the uniform distribution applies over an interval with width $\alpha > 0$ on either side of the mean rate. Thus, if the long-term average rate is i, then we have a uniform distribution over the interval $\left[i-\alpha, i+\alpha\right]$.

Now assume that successive rates of interest can be linked by the recursion formula

$$i_t = i + k\left(i_{t-1} - i\right) \tag{12.27}$$

where $0 \le k \le 1$. This dependency relationship assumes that the uniform distribution is applicable centered on i_{t-1}, i.e. over the interval $\left[i_{t-1} - \alpha, i_{t-1} + \alpha\right]$, for each successive value of $t-1$.

The constant k is the relative weighting given to the long-term average rate and the prior period's rate. If $k = 0$, then we have independence and the results of Section 12.2 apply. If $k = 1$, then we give total weighting to the prior period's rate. An intermediate value of k gives partial weighting to both i and i_{t-1}. In fact, we are performing a linear interpolation between the two.

This simple illustration actually involves an application of an *autoregressive process of order one* - AR(1). Such a process makes the rate in one period dependent upon the rate in the prior period.

Successful results have been obtained by applying the lognormal distribution in a dependent fashion. This will be accomplished by specifying the form of $\delta_{[t]}$ as defined in formula (12.26). We assume that the long-term average force of interest is given by δ, i.e.

$$\mathrm{E}\left[\delta_{[t]}\right] = \delta \tag{12.28}$$

for $t = 1, 2, 3, \ldots$

We now apply the AR(1) process and develop it more fully than above. This process assumes that $\delta_{[t]}$ 1is based on the long-term average force and the prior period's force. Thus, it has the form

$$\delta_{[t]} = \delta + k\left(\delta_{[t-1]} - \delta\right) + e(t). \tag{12.29}$$

The similarity with formula (12.27) is evident. The expression $e(t)$ is the error term and it is assumed that the $e(t)$'s for $t = 1, 2, 3, \ldots$ are independent and identically distributed according to the normal distribution with mean $\mu = 0$ and variance σ^2.

We state the following results without proof. The variance of $\delta_{[t]}$ is given by

$$\mathrm{Var}\left[\delta_{[t]}\right] = \frac{\sigma^2}{1-k^2} \tag{12.30}$$

and the covariance between $\delta_{[s]}$ and $\delta_{[t]}$ is given by

$$\mathrm{Cov}\left[\delta_{[s]}, \delta_{[t]}\right] = \frac{\sigma^2}{1-k^2} k^{t-s} \tag{12.31}$$

for $t > s$. The above formulas require that $|k| < 1$. Note that if $k = 0$, we have independence and the results of Section 12.2 apply.

A more sophisticated time series procedure is the *autoregressive process of order two* - AR(2). This process assumes that $\delta_{[t]}$ is based on the long-term average force and the forces from the prior two periods. Thus, it has the form

$$\delta_{[t]} = \delta + k_1\left(\delta_{[t-1]} - \delta\right) + k_2\left(\delta_{[t-2]} - \delta\right) + e(t). \tag{12.32}$$

The error term $e(t)$ is defined the same as in the AR(1) process.

The variance of $\delta_{[t]}$ is given by

$$\mathrm{Var}\left[\delta_{[t]}\right] = \frac{1-k_2}{1+k_2} \cdot \frac{\sigma^2}{(1-k_2)^2 - k_1^2}. \tag{12.33}$$

The covariance between $\delta_{[s]}$ and $\delta_{[t]}$ is given by

$$\operatorname{Cov}\left[\delta_{[s]}, \delta_{[t]}\right] = \operatorname{Var}\left[\delta_{[t]}\right]\left[\tau g_1^{t-s} + (1-\tau)\, g_2^{t-s}\right] \tag{12.34}$$

for $t > s$, where

$$\tau = \frac{g_1\left(1-g_2^2\right)}{\left(g_1-g_2\right)\left(1+g_1 g_2\right)} \tag{12.35}$$

and where g_1 and g_2 are the reciprocals of the roots of the characteristic equation

$$f(x) = 1-k_1x-k_2x^2 = 0. \tag{12.36}$$

It is possible for the characteristic equation to have imaginary roots. The above formulas require three conditions:

$$\begin{aligned} k_1 + k_2 &< 1 \\ k_2 - k_1 &< 1 \\ -1 < k_2 &< 1. \end{aligned}$$

Again, note that if $k_1 = k_2 = 0$, we have independence and the results of Section 12.2 apply.

The above cited approach to implementing the AR(1) and AR(2) processes is analytical in nature. However, another approach which can readily be used is simulation. Other models involving dependency can also be constructed and then implemented with simulation. It is important that any model be tested with empirical data before using it to see how well the model handles actual known results.

***Example 12.5** Assume that the long-term average effective rate of interest in a particular situation is 6% and that the prior year's rate is 9%. Compare the pattern produced by formula (12.27) over a three-year period, assuming each year's rate turns out to exactly equal its estimated rate based on the long-term average rate and the prior year's rate:*

(1) If $k = .2$.

(2) if $k = .8$.

1. We have

$$\begin{aligned} i_1 &= .06+.2(.09-.06) &&= .066 \\ i_2 &= .06+.2(.066-.06) &&= .0612 \\ i_3 &= .06+.2(.0612-.06) &&= .06024. \end{aligned}$$

The regression of values to the mean rate of 6% is quite rapid.

2. We have

$$\begin{aligned} i_1 &= .06+.8(.09-.06) &&= .084 \\ i_2 &= .06+.8(.084-.06) &&= .0792 \\ i_3 &= .06+.8(.0792-.06) &&= .07536. \end{aligned}$$

Here the regression to the mean is much slower.

The purpose of this example is to illustrate the implicit pattern produced by different values of k. Of course, in practice each year's actual rate will quite likely differ from the estimated rate based on the long-term average rate and the prior year's rate, so that the smooth pattern above will be much bumpier. However, the effect of the choice of k would be just as pronounced in terms of the magnitude of the regression toward the long-term average rate as in the above illustration.

Example 12.6 ***It is known that $\delta_{[t]}$ follows an AR(1) process with mean = .09, variance = .003, and covariance between adjacent values = .002. The estimated value of $\delta_{[4]}$ is .075. Find the actual-value of $\delta_{[3]}$.***

We divide formula (12.31) by formula (12.30) to obtain

$$\frac{\text{Cov}}{\text{Var}} = k = \frac{.002}{.003} = \frac{2}{3}.$$

We will denote actual values by δ^A and estimated values by δ^E. From formula (12.29) we have

$$\begin{aligned} \delta^E_{[4]} &= \delta + k\left(\delta^A_{[3]} - \delta\right) \\ .075 &= .09 + \frac{2}{3}\left(\delta^A_{[3]} - .09\right) \end{aligned}$$

which gives

$$\delta^A_{[3]} = .0675.$$

Example 12.7 It is known that $\delta_{[t]}$ follows an AR(2) process with a mean equal to .08. The following values are given:

Z	*Actual $\delta_{[z]}$*	*Estimated $\delta_{[z]}$*
1	*.100*	*.086*
2	*.110*	*.094*
3	*.090*	*.102*
4	*.095*	*.094*

Find the estimated value for $\delta_{[5]}$.

If we apply formula (12.32) for $z = 3$ and 4, we have

$$.102 = .08 + k_1(.11 - .08) + k_2(.10 - .08)$$

and

$$.092 = .08 + k_1(.09 - .08) + k_2(.11 - .08)$$

which simplifies to

$$\begin{aligned} .03k_1 + .02k_2 &= .022 \\ .01k_1 + .03k_2 &= .012. \end{aligned}$$

These are two equations in two unknowns, which can be solved to give $k_1 = .6$ and $k_2 = .2$. Note that the values of k satisfy the three necessary conditions. Thus, we have

$$\delta_{[5]}^E = .08 + .6(.095 - .08) + .2(.09 - .08) = .091.$$

12.5 BINOMIAL LATTICES

Another dependent interest rate model is the *binomial model.* This model generates a series of future *interest rate paths* involving a sequence of up and down moves in the rate of interest. When displayed graphically the representation is often called a *binomial lattice* or a *binomial tree.*

The binomial model starts with a current rate of interest which remains level over some specified period and then moves either up or down the with an assigned probability. It cannot remain level, thus, the name "binomial" refers to the fact that there is a two-way outcome whose probabilities sum to one.

The process then repeats itself over successive periods into the future. The number of periods is entirely up to the modeler based on the particular application at hand. Each successive period is of equal length and the probabilities of an up move and a down move remain constant each period.

The binomial method is an example of a *random walk model*, a term encountered in applied statistics. The starting value for each period is the ending point of the prior period. Also, the outcome in each period is independent of the outcomes in prior periods.

Binomial lattices can be either closed or open. In a *closed lattice* the same value is obtained after two successive periods if there is one up move and one down move in either order. In an *open lattice* different points would be reached, Figure 12.1 graphically illustrates the difference.

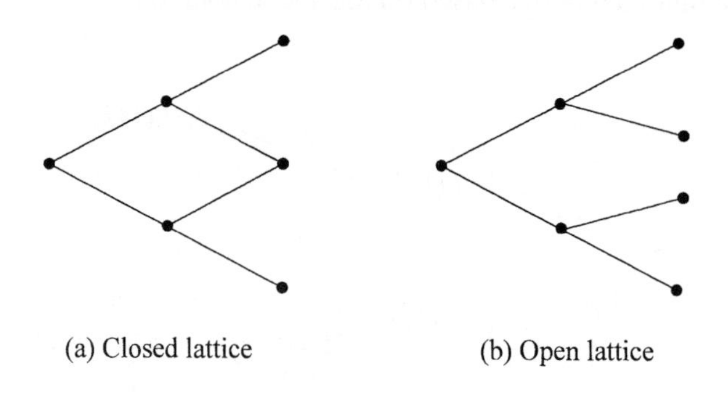

Figure 12.1

After n periods a closed lattice will have $n+1$ endpoints and an open lattice with no duplicates at all will have 2^n endpoints. Open lattices are obviously more complex than closed lattices.

A closed lattice is called an *additive binomial model* if each up and down move is the same amount. For example, if each interest rate move is plus or minus 1%, the model is said to be "additive."

A closed lattice is called a *multiplicative binomial model* if each up and down move is a constant multiple of the prior rate. The multiplicative model has the distinct advantage that rates will never become negative as they could with an additive model.

As in prior chapters, we denote the interest rate for the period from time $t-1$ to t as i_t. Thus, the lattice starts at i_1, the interest rate for the first period, and then branches out from there.

A frequently used multiplicative model is defined by

$$i_{t+1} = i_t(1+k) \quad \text{if up move} \tag{12.37a}$$

or

$$i_{t+1} = \frac{i_t}{1+k} \quad \text{if down move} \tag{12.37b}$$

The parameter k is often called the *volatility parameter* in this type of multiplicative model.

We denote the probability of an up move by p. The probability of a down move will then be $1-p$. Figure 12.2 displays a generic two-period multiplicative binomial lattice based on the above notation.

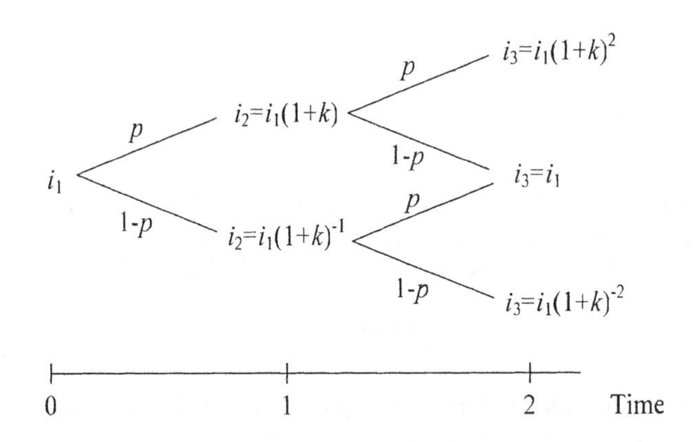

Figure 12.2 Two-period binomial lattice

We next consider the number of interest rate paths through the lattice. If there are n periods in the model, there will be a total of 2^n such paths.

Some of the paths may or may not be duplicates of each other depending on the particular application. For example, in Figure 12.2 the middle value for $i_3 = i_1$ is based on one up move and one down move in either order. However, the two paths are not equivalent when it comes to calculating present values over two years. Both paths use rate i_1 in the first year, but have different i_2's in the second year.

Although we have now shown how to construct an interest rate lattice, there usually is more to the story. The typical reason to construct such a lattice in the first place is to calculate some financial value for each interest rate path through the lattice. Finally, a weighted average value for all the paths can be calculated.

One of the most common applications of an interest rate lattice is bond valuation. We will demonstrate some illustrative bond calculations in Examples 12.9 and 12.10.

The valuation technique is a recursive process that starts at the right-hand end of the lattice and works its way back to the beginning on the left. We will assume a coupon bond in which the coupon paying period and the period in the lattice coincide.

Let V be the value of the bond, i.e. present value of future cash flows, at the beginning of a period. Then we define the following values at the end of the period:

R_U – cash flow in an up move
R_D – cash flow in a down move
V_U – value in a up move
V_D – value in a down move

Note the distinction between cash flows occurring at the end of the period, denoted by R, and the present value of future cash flows occurring later, denoted by V.

The recursion formula is given by

$$V = \frac{p(R_U + V_U) + (1-p)(R_D + V_D)}{1+i_t} \tag{12.38}$$

where i_t is the rate of interest for the particular period in question from the lattice.

The reader may be curious about choosing the length of periods in general. In formula (12.38) we chose the period in the lattice to coincide with the coupon frequency on the bond for convenience. This would typically result in a semiannual frequency for bonds, but typically a monthly frequency for mortgages.

Practical applications are done on computer and generally a short enough period can be chosen to avoid cash flows in the middle of a period. Formula (12.38) still works if there are no cash flows simply by setting $R_U = R_D = 0$. In fact, using lattices with more branches and shorter periods over a given time interval for the entire calculation may well improve the accuracy of the results in many applications.

It is also possible under certain conditions to shrink the period to zero and create a completely continuous model. We will not attempt to develop such a model in this section. However, we do note that Section 12.6 will present some continuous stochastic interest rate models.

Example 12.8 ***A binomial lattice with annual effective rates is constructed to value a three-year zero coupon bond maturing for $1000. The starting interest rate in the lattice is 10%. The multiplicative model with probability p = .5 and volatility parameter k = .2 is to be utilized.***
(1) Calculate the value of this bond from the lattice.
(2) Calculate the value of this bond using a level 10% yield rate.

1. With a zero coupon bond we have no cash flows until time $t=3$. The lattice will have 3 periods and is displayed in Figure 12.3.

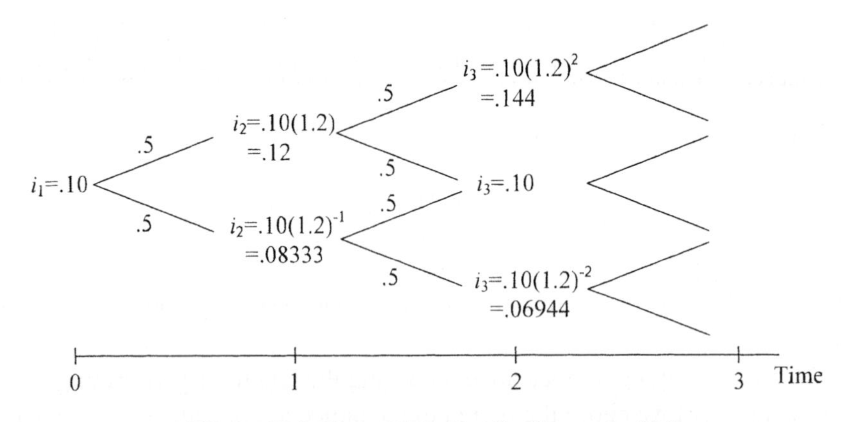

Figure 12.3 Binomial lattice for Example 12.5

Note that the branches between times $t=2$ and $t=3$ will not be used for any calculations in this example. All the rates of interest to be used are already known at time $t=2$ (i.e. the beginning of year 3).

Since there are no cash flows until time $t=3$, we can streamline the process described in this section. Rather than using formula (12.38) we can simply discount the maturity value of $1000 for 3 years at the appropriate rates of interest from the lattice. Values required in the calculation are given below:

Path	Probability	Present Value	
UU	.25	$(1.1)^{-1}(1.12)^{-1}(1.144)^{-1}$	= .709518
UD	.25	$(1.1)^{-1}(1.12)^{-1}(1.1)^{-1}$	= .737898
DU	.25	$(1.1)^{-1}(1.08333)^{-1}(1.1)^{-1}$	= .762876
DD	.25	$(1.1)^{-1}(1.08333)^{-1}(1.06944)^{-1}$	= .784676

The value of the 3-year zero coupon bond is the weighted average across the various interest rate paths, i.e.

$$1000(.25)(.709518+.737898+.762876+.784676) = \$748.74.$$

2. The value of this bond using a constant yield rate of 10% is equal to

$$1000(1.1)^{-3} = \$751.31.$$

Note that the value is greater than the value obtained in part 1 despite the complete symmetry of interest rates in part 1 around the starting value $i_1 = .10$. Intuitively, this makes sense. Part 1 has significant interest rate uncertainty, while part 2 does not. Greater interest rate uncertainty leads to higher yield rates, and thus lower prices. This is true even for zero coupon bonds.

***Example 12.9** You wish to value a one-year $1000 par value 7.6% bond with semiannual coupons. The current yield rate is 8% convertible semiannually. A binomial lattice with semiannual periods is to be used. The multiplicative model with p = .4 and volatility parameter k = .2 is selected. Calculate the value of this bond using this binomial lattice.*

The starting interest rate is the current semiannual yield rate of .08/2=.04. The binomial lattice is displayed in Figure 12.4.

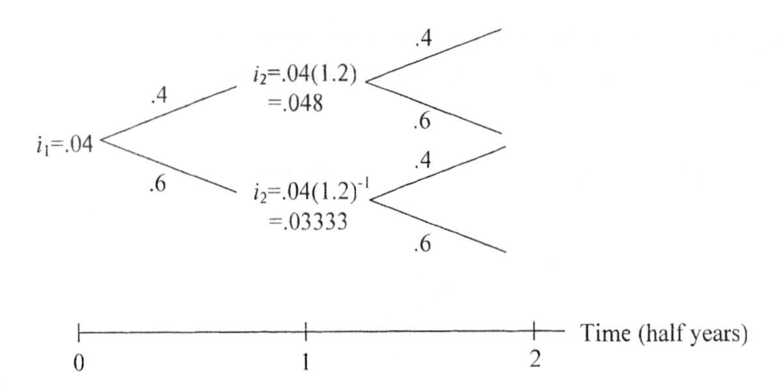

Figure 12.4 Binomial lattice for Example 12.6

Similarly to Example 12.8, the values of i_2 do not need to be computed, since they will not be used for any calculations. All the rates of interest to be used are already known at time $t=1$ (i.e. the beginning of period 2).

Since this is a coupon bond, we will need to apply formula (12.38) recursively going backwards though the lattice. At time $t=2$ in all cases we have

$$R_U \;=\; R_D \;=\; 1038 \quad \text{(maturity value + coupon)}$$

and

$$V=0 \;\; \text{(bond has matured)}.$$

Applying formula (12.38) at time $t=1$ on the up branch, we have

$$\begin{aligned} V &= \frac{p(R_U+V_U)+(1-p)(R_D+V_D)}{1+i_1} \\ &= \frac{(.4)(1038+0)+(.6)(1038+0)}{1.048} \\ &= 990.46. \end{aligned}$$

Applying formula (12.38) at $t=1$ on the down branch, we have

$$\begin{aligned} V &= \frac{(.4)(1038+0)+(.6)(1038+0)}{1.03333} \\ &= 1004.52. \end{aligned}$$

Finally, applying formula (12.38) at time $t=0$, we have

$$V = \frac{(.4)(38+990.46)+(.6)(38+1004.52)}{1.04}$$
$$= \$997.02.$$

Example 12.10 Rework Example 12.9 if the bond is callable on any coupon date at par.

The bond will not be called immediately at time $t = 0$, since its value of \$997.02 is less than its par value of \$1000. Also, it would not be called at time $t = 1$ if interest rates move up, since its value at that point would be \$990.46.

However, the bond would be called at time $t = 1$ if interest rates move down, since the value at that point would be \$1004.25. Thus, we must recompute the value at time $t = 0$ replacing \$1004.52 with the call value of \$1000. This gives a value at time $t = 0$ of

$$V = \frac{(.4)(38+990.46)+(.6)(38+1000)}{1.04}$$
$$= \$994.41.$$

Thus, the value of a callable bond is less than the value of an otherwise identical noncallable bond. Intuitively, this makes sense. Since callable bonds involve greater uncertainty, the price of the callable bond should be lower to compensate buyers for the greater uncertainty.

Actually, in practical applications one of the primary uses of binomial lattices is the valuation of securities and other financial instruments with interest sensitive cash flows. Callable bonds are an important example of such a security.

12.6 CONTINUOUS STOCHASTIC MODELS

The final category of dependent interest rate models consists of *continuous stochastic models*. These are actually a family of models constructed in a similar fashion, but with different properties and characteristics. We will discuss four such models in increasing order of complexity and sophistication.

The theory underlying continuous stochastic models is relatively advanced. It involves the application of stochastic calculus and the solution of differential equations.

We will not attempt to develop all the underlying theory in this basic textbook. Thus, we will present the material heuristically and will use discrete approximations in numerical applications of the models.

Since the models are continuous in nature, it would seem natural to use the force of interest δ_t, as defined in Chapter 1. Of course, a varying force of interest can always be converted into an equivalent rate of interest over some interval of time, if necessary. Thus, these models will use a starting value, δ_0, and generate values of δ_t thereafter from the models.

All the models presented in Section 12.6 are based on a *Weiner process*. If a variable z_t follows a Weiner process, then changes in z_t over small time intervals will be independent and will follow a normal distribution. We then apply the property that the mean of a normal distribution is proportional to time t and the standard deviation is proportional to $\sqrt{t}$.

Let y be a value from the standard normal distribution, i.e. with $\mu=0$ and $\sigma=1$. We would then have the following relationship over some short time interval

$$\Delta z = y\sqrt{\Delta t}. \qquad (12.39)$$

Now Δz itself is normally distributed with mean 0 and standard deviation $\sqrt{\Delta t}$. Finally, we obtain a continuous model by taking the limit as $\Delta t \to 0$ and denoting the result by the differential dz.

Random walk model (Brownian motion)

The simplest continuous stochastic model is the *random walk model*, which is often called *Brownian motion*. It is a well-known model in applied statistics with many different types of applications. The reader will recall that we saw a discrete version of a random walk model in Section 12.5.

The random walk model is then defined by

$$d\delta = adt + \sigma dz. \qquad (12.40)$$

The parameter a is usually called a *drift parameter*, since it will cause the random walk to drift upwards if $a>0$ or downwards if $a<0$. The standard deviation of the process, i.e. σ, is often called the *volatility parameter*.

The discrete approximation for this model is

$$\Delta\delta = a\Delta t + \sigma\Delta z \tag{12.41a}$$

which becomes the following upon substituting formula (12.39)

$$\Delta\delta = a\Delta t + \sigma y\sqrt{\Delta t}\,. \tag{12.41b}$$

Note that the drift parameter a is proportional to t, while the standard deviation σ of the process is proportional to $\sqrt{t}$.

In other words, over t periods the mean of this process is

$$\mathrm{E}\left[\delta_t\right] = \delta_0 + at \tag{12.42}$$

and the variance is

$$\mathrm{Var}\left[\delta_t\right] = \sigma^2 t \tag{12.43}$$

The following observations about this model are relevant:

1. The use of the drift parameter a over long periods of time is questionable, since it will result in an indefinite secular increase or decrease in δ_t. However, its use may be appropriate over shorter intervals, depending on circumstances. Also, note that drift can be completely eliminated by setting $a=0$.

2. This model can result in negative values for δ_t, which clearly is unreasonable.

3. The volatility is the same whether δ_t is large or small. Many modelers might be more comfortable with volatility that depends on how large or small δ_t is at a given point in time.

4. Values of δ_t do not possess *mean reversion.* In other words they show no tendency to gradually move toward some long term average rate over time. Thus if the long term average δ is 5% and the current $\delta_t = 10\%$, it is just as likely that the next move will be even higher as it is that it will move lower.

Rendleman - Bartter model

The *Rendleman-Bartter model* can be characterized as a geometric random walk model. The model is defined by

$$d\delta = a\delta dt + \sigma\delta dz. \tag{12.44}$$

The concept is to make the two parameters a and σ proportional to the current magnitude of δ_t.

The discrete approximation for this model is

$$\Delta\delta = a\delta\Delta t + \sigma\delta\Delta z \tag{12.45a}$$

or

$$\Delta\delta = a\delta\Delta t + \sigma\delta y\sqrt{\Delta t}. \tag{12.45b}$$

Observation 1 above is also applicable to this model. However, this model does not have the weaknesses described in observations 2 and 3, which were the primary motivations for its development in the first place. However, the weakness in observation 4 is still present.

In addition, this model has another weakness. Because volatility is proportional to how large δ_t is at a given point in time, further upward moves applied to an already high value of δ_t could drive the δ_t values to unrealistically high levels.

Vasicek model

Our third model is the *Vasicek model*. The primary purpose of this model is to reflect mean reversion. The model is defined by

$$d\delta = c(b-\delta)dt + \sigma dz. \tag{12.46}$$

The term $c(b-\delta)dt$ provides the mean reversion. The parameter b is the long term force of interest toward which the model reverts. The parameter c measures the *rate of reversion* to the mean. For example, if $c = .2$ then the model, on average, closes 20% of the gap between the current δ_t and the long term δ every period.

The discrete approximation for this model is

$$\Delta\delta = c(b-\delta)\Delta t + \sigma\Delta z \tag{12.47a}$$

or

$$\Delta\delta = c(b-\delta)\Delta t + \sigma y\sqrt{\Delta t}\,. \tag{12.47b}$$

The weakness cited in observation 4 above clearly is solved by this model, which constitutes the primary motivation for the model in the first place. Also, the possible weakness in observation 1 is not present. However, the weaknesses in observations 2 and 3 are still present.

It is instructive to note two special limiting cases of the Vasicek model. If $c=0$, the model becomes the random walk model with no drift. If $c=1$, the model actually becomes a normal distribution with $\mu=b$. In a certain sense, we could conceptualize the Vasicek model as blending the normal distribution and Brownian motion.

Cox-Ingersoll-Ross model

Our fourth, and final, continuous stochastic model is the *Cox-Ingersoll-Ross model.* It is the most sophisticated of these four models and attempts to eliminate all the weaknesses described above for the other three models. It does this by adjusting the Vasicek model to make the volatility parameter σ proportional to $\sqrt{\delta}$.

Thus, this model is defined by

$$d\delta = c(b-\delta)dt + \sigma\sqrt{\delta}dz \tag{12.48}$$

The discrete approximation for this model is

$$\Delta\delta = c(b-\delta)\Delta t + \sigma\sqrt{\delta}\Delta z \tag{12.49a}$$

or

$$\Delta\delta = c(b-\delta)\Delta t + \sigma\sqrt{\delta}y\sqrt{\Delta t}\,. \tag{12.49b}$$

Because of its attractive properties, the Cox-Ingersoll-Ross model has become quite widely used by interest rate modelers wishing to utilize a continuous stochastic model.

Practical considerations

We close this section by listing four practical considerations in applying these models.

1. The discrete versions of these models require us to define t carefully and how often we wish to compute a new force of interest. For example, we might wish to define $t=1$ as a one-year period of time, but improve the accuracy of the model with more frequent changes in the force of interest. Thus, for example, if we set $\Delta t = 1/4$ we would generate quarterly values of δ_t; or if we set $\Delta t = 1/12$, we would generate monthly values.

2. The models require us to estimate a volatility parameter σ and possibly other parameters a, b, and/or c. These parameters must be consistent with how we have defined one time period, i.e. $t=1$, above.

3. The discrete models are often implemented using simulation. The concept is to generate random numbers which in turn are used to generate values of y from the standard normal distribution, i.e. with $\mu = 0$ and $\sigma = 1$. Thus, if we wish to generate a value δ_1 using monthly values over the year, we will need 12 simulated standard normal variables y.

4. In using the discrete models, the ending value in one period becomes the starting value for the next period. Thus, the models are applied recursively from period to period.

***Example 12.11** The current force of interest is .07. Estimate the force of interest one year into the future, i.e. at time t = 1. Use the random walk model (Brownian motion) with quarterly adjustments, i.e. Δt = .25. The volatility parameter σ = .01 and the drift parameter a = – .004. The following four standard normal variables were generated using simulation:* **+2, –.5, +1, 0.**

The four standard normal variables can be interpreted as the number of standard deviations above or below the mean which equals 0. They were chosen somewhat arbitrarily to illustrate more clearly the operation of the model. Clearly, on average, these four particular values are somewhat greater than the mean.

The interpretation of the drift parameter is that it will reduce the force of interest by .004, or .4%, per year under neutral conditions. The interpretation of the volatility parameter is that the standard deviation of the force of interest over one year is .01, or 1%, in relation to the current force of interest of 7%.

We now apply formula (12.41*b*) four times recursively

$$\Delta\delta = a\Delta t + \sigma y\sqrt{\Delta t}$$

with a starting value $\delta_0 = .07$. This gives the following results:

$$\begin{aligned}
\delta_{.25} &= .07 - .004(.25) + (.01)(2)\sqrt{.25} &&= .0790 \\
\delta_{.50} &= .0790 - .004(.25) + (.01)(-.5)\sqrt{.25} &&= .0755 \\
\delta_{.75} &= .0755 - .004(.25) + (.01)(1)\sqrt{.25} &&= .0795 \\
\delta_{1} &= .0795 - .004(.25) + (.01)(0)\sqrt{.25} &&= .0785.
\end{aligned}$$

Thus, the answer is .0785, or 7.85%.

The effect of the drift parameter $a = -.004$ is to move the force of interest down at the rate of $-.001$ per quarter. However, this effect is more than offset by positive values of y well above the mean. The entire movement in the fourth quarter is attributable to drift. If the drift parameter had been zero, then the force of interest would have been unchanged over that quarter.

Example 12.12 Rework Example 12.11 using the Rendelman-Bartter model.

We will apply formula (12.45*b*) four times recursively. In order to get results comparable to Example 12.11, we will multiply the parameters a and σ by 1/.07 to neutralize the effect of putting δ into the formula.

We have

$$\Delta\delta = a\delta\Delta t + \sigma\delta y\sqrt{\Delta t}$$

which produces:

$$\begin{aligned}
\delta_{.25} &= .07 - \frac{.004}{.07}(.07)(.25) + \frac{.01}{.07}(.07)(2)\sqrt{.25} &&= .0790 \\
\delta_{.50} &= .0790 - \frac{.004}{.07}(.0790)(.25) + \frac{.01}{.07}(.0790)(-.5)\sqrt{.25} &&= .0751 \\
\delta_{.75} &= .0751 - \frac{.004}{.07}(.0751)(.25) + \frac{.01}{.07}(.0751)(1)\sqrt{.25} &&= .0794 \\
\delta_{1} &= .0794 - \frac{.004}{.07}(.0794)(.25) + \frac{.01}{.07}(.0794)(0)\sqrt{.25} &&= .0783
\end{aligned}$$

Thus, the answer is .0783, or 7.83%.

The effect of using the geometric version of Brownian motion is not all that evident over this short period with relatively modest changes in the force of interest. The effect would become more evident if interest levels were to rise or fall more dramatically.

Example 12.13 Rework Example 12.11 using the Vasicek model with parameters b = .05 and c = .20.

The interpretation of the parameter $b = .05$ is that the long term force of interest is 2% below its current level. The interpretation of the parameter $c = .20$ is that the rate of reversion to the mean is 20% per year. We will apply formula (12.47*b*) four times recursively

$$\Delta\delta = c(b-\delta)\Delta t + \sigma y\sqrt{\Delta t}\,.$$

We have

$$\begin{aligned}
\delta_{.25} &= .07+.2(.05-.07)(.25)+(.01)(2)\sqrt{.25} &&= .0790\\
\delta_{.5} &= .0790+.2(.05-.0790)(.25)+(.01)(-.5)\sqrt{.25} &&= .0751\\
\delta_{.75} &= .0751+.2(.05-.0751)(.25)+(.01)(1)\sqrt{.25} &&= .0788\\
\delta_{1} &= .0788+.2(.05-.0788)(.25)+(.01)(0)\sqrt{.25} &&= .0774.
\end{aligned}$$

Thus, the answer is .0774, or 7.74%.

The results in this example are quite close to Example 12.11. This result is attributable to the fact that the reversion to the mean is approximately $.2(.05-.07) = -.004$ per year, which is the same as the drift parameter a in Example 12.11.

Example 12.14 Rework Example 12.13 using the Cox-Ingersoll-Ross model.

We will apply formula (12.49*b*) four times recursively. In order to get results comparable to Example 12.13, we will multiply the parameter σ by $1/\sqrt{.07}$ to neutralize the effect of putting $\sqrt{\delta}$ into the formula.

We have

$$\Delta\delta = c(b-\delta)\Delta t + \sigma\sqrt{\delta}\,y\sqrt{\Delta t}$$

which produces

$$\delta_{.25} = .07+.2(.05-.07)(.25)+\frac{.01}{\sqrt{.07}}\sqrt{.07}\,(2)\sqrt{.25} = .0790$$

$$\delta_{.5} = .0790+.2(.05-.0790)(.25)+\frac{.01}{\sqrt{.07}}\sqrt{.0790}\,(-.5)\sqrt{.25} = .0749$$

$$\delta_{.75} = .0749+.2(.05-.0749)(.25)+\frac{.01}{\sqrt{.07}}\sqrt{.0749}\,(1)\sqrt{.25} = .0788$$

$$\delta_{1} = .0788+.2(.05-.0788)(.25)+\frac{.01}{\sqrt{.07}}\sqrt{.0788}\,(2)\sqrt{.25} = .0774.$$

Thus, the answer is .0774, or 7.74%.

Under these relatively mild conditions over a short period of time the Cox-Ingersoll-Ross model gives almost identical results to the Vasicek model. Larger differences would become more apparent with greater movements in interest levels up or down over longer periods of time.

12.7 SCENARIO TESTING

In practical applications for many of the situations described in Chapters 11 and 12 an approach called *scenario testing* has become quite popular. This technique is, in essence, a type of sophisticated simulation which requires extensive computer capability to implement, since the volume of calculations is typically quite high. In this approach, each "scenario" refers to a different interest rate path.

For example, consider an analysis involving the matching of assets and liabilities for a financial institution. It is necessary to estimate future cash inflows from the assets and future cash outflows from the liabilities.

These cash inflows and outflows may involve inherent uncertainty as to amount, probability of payment, and timing. It is important to recognize in the construction of the scenarios that these cash flows may also be affected by the interest rate path under consideration. For example, on the asset side as we have previously noted, cash inflows arising from bonds being called and from the prepayment of mortgages are affected by the level of interest rates. Similarly, on the liability side, cash outflows may also be affected by the level of interest rates.

The level of surplus, which may be positive or negative, is computed at the end of the projection period for each scenario. These results provide an indication of the range of possible outcomes. Also, other statistical measures can be computed on the set of outcomes, e.g. the mean and the standard deviation.

There are a number of decisions that must be made in applying scenario testing. One such decision is the number of scenarios to use, i.e. the number of different interest rate paths to consider. Increasing the number of paths presumably provides a better picture of the likely distribution of results. However, at some point the "law of diminishing returns" takes hold. It is not automatically true that doubling the stack of computer printouts necessarily produces more valuable information. Also, time and expense considerations are generally significant. Thus, the importance of the study is relevant in determining how much effort to devote. In the final analysis, the number of scenarios to use is judgmental.

Another decision is the frequency of changes in the interest rates to use in the scenario testing, i.e. monthly, quarterly, annually, etc. Again, this is a trade-off between increasing the level of sophistication, while also increasing the complexity, time, and expense of doing the analysis. Again, the decision is judgmental and is based on many of the same considerations as in determining the number of scenarios to use.

An important consideration in developing the interest rate paths for the various scenarios is the yield curve. In fact, in many cases of scenario testing the entire yield curve is projected. Experience has shown that generally short-term rates of interest are more volatile than long-term rates of interest. Thus, variations in the future behavior of the yield curve should be an integral part of scenario testing. In other words, the analyst should not ignore the yield curve and thereby implicitly assume that its shape is the same under all the scenarios.

A related issue is the assumption involving reinvestment rates. This assumption is particularly important if the analysis involves an extensive period of time. This may involve assumptions about future behavior, as well as the purely financial assumptions.

Another important consideration in constructing scenarios is the possibility of risk-free arbitrage in one or more of the various interest rate paths. The existence of the possibility of risk-free arbitrage in a given interest rate path, or set of paths when projecting an entire yield curve, raises questions about the internal consistency of the scenario or scenarios involved. There are techniques for eliminating risk-tree arbitrage, but those techniques are beyond the scope of this book.

There are three general methods followed in determining the interest rate paths for scenario testing. The first is the *preset method.* Under this method the analyst directly specifies all the interest rates in the various interest rate paths. This method offers maximum flexibility to the analyst in the choice of scenarios. It also has been specified by certain regulators of financial institutions.

Typically the scenarios being tested include a mixture of optimistic, midrange, and pessimistic scenarios with at least one "worst case" scenario thrown in. Interest rate paths of both high and low volatility are generally included. Paths reflecting a major secular trend up or down over time are also generally included. Paths reflecting a major depression or hyperinflation may be utilized when considering "worst case" scenarios.

However, in forming conclusions based on the scenarios, it is important for the analyst to assign probabilities to the various scenarios. One common mistake is to assume that all scenarios are equally likely. Once probabilities are assigned to the various scenarios, then statistical measures such as the mean and the standard deviation can be computed across all scenarios.

Although offering great flexibility to the analyst, the preset method does have some significant weaknesses. One weakness is that the method is inherently arbitrary since the interest rate paths are based on the subjective judgment of the analyst or paths prescribed by regulators. Another weakness is that the method can be quite time consuming, since it is necessary to specify all the different interest rates required for the various scenarios. The other two methods do not require the same subjective judgments by the analyst and generate the interest rate paths in a more systematic and efficient manner.

The second type of method is a *probabilistic method.* One common probabilistic method is to use a binomial lattice technique. It should be noted that there is a precise inverse relationship between bond prices and the rate of interest. Thus, assuming bond prices move in a random walk is equivalent to assuming that interest rates move in a random walk. Under this method the probability of an upward movement in the rate of interest each period is p, while the probability of a downward movement is $1-p$. If $p = 1/2$, then rates will move up and down randomly around their current level, assuming that the increase factor and decrease factor are reciprocals. If $p > 1/2$ there will be a secular trend upward over time, while the opposite will be true if $p < 1/2$. The volatility of results is controlled by the magnitude of the possible upward and downward movements.

The third type of method is a *stochastic method.* Probably the most common stochastic method used is to assume that successive values of $1+i_t$ follow a lognormal distribution. One advantage with the stochastic method is the ability to readily adjust for the volatility of the interest rate. It can be shown that if common assumptions are used throughout, then this method becomes the limiting case of the binomial lattice method as the intervals in the binomial lattice shrink to zero.

One problem with both the probabilistic and stochastic methods is that interest rates may appear in some of the interest rate paths after a number of periods which seem unreasonably high or unreasonably low. One way of dealing with this problem is to lower the assumed volatility assumption in the movement of interest rates. Another way is to put bounds on how high or low the rates can go. However, neither method of dealing with the problem is ideal.

Time series analysis is useful in connection with the construction of scenarios. This forces the analyst to consider past data in the construction of scenarios. However, it is also important to remember the admonition that "the future will not duplicate the past." Thus, some of the scenarios may well involve conditions that have not previously occurred.

Finally, it is important not to ignore the importance of intermediate results by focusing too heavily on results at the end of the projection period. For example, for a particular scenario if we show a positive result at the end of the projection period, but are in a significant negative position midway through the period, we may not have a favorable scenario. At a minimum, a closer analysis of this particular scenario is in order.

The above is a brief descriptive discussion of scenario testing. It is difficult to be very specific in discussing the technique, since there are probably as many different ways of conducting scenario testing as there are analysts doing it (maybe even more!). Nevertheless, this section should be useful in providing the reader with a general appreciation of the various methods used and some of the considerations involved.

Example 12.15 ***\$1000 is invested for five years at an unknown force of interest which changes annually. It is assumed that the force of interest follows an AR(1) process in which $\delta = .08$, $k = .7$, and $\sigma = .005$. Five random numbers are generated which produce the following values from the standard normal distribution: +.82, –1.61, +.43, +1.02, –.79. The force of interest for the year just ending was .10. Find the accumulated value of the investment at the end of five years for this interest rate path.***

Five successive values of $\delta_{[t]}$ are generated using formula (12.29) as follows:

$$\begin{aligned}
\delta_{[1]} &= .08 + .7(.1000 - .08) + .82(.005) = .0981 \\
\delta_{[2]} &= .08 + .7(.0981 - .08) - 1.61(.005) = .0846 \\
\delta_{[3]} &= .08 + .7(.0846 - .08) + .43(.005) = .0854 \\
\delta_{[4]} &= .08 + .7(.0854 - .08) + 1.02(.005) = .0889 \\
\delta_{[5]} &= .08 + .7(.0889 - .08) - .79(.005) = .0823
\end{aligned}$$

Thus, the accumulated value at the end of five years for this interest rate path is

$$1000e^{.0981}e^{.0846}e^{.0854}e^{.0889}e^{.0823} = 1000e^{.4393} = \$1552$$

to the nearest dollar.

In an actual problem of this type a large number of interest rate paths would be generated in like fashion. Statistical measures, such as the mean and standard deviation, could be computed for the distribution of accumulated values produced by the simulation.

***Example 12.16** An insurance company issues a one-year guaranteed investment contract (GIC) which credits an annual effective rate of 8.5%. The company decides to invest the proceeds from the sale of the GIC in three-month instruments at the beginning of each quarter. The rate of interest earned for the first quarter is 8.4% convertible quarterly. It is assumed that future interest rates move according to the random walk model in which the probability of an upward movement in the rate of interest is .4, and the amount of upward and downward movements each quarter are .5% and .4% convertible quarterly, respectively. Find the probability that the company will lose money on the GIC.*

The binomial lattice in this case is an open lattice as illustrated in Figure 12.1 and not the more typical closed lattice. Thus, there are $2^3 = 8$ interest rate paths.

We will work in quarterly rates of interest. The rate of interest for the first quarter is .021. The amount of each upward movement in the rate of interest is .00125, while the amount of downward movement is .001.

The results for the eight interest rates paths are summarized in Table 12.2.

Table 12.2 Summary of Interest Rate Paths for Example 12.16

Number	*Path*	*Probability*	*Accumulated Value*
1	UUU	.064	(1.021)(1.02225)(1.0235)(1.02475) = 1.09468
2	UUD	.096	(1.021)(1.02225)(1.0235)(1.0225) = 1.09228
3	UDU	.096	(1.021)(1.02225)(1.02125)(1.0225) = 1.08988
4	UDD	.144	(1.021)(1.02225)(1.02125)(1.02025) = 1.08748
5	DUU	.096	(1.021)(1.02)(1.02125)(1.0225) = 1.08748
6	DUD	.144	(1.021)(1.02)(1.02125)(1.02025) = 1.08509
7	DDU	.144	(1.021)(1.02)(1.019)(1.02025) = 1.08270
8	DDD	.216	(1.021)(1.02)(1.019)(1.019) = 1.08031

Under the GIC the company must pay 1.085 at the end of the year per dollar invested. It will lose money for paths 7 and 8 in Table 12.2. Thus, the probability of loss is $.144 + .216 = .36$.

12.8 MORE ADVANCED MODELS

This chapter undoubtedly appears complex and challenging to many readers. Despite that appearance, this chapter has been a relatively basic introduction to stochastic interest models. The purpose of this final section is to provide a brief non-technical description of four other more sophisticated models in widespread use which go beyond the scope of this book.

1. First is the development of multi-period *arbitrage-free models* involving a yield curve. The need for this type of model was identified in Section 12.7.

2. The Vasicek and Cox-Ingersoll-Ross models both involve reversion to a long-term force of interest as their primary feature. A more complex model in this general category is a *double mean-reverting model* in which the long-term force of interest itself reverts to an even longer-term true level. Although sounding needlessly complicated at first, this model has proven able to generate more realistic interest scenarios for scenario testing.
3. The *Black-Derman-Toy model* is a more complex model incorporating yield curves into a binomial lattice. It also is designed to match actual real-world

data through a process called *calibration*. This model has proven to do an excellent job of modeling yield curve volatility over time.

4. Finally, we have various types of *regime-switching models*. These models switch randomly between two or more distributions. They having proven effective in certain types of applications, particularly in modeling equity returns.

APPENDIX 12

Derivation of the variance of annuity

It is desired to find the variance of the sum

$$s = x_1 + x_1x_2 + \cdots + x_1x_2\ldots x_n$$

where $x_1x_2\ldots x_n$ are independent and identically distributed random variables. Both formula (3.23) for $a_{\overline{n}|}$ and formula (3.25) for $\ddot{s}_{\overline{n}|}$ are of this form.

Let m_1 and m_2 be the first and second moments about the origin, i.e.

$$\mathrm{E}\left[x_k\right] = m_1 \quad \text{and} \quad \mathrm{E}\left[x_k^2\right] = m_2$$

for $k = 1,\ 2, \ldots,\ n$. From independence we have

$$\mathrm{E}\left[s\right] = \sum_{k=1}^{n} m_1^k$$

which we will denote by $s_n\left(m_1\right)$.

The formula that we wish to prove is

$$\mathrm{Var}\left[s\right] = \frac{m_2 + m_1}{m_2 - m_1}\, s_n\left(m_2\right) - \frac{2m_2}{m_2 - m_1}\, s_n\left(m_1\right) - \left[s_n\left(m_1\right)\right]^2 .$$

The proof is by mathematical induction.

Let $n = 1$. We know that

$$\mathrm{Var}\left[s\right] = \mathrm{Var}\left[x_1\right] = m_1 - m_1^2 .$$

The right-hand side of the formula to be proven is

$$\frac{m_2 + m_1}{m_2 - m_1} m_2 - \frac{2m_2}{m_2 - m_1}\, m_1 - m_1^2 = m_2 - m_1^2 .$$

Thus, the formula holds for $n = 1$.

Now assume that the formula holds for $n - 1$. Define

$$t = x_1 + x_1 x_2 + \cdots + x_1 x_2 \ldots x_{n-1}.$$

We have

$$\begin{aligned} \operatorname{Var}[s] &= \operatorname{Var}[t + x_1 x_2 \ldots x_n] \\ &= \operatorname{Var}[t] + \operatorname{Var}[x_1 x_2 \ldots x_n] + 2\operatorname{Cov}[t,\ x_1 x_2 \ldots x_n]. \end{aligned}$$

We need to evaluate these three terms.

From the induction assumption

$$\operatorname{Var}[t] = \frac{m_2 + m_1}{m_2 - m_1}\, s_{n-1}(m_2) - \frac{2m_2}{m_2 - m_1}\, s_{n-1}(m_1) - \left[s_{n-1}(m_1)\right]^2$$

$$= \frac{m_2 + m_1}{m_2 - m_1}\left(m_2 + m_2^2 + \cdots + m_2^{n-1}\right) \qquad \text{(A)}$$

$$- \frac{2m_2}{m_2 - m_1}\left(m_1 + m_1^2 + \cdots + m_1^{n-1}\right) \qquad \text{(B)}$$

$$- \left(m_1 + m_1^2 + \cdots + m_1^{n-1}\right)^2 \qquad \text{(C)}$$

From independence

$$\begin{aligned} \operatorname{Var}[x_1 x_2 \ldots x_n] &= m_2^n - m_1^{2n} \\ &= \underbrace{\frac{m_2^{n+1} - m_2^n m_1}{m_2 - m_1}}_{\text{(D)}} - \underbrace{m_1^{2n}}_{\text{(E)}}. \end{aligned}$$

For the covariance term we have

$$2\operatorname{Cov}[t, x_1 x_2 \ldots x_n] = 2\mathrm{E}[t x_1 x_2 \ldots x_n] - 2\mathrm{E}[t]\,\mathrm{E}[x_1 x_2 \ldots x_n]$$

$$= 2\left(m_2 m_1^{n-1} + m_2^2 m_1^{n-2} + \cdots + m_2^{n-1} m_1\right) - 2\left(m_1 + m_1^2 + \cdots + m_1^{n-1}\right) m_1^n$$

$$= 2 \cdot \frac{m_2^n m_1 - m_1^n m_2}{m_2 - m_1} - 2m_1^n\left(m_1 + m_1^2 + \cdots + m_1^{n-1}\right)$$

$$= \underbrace{\frac{2m_1 m_2^n}{m_2 - m_1}}_{\text{(F)}} - \underbrace{\frac{2m_1^n m_2}{m_2 - m_1}}_{\text{(G)}} - \underbrace{2m_1^n\left(m_2 + m_1^2 + \cdots + m_1^{n-1}\right)}_{\text{(H)}}.$$

We need to show that the sum of the three terms gives us our induction hypothesis. The reader should verify that (A) + (D) + (F) give the first term in the formula to be proven; (B) + (G) gives the second term; and (C) + (E) + (H) give the third term.

Thus, the proof by mathematical induction is complete.

EXERCISES

12.2 Independent rates of interest

1. Derive formula (12.9).

2. Derive formula (12.11).

3. A sum of $1000 is invested for three years. The effective rate of interest is 8% for the first year. The effective rate of interest for the second year is equally likely to be 1% higher or lower than the rate for the first year. Similarly, the effective rate of interest for the third year is equally likely to be 1% higher or lower than the rate for the second year.
   a) Find the mean interest rate for each year in the three-year period.
   b) Find the standard deviation of the interest rate for each year in the three-year period.
   c) Find the maximum possible accumulation at the end of three years.
   d) Find the minimum possible accumulation at the end of three years.
   e) Find the accumulation at the end of three years at the mean interest rate.
   f) Find the mean value of the accumulation at the end of three years.
   g) Find the standard deviation of the accumulation at the end of three years.

4. Assume that i_t is an effective rate of interest distributed as in Example 12.1, i.e. uniformly on the interval [.07, .09] for $t = 1, 2, 3$.
   a) Find i such that $\mathrm{E}\left[(1+i_t)^{-1}\right] = (1+i)^{-1}$.
   b) Find the mean of the present value of 1 to be paid at the end of three years.
   c) Find k such that $\mathrm{E}\left[(1+i_t)^{-2}\right] = (1+k)^{-1}$.
   d) Find the standard deviation of the present value in (*b*).

5. Rework Exercise 4(*b*) and (*d*) for the present value of payments of 1 to be made at the end of each year for three years.

6. Assume that $i_t^{(2)}$ is a nominal rate of interest that follow a normal distribution with $\mu = 6\%$ and $\sigma = 1\%$ for $t = .5,\ 1,\ 1.5,\ 2$.
   a) Find the mean and standard deviation of the accumulated value of 100 at the end of two years.
   b) Rework (*a*) for the accumulated value of payments of 100 to be made at the beginning of each half year for two years.

7. Develop formulas for:

   a) $\mathrm{E}\left[s_{\overline{n}|}\right]$, based on formula (12.5).

   b) $\mathrm{Var}\left[s_{\overline{n}|}\right]$, based on formula (12.8).

   c) $\mathrm{E}\left[\ddot{a}_{\overline{n}|}\right]$, based on formula (12.11).

   d) $\mathrm{Var}\left[\ddot{a}_{\overline{n}|}\right]$, based on formula (12.14).

12.3 The lognormal model

8. In Example 12.3(1), for the standard deviation, confirm that the answer can be obtained by the alternate approach of using formula (12.4a).

9. Assume that $1+i_t$ follows a lognormal distribution with μ and σ^2. Find the formulas for:

   a) $\mathrm{E}\left[\ddot{s}_{\overline{n}|}\right]$

   b) $\mathrm{Var}\left[\ddot{s}_{\overline{n}|}\right]$

   c) $\mathrm{E}\left[a_{\overline{n}|}\right]$

   d) $\mathrm{Var}\left[a_{\overline{n}|}\right]$

10. Assume that $1+i_t$ follows a lognormal distribution with $\mu = .06$ and $\sigma^2 = .0001$. Find the mean and standard deviation for:

    a) $a(10)$

    b) $\ddot{s}_{\overline{10}|}$

    c) $a^{-1}(10)$

    d) $a_{\overline{10}|}$

11. Assume that $\mathrm{E}\left[i_t\right]=.067$ and $\mathrm{Var}\left[i_t\right]=.011445$. Also assume $1+i_t$ follows a lognormal distribution. Find the mean and the variance of $\delta_{[t]}$.

12. Assume that $\mathrm{E}\left[i_t\right]=.08$ for t = 1, 2, 3. Also assume that $1+i_t$ follows a lognormal distribution with $\sigma^2=.0001$. Find a two-tailed 95% confidence interval for the accumulated value of an investment of 1 at the end of three years.

13. Using the same data as in Exercise 12, find the mean and variance of the accumulated value of an investment of 1 made at the end of each year of three years.

14. A 35-year old invests an amount of money now to obtain a retirement fund of at least \$100,000 at age 65. The return for each year is independent of the returns in any other year. Use the Central Limit Theorem to determine the amount that the 35-year old would need to invest now to have a 95% probability of being sufficient when $\ln(1+i_t)$ is distributed uniformly on the interval $[.07,.09]$.

12.4 Time series models

15. Estimate $\delta_{[t]}$ for t = 6, 7, 8 given the data in Example 12.6, assuming future actual values are equal to estimated values.

16. *a*) Show that formula (12.33) simplifies to formula (12.30) if $k_2 = 0$.
    b) Show that formula (12.34) simplifies to formula (12.31) if $k_2 = 0$.

17. Estimate σ^2 for the AR(2) process in Example 12.7 based on the data for Z = 1, 2, 3, 4, assuming errors are distributed normally with mean = 0 and assuming that the population variance is equal to the sample variance.

18. Assume that the value of σ^2 for the AR(2) process in Example 12.7 is actually equal to .0002.
    a) Find $\mathrm{Var}\left[\delta_{[t]}\right]$.
    b) Find $\mathrm{Cov}\left[\delta_{[t]},\ \delta_{[t+2]}\right]$.

19. It is known that $\delta_{[t]}$ is normally distributed and follows an AR(1) process. The following values are given:

Z	*Actual* $\delta_{[z]}$	*Estimated* $\delta_{[z]}$
1	.100	.104
2	.105	.096
3	.095	.100

    a) Find $\delta^{E}_{[4]}$.
    b) If $\mathrm{Var}\left[\delta_{[t]}\right]$ = .0001, find $\mathrm{Cov}\left[\delta_{[3]},\ \delta_{[6]}\right]$.

20. An investment fund earned 6% effective during the past year. For each of the next two years the yield on the investment fund i_t is equally likely to be:

$$.02 + k(i_{t-1} - .06)$$
$$.06 + k(i_{t-1} - .06)$$
$$.10 + k(i_{t-1} - .06).$$

a) Show that

$$\mathrm{E}[a(2)] = (1.06)^2 + \frac{1}{3}(.0032)k.$$

b) Show that

$$\mathrm{Var}[a(2)] = \frac{1}{9}(.02158336 + .02157312k + .01079168k^2).$$

12.5 Binomial lattices

21. Rework Example 12.8 (1) applying formula (12.38).

22. An additive binomial model with annual effective rates is constructed to value a three-year zero coupon bond maturing for \$1000. The starting interest rate in the lattice is 10%. Each interest rate moves upwards by 1% with probability $p = .5$ or downwards by 1% with probability $1 - p = .5$.

a) Calculate the value of this bond form the lattice.

b) Calculate the standard deviation of the present value of this bond from the lattice.

c) Compare the value of the bond from the lattice and the value using the mean interest rate.

23. A one-year 9% bond with semiannual coupons matures for \$1000. A binomial lattice with semiannual periods is to be used. The current yield rate is 9% convertible semiannually. Each nominal interest rate moves upwards by 1% with probability $p = .3$ or downwards by 1% with probability $1 - p = .7$.

a) Calculate the value of this bond from the lattice.

b) Calculate the level continuous rate of return.

24. Rework Exercise 23(*a*) if the bond is callable on any coupon date in the future at par.

25. Rework Example 12.9 if the current yield rate is 8% convertible quarterly. Apply a binomial lattice with quarterly intervals.

26. A multiplicative binomial model with probability $p = .4$ and volatility parameter $k = .2$ is to be utilized. The starting interest rate in the lattice is 10%.
    a) Find the mean value of $a(3)$.
    b) Find the mean value of $a^{-1}(3)$.
    c) Find the mean value of $a_{\overline{3|}}$.
    d) Find the mean value of $\ddot{s}_{\overline{3|}}$.

12.6 Continuous stochastic models

27. Formulas (12.42) and (12.43) give the mean and variance of the process δ_t under the random walk model. Find $\mathrm{E}[\delta_t]$ and $\mathrm{Var}[\delta_t]$ under the other three models.

28. For the Vasicek model defined by formula (12.46):
    a) Show that when $c = 0$, the model becomes the random walk model with no drift.
    b) Show that when $c = 1$, the model becomes a normal distribution with $\mu = b$.

29. The current force of interest is .06. Under the random walk model with semiannual adjustments, the estimated forces of interest are: $\delta_{.5} = .0675$, $\delta_1 = .065$, $\delta_{1.5} = .063$, and $\delta_2 = .0685$. Find the estimated forces of interest using the Rendelman-Bartter model with the same parameters a and σ.

30. A one-year $1000 par value bond has 7.8% semiannual coupons. The current force of interest is .08. Use the random walk model with semiannual adjustments to estimate the force of interest in the future. The volatility parameter $\sigma = .01$, and $a = .006$.
    a) Find the value of the bond.
    b) Find the level yield rate.
    c) Find the value of the bond, if a standard normal variable was generated to be .5 using simulation.

31. Discard the four standard normal variables generated using simulation in Examples 12.11-12.14. Rework these four Examples to find the maximum and minimum possible force of interest rate one year into the future. Assume the range of the standard normal variables is 4, i.e. ± 2 standard deviations.

12.7 Scenario testing

32. Assume that the effective rate of interest for the year just ended is 8%. Interest rate paths are to be generated over the next 10 years with a binomial lattice. Assume that the effective rate will either increase or decrease by 10% of its prior level each year and that movement in either direction is equally likely.
    a) Find the maximum possible effective rate after 10 years.
    b) Find the minimum possible effective rate after 10 years.
    c) Find the effective rate after 10 years if there are 5 increases and 5 decreases.
    d) Explain why the answer to (*c*) is not 8%.
    e) Find the probability of the outcome in (*c*).
    f) It is decided that outcomes in excess of 15% are unrealistic. Find the probability that the rate is capped at 15% at the end of 10 years.

33. Short-term interest rates are typically more volatile than long-term interest rates. In order to reflect this phenomenon, a projection technique is adopted for which successive spot rates in the interest rate path are generated from the formula

$$i_{t+1} = i_t \, e^{kz\sigma},$$

where σ is the standard deviation of the spot rate, z is a value from the standard normal distribution, and k is a constant. The standard deviation σ is larger for short-term rates than for long-term rates. Assume that the current one-year spot rate is 7% with a standard deviation of .1, while the current five-year spot rate is 8% with a standard deviation of .05. Rates are to be projected over the next five years for both spot rates. Five random numbers are generated from the standard normal distribution: +1.65, −.26, +.73, +1.17, +.98. These values are used to project an interest rate path for both spot rates. The constant k is set equal to 1. Find the two spot rates at the end of five years and show that the yield curve became inverted.

13

Options and other derivatives

13.1 INTRODUCTION

The final topic to be presented in this book is a brief introduction to options and other derivatives. There are some aspects of this topic that have a relationship with the material covered in Sections 12.3 and 12.5.

However, this is a large topic and easily warrants its own dedicated chapter. In fact, entire books have been devoted to this subject. Thus, the presentation in Chapter 13 will be able to cover only the most basic definitions, concepts, valuation methods, and applications.

Section 8.8 provides a short descriptive introduction to four types of *derivatives;* namely (1) *options,* (2) *futures,* (3) *forwards* and (4) *swaps.* As a refresher from Section 8.8, a "derivative" is a financial instrument which has no inherent value by itself, but rather derives its value based on a relationship with some other security, financial instrument, index, etc.

We will confine our treatment of options only to those with common stocks as the underlying security. Such options have been in existence the longest and still constitute a large and actively traded public market. In Section 13.8 we will briefly mention some extension beyond the universe of common stocks.

As mentioned in Section 8.8, there are two primary motivations for buying or selling options. These motivations lie at opposite ends of the spectrum. The first motivation is speculation. Options are highly leveraged to their underlying security, so that small changes in the price of the underlying security can lead to large changes in the value of a related option.

The second motivation is hedging. There are a variety of option strategies that have been developed as risk reduction techniques. The concept of these strategies is to lessen the financial effects arising from volatility in the underlying security.

13.2 DEFINITIONS AND CONCEPTS

In this section we will present a number of definitions and concepts related to options. This material is descriptive and will be followed in succeeding sections with a more analytical treatment.

These are two fundamental types of options. A *call* is a contract that gives its owner the option to buy the underlying security on some future date at a specified price fixed in the contract. Analogously, a *put* gives its owner the option to sell the underlying security under the same conditions.

The fixed price specified in the option contract is called the *exercise price*, or *strike price*. The actual process of buying or selling the underlying security in the future is called an *option exercise*. Options have a finite life defined in the option contract. The *expiration date* or *expiry* is the date on which the option must be exercised or else the contract expires and becomes worthless.

Options are synthetic, manufactured contracts. There is not a definite, determinable number of options related to the capital structure of a company, as there is with securities such as stocks and bonds. The number of option contracts in existence at any point in time is driven directly by supply and demand for the options. Thus, for every buyer of an option there must be a seller. An option seller is often called an *option writer*.

This means that for every "long" option position there must be an offsetting "short" option position. Unless someone is willing to sell an option, there would be nothing for a potential option buyer to buy.

It would be possible for 100% of the securities (stocks and bonds) of a company to be owned by someone and have no short positions at all. That would not be possible with options on the company's securities. In fact, options are created on option exchanges, or by other external parties, and the company in question has no direct involvement with the options on its securities at all.

The reader may recall that short selling of securities was covered in Section 7.8. Although there are some similarities between selling options and short selling securities, there are also fundamental differences.

The primary difference lies with the option exercise. Short sellers of a security must buy the security back at some future date to "cover the short." Option sellers could, in a similar fashion, also cover their position by buying back the option before the expiration date. However, if the owner of a call exercises the option, the option seller must deliver the stock to the call owner and in exchange will receive the strike price from the call owner. In the case of the exercise of a put, the option seller must buy the stock from the put owner, and in exchange must pay the strike price to the put owner.

In is important to note that option buyers have *rights*, i.e. the option may or may not be exercised by the buyer. Thus, the name "option" is aptly chosen. However, option sellers have *obligations*. If the buyer exercises the option, the seller has no choice. The option seller must sell the stock in the case of a call exercise, or buy the stock in the case of a put exercise.

We will discuss option valuation in detail in later sections. However, there are a few terms that we will introduce in this definitional section. These terms should provide a glimpse into some properties of option valuation.

The *inherent value* of an option is the value of the option as if today were the expiration date of the option. This value can be, and often is, equal to zero. Inherent value is based on the relationship between the stock price and the exercise price.

Let the current stock price be denoted by S and the exercise (strike) price by E. The inherent value of a call (IVC) is given by

$$IVC = \begin{cases} S-E & \text{if } S>E \\ 0 & \text{if } S \leq E. \end{cases} \tag{13.1}$$

Similarly, the inherent value of a put (IVP) is given by

$$IVP = \begin{cases} E-S & \text{if } S<E \\ 0 & \text{if } S \geq E. \end{cases} \tag{13.2}$$

If an option has a positive inherent value, then it is said to be "in the money." If an option has an inherent value equal to zero, it is said to be "out of the money," If the current stock price is exactly equal to the exercise (strike) price, the option is said to be "at the money."

However, options with time remaining until expiry will trade in the market at prices considerably higher than inherent value. This happens because the stock may make a move in a favorable direction for the option owner prior to expiry. Of course, the stock may also make a move in the opposite direction prior to expiry and the option may lose value or become worthless at expiry.

The difference between the current price of the option and its inherent value is called the *time value* of the option. Thus, inherent value and time value constitute a two-way decomposition of total option value.

Let the current value of a call be denoted by C and the current value of a put be denoted by P. The time value of a call (TVC) is given by

$$TVC = C - IVC. \tag{13.3}$$

Similarly, the time value of a put (TVP) is given by

$$TVP = P - IVP. \tag{13.4}$$

Note that in the case of an "out of the money" option, the entire option value is time value.

Example 13.1 ***A stock currently sells for $50. A call option with an exercise (strike) price of $50 currently sells for $2.50.***

(1) Find the percentage gain to an investor in the common stock, if the stock goes up to $55 at the expiry date of the option.

(2) Find the percentage gain to an investor in the option over the same period.

(3) Rework (1) if the stock price stays constant.

(4) Rework (2) if the stock price stays constant.

(5) Find the "break-even" price to which the stock must go, so that the option owner neither makes nor loses money at expiry.

1. The percentage gain for investing in the stock is

$$\frac{55-50}{50} = +10\%.$$

2. The option will be worth $55-50 = 5$ at expiry, so the percentage gain from investing in the option is

$$\frac{5-2.50}{2.50} = +100\%.$$

3. The percentage gain for investing in the stock is

$$\frac{50-50}{50} = 0\%.$$

4. The option will be worthless at expiry, so the percentage gain from investing in the option is

$$\frac{0-2.50}{2.50} = -100\%.$$

   Comparing (2) with (1) and (4) with (3) demonstrates the great amount of "leverage" that arises from investing in options in comparison with investing in the common stock itself.

5. For the option owner to come out even, the option must be worth 2.50 at expiry. This will happen of the stock price at expiry is exactly \$52.50, which is called the "break-even" price for the option owner.

Example 13.2 ***A stock currently sells for \$49. A call option with an exercise price of \$50 currently sells for \$1.50. A put option with the same exercise price sells for \$3.50. Find the following:***
(1) IVC.
(2) TVC.
(3) IVP.
(4) TVP.

1. Since $S < E$, then $IVC = 0$.

2. Since $IVC = 0$, $TVC = C = \$1.50$, i.e. the entire value of the call is time value.

3. Since $S < E$, then $IVP = E - S = 50 - 49 = \$1$

4. $TVP = P - IVP = 3.50 - 1 = \$2.50$.

13.3 POSITION AND PROFIT DIAGRAMS

It is quite helpful in analyzing options to display graphically the relationships presented in Section 13.2. A *position diagram* is a graphical display of inherent value, i.e. the value of the option position on the expiration date of the option.

Figure 13.1 displays a set of four position diagrams for the following cases:

(a) Long call
(b) Short call
(c) Long put
(d) Short put

Stock price is shown on the x-axis and the position value at expiry is shown on the y-axis.

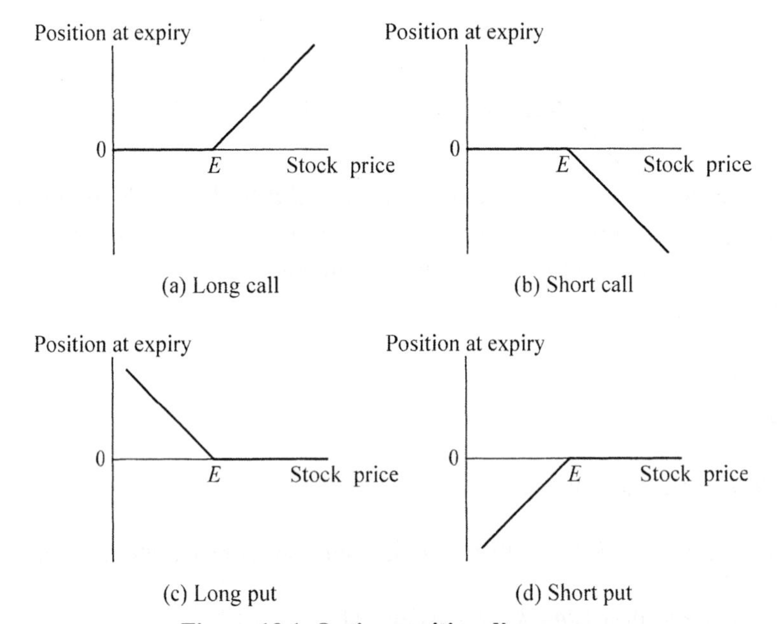

Figure 13.1 Option position diagrams

Figure 13.1(a) is a graphical representation of *IVC* from formula (13.1). Figure 13.1(b) is the mirror image of 13.1(a) for the other side of the transaction. Similarly, Figure 13.1(c) is a graphical representation of *IVP* from formula

(13.2). Finally, Figure 13.1(d) is the mirror image of 13.1(c) for the other side of the transaction.

We next present four additional position diagrams that do not involve options. These will be important in graphically displaying combination positions in Section 13.5. They also provide valuable insight into how option positions differ from other basic financial transactions.

Figure 13.2 displays the following four cases:

(a) Long stock
(b) Short stock
(c) Lending money
(d) Borrowing money

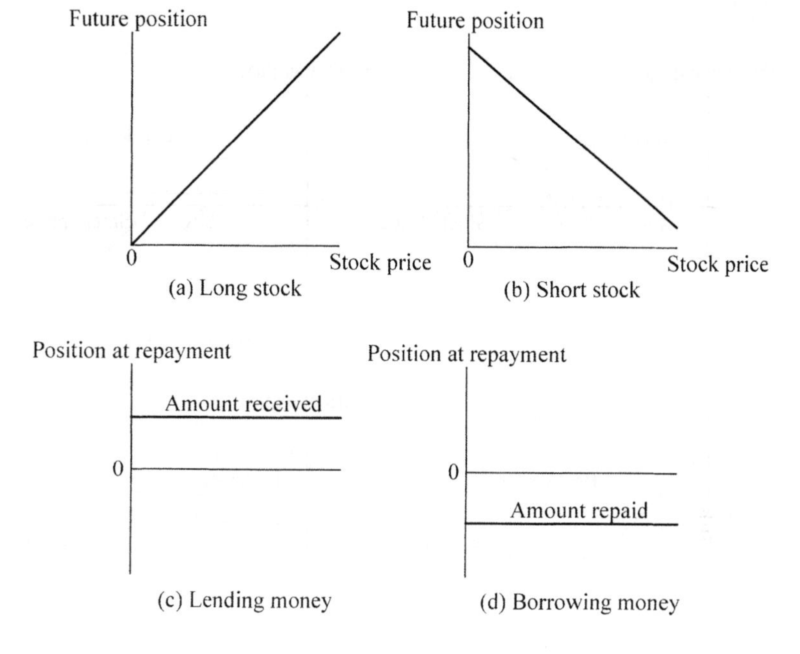

Figure 13.2 Other position diagrams

Figure 13.2(a) simply indicates that a stock owner will have a future position equal to the value of the stock. Figure 13.2(b) shows the future position for a short seller of the stock. The maximum value occurs if the stock price falls to zero. The future position can actually cross the *x*-axis and go negative if the stock price continues to rise. There is no upper limit on potential future losses in a short stock position.

Figures 13.2(c) and 13.2(d) involve simple borrowing and lending transactions. In the case of lending, there will be a cash inflow at loan repayment. In the case of borrowing, there will be a cash outflow at loan repayment.

The position diagrams in Figure 13.1 do not show net profit at option expiry, since they do not reflect the original cost of the option. In a long position, there is a cash outflow when the option is originally bought. In a short position, there is a cash inflow when the option is originally sold.

A *profit diagram* is an adjusted position diagram to reflect the original price of the option. Figure 13.3 contains profit diagrams for the four cases illustrated in Figure 13.1.

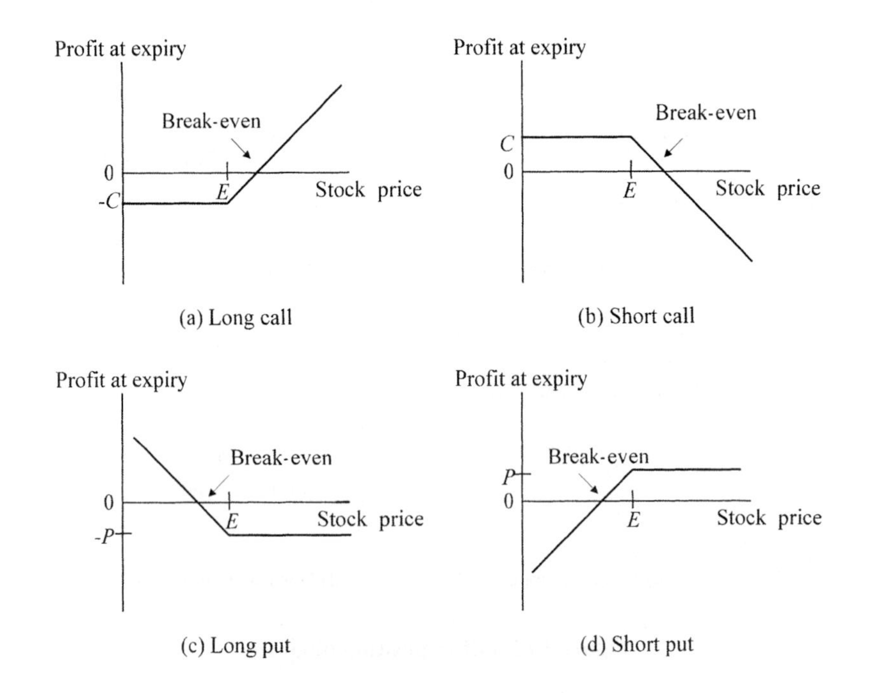

Figure 13.3 Option profit diagrams

Example 13.3 Display profit diagrams, as presented in Figure 13.3, for the stock and its options contained in Example 13.2.

The profit diagrams are displayed in figure 13.4.

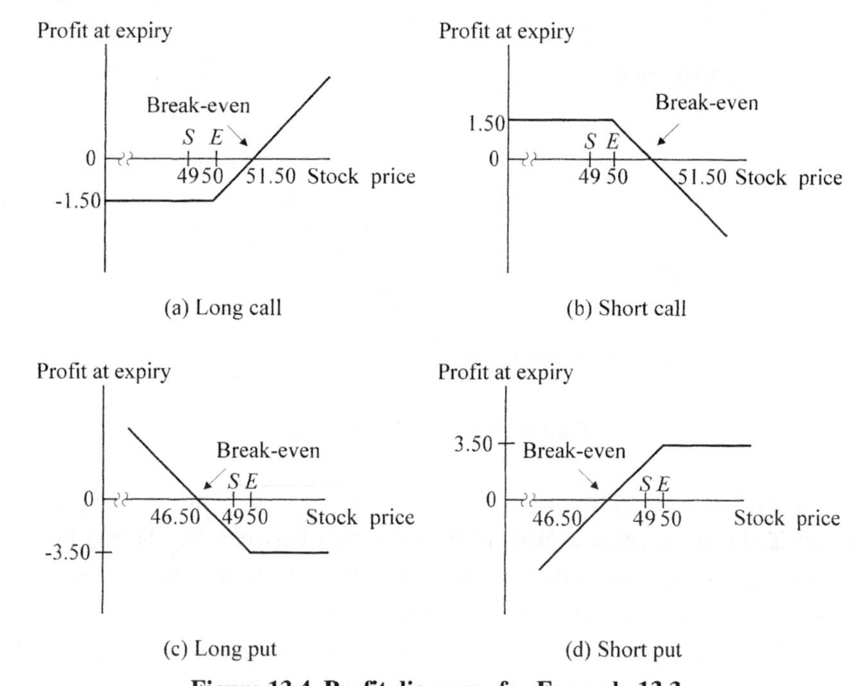

Figure 13.4 Profit diagrams for Example 13.3

Note that the current stock price $S = 49$ has been added to the four diagrams. However, it is not an inherent part of the profit diagram. Of course, the current value of S is a major determinant of the call price C and put price P. The factors that affect the value of an option will be developed more fully in the next section.

13.4 DETERMINANTS OF OPTION VALUE

In this section we will extend the largely descriptive presentation thus far in this chapter and identify the determinants of option value. Actual methods and techniques for determining option values will be presented in Sections 13.6 and 13.7.

We will focus on a call option for purposes of this presentation. The reader is encouraged to work through the same steps for a put option. Figure 13.1(a) graphically displays the inherent value of a call (*IVC*), i.e. the value of a call at expiry. However, it does not display the time value of a call (TVC), nor the total value of a call *C*. Figure 13.5 is an extension of Figure 13.1(a) that displays these relationships.

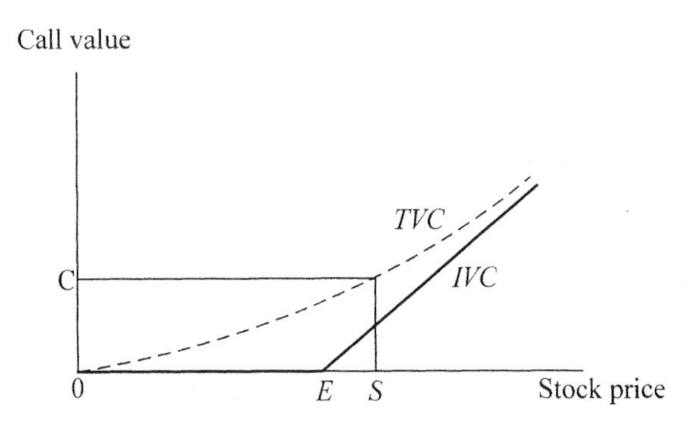

Figure 13.5 Value of a call

The dashed line represents the total value of a call *C* prior to expiry as a function of the stock price *S*. The vertical distance between the dashed line and the solid line is the time value of the call (*TVC*). Note that to the left of the exercise (strike) price *E*, the entire call value is time value.

There are three interesting observations that can be drawn from Figure 13.5.

1. As *S* falls well below *E*, the value of *C* approaches zero. In this situation it is becoming increasingly likely that the *IVC* will be zero at expiry.

2. As *S* rises well above *E*, the dashed line approaches the solid line asymptotically. This can be interpreted as *C* changing ever more closely in tandem with changes in *S*. In the limit, *C* is approaching *S* minus the present value of *E* at the date of expiry.

3. Time value, i.e. *TVC*, is largest when *S* is "close" to *E* (i.e. close to "at the money") rather than far away from *E* (i.e. well "out of the money" or well "in the money.")

We now have enough background to address the determinants of the value of a call, i.e. why the dotted line in Figure 13.5 lies where it does. We assume that the underlying stock does not pay dividends. Payment of dividends is a complicating matter and will be covered in Section 13.8.

There are five determinants of the value of a call:

1. *Stock price (S)* - Clearly, from Figure 13.5 the value of C increases as the value of S increases, and conversely. The opposite result holds for puts.

2. *Exercise price (E)* - For any given call option, E does not vary. However, consider the comparative values of a set of calls on a company's stock for various values of E. The higher the value of E the lower the value of C, and conversely. This should be obvious from formula (13.1), as well from general reasoning. The opposite result holds for puts.

3. *Time to expiry (t)* - In Figure 13.5 as time elapses the dashed line will move toward the solid line and will coincide with it at expiry. Thus, as t decreases, the value of C will decrease, and conversely. Longer-term calls will be worth more than shorter-term calls, all else being equal. The same result will hold for puts using the same reasoning.

   We should pause a moment to recognize that implicit in the above discussion is an assumption that the call can only be exercised on its expiration date. If it could be exercised earlier than that, the analysis would become more complex.

   European options have exactly this property; namely, that the only exercise date possible is the expiration date of the option. Thus, through Section 13.7 we will be analyzing only European options. We will identify some other varieties of options with different exercise features in Section 13.8.

4. *Volatility of stock price* (σ) - We have not yet discussed the *volatility* of the stock price. We will measure that volatility by the standard deviation of the stock price, denoted by σ, over some base time period. The standard deviation over t periods will be $\sigma\sqrt{t}$ from basic statistics.

Although we have not yet developed any analytical tools to address this question, it should be intuitively clear that higher values of σ will lead to higher values of C, and conversely. In everyday language, the greater the volatility of the underlying stock, the greater the chance that it will make a move favorable to the value of a call prior to expiry. The same result holds for puts using the same reasoning.

5. *Interest rate (i or δ)* - Finally, we come to effect of interest. Interest can either be measured as a rate of interest i or a force of interest δ.

   Again, we have not yet developed any analytical tools to address this question. However, property 2 discussed above in connection with Figure 13.5 provides a clue. It observes that the upper limit of C as S increases is equal to S minus the present value of E. As the interest rate increases this present value will decrease causing the call value to increase, and conversely. When we do develop the analytical tools needed, we will see that this rudimentary, intuitive argument does provide the correct relationship in general.

   One additional question that arises is what rate or force of interest should be used. This is a challenging question and a complete analysis lies beyond the scope of this book. It turns out that the rate should be a risk-free rate, most easily captured as the rate on a zero coupon Treasury security over time period t, the life of the option. Any other rate is subject to arbitrage opportunities, but this risk-free rate is not.

Example 13.4 ***Develop a graphical representation of the value of a put analogous to Figure 13.5.***

We start with Figure 13.1(c) and extend it. This results in Figure 13.6 which provides the analogous graph to Figure 13.5 for a put.

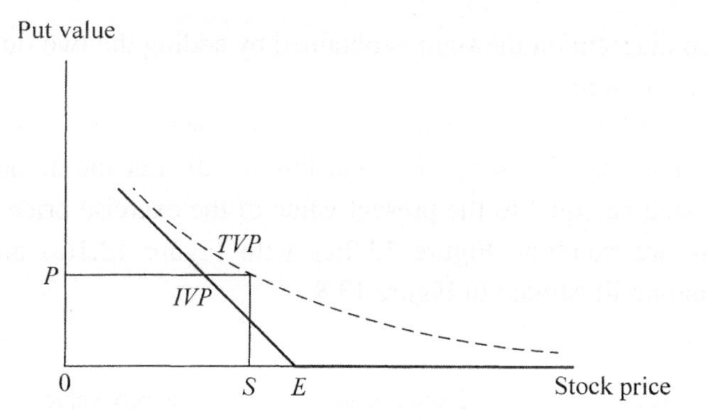

Figure 13.6 Value of a put

Again, the dashed line represents the total value of a put *P* prior to the expiry as a function of the stock price *S*. The vertical distance between the dashed line and the solid line is the time value of the put (*TVP*). Note that to the right of the exercise (strike) price *E*, the entire put value is time value.

13.5 COMBINATION POSITIONS

The position and the profit diagrams considered in Section 13.3 were based on only one position. A wide variety of interesting, and important, outcomes can be obtained by combining positions. These outcomes can be displayed by combining two or more of the eight position diagrams displayed in Figures 13.1 and 13.2.

To illustrate the approach, consider the combination of buying a stock and buying a put. If we combine Figures 13.2(a) with Figure 13.1(c), we obtain the position diagram illustrated in Figure 13.7.

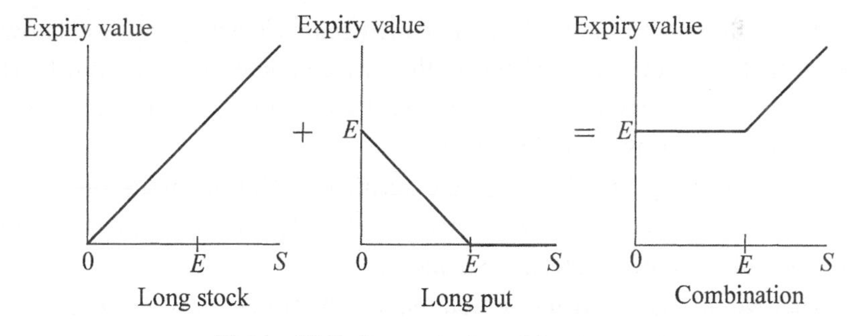

Figure 13.7 Long stock and long put

The position diagram on the right is obtained by adding the two outcomes to the left of the equals sign.

Next consider what happens if we lend money (e.g. in a bank deposit earning the risk-free Treasury rate) and buy a call. Let the amount of money loaned/invested be equal to the present value of the exercise price of the call E. In this case we combine Figure 13.2(c) with Figure 13.1(a) and obtain the position diagram illustrated in Figure 13.8.

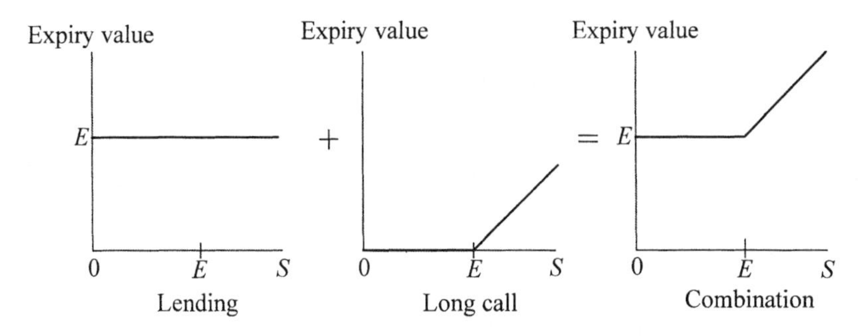

Figure 13.8 Lending money and long call

Figures 13.7 and 13.8 have exactly the same outcome! Two different positions that produce the same outcome are often called a *replicating transaction*.

This particular replicating transaction is very important in analyzing options. If we express it algebraically rather than graphically we obtain

$$S + P = v^t E + C \tag{13.5}$$

The relationship in formula (13.5) is called *put-call parity*. If we know any three of the four values S, E, C and P, then we can determine the fourth. This is a dramatic result in practice. For example, if we know S, E, and C, the value of P can be obtained from formula (13.5).

The reader may find this outcome surprising. Options trade on exchanges and the reader might naturally assume that supply and demand in the option market would separately determine S and P.

What would happen if the option market set prices for S and P that did not satisfy put-call parity? If this were to happen, it would create a golden arbitrage opportunity that would quickly be exploited until put-call parity were reestablished. The reader might want to refer back to Section 10.6 for a more detailed discussion of arbitrage.

It is also enlightening to consider Figure 13.7 on a stand-alone basis. The position diagram for this particular combination shows an upside potential if S increases, but also has downside protection if S decreases. This is an outcome that might appeal to conservative investors in common stock. It is an excellent example of using options to reduce risk by *hedging*, a term we have encountered in earlier chapters.

This particular investment strategy can easily be used by individual investors and is often called a *protective put*. In this strategy the cost of the put is essentially "insurance" against the value of the common stock decreasing.

Another elementary hedging strategy that can also be easily utilized by individual investors is the *covered call*. It is a combination of buying a stock and selling a call. Figure 13.9 displays this combination position. In this case we combine Figure 13.2(a) with Figure 13.1(b).

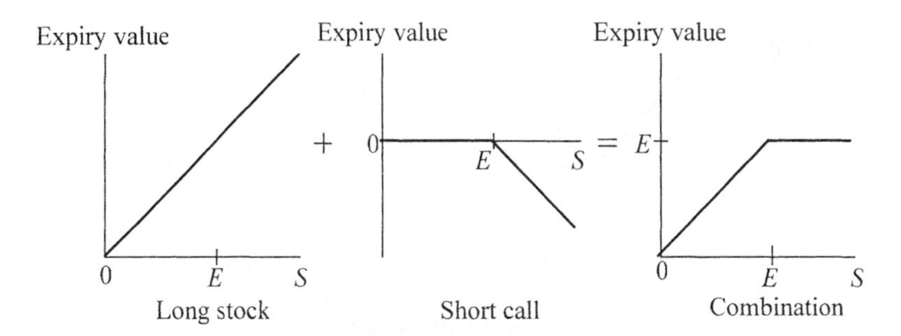

Figure 13.9 Long stock and short call

This might initially appear to be a totally unfavorable outcome. We have the downside risk in the stock together with no upside potential. Why would anyone do this?

We must remember, though, that Figure 13.9 is a position diagram, not a profit diagram. The investor receives the value of the call when it is originally sold. A covered call strategy might actually be quite appealing as a way of generating extra return from stocks that are not likely to increase in value significantly over the life of the call option.

At this point we have merely scratched the surface of combination positions that could be created in practice. Constructing complex combination positions in options and other derivatives has become a widespread activity, particularly among large, institutional investors. There do not appear to be many limits on the complex, even exotic, strategies that have been developed by experts in this area.

Example 13.5 Construct a position diagram and a profit diagram arising from buying both a put and a call with the same exercise price.

In this case we combine Figures 13.1(a) and (c). The position diagram is displayed in Figure 13.10(a) and the profit diagram in 13.10(b). Figure 13.10(b) is lower than 13.10(a) by the cost of buying the two options.

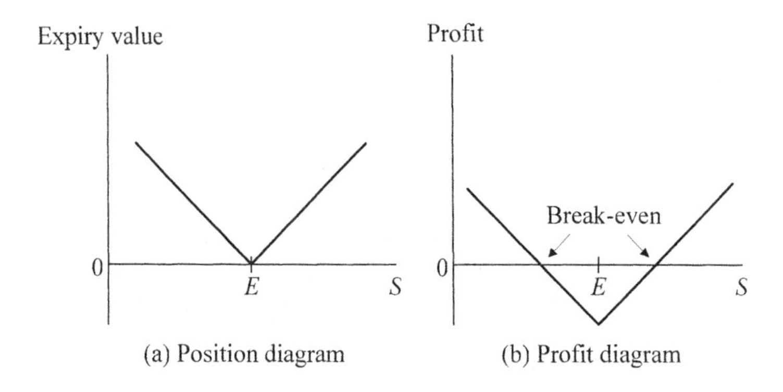

(a) Position diagram (b) Profit diagram

Figure 13.10 Straddle

This particular investment strategy is called a *straddle*. This strategy will gain if the stock price makes a large move either up or down, but will lose if the stock price stays about the same. It has two "break-even" values, one above E and one below E.

13.6 BINOMIAL LATTICES

Sections 13.1 through 13.5 have provided considerable background and insight into options. However, these sections have stopped short of developing methods for actually valuing options. Section 13.6 presents a discrete model for such valuation, while Section 13.7 presents a continuous model.

The discrete method is called the *binomial method* and is based on *binomial lattices*. It is quite similar in many respects to binomial lattices for interest rates discussed in Section 12.5. The reader is encouraged to reread Section 12.5 before reading this section. The discussion in this section is streamlined in certain places, since it assumes the reader is familiar with Section 12.5.

There also are some differences between the binomial lattices for interest rates and the binomial lattices for options. We will attempt to highlight these differences, since the two methods have so many similarities. Rather than interest rates moving up and down, as in Section 12.5, it is stock prices moving up and down. We then value an option based on the stock prices at the right-hand end of the lattice.

We are not focused on interest rate paths as we were in Section 12.5. Rather, the paths represent a progression of stock prices. There is only one interest rate throughout the entire lattice, the risk-free rate as discussed in Section 12.4.

The lattice may be open or closed as illustrated in Figure 12.1. We will focus on closed lattices which will have $n+1$ endpoints after n periods. Closed lattices may be "additive" or "multiplicative," as defined in Section 12.5. For the multiplicative model, we have the following formulas similar to formula (12.37):

$$S_{t+1} = S_t(1+k) \text{ if up move} \tag{13.6a}$$

and

$$S_{t+1} = \frac{S_t}{1+k} \text{ if down move} \tag{13.6b}$$

where S_t represents the stock price after t periods in the lattice.

The modeler can select the value of k. However, it can be shown that an excellent value of k is given by

$$k = e^{\sigma\sqrt{h}} - 1 \tag{13.7}$$

where σ is the standard deviation of the stock price and h is the length of successive time intervals through the lattice. The rationale for this choice of k is not yet evident, but will become evident in Section 13.7.

Under this structure a two-period binomial lattice for the multiplicative binomial model analogous to Figure 12.2 is given in Figure 13.11. Binomial lattices with periods other than two are constructed similarly to Figure 13.11.

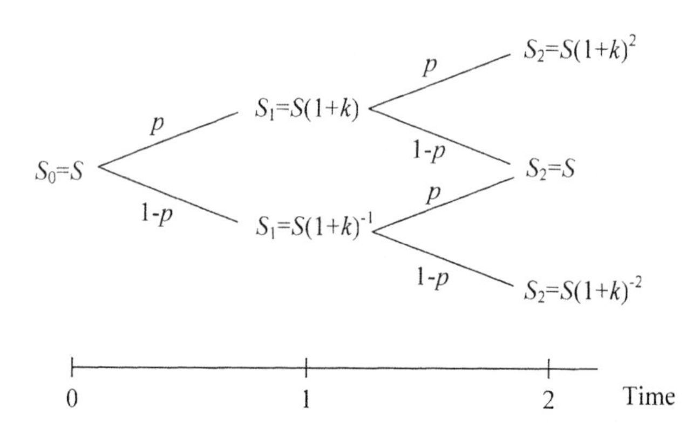

Figure 13.11 Two-period binomial lattice

We are now equipped with enough background to develop the binomial method. Rather than present a theoretical derivation we will work through a numerical illustration to strengthen conceptual understanding of the technique. For simplicity in the illustration we will use only one period in the lattice. The multiplicative model is not used in order to simplify the calculations.

There are two possible approaches used in applying the binomial method. Both methods will give the same answer, if applied consistently.

The first method is the *option delta method.* A stock is currently selling for \$70. We assume that in one year the price must either be \$55 or \$95. We seek to find the value of a European call which expires at the end of one year with an exercise price of \$75. We will assume that the one-year risk-free rate of interest is 10%. If the stock falls to \$55, the call will be worthless. If the stock rises to \$95, the call will be worth \$20 at expiry.

Now compare these outcomes with those that would result from buying one share of stock and borrowing \$50. If the stock falls to \$55, we can sell it and use the proceeds to pay off the loan for 50(1.1) = \$55 leaving a zero balance. If the stock rises to \$95, we can sell it and use the proceeds to pay off the loan, leaving a net balance of 95 – 55 = \$40.

The outcomes from this second transaction are identical to those that would result from buying two calls. This is another example of a replicating transaction. Thus, the two transactions have the same value, i.e.

$$\begin{aligned}\text{value of 2 calls} &= \text{value of stock} - \text{bank loan}\\ &= 70 - 50 = \$20\end{aligned}$$

The value of 1 call is then \$10.

If the call sells for something other than \$10, an arbitrage opportunity exists. If the call sells for more than \$10, then an investor can make a certain profit by buying one share of stock, selling two calls, and borrowing \$50. On the other hand, if the call sells for less than \$10, then an investor can also make a certain profit by selling one share of stock, buying two calls, and lending the balance. Since arbitrage opportunities are quickly eliminated in efficient markets, the value of the call must be \$10.

The number of shares necessary to replicate one call is often called the *option delta* or the *hedge ratio*. In the above illustration the option delta is 1/2.

We now develop general formulas for this technique. Denote the option delta by Δ. It is defined as follows

$$\begin{aligned}\Delta &= \frac{\text{range of option values}}{\text{range of stock values}}\\ &= \frac{V_U - V_D}{S_U - S_D}\end{aligned} \tag{13.8}$$

where

V_U = value of option in an up move
V_D = value of option in a down move
S_U = value of stock in an up move
S_D = value of stock in a down move

The value of a call given by

$$C = S\Delta - \frac{S_D\Delta}{1+i}. \tag{13.9}$$

In the above illustration we have

$$\Delta = \frac{20-0}{95-55} = \frac{20}{40} = \frac{1}{2}$$

and

$$C = (70)\left(\frac{1}{2}\right) - \frac{(55)\left(\frac{1}{2}\right)}{1.1} = 10$$

confirming the answer obtained by general reasoning above.

The corresponding value for a put is

$$P = S\Delta - \frac{S_U\Delta}{1+i}. \tag{13.10}$$

The reader should carefully note that the option delta Δ is negative for puts.

The second method is the *risk neutral method.* Let us pretend that investors are indifferent about risk. If investors are indifferent about risk, then the expected return on the stock must be 10%. Let p be the probability that the stock price rises and $1 - p$ be the probability that it falls. If the stock price rises from \$70 to \$95, then the yield rate is +35.71%. If the stock price falls from \$70 to \$55, then the yield rate is −21.43%.

Thus, under the assumption of risk-neutrality, we have

$$.3571p + (-.2143)(1-p) = .1$$

which can be solved to give $p = .55$.

Now if we compute the expected present value of the call using a technique similar to formula (12.38), we have

$$\frac{.55(20) + .45(0)}{1.1} = \$10$$

which is the same answer we obtained earlier. Thus, if we are to eliminate the possibility of risk-free arbitrage, we must compute values assuming risk neutrality. Moreover, the probabilities of the two different outcomes are determined by the requirement to eliminate risk-free arbitrage.

We now develop general formulas for this technique. We have

$$S(1+i) = pS_U + (1-p)S_D \tag{13.11}$$

and then solve formula (13.11) for p. The value of the call is given by

$$C = \frac{p \cdot V_U + (1-p)V_D}{1+i} \tag{13.12}$$

a formula similar to formula (12.38). The reader should confirm that formulas (13.11) and (13.12) reproduce the illustrative calculation above.

Finally, we see that the value of a put is also given by formula (13.12)

$$P = \frac{p \cdot V_U + (1-p)V_D}{1+i} \tag{13.12}$$

Although the same formula is used for both calls and puts, the value of V_U and V_D differ between the two types of options.

We are now equipped with enough background to develop a generalized formula for n periods. As before, let the exercise price be denoted by E. The value of the call at expiry for each outcome is the greater of zero and the excess of the stock price at expiry over the exercise price. Thus, we have the following general expression for the value of a European call using an n - period binomial lattice:

$$C = \frac{1}{(1+i)^n} \sum_{t=0}^{n} \binom{n}{t} p^{n-t}(1-p)^t \max\left[0, S(1+k)^{n-2t} - E\right]. \tag{13.13}$$

In applying formula (13.13) we determine the value of p as above for the one-period case. All the other values are known and the formula can be evaluated. The formula may be tedious to calculate by hand, but can easily be evaluated by computer.

Example 13.6 Find the value of the put with the same values of S, E, i, and t as the call illustrated in this section using:

(1) Put-call parity.

(2) The option delta method.

(3) The risk neutral method.

1. We have:

$S = 70$

$E = 75$

$i = .1$

$t = 1$

$C = 10$ obtained earlier.

Applying formula (13.5) for put-call parity, we have

$$S+P = v^t E+C$$

$$70+P = (1.1)^{-1}(75)+10$$

and solving for P, we have

$$P = 68.18+10-70 = 8.18.$$

2. In addition to the values in part 1, we have:

$$S_U = 95$$
$$S_D = 55$$
$$V_U = 0$$
$$V_D = 75-55 = 20.$$

Now applying formula (13.8) we have

$$\Delta = \frac{V_U - V_D}{S_U - S_D}$$

or

$$\Delta = \frac{0-20}{95-55} = \frac{-20}{40} = -.5.$$

Note that Δ for a put is the negative of the value of the corresponding call. Applying formula (13.10) we have

$$P = S\Delta - \frac{S_U \Delta}{1+i}$$

$$= (70)(-.5) - \frac{(95)(-.5)}{1.1} = 8.18.$$

3. Applying formula (13.11) we have

$$S(1+i) = pS_U + (1-p)S_D$$

or

$$70(1.1) = p(95)+(1-p)(55).$$

Solving for p we obtain

$$p = \frac{70(1.1)-55}{95-55} = .55.$$

Note that this is the same value for p as obtained when the call value was determined. Finally, applying formula (13.12) we have

$$\begin{aligned} P &= \frac{p \cdot V_U + (1-p)V_D}{1+i} \\ &= \frac{(.55)(0)+(1-.55)(20)}{1.1} = 8.18. \end{aligned}$$

Example 13.7 Find the value of a European call expiring in one year with an exercise price of \$100 for a stock currently selling for \$90. The standard deviation for the continuous rate of return for this stock is .3, and the risk free force of interest is 10%. Use the binomial method applied in four steps, i.e. on a quarterly basis.

From formula (13.7) we have

$$k = e^{\sigma\sqrt{h}} - 1 = e^{.3\sqrt{.25}} - 1 = .16183.$$

We now need to compute p on a basis which eliminates risk-free arbitrage. Our upside value is $90(1 + k) = 104.565$ and our downside value is $90(1 + k)^{-1} = 77.464$.

Using formula (13.11), modified to reflect a force of interest rather than a rate of interest to determine p, we have

$$104.565p + 77.464(1-p) = 90e^{.25(.1)} = 92.278$$

which can be solved to give $p = .5466$.

We have $n + 1 = 5$ possible outcomes:

$$\begin{aligned} 90(1+k)^4 &= 163.988 \\ 90(1+k)^2 &= 121.486 \\ 90 &= 90.000 \\ 90(1+k)^{-2} &= 66.674 \\ 90(1+k)^{-4} &= 49.394 \end{aligned}$$

We now apply formula (13.13) to obtain

$$C = e^{-.1}\left[(.5466)^4(163.988-100) + \binom{4}{1}(.5466)^3(.4534)(121.486-100)\right] = \$10.93.$$

Thus, the binomial method applied on a quarterly basis produces a value for the call of \$10.93.

13.7 BLACK SCHOLES FORMULA

Perhaps the most famous option pricing method of all is the Black Scholes formula. It is a continuous model in contrast to the discrete models presented in Section 13.6. It was first published in a 1973 paper by F. Black and M. Scholes entitled *The Pricing of Options and Corporate Liabilities.*

The Black-Scholes formula for the value of a European call is given by

$$C = SN(d_1) - Ee^{-\delta t}N(d_2) \tag{13.14}$$

where

C = value of the European call
S = current stock price
E = exercise (strike) price
δ = risk-free force of interest
t = time remaining until expiry
N = cumulative distribution function for the standard normal

$$d_1 = \frac{\ln(S/E) + \left(\delta + \frac{1}{2}\sigma^2\right)t}{\sigma\sqrt{t}} \tag{13.15a}$$

$$d_2 = \frac{\ln(S/E) + \left(\delta - \frac{1}{2}\sigma^2\right)t}{\sigma\sqrt{t}} \tag{13.15b}$$

σ = standard deviation of the stock price

Interestingly enough, the Black-Scholes formula is based on the assumption that $1 + i_t$ follows the lognormal distribution, just as described in Section 12.3. Formula (13.14) also assumes that the underlying stock or other asset does not pay dividends prior to the expiry date. The derivation of formula (13.14) is lengthy and is given in the Appendix 13 at the end of the chapter.

The corresponding formula for the value of a European put is given by

$$P = Ee^{-\delta n}\left[1 - N(d_2)\right] - S\left[1 - N(d_1)\right] \tag{13.16}$$

where P is the value of the put and all other symbols are defined the same as in formula (13.14). Alternatively, the value of the put could also be determined by put-call parity, i.e. using formula (13.5).

Empirical tests of the Black-Scholes formula suggest that the formula works quite well under many conditions. It tends to develop greater errors in the following situations:

1. When the exercise price E is far from the current stock price S.

2. For securities with volatility much above or below average, i.e. σ being quite high or low.

3. If the expiry date is far in the future, i.e. for high values of t.

It can be shown that the limit of the binomial method as the number of periods increase without limit and the length of each interval shrinks to zero will be the Black Scholes formula under certain conditions. In particular, if the multiplicative binomial method, as presented in Section 13.6, is applied with

$$k = e^{\sigma\sqrt{h}} - 1 \tag{13.7}$$

given earlier, the Black Scholes formula will be obtained in the limit as $h \to 0$.

Example 13.8 ***Use the Black-Scholes formula to find the value of a European call expiring in one year with an exercise price of \$100 for a stock currently selling for \$90. The standard deviation for the continuous rate of return for this stock is .3, and the risk-free force of interest is 10%.***

Applying formulas (13.15a) and (13.15b) we have

$$d_1 = \frac{\ln(90/100) + (.1+.09/2)(1)}{.3(1)} = .132$$

and

$$d_2 = \frac{\ln(90/100) + (.1-.09/2)(1)}{.3(1)} = -.168.$$

From tables for the cumulative normal distribution we have

$$N(.132) = .5525$$

and

$$N(-.168) = .4333.$$

Now substituting into formula (13.14) we have

$$C = (90)(.5525) - (100)(e^{-.1})(.4333) = \$10.52.$$

This result should be compared with Example 13.7 in which the value of this same option was obtained using the binomial method with quarterly periods. The answer obtained using that method was \$10.93. If the binomial method were applied with more periods and shorter intervals the answer would approach the Black-Scholes answer of \$10.52 in the limit.

13.8 SOME EXTENSIONS

In this final section, we present some extensions to the material developed in Sections 13.1 through 13.7.

Dividends

The formulas developed earlier did not include dividends. If the stock pays dividends, the net effect will be to depress the stock price somewhat. The basis for this statement is that had the company not paid the dividend, the cash used to pay the dividend would still reside within the company and belong to the stockholders.

Assume that dividends are paid continuously at the rate of r per period. The conventional approach is to adjust the Black Scholes formula (13.14) by replacing S with Se^{-rt}.

Similar adjustments could be made in the binomial method by adjusting stock prices downward by the amount of the dividends paid on a discrete basis as they occur.

Option types

Throughout Chapter 13 we have considered European options which can only be exercised on the expiration date. European options can readily be analyzed using the techniques already presented.

However, there are a variety of other options types. Perhaps most significantly, *American options* can be exercised at any time. In many cases the optimal time to exercise an American option is at expiration, making it functionally equivalent to a European option. However, in other cases early exercise may be optimal.

Two other option types deserve mention. *Bermuda options* can be exercised during some, but not all, periods in the life of the option. Thus, this type of option might be considered to lie between European options and American options in a certain sense.

A particularly intriguing and complex option type is the *Asian option*. In this type of option the payoff is calculated using the average of stock prices at more than one date, rather than only using the price on the date of exercise.

Valuation of these other types of options is more complex than for European options and involves techniques beyond the scope of this book.

Embedded options

Many securities contain *embedded options*, which are not identified as separate financial instruments, but are included as part of a package.

As an example, consider the relationship between a noncallable bond and an otherwise identical callable bond. The noncallable bond will sell at a higher price than the callable bond, since bond purchasers are willing to pay more for a bond which cannot be called early at an uncertain date. Thus we have the following relationship

$$B^{nc} = B^{c} + C \qquad (13.17)$$

where

B^{nc} = value of the noncallable bond
B^{c} = value of the callable bond
C = value of the call option

When investors buy callable bonds, in essence they are buying noncallable bonds and simultaneously selling call options to the bond issuers.

Another example of an embedded option involves prepayments under mortgages backed securities (MBS) and collateralized mortgage obligations

(CMOs) described in Section 8.8. These are quite analogous conceptually to callable bonds, i.e. both involve borrowers exercising an option to repay loans ahead of schedule.

Yet a third example lies in many insurance and annuity contracts. For example, most variable annuity contracts have embedded options that allow contract owners to obtain values other than the market value of the underlying securities under certain conditions specified in the contract.

Many other examples could be cited. The main point is that option pricing theory has many applications well beyond simple options on common stocks trading on option exchanges as presented in this chapter.

The Greeks

More advanced option analysis considers option price sensitivity to various factors. These sensitivities are commonly called *the Greeks*. The five most common of "the Greeks" are as follows:

- *Delta* - the partial derivative of the option price with respect to the stock price.
- *Gamma* - the partial derivative of delta with respect to the stock price.
- *Theta* - the partial derivative of the option price with respect to time.
- *Vega* - the partial derivative of the option price with respect to volatility.
- *Rho* - the partial derivative of the option price with respect to the interest rate.

We will not attempt to define these sensitivities more completely, nor discuss how they might be applied in practice. Perhaps the reader's curiosity will be piqued by this colorful lineup and it will stimulate an interest in investigating option theory more deeply.

APPENDIX 13

Derivation of the Black-Scholes formula

Let S_t be a random variable of an asset at time *t*, where $S_0 = S$. Let $f_t(x)$ be probability density function for S_t.

Then the value of a European call is given by

$$C = e^{-\delta n} \int_E^{\infty} (x-E) f_n(x) dx$$

since the value of the call is equal to the expected present value of the excess of the asset price at expiry over the exercise price (but not less than zero).

Assume that $1+i_t$ follows the lognormal distribution. Then $\ln(S_n / S)$ is normally distributed with mean = $n\mu$ and variance = $n\sigma^2$. From the lognormal distribution we have

$$\mathrm{E}[S_n / S] = e^{n(\mu+\sigma^2/2)}$$

and

$$f_n(x) = \frac{1}{x\sigma\sqrt{2\pi n}} e^{-\frac{[\ln(x/S)-n\mu]^2}{2n\sigma^2}}.$$

Also assume that the asset at time 0 is equal to its expected present value

$$S = \mathrm{E}\left[e^{-\delta n} S_n\right] = e^{-\delta n} S e^{n\mu+n\sigma^2/2}$$

or

$$1 = e^{-\delta n+n\mu+n\sigma^2/2}.$$

This implies that $\mu = \delta - \sigma^2 / 2$.

When we combine all these results we have

$$C = e^{-\delta n} \int_E^\infty \frac{x-E}{x\sigma\sqrt{2\pi n}} e^{-\frac{\left[\ln(x/S)-n(\delta-\sigma^2/2)\right]^2}{2n\sigma^2}} dx.$$

We now evaluate this integral by making a change of variable. Let

$$y = \frac{\ln(x/S)-n(\delta-\sigma^2/2)}{\sigma\sqrt{n}}$$

so that

$$dy = \frac{1}{x\sigma\sqrt{n}} dx$$

and

$$x = Se^{\left[n(\delta-\sigma^2/2)+y\sigma\sqrt{n}\right]}$$

Let the lower limit after the change of variable be F, so that

$$E = Se^{\left[n(\delta-\sigma^2/2)+F\sigma\sqrt{n}\right]}$$

or

$$F = \frac{\ln(E/S)-n(\delta-\sigma^2/2)}{\sigma\sqrt{n}}.$$

Thus, after the first change of variable we have

$$C = e^{-\delta n} \int_F^\infty \frac{Se^{\left[n(\delta-\sigma^2/2)+y\sigma\sqrt{n}\right]}-E}{\sqrt{2\pi}} e^{-y^2/2} dy$$

$$= S \int_F^\infty \frac{e^{-(y-\sigma\sqrt{n})^2/2}}{\sqrt{2\pi}} dy - Ee^{-\delta n} \int_F^\infty \frac{e^{-y^2/2}}{\sqrt{2\pi}}.$$

However, the first integral is the area to the right of $F - \sigma\sqrt{n}$, or to the left of $-F + \sigma\sqrt{n}$, in the standard normal distribution. Similarly, the second integral is the area to the right of F or to the left of $-F$.

Thus, if we denote the cumulative distribution function for the standard normal distribution by N, we have

$$C = SN\left(-F + \sigma\sqrt{n}\right) - Ee^{-\delta n}N\left(-F\right).$$

Now let

$$d_1 = -F + \sigma\sqrt{n} = \frac{\ln\left(S/E\right) + n\left(\delta - \sigma^2/2\right) + \sigma^2 n}{\sigma\sqrt{n}}$$

$$= \frac{\ln\left(S/E\right) + n\left(\delta + \sigma^2/2\right)}{\sigma\sqrt{n}}$$

and

$$d_2 = -F = \frac{\ln\left(S/E\right) + n\left(\delta - \sigma^2/2\right)}{\sigma\sqrt{n}}.$$

This gives

$$C = SN\left(d_1\right) - Ee^{-\delta n}N\left(d_2\right)$$

which is the Black-Scholes formula.

EXERCISES

13.2 Definitions and concepts

1. A stock currently sells for \$80 and a put option with an exercise price of \$80 currently sells for \$2.
   a) Find the percentage gain to an investor in the common stock and the option, if the stock goes up to \$84 at the expiration date of the option.
   b) Rework (*a*) if the stock price stays constant.
   c) Rework (*a*) if the stock price goes down to \$78 at the expiration date of the option.
   d) Rework (*a*) if the stock price goes down to \$76 at the expiration date of the option.
   e) Find the "break-even" price to which the stock must go, so that the option owner neither makes nor loses money at expiry.
   f) Find TVP.

2. A stock sells for \$100, a call option with an exercise price of \$98 currently sells for \$6, a put option with the same exercise price sells for \$2. Find the following:
   a) IVC.
   b) TVC.
   c) IVP.
   d) TVP.

13.3 Position and profit diagrams

3. An investor buys a call with an exercise price of \$40 for \$3, while simultaneously selling a call on the same stock with an exercise price of \$45 for \$1. Both options have the same expiry date. (Note: this is an example of an option strategy called a *spread*.) Calculate the profit position at expiry if:
   a) S = \$35.
   b) S = \$40.
   c) S = \$42.50.
   d) S = \$45.
   e) S = \$50.

4. Display profit diagrams for long stock and for short stock.

5. Based on Figure 13.3, if an investor purchases one long call option and one long put option, find:
   a) Two "break-even" stock prices.
   b) The largest amount of loss.

6. There are two call options with the exercise price of \$50. Call option A with time to expiration of six months sells for \$5. Call option B with the time to expiration of one year sells for \$4.
   a) Construct a strategy that is certain to make a profit.
   b) What is the profit if the stock is at \$48, \$50 and 52 in one year? Ignore the time value of money.

13.4 Determinants of option value

7. Develop graphical representations of the values of a short call and a short put analogous to Figures 13.5 and 13.6.

8. Explain how the determinants S, E, t, σ and i affect the value of a put.

9. Explain why the arbitrage opportunity exists in Exercise 6.

10. Find the following limiting values for the value of a call option:
    a) $S = 0$.
    b) S is very large in relation to E.
    c) $E = 0$.
    d) E is very large in relation to S.
    e) $n = 0$.
    f) n is very large.

13.5 Combination positions

11. Use the put-call parity Formula (13.5) to verify Observation 2 in the list of five determinants in Section 13.4, in which the upper limit of C as S increases is equal to S minus the present value of E.

12. A three-month call option with an exercise price of \$50 sells for \$1. The current stock price is \$49. The interest rate is 9% convertible monthly. Find the price of a three-month put option with the same exercise price.

13. Consider the same call and put options as in Exercise 12. If the put option actually sells for \$2, develop an arbitrage strategy that guarantees a certain profit. Determine the amount of that profit and when it is realized.

14. Similar to a straddle, a *strangle* also involves buying a call and buying a put with the same term to expiry on the same stock. However for a strangle, the exercise price of the call is higher than for the put. Display the profit diagram for a strangle.

15. In a *butterfly spread*, a trader buys one call with a low exercise price and buys one call with a high exercise price, while selling two calls with a medium exercise price. Assume the long call with exercise price $55 sells for $3, the long call with exercise price $45 sells for $6 and the short call with exercise price $50 sells for $4.
    a) What is the profit when the stock price is $45, $50, $55 at expiry?
    b) Display the profit diagram for a butterfly spread.

13.6 Binomial lattices

16. A stock is currently selling for $100. In one year it will be worth either $90 or $110. A one-year call is issued with an exercise price of $100. The one-year risk-free effective rate of interest is 6%.
    a) Find the probability that the stock will sell for $110 in one year assuming risk-neutrality.
    b) Find the value of the call which will eliminate risk-free arbitrage.

17. A replicating transaction involving one call, as described in Section 13.5, is constructed for Exercise 16.
    a) Find the hedge ratio or option delta.
    b) Find the amount of the loan.

18. Find the value of a two-year call based on the data in Exercise 16 if the increase and decrease factors remain unchanged for the second year.

19. Rework Example 13.7 using eight steps instead of four steps.
    a) Find k.
    b) Find p.
    c) Find C.

20. Find the value of a two-year put with an exercise price of $100 based on the data in Exercise 16 if increase and decrease factors remain unchanged for the second year.

21. Similar to formula (13.13), show that the expression for the value of a European put using an n period binomial lattice is:

$$P = \frac{1}{(1+i)^n} \sum_{t=0}^{n} \binom{n}{t} p^{n-t} (1-p)^t \max\left[0, E - S(1+k)^{n-2t}\right]$$

13.7 Black Scholes formula

22. Verify algebraically that the Black-Scholes formula for a call given by formula (13.14) and the Black-Scholes formula for a put given by formula (13.16) satisfy put-call parity.

23. Find the value of the European put with the same expiry date and exercise price as the European call in Example 13.8.

24. In order to illustrate the sensitivity of the Black-Scholes formula, rework Example 13.8 changing the following parameters one-by-one while holding all the other parameters constant.
    a) $S = 80$
    b) $S = 100$
    c) $\delta = .05$
    d) $\delta = .15$
    e) $\sigma = .15$
    f) $\sigma = .45$
    g) $n = .5$
    h) $n = 1.5$

13.8 Some extensions

25. The Black-Scholes formula can be applied to a stock paying dividends by subtracting the present value of the dividends to be paid prior to expiry from S and then applying the formula in the normal fashion. Rework Example 13.8 if the stock pays a $3.60 dividend at the end of the year.

26. Bond A is a $100 par value two-year corporate bond maturing at par with $10 annual coupons bought to yield 10% effective. Bond B is an otherwise identical bond which can be called at the end of one year at 102. Use the Black-Scholes formula to estimate the price of Bond B. Assume that the risk-free force of interest is 9% and the standard deviation of the yield rate on corporate bonds is 8.3%.

27. The put-call parity formula can be applied to a stock paying dividends by subtracting the present value of the dividends to be paid prior to expiry from S. Rework Exercise 12 if the stock pays a \$.50 dividend at the end of each month.

28. A common stock has the following quarterly prices over the next year:

Time	Price
0	10.00
.25	10.10
.50	10.51
.75	11.93
1	12.74

Find the payoff for a one-year Asian call, if the payoff is based on the stock prices at the end of each quarter and if the strike price is \$9.

Appendix A

Table numbering the days of the year

For leap years the number of the day is one greater than the tabular number after February 28													
Day of Month	January	February	March	April	May	June	July	August	September	October	November	December	Day of Month
1	1	32	60	91	121	152	182	213	244	274	305	335	1
2	2	33	61	92	122	153	183	214	245	275	306	336	2
3	3	34	62	93	123	154	184	215	246	276	307	337	3
4	4	35	63	94	124	155	185	216	247	277	308	338	4
5	5	36	64	95	125	156	186	217	248	278	309	339	5
6	6	37	65	96	126	157	187	218	249	279	310	340	6
7	7	38	66	97	127	158	188	219	250	280	311	341	7
8	8	39	67	98	128	159	189	220	251	281	312	342	8
9	9	40	68	99	129	160	190	221	252	282	313	343	9
10	10	41	69	100	130	161	191	222	253	283	314	344	10
11	11	42	70	101	131	162	192	223	254	284	315	345	11
12	12	43	71	102	132	163	193	224	255	285	316	346	12
13	13	44	72	103	133	164	194	225	256	286	317	347	13
14	14	45	73	104	134	165	195	226	257	287	318	348	14
15	15	46	74	105	135	166	196	227	258	288	319	349	15
16	16	47	75	106	136	167	197	228	259	289	320	350	16
17	17	48	76	107	137	168	198	229	260	290	321	351	17
18	18	49	77	108	138	169	199	230	261	291	322	352	18
19	19	50	78	109	139	170	200	231	262	292	323	353	19
20	20	51	79	110	140	171	201	232	263	293	324	354	20
21	21	52	80	111	141	172	202	233	264	294	325	355	21
22	22	53	81	112	142	173	203	234	265	295	326	356	22
23	23	54	82	113	143	174	204	235	266	296	327	357	23
24	24	55	83	114	144	175	205	236	267	297	328	358	24
25	25	56	84	115	145	176	206	237	268	298	329	359	25
26	26	57	85	116	146	177	207	238	269	299	330	360	26
27	27	58	86	117	147	178	208	239	270	300	331	361	27
28	28	59	87	118	148	179	209	240	271	301	332	362	28
29	29		88	119	149	180	210	241	272	302	333	363	29
30	30		89	120	150	181	211	242	273	303	334	364	30
31	31		90		151		212	243		304		365	31

Appendix B

Illustrative mortgage loan amortization schedule

The following table is an amortization schedule for a $100,000 real estate mortgage with monthly payments at 10% interest convertible monthly.

The ending balance of $3.55 is attributable to accumulated roundoff error. The monthly payment used in the schedule is equal to $877.57 rounded to the nearest cent. The monthly payment carrying more decimal places would have been $877.57158.

In practice, most lenders would probably use a monthly payment of $877.58 so that the final payment would be smaller than all the prior payments rather than larger.

Month	Principal	Interest	Balance	Month	Principal	Interest	Balance
1	44.24	833.33	99,955.76	61	72.78	804.79	96,501.66
2	44.61	832.96	99,911.16	62	73.39	804.18	96,428.27
3	44.98	832.59	99,866.18	63	74.00	803.57	96,354.27
4	45.35	832.22	99,820.83	64	74.62	802.95	96,279.65
5	45.73	831.84	99,775.10	65	75.24	802.33	96,204.41
6	46.11	831.46	99,728.99	66	75.87	801.70	96,128.54
7	46.50	831.07	99,682.49	67	76.50	801.07	96,052.05
8	46.88	830.69	99,635.61	68	77.14	800.43	95,974.91
9	47.27	830.30	99,588.34	69	77.78	799.79	95,897.13
10	47.67	829.90	99,540.67	70	78.43	799.14	95,818.70
11	48.06	829.51	99,492.61	71	79.08	798.49	95,739.62
12	48.46	829.11	99,444.14	72	79.74	797.83	95,659.88
13	48.87	828.70	99,395.27	73	80.40	797.17	95,579.48
14	49.28	828.29	99,346.00	74	81.07	796.50	95,498.40
15	49.69	827.88	99,296.31	75	81.75	795.82	95,416.65
16	50.10	827.47	99,246.21	76	82.43	795.14	95,334.22
17	50.52	827.05	99,195.69	77	83.12	794.45	95,251.10
18	50.94	826.63	99,144.75	78	83.81	793.76	95,167.29
19	51.36	826.21	99,093.39	79	84.51	793.06	95,082.78
20	51.79	825.78	99,041.60	80	85.21	792.36	94,997.57
21	52.22	825.35	98,989.37	81	85.92	791.65	94,911.65
22	52.66	824.91	98,936.71	82	86.64	790.93	94,825.01
23	53.10	824.47	98,883.62	83	87.36	790.21	94,737.65
24	53.54	824.03	98,830.08	84	88.09	789.48	94,649.56
25	53.99	823.58	98,776.09	85	88.82	788.75	94,560.73
26	54.44	823.13	98,721.65	86	89.56	788.01	94,471.17
27	54.89	822.68	98,666.77	87	90.31	787.26	94,380.86
28	55.35	822.22	98,611.42	88	91.06	786.51	94,289.80
29	55.81	821.76	98,555.61	89	91.82	785.75	94,197.97
30	56.27	821.30	98,499.34	90	92.59	784.98	94,105.39
31	56.74	820.83	98,442.59	91	93.36	784.21	94,012.03
32	57.22	820.35	98,385.38	92	94.14	783.43	93,917.89
33	57.69	819.88	98,327.69	93	94.92	782.65	93,822.97
34	58.17	819.40	98,269.52	94	95.71	781.86	93,727.26
35	58.66	818.91	98,210.86	95	96.51	781.06	93,630.75
36	59.15	818.42	98,151.71	96	97.31	780.26	93,533.44
37	59.64	817.93	98,092.07	97	98.12	779.45	93,435.31
38	60.14	817.43	98,031.94	98	98.94	778.63	93,336.37
39	60.64	816.93	97,971.30	99	99.77	777.80	93,236.60
40	61.14	816.43	97,910.16	100	100.60	776.97	93,136.00
41	61.65	815.92	97,848.50	101	101.44	776.13	93,034.57
42	62.17	815.40	97,786.34	102	102.28	775.29	92,932.29
43	62.68	814.89	97,723.66	103	103.13	774.44	92,829.15
44	63.21	814.36	97,660.45	104	103.99	773.58	92,725.16
45	63.73	813.84	97,596.72	105	104.86	772.71	92,620.30
46	64.26	813.31	97,532.45	106	105.73	771.84	92,514.56
47	64.80	812.77	97,467.65	107	106.62	770.95	92,407.95
48	65.34	812.23	97,402.31	108	107.50	770.07	92,300.44
49	65.88	811.69	97,336.43	109	108.40	769.17	92,192.04
50	66.43	811.14	97,270.00	110	109.30	768.27	92,082.74
51	66.99	810.58	97,203.01	111	110.21	767.36	91,972.53
52	67.54	810.03	97,135.46	112	111.13	766.44	91,861.40
53	68.11	809.46	97,067.36	113	112.06	765.51	91,749.34
54	68.68	808.89	96,998.68	114	112.99	764.58	91,636.34
55	69.25	808.32	96,929.43	115	113.93	763.64	91,522.41
56	69.82	807.75	96,859.61	116	114.88	762.69	91,407.53
57	70.41	807.16	96,789.20	117	115.84	761.73	91,291.69
58	70.99	806.58	96,718.21	118	116.81	760.76	91,174.88
59	71.58	805.99	96,646.62	119	117.78	759.79	91,057.10
60	72.18	805.39	96,574.44	120	118.76	758.81	90,938.34

Month	Principal	Interest	Balance	Month	Principal	Interest	Balance
121	119.75	757.82	90,818.59	181	197.03	680.54	81,468.19
122	120.75	756.82	90,697.84	182	198.67	678.90	81,269.52
123	121.75	755.82	90,576.09	183	200.32	677.25	81,069.19
124	122.77	754.80	90,453.32	184	201.99	675.58	80,867.20
125	123.79	753.78	90,329.53	185	203.68	673.89	80,663.52
126	124.82	752.75	90,204.70	186	205.37	672.20	80,458.15
127	125.86	751.71	90,078.84	187	207.09	670.48	80,251.07
128	126.91	750.66	89,951.92	188	208.81	668.76	80,042.25
129	127.97	749.60	89,823.95	189	210.55	667.02	79,831.70
130	129.04	748.53	89,694.92	190	212.31	665.26	79,619.40
131	130.11	747.46	89,564.80	191	214.08	663.49	79,405.32
132	131.20	746.37	89,433.61	192	215.86	661.71	79,189.46
133	132.29	745.28	89,301.32	193	217.66	659.91	78,971.81
134	133.39	744.18	89,167.93	194	219.47	658.10	78,752.33
135	134.50	743.07	89,033.42	195	221.30	656.27	78,531.03
136	135.62	741.95	88,897.80	196	223.14	654.43	78,307.89
137	136.76	740.81	88,761.04	197	225.00	652.57	78,082.88
138	137.89	739.68	88,623.15	198	226.88	650.69	77,856.00
139	139.04	738.53	88,484.10	199	228.77	648.80	77,627.23
140	140.20	737.37	88,343.90	200	230.68	646.89	77,396.56
141	141.37	736.20	88,202.53	201	232.60	644.97	77,163.96
142	142.55	735.02	88,059.98	202	234.54	643.03	76,929.42
143	143.74	733.83	87,916.24	203	236.49	641.08	76,692.93
144	144.93	732.64	87,771.31	204	238.46	639.11	76,454.47
145	146.14	731.43	87,625.17	205	240.45	637.12	76,214.02
146	147.36	730.21	87,477.81	206	242.45	635.12	75,971.57
147	148.59	728.98	87,329.22	207	244.47	633.10	75,727.09
148	149.83	727.74	87,179.39	208	246.51	631.06	75,480.58
149	151.08	726.49	87,028.32	209	248.57	629.00	75,232.02
150	152.33	725.24	86,875.98	210	250.64	626.93	74,981.38
151	153.60	723.97	86,722.38	211	252.73	624.84	74,728.65
152	154.88	722.69	86,567.50	212	254.83	622.74	74,473.82
153	156.17	721.40	86,411.32	213	256.95	620.62	74,216.87
154	157.48	720.09	86,253.85	214	259.10	618.47	73,957.77
155	158.79	718.78	86,095.06	215	261.26	616.31	73,696.52
156	160.11	717.46	85,934.95	216	263.43	614.14	73,433.09
157	161.45	716.12	85,773.50	217	265.63	611.94	73,167.46
158	162.79	714.78	85,610.71	218	267.84	609.73	72,899.62
159	164.15	713.42	85,446.56	219	270.07	607.50	72,629.54
160	165.52	712.05	85,281.05	220	272.32	605.25	72,357.22
161	166.89	710.68	85,114.15	221	274.59	602.98	72,082.63
162	168.29	709.28	84,945.87	222	276.88	600.69	71,805.74
163	169.69	707.88	84,776.18	223	279.19	598.38	71,526.56
164	171.10	706.47	84,605.08	224	281.52	596.05	71,245.04
165	172.53	705.04	84,432.55	225	283.86	593.71	70,961.18
166	173.97	703.60	84,258.59	226	286.23	591.34	70,674.95
167	175.42	702.15	84,083.17	227	288.61	588.96	70,386.34
168	176.88	700.69	83,906.29	228	291.02	586.55	70,095.32
169	178.35	699.22	83,727.94	229	293.44	584.13	69,801.88
170	179.84	697.73	83,548.11	230	295.89	581.68	69,505.99
171	181.34	696.23	83,366.77	231	298.35	579.22	69,207.64
172	182.85	694.72	83,183.92	232	300.84	576.73	68,906.80
173	184.37	693.20	82,999.55	233	303.35	574.22	68,603.45
174	185.91	691.66	82,813.65	234	305.87	571.70	68,297.58
175	187.46	690.11	82,626.19	235	308.42	569.15	67,989.16
176	189.02	688.55	82,437.17	236	310.99	566.58	67,678.16
177	190.59	686.98	82,246.58	237	313.59	563.98	67,364.58
178	192.18	685.39	82,054.40	238	316.20	561.37	67,048.38
179	193.78	683.79	81,860.61	239	318.83	558.74	66,729.54
180	195.40	682.17	81,665.21	240	321.49	556.08	66,408.05

Month	Principal	Interest	Balance	Month	Principal	Interest	Balance
241	324.17	553.40	66,083.88	301	533.36	344.21	40,771.95
242	326.87	550.70	65,757.01	302	537.80	339.77	40,234.15
243	329.59	547.98	65,427.42	303	542.29	335.28	39,691.86
244	332.34	545.23	65,095.08	304	546.80	330.77	39,145.06
245	335.11	542.46	64,759.97	305	551.36	326.21	38,593.70
246	337.90	539.67	64,422.06	306	555.96	321.61	38,037.74
247	340.72	536.85	64,081.34	307	560.59	316.98	37,477.15
248	343.56	534.01	63,737.78	308	565.26	312.31	36,911.89
249	346.42	531.15	63,391.36	309	569.97	307.60	36,341.92
250	349.31	528.26	63,042.05	310	574.72	302.85	35,767.20
251	352.22	525.35	62,689.83	311	579.51	298.06	35,187.69
252	355.15	522.42	62,334.68	312	584.34	293.23	34,603.35
253	358.11	519.46	61,976.57	313	589.21	288.36	34,014.14
254	361.10	516.47	61,615.47	314	594.12	283.45	33,420.03
255	364.11	513.46	61,251.36	315	599.07	278.50	32,820.96
256	367.14	510.43	60,884.22	316	604.06	273.51	32,216.89
257	370.20	507.37	60,514.02	317	609.10	268.47	31,607.80
258	373.29	504.28	60,140.73	318	614.17	263.40	30,993.63
259	376.40	501.17	59,764.33	319	619.29	258.28	30,374.34
260	379.53	498.04	59,384.80	320	624.45	253.12	29,749.89
261	382.70	494.87	59,002.10	321	629.65	247.92	29,120.23
262	385.89	491.68	58,616.21	322	634.90	242.67	28,485.33
263	389.10	488.47	58,227.11	323	640.19	237.38	27,845.14
264	392.34	485.23	57,834.77	324	645.53	232.04	27,199.61
265	395.61	481.96	57,439.16	325	650.91	226.66	26,548.70
266	398.91	478.66	57,040.25	326	656.33	221.24	25,892.37
267	402.23	475.34	56,638.01	327	661.80	215.77	25,230.57
268	405.59	471.98	56,232.42	328	667.32	210.25	24,563.26
269	408.97	468.60	55,823.46	329	672.88	204.69	23,890.38
270	412.37	465.20	55,411.08	330	678.48	199.09	23,211.90
271	415.81	461.76	54,995.27	331	684.14	193.43	22,527.76
272	419.28	458.29	54,576.00	332	689.84	187.73	21,837.92
273	422.77	454.80	54,153.23	333	695.59	181.98	21,142.34
274	426.29	451.28	53,726.93	334	701.38	176.19	20,440.95
275	429.85	447.72	53,297.09	335	707.23	170.34	19,733.72
276	433.43	444.14	52,863.66	336	713.12	164.45	19,020.60
277	437.04	440.53	52,426.62	337	719.06	158.51	18,301.54
278	440.68	436.89	51,985.94	338	725.06	152.51	17,576.48
279	444.35	433.22	51,541.58	339	731.10	146.47	16,845.38
280	448.06	429.51	51,093.53	340	737.19	140.38	16,108.19
281	451.79	425.78	50,641.74	341	743.34	134.23	15,364.85
282	455.56	422.01	50,186.18	342	749.53	128.04	14,615.32
283	459.35	418.22	49,726.83	343	755.78	121.79	13,859.55
284	463.18	414.39	49,263.65	344	762.07	115.50	13,097.47
285	467.04	410.53	48,796.61	345	768.42	109.15	12,329.05
286	470.93	406.64	48,325.68	346	774.83	102.74	11,554.22
287	474.86	402.71	47,850.82	347	781.28	96.29	10,772.94
288	478.81	398.76	47,372.01	348	787.80	89.77	9,985.14
289	482.80	394.77	46,889.21	349	794.36	83.21	9,190.78
290	486.83	390.74	46,402.38	350	800.98	76.59	8,389.80
291	490.88	386.69	45,911.50	351	807.66	69.91	7,582.14
292	494.97	382.60	45,416.52	352	814.39	63.18	6,767.76
293	499.10	378.47	44,917.42	353	821.17	56.40	5,946.59
294	503.26	374.31	44,414.17	354	828.02	49.55	5,118.57
295	507.45	370.12	43,906.71	355	834.92	42.65	4,283.66
296	511.68	365.89	43,395.03	356	841.87	35.70	3,441.78
297	515.94	361.63	42,879.09	357	848.89	28.68	2,592.90
298	520.24	357.33	42,358.84	358	855.96	21.61	1,736.93
299	524.58	352.99	41,834.26	359	863.10	14.47	873.84
300	528.95	348.62	41,305.31	360	870.29	7.28	3.55

Appendix C

Basic mathematical review

A. Progressions

1. *Arithmetic progression*

   The following is an arithmetic progression with n terms:

   $$a \quad a+d \quad a+2d \quad \cdots \quad a+(n-1)d$$

   If we let $l = a+(n-1)d$, then the sum s of the arithmetic progression is

   $$s = \frac{n}{2}(a+l).$$

2. *Geometric progression*

   The following is a geometric progression with n terms:

   $$a \quad ar \quad ar^2 \quad \cdots \quad ar^{n-1}$$

   If we let $l = ar^{n-1}$, then the sum s of the geometric progression is

   $$s = a\frac{(r^n-1)}{r-1} = \frac{rl-a}{r-1}.$$

   If the common ratio r satisfies $-1 < r < 1$, then the sum of an infinite geometric progression as n approaches infinity becomes

   $$s = \frac{a}{1-r}.$$

3. *Harmonic progression*

   The following is a harmonic progression with n terms:

   $$\frac{1}{a} \quad \frac{1}{a+d} \quad \frac{1}{a+2d} \cdots \frac{1}{a+(n-1)d}$$

   In other words, the reciprocals are an arithmetic progression.

B. Means

1. *Arithmetic mean*

   The arithmetic mean of n numbers $a_1, a_2, \ldots, a_n$ is

$$\frac{a_1 + a_2 + \cdots + a_n}{n}.$$

2. *Geometric mean*

   The geometric mean of n numbers $a_1, a_2, \ldots, a_n$, all greater than zero, is

$$(a_1 a_2 \ldots a_n)^{1/n}.$$

3. *Harmonic mean*

   The harmonic mean of n non-zero numbers $a_1, a_2, \ldots, a_n$, is

$$\frac{1}{\frac{1}{n}\left(\frac{1}{a_1}\right)}.$$

C. Summing powers of integers

1. $1 + 2 + \cdots + n = \frac{1}{2}n\,(n+1)$

2. $1^2 + 2^2 + \cdots + n^2 = \frac{1}{6}n\,(n+1)(2n+1)$

3. $1^3 + 2^3 + \cdots + n^3 = \frac{1}{4}n^2\,(n+1)^2$

D. Binomial theorem

$$(1+x)^n = 1 + nx + \frac{n(n-1)}{2!}x^2 + \frac{n(n-1)(n-2)}{3!}x^3 + \cdots$$

This expression converges if n is a positive integer or if $-1 < x < 1$.

E. Series expansions

1. $e^x = 1 + x + \frac{x^2}{2!} + \frac{x^3}{3!} + \cdots$ for all x.

2. $\ln(1+x) = x - \frac{x^2}{2} + \frac{x^3}{3} - \frac{x^4}{4} + \cdots$ if $-1 < x \le 1$

F. Taylor series

$$f(x+h) = f(x) + hf'(x) + \frac{h^2}{2!}f''(x) + \frac{h^3}{3!}f'''(x) + \cdots$$

if the infinite series converges.

G. Descartes' rule of signs

Let $f(x)$ be the nth degree polynomial

$$f(x) = a_n x^n + a_{n-1} x^{n-1} + \cdots + a_1 x + a_0 .$$

The maximum number of positive roots of $f(x) = 0$ is the number of sign changes in the coefficients $a_n, a_{n-1}, \ldots, a_1, a_0$ (ignoring zeroes). The maximum number of negative roots is given by the number of sign changes in $f(-x)$.

Appendix D

Statistical background

A. Moments

1. The mean of a random variable X, denoted by μ_x, is the first moment about the origin

$$\mu_x = \mathrm{E}[X].$$

2. The variance of a random variable X, denoted by σ_x^2 or $\mathrm{Var}[X]$, is the second moment about the mean

$$\sigma_x^2 = \mathrm{Var}[X] = \mathrm{E}\left[(X-\mu)^2\right] = \mathrm{E}\left[X^2\right] - \{\mathrm{E}[X]\}^2.$$

3. The standard deviation of a random variable X, denoted by σ_x, is the square root of the variance.

4. The covariance of two random variables X and Y, denoted by σ_{xy} or $\mathrm{Cov}[X, Y]$, is defined as

$$\sigma_{xy} = \mathrm{Cov}[X, Y] = \mathrm{E}\left[(X-\mu_x)(Y-\mu_y)\right] = \mathrm{E}[XY] - \mathrm{E}[X]\mathrm{E}[Y].$$

5. If the random variables X and Y are independent, then $\mathrm{E}[XY] = \mathrm{E}[X]\mathrm{E}[Y]$ and $\sigma_{xy} = \mathrm{Cov}[X, Y] = 0$.

6. The mean of $aX + bY$, where a and b are constants, is given by

$$a\mu_x + b\mu_y .$$

7. The variance of $aX + bY$, where a and b are constants, is given by

$$a^2\sigma_x^2 + b^2\sigma_y^2 + 2ab\sigma_{xy} .$$

B. Distributions

1. *Binomial distribution*

   A discrete distribution defined by

$$f(x) = \binom{n}{x} p^x (1-p)^{n-x}$$

where n is a positive integer, $0 < p < 1$, and $x = 0, 1, 2, \ldots, n$. The moments are:

$$\text{mean} = np$$

and

$$\text{variance} = npq.$$

2. *Uniform distribution*

   A continuous distribution defined by

$$f(x) = \frac{1}{b-a}$$

where $a \le x \le b$. The moments are:

$$\text{mean} = \frac{a+b}{2}$$

and

$$\text{variance} = \frac{(b-a)^2}{12}.$$

3. *Normal distribution*

   A continuous distribution defined by

$$f(x) = \frac{1}{\sigma\sqrt{2\pi}} e^{-\frac{1}{2}\left(\frac{x-\mu}{\sigma}\right)^2}$$

where $-\infty < \mu < \infty, \sigma > 0$, and $-\infty < x < \infty$. The moments are:

$$\text{mean} = \mu$$

and

$$\text{variance} = \sigma^2.$$

Values of the cumulative distribution function are tabulated and used in finding probabilities from this distribution. A table of such values appears at the end of this Appendix.

4. *Lognormal distribution*
If $Y = \ln X$ and Y has a normal distribution, then $X > 0$ has a lognormal distribution. The moments are:

$$\text{mean} = e^{\mu+\frac{\sigma^2}{2}}$$

and

$$\text{variance} = e^{2\mu+\sigma^2}\left(e^{\sigma^2}-1\right).$$

Note that the mean $\neq \mu$ and the variance $\neq \sigma^2$.

C. Normal approximation to the binomial distribution

For large values of n, the normal distribution can be used as an approximation to the binomial distribution. In testing for the parameter p, the mean and variance are:

$$\text{mean} = p$$

and

$$\text{variance} = \frac{p(1-p)}{n}.$$

D. Central Limit Theorem

Another important application of the normal distribution is the *Central Limit Theorem.* This theorem justifies using the normal distribution as an acceptable approximation for the sum of n independent random variables for large values of n, regardless of the underlying distribution of the individual random variables.

In applying this theorem, simply add the means and variances of the n individual random variables. These two sums become the mean and variance, respectively, of the approximation normal distribution completely specifying it.

The normal distribution is typically converted to a distribution with a mean equal to 0 and standard deviation equal to 1 by the formula

$$Z = \frac{x-\mu}{\sigma}.$$

In this formula, Z represents the number of standard deviations that X is located above or below the mean.

A frequent application is the testing of sample means $\bar{X}$. The means and variance are:

$$\text{mean} = \mathrm{E}(\bar{X}) = \mu$$

$$\text{variance} = E\left[\left(\bar{X}-\mu\right)^2\right] = \frac{\sigma^2}{n}.$$

E. Simulation

If X is a random variable, let Y be the cumulative distribution function

$$Y = F(x), \text{ where } 0 \leq y \leq 1.$$

Use a random number to find a value of Y. If the inverse function exists, then the simulated value of X is given by

$$X = F^{-1}(y).$$

Other techniques have been developed for distributions in which the inverse function does not exist or is overly complicated. Special algorithms have also been developed for certain distributions to decrease computer run time.

F. Normal distribution table

The table below gives the value of the cumulative normal distribution function $\Phi(z)$ for certain values of z where

$$\Phi(z) = \Pr(Z \leq z) \text{ for } z \geq 0.$$

The integer z is given in the top row, and the first decimal place of z is given in the left column. Since the normal distribution is symmetric, the value of the cumulative distribution function for negative z is given by

$$\Phi(z) = 1 - \Phi(-z) \text{ for } z < 0.$$

z	0	1	2	3
0.0	0.5000	0.8413	0.9772	0.9987
0.1	0.5398	0.8643	0.9821	0.9990
0.2	0.5793	0.8849	0.9861	0.9993
0.3	0.6179	0.9032	0.9893	0.9995
0.4	0.6554	0.9192	0.9918	0.9997
0.5	0.6915	0.9332	0.9938	0.9998
0.6	0.7257	0.9452	0.9953	0.9998
0.7	0.7580	0.9554	0.9965	0.9999
0.8	0.7881	0.9641	0.9974	0.9999
0.9	0.8159	0.9713	0.9981	1.0000

Values of z for selected values of $\Pr(Z \leq z)$							
z	0.842	1.036	1.282	1.645	1.960	2.326	2.576
$\Pr(Z \leq z)$	0.800	0.850	0.900	0.950	0.975	0.990	0.995

Appendix E

Iteration methods

A. General background

1. A general formula for an equation to be solved using iteration is given by

$$f(x) = 0.$$

The roots of this equation are those values of x for which $f(x)=0$.

2. Many iteration methods express the formula for the equation to be solved in the form

$$x = g(x).$$

The iteration then proceeds by assuming a starting value x_0 and generating successive values $x_1, x_2, \ldots$ from

$$x_{n+1} = g(x_n).$$

3. The iteration procedure described above will converge if

$$|g'(r)| < 1$$

and will diverge if

$$|g'(r)| \geq 1$$

4. The iteration stops when the desired level of accuracy is obtained for a converging iteration or when it is found that the iteration is diverging.

B. Successive bisection

1. This method requires two starting values, x_0 and x_1, which have functional values $f(x_0)$ and $f(x_1)$ of opposite sign.

2. Bisect the interval, i.e. $x_2 = .5(x_0 + x_1)$, and find its functional value.

3. Then choose x_2 and either x_0 or x_1, such that $f(x_2)$ and the choice of $f(x_0)$ or $f(x_1)$ are of opposite sign.

4. Continue the bisection process as many times as necessary to achieve the desired level of accuracy.

5. This method is very simple to apply on a computer and convergence is guaranteed if $f(x)$ is continuous. However, the rate of convergence may be rather slow.

C. Successive inverse interpolation

1. This method also requires two starting values, x_0 and x_1, which have functional values of opposite sign.

2. The iteration formula is given by

$$x_{n+2} = \frac{x_n f(x_{n+1}) - x_{n+1} f(x_n)}{f(x_{n+1}) - f(x_n)}.$$

3. Two variations exist in applying this method after the first iteration. In the first variation the two most recently computed values of x for which the values of $f(x)$ are of opposite sign are used. In the second variation the two most recently computed values of x are used regardless of the sign of $f(x)$.

D. Newton-Raphson method

1. The iteration formula is given by

$$x_{n+1} = x_n - \frac{f(x_n)}{f'(x_n)}.$$

2. For this method $g'(r) = 0$, which produces an extremely fast rate of convergence called "second-order convergence."

3. This method does require that $f'(x)$ can be computed and is non-zero.

Answers to the exercises

Chapter 1

1. *a*) $\frac{1}{3}(t^2 + 2t + 3)$ *c*) $2n + 1$

3. \$260

4. \$300

5. *a*) 1/24 *b*) 1/29

6. *a*) .1 *b*) .1

8. \$1190.91

9. *a*) 9.2% *b*) 3 1/3 years

10. \$582.50

11. 16

12. \$1150

13. \$3456

14. $\dfrac{i-j}{1+j}$

15. $c-a-b$

16. 1.523

17. \$748.97

18. $\dfrac{3+\sqrt{5}}{2}$

19. \$3281.25

20. *a*) 1/15 *b*) 1/6

21. 12.08%

22. $2800

23. *a)* $4225.27 *b)* $4225.46

26. *a)* $4\left[1-\left(1+\frac{i^{(3)}}{3}\right)^{-3/4}\right]$ *b)* $6\left[\left(1-\frac{d^{(2)}}{2}\right)^{-1/3}-1\right]$

28. *a)* $112.65 *b)* $114.71

29. 8

30. 20

31. r^{-4}

32. $d < d^{(m)} < \delta < i^{(m)} < i$

33. *a)* $\ln a + 2t \ln b + c^t \ln c \ln d$ *b)* Formula (1.26)

34. 5

35. 14/205

36. $\dfrac{\ln i - \ln \delta}{\delta}$

37. 7.53%

38. *a)* $(1+r)^{n(n+1)/2}(1+i)^n$ *b)* $(1+r)^{(n+1)/2}(1+i)-1$

39. 7.86%

40. $e^{.3}$

41. 9.48%

42. *a)* 23.6% *b)* 14.9% *c)* 18.6% *d)* .922

43. $677,057

44. 9.46%

45. 38.88

46. $2/n$

47. 120/121

48. *a)* $\delta + \frac{\delta^2}{2!} + \frac{\delta^3}{3!} + \frac{\delta^4}{4!} + \cdots$

b) $i - \frac{i^2}{2} + \frac{i^3}{3} - \frac{i^4}{4} + \cdots$

c) $i - i^2 + i^3 - i^4 + \cdots$

d) $d + \frac{d^2}{2} + \frac{d^3}{3} + \frac{d^4}{4} + \cdots$

49. *a)* $(1+i)^{-2}$ *b)* $(1+i)^{-1}$ *c)* $-v^{-1}$ *d)* $e^{-\delta}$

50. *a)* (1) $e^{at+bt^2/2}$ (2) $e^{(a-b/2)+bn}$

b) (1) $e^{a(b^t-1)/\ln b}$ (2) $e^{a(b-1)b^{n-1}/\ln b}$

Chapter 2

1. $1593.00
2. $535.13
3. $917.76
4. $483.11
5. *a)* $275 *b)* $260
6. 36.4 years
7. 9.66 years
8. 6.25 years
9. $\frac{2n^2+n}{3}$
10. 114
11. 2.33 years
12. 1.43 years
13. 7.46%
14. $\frac{\sqrt{19}-4}{3}$
15. 3.51%

16. 1.5%

17. $\frac{\ln 2}{50}$

18. 4%

19. *a*) 1340 *b*) 1321

20. *a*) \$101.92 *b*) \$100.00 *c*) \$103.33

21. *c*) Invest for the month of February

22. *a*) 16% *b*) 17.74%

23. *a*) 1.0124 *b*) .9938

24. \$5437.17

25. 1.0259

26. *a*) 7.00% *b*) 7.71% *c*) 7.53%

27. \$1540.34

28. 11.15%

29. 14.80%

30. \$1276

31. \$690.30

32. \$17,936

33. \$700

Chapter 3

1. \$651.72

2. \$1489.36

3. \$321.86

4. \$5227.12

5. $n^2\left[1-\left(\frac{n}{n+1}\right)^n\right]$

6. $\frac{2x-y}{x^2+2x-y}$

7. 5.695

8. \$2389.72

9. \$24,305

12. *a*) \$3256.88 *b*) \$5403.15 *c*) \$6959.37

13. $a_{\overline{45|}}$

14. $x = 4 \quad y = 7 \quad z = 4$

15. 1.8

16. 2

17. \$16,178

18. $1000\left[(1+i)^{30} - (1+i)^{10}\right]$

19. 4

20. \$102,412

21. 4

22. 30/49

23. *a*) 4.5195 *b*) 4.5230 *c*) 4.5160

24. \$146.07 at time 21

25. 9

26. 14

27. *a*) 29 *b*) 30.5

28. *a*) 9.24% *b*) 9.80%

29. $\dfrac{4\sqrt{2}-5}{7}$

30. 8.69%

31. 30.2

32. *a*) 8.145 *b*) 8.230

33. *a*) 4.1543 *b*) 4.1831

34. $\dfrac{P(1+i)^{1/2}}{1+2a_{\overline{4}|i}+2(1+i)^{-4}a_{\overline{5}|j}}$

35. $\displaystyle\sum_{t=9}^{28}\frac{11}{t}$

36. $n-\frac{1}{2}n(n+1)d$

37. $\log_2(n+1)$

38. 14.5

39. .0018

40. 574.60

41. 12.25%

42. $\dfrac{10{,}000}{4a_{\overline{20}|}-a_{\overline{15}|}-a_{\overline{10}|}-a_{\overline{5}|}}$

43. 7%

44. $980

45. $\dfrac{s_{\overline{41}|}-s_{\overline{15}|}-26}{i}$

Chapter 4

1. $35,824

2. $11,466

3. 6%

4. 10.0%

5. $35,824

6. *a)* $\dfrac{200}{s_{\overline{4}|}}\left(a_{\overline{176}|}-a_{\overline{32}|}\right)$ *b)* $\dfrac{200}{a_{\overline{4}|}}\left(a_{\overline{180}|}-a_{\overline{36}|}\right)$

7. $300\dfrac{1-(.9925)^{120}}{1-(.9925)^{6}}$

8. 20%

9. $100\dfrac{1-e^{-.4}}{1-e^{-.02}}$

10. $\dfrac{1 - v^{48}}{1 - v^{4/3}}$

11. \$11,466

13. $\dfrac{\ln 20\left[1-(1-d)^{.5}\right]}{\ln(1-d)}$

14. 1/30

15. $\dfrac{1-v^{36}}{1-v^{3/4}}$

17. 27.47 years

18. 1/6

19. $\ln(n+1)$

20. $1 - \dfrac{1}{\delta}\ln\dfrac{i}{\delta}$

22. $6a_{\overline{20}|} + \dfrac{a_{\overline{20}|} - 20v^{20}}{i}$

24. $a_{\overline{n}|}/d$

25. 66

26. 1/21

27. 6250 – 325*A*

28. \$7851

29. 5%

30. \$16,607

31. 15%

32. \$108,576

33. \$1385

35. *a*) 3 *b*) 25/12

37. 48

38. 112.59

39. 3

40. 156.25

41. $\dfrac{1}{\delta_i - \delta_k}$

42. *a)* $\int_0^n (n-t)\, v^t dt$ *b)* $\dfrac{n - \bar{a}_{\overline{n}|}}{\delta}$

43. 84.5

44. 3.71

45. 40

47. *a)* $\dfrac{q}{p-q}$ *b)* $\dfrac{2q}{p-q}$

49. $\dfrac{a^3}{(2a-b)^2}\left[2a - b - (b-a)\ln\dfrac{a}{b-a}\right]$

50. *a)* (2) $-\dfrac{n(n+1)}{2}$ *b)* (2) $-\dfrac{n^2}{2}$

Chapter 5

1. \$635.32

2. \$4918

3. \$16,514

4. \$17,143

5. $20{,}000\dfrac{a_{\overline{15}|}(1+i)^2}{a_{\overline{20}|}a_{\overline{13}|}}$

7. \$20,636

8. \$641.86

10. \$724.59

11. *a)* $i\left(a_{\overline{6}|\,i} + v_i^6 a_{\overline{10}|\,j}\right)$ *b)* v_j^6

13. *a*) .4*L* *b*) .9*L*

14. \$72

15. \$754.95

16. \$479.73

17. *a*) \$1000 *b*) \$500 *c*) \$600 *d*) \$900 *e*) \$5900

19. \$676.43

20. \$7610

21. \$2221

22. *a*) \$229.87 *b*) \$229.62

23. 7%

24. \$213.32

25. \$6184

26. \$14,523

27. \$1344.89

28. \$966.08

29. \$78.20

30. \$908.87

31. *a*) \$1287.76 *b*) \$276.24

32. 4%

33. 9%

34. \$6889

35. \$97.44

36. 2.8659

38. *a*) $k\bar{a}_{\overline{n-k}|} + (\bar{I}\,\bar{a})_{\overline{n-k}|}$ *b*) $(\bar{I}\,\bar{a})_{\overline{n}|}(1+i)^k - (\bar{I}\,\bar{s})_{\overline{k}|}$

39. *a*) .5 *b*) .375

40. *a*) $\alpha\beta e^{-\beta t}$ *b*) α *c*) $\dfrac{\alpha\beta}{\beta+\delta}$ *d*) $\dfrac{\alpha\beta}{\beta+\delta}e^{-\beta t}$

41. $310

42. *a*) $79.59 *b*) 1.02

43. $272.42

46. $5736

47. *a*) $757.19 *b*) $826.40

48. 13

49. *a*) $\dfrac{\left(80{,}000 / a_{\overline{20}|.08}\right) a_{\overline{11}|.08} - 5000}{a_{\overline{9}|.09}}$

b) $\dfrac{80{,}000(1.09)^9 - \left(80{,}000 / a_{\overline{20}|.08}\right) s_{\overline{9}|.09} - 5000}{a_{\overline{9}|.09}}$

50. $571

Chapter 6

1. *a*) $385.54 *b*) $422.41 *c*) 9.56%

2. $844.77

3. *a*) 7.91% *b*) 8.51%

4. $115.87

5. $794.83

6. $945

7. $1200

8. $1291

9. $1100

10. *a*) 8.40% *b*) 8.00% *c*) 9.14% *d*) 10.00%

11. $1 - .5p$

12. $20

13. $33.98

14. $573.60

15. $X/2$

16. *a)* 1037.17   *b)* 964.54
    1027.88   973.41
    1018.59   982.27
    1009.29   991.14
    1000.00   1000.00

17. *a)* Theoretical = Semi-Theoretical < Practical
    b) Semi-Theoretical < Theoretical
    Semi-Theoretical < Practical
    Practical $\lesseqgtr$ Theoretical

18.

	$B^f_{1/3}$	$Fr_{1/3}$	$B^m_{1/3}$
Theoretical	980.35	13.12	967.23
Practical	980.62	13.33	967.29
Semi-Theoretical	980.35	13.33	967.02

19. $919.15

20. *a)* 8.64%   *b)* 8.71%

21. 8.4%

22. 9.13%

23. 6.3%

24. *a)* $1148.77   *b)* $846.28   *c)* 10.52%
    d) $1196.00   *e)* $875.38

25. $1086

26. $922.05

27. 25

28. 9.24%

29. $10,945

30. $7057

31. $$80,000 + 2000\left[\frac{3a_{\overline{46}|} - a_{\overline{40}|} - a_{\overline{28}|} - a_{\overline{10}|}}{a_{\overline{6}|}}\right]$$

32. $A = 105i^{(2)} - 8 \qquad B = 8$

33. $844.20

34. $1115

35. $17.14

36. $33.81

37. 15.7%

38. 6.57%

39. *a*) $2,050,000 *b*) $2,000,000 *c*) $2,150,000 *d*) $2,096,200

40. $\frac{1}{\delta}[(100\delta - 9)e^{-12\delta} + 9]$

41. $A = 3$ $B = -2$

42. 11 years

43. $1490.54

44. $955

45. $1055

Chapter 7

1. $20,206

2. *a*) 75.05 *b*) −57.85

3. 3

4. $544,037

5. $5460

6. *a*) − $498,666 *b*) 13.72%

7. *a*) 3 *b*) Yes

8. .02

9. $A = -2600$ $B = 1680$

10. *a*) $17,269 *b*) 5.62%

12. 6.16%

13. $4448

14. 8.04%

15. 9.75%

16. 10.0%

17. 6.49%

18. $10,867

19. $943

20. $2691

21. 8%

22. *a)* $\dfrac{ti}{1+(1-t)i}$ *b)* $\dfrac{(1-t)i}{1+ti}$

24. *a)* Yes *b)* No

25. *a)* 6.52% *b)* 9.54%

26. $2200

27. *a)* 8.57% *b)* 9.18%

28. 236.25

29. – 25%

30. *b)* $i^{DW} = \dfrac{C-A-D}{A+\frac{1}{2}D}$ $i^{TW} = \left(\dfrac{B}{A}\right)\left(\dfrac{C}{B+D}\right)-1$

c) $i^{DW} = \dfrac{C-A-D}{A+\frac{1}{2}D}$ $i^{TW} = \left(\dfrac{B-D}{A}\right)\left(\dfrac{C}{B}\right)-1$

31. $4484.12

32. 6.5708

33. $R > P > Q$

34. 7.75%

35. 9.47%

36. *a)* $\dfrac{\partial}{\partial t}\ln a(s,t)$ *b)* $e^{\int_s^t \delta_{s,r}dr}$ *c)* $a(t)/a(s)$ *d)* $(1+i)^t$ *e)* 1

37. $\dfrac{7+4m}{50m}$

38. 44
39. \$23,300
40. \$900
41. Earlier receipt of dividends. Partial release of margin.
42. MIRR = 7.90%. Project should be rejected.
43. Pay cash
44. *b*) Graph does not cross the x-axis.
45. They are equivalent, but both should be rejected.
47. 1.191
48. Rejected
49. 14.8%
50. \$3870
51. \$100.66
52. \$1167
53. September 1
54. $(n+1)^2$

Chapter 8

1. 51.2%
2. 14.65%
3. 34.49%
4. *a*) \$205.72 *b*) 16.38% *c*) 12.00%
5. $Y < Z < X$
6. *a*) \$2692.83 *b*) \$2660.00
7. *a*) \$11,550 *b*) \$11,500
8. *a*) 38.2% and 261.8% *b*) 30%
10. 14.3%
11. *a*) Option A *b*) \$1882

12. $1911

13. *a*) A: $15,511 B: $10,349
 b) A: $6047 B: $6026

14. *a*) $375.24 *b*) .63% monthly *c*) .73% monthly

15. 8.89%

16. *a*) – $580,177 *b*) – $613,805 *c*) "Buy" option

17. *a*) $4043.35 *b*) 9.17%

19. $16,787

20. 9.14%

21. $13,752

22. *a*) $8318 *b*) Yes

23. $11,164

24. $92,988

25. *a*) $764 *b*) $872 *c*) $800 *d*) $822.15

26. $5

27. 14.7%

28. 14.3%

29. 4.31

33. *a*) (1) $1340.10 (2) $1000.00 (3) $250.00
 b) (1) $11,408.50 (2) $10,000.00 (3) $6875.00

34. 8.39%

35. $5000

36. $36,329

37. $286.33

38. $177

39. $5253

40. $2216

41. $n\dfrac{\ln(1-S/A)-\ln[-\ln(S/A)]}{\ln(S/A)}$

42. *a*) \$1715.55 *b*) \$34,311

43. 4.61%

44. \$42.70

45. \$46.06

46. \$365.63

47. \$116,500

48. \$72,172

Chapter 9

1. 1.00

2. .82

3. 12.9%

4. \$211,807

5. \$306

6. 1.17

7. *a*) Coupon 1 = \$520 Coupon 2 = \$546 Maturity Value = \$10,920
   b) Nominal = 6.95% Real = 2.41%

8. \$1191.50

9. *a*) \$25,633 *b*) \$23,736 *c*) \$16,658

10. *a*) Option A *b*) Option B

11. 5.57% compared to 5.37%

12. \$935.26

13. 38.9% compared to 34.4%

14. \$1921.73

15. 1.40%

16. $363,000

17. 116.8%

18. $30,267

19. *a)* 11.45% *b)* 9.06%

20. $i^b = 15.1\%$ $i^a = 10.0\%$

21. *a)* $104.25 *b)* $2378.84 *c)* $8575

22. $21,512

23. 11.3%

24. *a)* $309,548 *b)* $271,079

25. 115.1

26. + 21.2%

27. line 1–1.2 line 2–9.48 line 3–56.84

28. *a)* 4.3% *b)* – 0.62%

29. *a)* € 6.61 million
b)

Time	0	1	2	3	4	5
$ million	–96	12.23	24.91	29.19	34.92	32.94

c) $7.94 million

30. – 6.52%

31. 8.07%

32. $767.55

33. *a)* $720 *b)* $240 *c)* 13.89%

34. .00685

35. *b)* c *c)* $1 - e^{-c}$ *d)* $1 - e^{-cn}$

36. *a)* $1,161,400 *b)* $16,600 *c)* 7.77%

37. *a)* $141,500 *b)* $128,300

38. 7.91%

Chapter 10

1.	*a*) \$3976.61		
2.	\$4786.78		
3.	*a*) Normal	*b*) Inverted	
4.	6.4646		
5.	\$11,946.50		
6.	*a*) \$841.67	*b*) \$1000.00	
7.	26.45%		
8.	*a*) 7.67%	*b*) 8.88%	
9.	*a*) Discount	*b*) \$73.97	
10.	*a*) 8.33%	*b*) 8.60%	*c*) \$1107.99
11.	*a*) \$926.03	*b*) 8.92%	
12.	$s_1 = 8\%$	$s_2 = 8\%$	$s_3 = 8\%$
13.	9.15%		
14.	Bond A: Bond B:	$P_A = \$1091.19$ $P_B = \$999.11$	$i_A = 5.09\%$ $i_B = 5.05\%$
15.	*a*) 9.46%	*b*) 10.51%	
16.	*a*) 8.60%	*b*) 7.66%	
17.	\$2617.18		
18.	$f_3 = 10.76\%$	$f_4 = 10.51\%$	${}_2f_3 = 10.63\%$
19.	10.51%		
20.	4.74%		
21.	\$13,153		
22.	6.150		

23. One-year bond: No.

Two-year bond: Yes. Buy the two-year bond. Sell one-year \$50 zero coupon bond short for \$46.73. Sell two-year \$550 zero coupon bond short for \$471.54. Arbitrage profit of \$2.27 at time $t = 0$.

24. *a)* Sell one-year zero coupon bond at 6%. Use proceeds to buy a two-year zero coupon bond at 7%. When one-year zero coupon bond matures, borrow proceeds at 7% for one year.

    b) \$10.70

25. Buy the coupon bond for 93.3425. Borrow the present value of the first coupon at 7%. Borrow the present value of the second coupon and maturity value at 9%. Arbitrage profit of \$.59 at time $t = 0$.

26. *a)* $.03 + .004t + .006t^2$ *b)* 4.12% *c)* 8.48% *d)* Normal

27. .6065

28. Minimum = \$128,614 Maximum = \$129,459

29. $r_1 = 3.9\%$ $r_2 = 5.8\%$ $r_3 = 7.1\%$

Chapter 11

2. 27

3. $\dfrac{v(\bar{I}\,\bar{a})_{\overline{n|}}}{\bar{a}_{\overline{n|}}}$

5. 5.99

6. *a)* 6.955 *b)* 93.50

7. 2.71

8. 1.715

9. *a)* 1.48 *b)* 3.23

11. *a)* \$3616 *b)* 2.2035 *c)* 1.7628 *d)* 4.9048

12. $\frac{1}{3}(n+1)(n+2)$

13. 1250

14. 97.71

15. *a)* 4.20 *b)* 20.74 *c)* \$98.14

16. *a)* 1.12 *b)* -52.73

17. $P(.07) = \$100{,}852$ $\qquad P(.09) = \$98{,}620$

19. 16.77

20. *a*) .540 *b*) .524

21. 5.04% and 6.95% rates of discount

22. 59

23. 8.18%

24. $2,977,990

25. $2503.48

26. $18,594

27. *a*) $2837.67 *b*) 6.80%

29. *a*) (1) -1.8012 (2) 0 (3) 1.8346
    b) (1) 1.8854 (2) 0 (3) -1.7531

30. *a*) $A_1 = \$71.44$ $\qquad A_5 = \$229.41$
    b) Yes

31. *a*) $3104.61 *b*) $8052.56

32. *a*) $4179.42 *b*) 1.967

33. *a*) $0 < p_1 < .6980$ *b*) No solution exists

34. *a*) $.2186 < p_1 < .5931$ *b*) No solution exists

35. Decrease: $-\$1313$ Increase: $+\$1323$

36. *a*) $179.37 *b*) 12.01%

38. $13,223 in 1-year zero coupon bonds
    $15,061 in 3-year zero coupon bonds
    $ 9624 in 5-year zero coupon bonds

40. *a*) .9354 *b*) .0004

Chapter 12

3. *a*) 8% in all years *b*) 0 in year 1; .01 in year 2; $.01\sqrt{2}$ in year 3
   c) \$1294.92 *d*) \$1224.94 *e*) \$1259.71 *f*) \$1259.82 *g*) 26.08

4. *a*) .07997 *b*) .79390 *c*) .16630 *d*) .00735

5. *b*) 2.5772 *d*) .0169

6. *a*) mean = 112.55 s.d. = 10.95
   b) mean = 430.91 s.d. = 30.74

7. *a*) $\ddot{s}_{\overline{n+1|}\,\bar{i}} - 1$ *b*) $\text{Var}\left[\ddot{s}_{\overline{n+1|}}\right]$ *c*) $1 + a_{\overline{n-1|}\,\bar{i}}$ *d*) $\text{Var}\left[a_{\overline{n-1|}}\right]$

9. *a*) Formula (12.5) with $\bar{i} = e^{\mu+\sigma^2/2} - 1$
   b) Formulas (12.6), (12.7), and (12.8) with $\bar{j} = e^{2\mu+2\sigma^2}$
   c) Formula (12.11) with $\bar{i} = e^{\mu-\sigma^2/2} - 1$
   d) Formulas (12.12), (12.13), and (12.14) with $\bar{k} = e^{-2\mu+2\sigma^2}$

10. *a*) mean = 1.823 s.d. = .058
    b) mean = 14.121 s.d. = .297
    c) mean = .549 s.d. = .017
    d) mean = 7.298 s.d. = .134

11. mean = .06 var = .01

12. (1.21693, 1.30247)

13. mean = 3.246 var = 65.62

14. \$9575.33

15. $\delta_{[6]} = .0896$ $\delta_{[7]} = .0880$ $\delta_{[8]} = .0867$

17. .0001513

18. *a*) .0004762 *b*) .0001300

19. *a*) .092 *b*) .0000512

22. *a*) 751.57 *b*) 15.25 *c*) 751.31

23. *a*) \$1001.85 *b*) 8.61%

24. \$998.63

25. \$997.83

26. *a*) 1.326 *b*) .749 *c*) 2.486 *d*) 3.626

27.
Rendelman-Bartter: mean = $\delta_0(1+at)$ var = $\sigma^2\delta_0^2t$
Vasicek: mean = $cb+(1-c)\delta_0$ var = σ^2t
Cox-Ingersoll-Ross: mean = $cb+(1-c)\delta_0$ var = $\sigma^2\delta_0t$

29. $\delta_{.5}=.06045$ $\delta_1=.06030$ $\delta_{1.5}=.06018$ $\delta_2=.06051$

30. *a*) \$995.15 *b*) $i^{(2)}=.1212$ *c*) \$993.46

31.
Random walk: max = .106 min = .026
Rendelman-Bartter: max = .114 min = .035
Vasicek: max = .103 min = .029
Cox-Ingersoll-Ross: max = .111 min = .034

32. *a*) 20.75% *b*) 2.79% *c*) 7.61% *e*) .2461 *f*) .0107

33. s_1 = 10.73% s_5 = 9.90%

Chapter 13

1.
a) Stock: + 5% Option: – 100% *e*) \$78
b) Stock: 0% Option: – 100% *f*) \$2
c) Stock: –2.5% Option: 0%
d) Stock: – 5% Option: + 100%

2. *a*) \$2 *b*) \$4 *c*) \$0 *d*) \$2

3. *a*) –\$2 *b*) –\$2 *c*) \$.50 *d*) \$3 *e*) \$3

4.

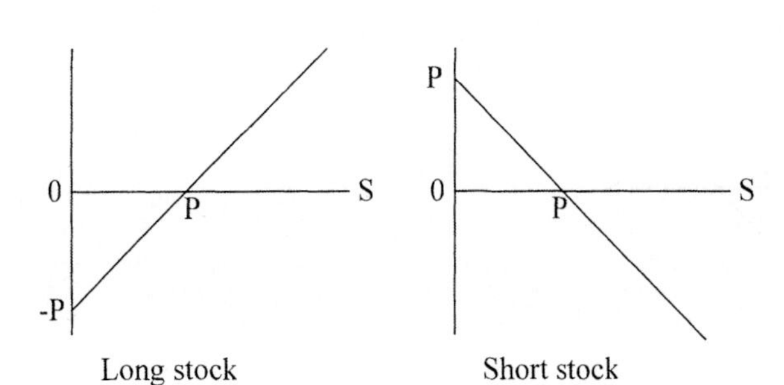

5. *a)* $E + C + P$ and $E - C - P$ *b)* $C + P$

6. *a)* Sell one \$5 option and buy one \$4 option. Adjust position in 6 months.
b) If $S \leq 50$ in 6 months, profit is:
\$1 if $S = 48$ in one year.
\$1 if $S = 50$ in one year.
\$3 if $S = 52$ in one year.
If $S > 50$ in 6 months, profit is:
\$3 if $S = 48$ in one year.
\$1 if $S = 50$ in one year.
\$1 if $S = 52$ in one year.

7.

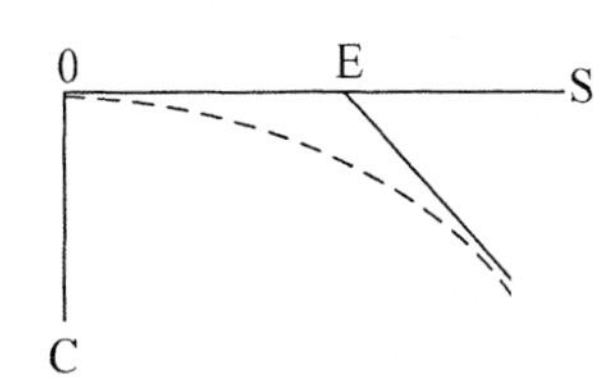

8. P increases as S decreases
E increases
t increases
σ increases
i decreases

9. Figure 13.5 provides the explanation

10. *a)* 0 *b)* $S - Ee^{-\delta n}$ *c)* S *d)* 0
e) $S - E$, if $S \geq E$; 0, if $S < E$ *f)* S

12. \$.89

13. Buy the call. Lend \$48.89. Sell the stock short. Sell the put. Guaranteed profit of \$1.11 at inception.

14.

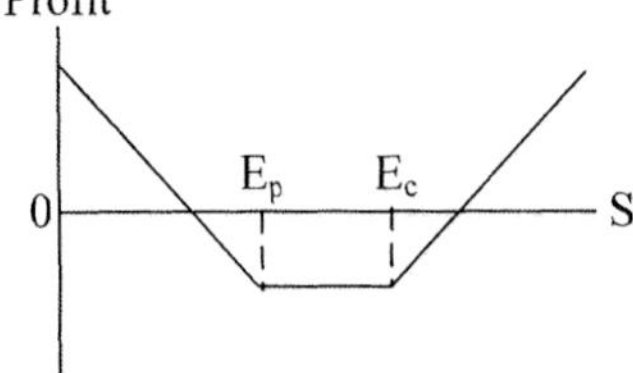

15. *a*) At $S = 45$, profit is $-\$1$
At $S = 50$, profit is $+\$4$
At $S = 55$, profit is $-\$1$

b)

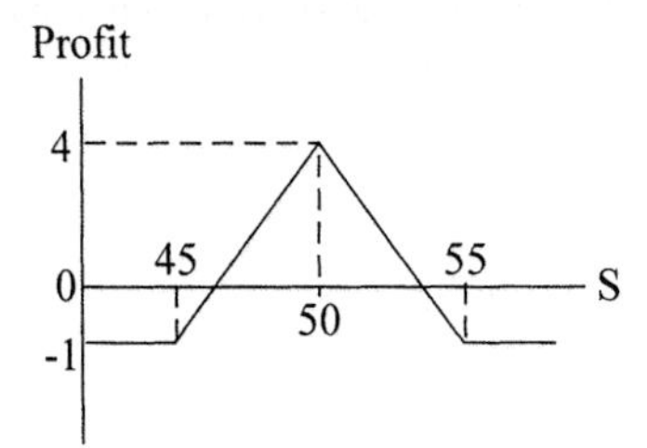

16. *a*) .8 *b*) \$7.55

17. *a*) ½ *b*) \$42.45

18. \$11.96

19. *a*) .11190 *b*) .5327 *c*) \$10.78

20. \$.96

23. \$11.00

24. *a*) 5.76 *b*) 16.73 *c*) 8.66 *d*) 12.58
e) 5.16 *f*) 15.82 *g*) 5.51 *h*) 14.88

25. \$8.80

26. \$97.99

27. \$2.37

28. \$2.32

Glossary of notation

Symbol	Section	Description
a	5.8	crossover duration with amortization involving step-rate amounts of principal
	12.6	drift parameter
	App. C	first term in a progression
$a(t)$	1.2	accumulation function
$a^{-1}(t)$	1.6	discount function, present value function
		present value of an n-period
$a_{\overline{n}\rceil}$	3.2	annuity-immediate
$\ddot{a}_{\overline{n}\rceil}$	3.3	annuity-due
$a_{\overline{n}\rceil}^{(m)}$	4.4	annuity-immediate payable $m$thly
$\ddot{a}_{\overline{n}\rceil}^{(m)}$	4.4	annuity-due payable $m$thly
$\bar{a}_{\overline{n}\rceil}$	4.5	continuous annuity
$a_{\overline{n}\rceil\, i\&j}$	5.4	annuity-immediate with different yield and sinking fund rates
$_{m\mid}a_{\overline{n}\rceil}$	3.4	m-period deferred annuity-immediate
$a_{\overline{\infty}\rceil}$	3.5	present value of a perpetuity-immediate
$\ddot{a}_{\overline{\infty}\rceil}$	3.5	present value of a perpetuity-due
A	7.5	amount in fund at beginning of year
	8.6	initial value of asset subject to depreciation
$A(t)$	1.2	amount function

Symbol	Section	Description
A_t	11.6	cash inflow generated by assets
B	7.5	amount in fund at end of year
B_t	5.2	outstanding loan balance
	6.4	book value of a bond
	7.3	outstanding investment balance
B'_k	7.6	outstanding investment balance at time t_k
B_t^p	5.2	prospective loan balance
B_t^r	5.2	retrospective loan balance
B_{t+k}^f	6.5	flat price of a bond
B_{t+k}^m	6.5	market price of a bond
B^c	13.8	value of a callable bond
B^{nc}	13.8	value of a noncallable bond
c	12.6	rate of reversion
$\bar{c}$	11.3	convexity
$\bar{c}_e$	11.4	effective convexity
C	6.3	redemption value of a bond
	13.4	value of a call
C_t	7.2	contribution, deposit, net cash flow
C'_k	7.6	contribution, deposit at time t_k
C'_t	7.10	contribution, deposit, gross cash flow
C_m	6.8	redemption value of a serial bond
C'	6.8	summation of redemption values of serial bonds
$\text{Cov}[X, Y]$	12.4	covariance of random variables X and Y
d	1.7	effective rate of discount
	1.7	rate of simple discount
	1.7	rate of compound discount
	8.6	factor in the declining balance method of depreciation
	App. C	common difference in an arithmetic progression

Symbol	Section	Description
d'	8.6	factor in a variation of the declining balance method of depreciation
$\bar{d}$	11.2	duration, Macaulay duration
$\bar{d}_e$	11.4	effective duration
d_n	1.7	effective rate of discount from time n - 1 to n
$d^{(m)}$	1.8	nominal rate of discount convertible $m$thly
d_1, d_2	13.7	constants in the Black-Scholes formula
D	5.4 6.10 8.3	sinking fund deposit dividend on stock depreciation during lease
D_t	8.6	depreciation charge
D_1, D_2	2.6	day of date
$(Da)_{\overline{n}\rvert}$	4.6	present value of a decreasing annuity
$(Ds)_{\overline{n}\rvert}$	4.6	accumulated value of a decreasing annuity
e^c	9.7	current exchange rate
e^e	9.7	expected future exchange rate
$e(t)$	12.4	error term in AR(1) and AR(2) processes
E	13.4	exercise (strike) price of an option
$\mathrm{E}[X]$	12.2	expected value of random variable X
EPV	9.8	expected present value
f	7.10	project financing rate
f_t	10.5	one-period forward rate
${}_mf_t$	10.5	m-period forward rate
$f(x)$	App. D	probability density function
F	6.3	face amount, par value of a bond
F_n	App. 4	present value of single payment at time n
Fr	6.3	bond coupon

Symbol	Section	Description
Fr_k	6.5	accrued bond coupon
$F(x)$	App. D	cumulative distribution function
g	6.3	modified coupon rate on a bond
$g(x)$	App. E	iteration formula
g_1, g_2	12.4	roots of the characteristic equation for the AR(2) process
G	6.3	base amount of a bond
G_n	App. 4	present value of level perpetuity starting at time n
h	12.5	length of time interval in binomial lattice
H	8.7	periodic charge of an asset
H_n	App. 4	present value of increasing perpetuity starting at time n
i	1.3	effective rate of interest
	1.4	rate of simple interest
	1.5	rate of compound interest
	5.4	interest rate on loan in sinking fund method
	6.3	yield rate on a bond
	7.2	yield rate, internal rate of return (IRR)
	7.4	investment rate when j is the reinvestment rate
	8.2	annual percentage rate (APR)
	9.4	nominal rate of interest with inflation
i'	4.7	adjusted interest rate for annuities varying in geometric progression
	8.4	quoted annual rate of interest on real estate mortgage
	9.4	real rate of interest without inflation
i_n	1.3	effective rate of interest from time n-1 to n
i^a	9.6	after-tax interest rate
i^b	9.6	before-tax interest rate
i^d	9.7	current domestic interest rate
i^f	9.7	current foreign interest rate
i^{DW}	7.6	dollar-weighted yield rate
i^{TW}	7.6	time-weighted yield rate

Symbol	Section	Description
i^y	7.7	portfolio rate of interest in calendar year *y*
i_t^y	7.7	investment year rate of interest for the *t*th year of investment in calendar year *y*
${}_a i_b$	7.5	amount of interest earned by 1 invested at time *b* over the following period of length *a*
i^{max}	8.5	approximate yield rate by maximum yield method
i^{min}	8.5	approximate yield rate by minimum yield method
i^{cr}	8.5	approximate yield rate by constant ratio method
i^{dr}	8.5	approximate yield rate by direct ratio method
$i^{(m)}$	1.8	nominal rate of interest convertible *m*thly
I	7.5	amount of interest earned during period
I_t	1.2 5.3 6.4	amount of interest earned on fund amount of interest paid on loan amount of interest earned on bond
$\bar{I}_t$	5.7	instantaneous rate at which interest is being paid
IRR	7.2	internal rate of return
IVC	13.2	inherent value of a call
IVP	13.2	inherent value of a put
$(Ia)_{\overline{n}\rvert}$	4.6	present value of an increasing annuity
$(Is)_{\overline{n}\rvert}$	4.6	accumulated value of an increasing annuity
$(Ia)_{\overline{\infty}\rvert}$	4.6	present value of an increasing perpetuity
$\left(I_{\overline{m}\rvert}\, a\right)_{\overline{n}\rvert}$	4.6	present value of an *n*-period increasing annuity with *m* increases, $m < n$.
$(Ia)_{\overline{n}\rvert}^{(m)}$	4.8	present value of an increasing annuity with periodic increases payable *m*thly
$\left(I^{(m)}a\right)_{\overline{n}\rvert}^{(m)}$	4.8	present value of an increasing annuity with *m*thly increases payable *m*thly

Symbol	Section	Description
$(\bar{I}\,\bar{a})_{\overline{n}\rceil}$	4.9	present value of a continuously increasing annuity payable continuously
j	various	a rate of interest, alternative notation to i
	5.4	sinking fund rate of interest
	7.4	reinvestment rate when i is the investment rate
	8.2	periodic rate used to determine the APR
	12.2	a rate defined by $1+j=\mathrm{E}\left[(1+i_t)^2\right]$ used to compute variances
j'	8.4	monthly rate of interest on real estate mortgage
j_k	7.6	subinterval yield rate in time-weighted calculations
k	various	a constant in several formulas, an index for summations
	1.2	constant of proportionality between the accumulation and amount functions
	3.6	fractional term for an annuity
	4.7	rate of change for annuity payments varying in geometric progression
	6.6	(P – C)/C used in determining bond yields
	7.5	average time at which net contributions made
	8.3	money factor in lease
	12.2	a rate defined by $(1+k)^{-1}=E\left[(1+i_t)^{-2}\right]$ used to compute variances
	12.4	constant in AR(1) process
	12.5	rate of change per step in binomial lattice
$k_1,\ k_2$	11.9	withdrawal amounts at different times in immunization
	12.4	constants in AR(2) process
K	6.3	present value of the redemption value of a bond
	8.2	finance charge
	8.7	capitalized cost
K_m	6.8	present value of the redemption value of a serial bond
K'	6.8	summation of present values of redemption values of serial bonds
l	App. C	last term in a progression

Symbol	Section	Description
L	5.2	original loan balance
	13.5	amount of loan in replicating transaction
L'	5.8	dividing amount of loan balance with amortization involving step-rate amounts of principal
L^*	8.4	amount financed on real estate mortgage for truth in lending purposes
L_t	11.6	cash outflow generated by liabilities
m_1	App. 12	first moment about the origin
m_2	App. 12	second moment about the origin
m_1^s	12.2	first moment of $1+i_t$ about the origin
m_2^s	12.2	second moment of $1+i_t$ about the origin
m_1^a	12.2	first moment of $(1+i_t)^{-1}$ about the origin
m_2^a	12.2	second moment of $(1+i_t)^{-1}$ about the origin
M	8.7	periodic maintenance expense
M_1, M_2	2.6	month of date
MIRR	7.10	modified internal rate of return
n	various	the term of a transaction
N	13.7	cumulative distribution function for the standard normal distribution
NPV	7.2	net present value
p	6.4	premium or discount on a $1 bond
	9.8	probability bond does not default
	12.5	probability of price increase in binomial lattice
p_t	9.8	probability bond does not default at time t
p_1, p_2	11.9	proportion of funds in different investments in immunization
P	6.3	price of a bond
	13.4	price of a put

Symbol	Section	Description
P_m	6.8	price of a serial bond
P_t	5.3	amount of principal repaid on loan
	6.4	amount of principal adjustment on bond
$\bar{P}_t$	5.7	instantaneous rate at which principal is being repaid
P'	6.8	summation of prices of serial bonds
$P(i)$	7.2	net present value
$P(s)$	10.3	net present value based on spot rates
PI	7.10	profitability index
q	9.8	probability bond defaults
Q	8.4	expenses at settlement on real estate mortgage that must be reflected in APR
r	6.3	coupon rate on a bond
	7.10	project return rate
	9.4	rate of inflation
	9.7	expected return on foreign investment
	App. C	common ratio in a geometric progression
R	4.3	equivalent payment per interest conversion period
	5.3	level installment payment to repay a loan
	8.6	level periodic return
R_t	5.6	varying installment payments to repay a loan
	7.2	return, withdrawal, net cash flow
	11.6	net cash flow in immunization
R_U	12.5	cash flow in an up move
R_D	12.5	cash flow in a down move
R'_t	7.10	return, withdrawal, gross cash flow
s	App. C	sum of a progression
	App. 12	sum of an annuity
s^2	12.2	variance of rate of interest
s_t	10.3	spot interest rate from yield curve

Symbol	Section	Description
		accumulated value of an n-period
$s_{\overline{n}\rvert}$	3.2	annuity-immediate
$\ddot{s}_{\overline{n}\rvert}$	3.3	annuity-due
$s_{\overline{n}\rvert}^{(m)}$	4.4	annuity-immediate payable $m$thly
$\ddot{s}_{\overline{n}\rvert}^{(m)}$	4.4	annuity-due payable $m$thly
$\bar{s}_{\overline{n}\rvert}$	4.5	continuous annuity
$s_n(m_1)$	App. 12	expected value of the sum of an annuity
S	8.6	salvage value of asset after depreciation
	13.4	current stock price
S_r	8.5	sum of the first r positive integers
S_t	App. 13	random variable for the value of an asset
t	various	an index representing time in many formulas
$\bar{t}$	2.4	method of equated time
TVC	13.2	time value of a call
TVP	13.2	time value of a put
U	8.7	units of production per time unit
v	1.6	discount factor, present value factor
v_k	1.10	present value factor in year k
$\bar{v}$	11.2	volatility, modified duration
V	12.5	present value in a binomial lattice
V_D	12.5	value in a down move
V_U	12.5	value in an up move
$\mathrm{Var}[X]$	12.2	variance of random variable X
$Y_1,\ Y_2$	2.6	year of date
Z	App. D	standard normal variable
δ	1.9	force of interest

Symbol	Section	Description
δ'	1.9	force of discount
$\delta_{[k]}$	1.10	level force of interest from time k - 1 to k
Δ	13.6	hedge ratio, option delta
	App. 11	difference operator
ε	11.7	increment in Taylor series
λ_t	10.7	continuous level spot rate
μ	12.3	mean of a distribution, parameter of the lognormal distribution
ξ	11.7	increment in final term in Taylor series
Π	various	product
σ^2	12.3	variance of a distribution, parameter of the lognormal distribution
Σ	various	summation
τ	12.4	constant in AR(2) process
Φ	App. C	cumulative distribution function of the standard normal distribution

Index

B

C

D

E

F

L

M

N

O

S